# INSPECTION OF INDUSTRIAL PLANT

# Inspection of Industrial Plant

A SURVEY OF
QUALITY ASSURANCE, SAFETY AND STANDARDS

**Second edition**

**Leslie Pilborough** C. Eng., MIEE, MIQA

Gower Technical

First edition published 1971 by Leonard Hill Books as *Inspection of Chemical Plant*, reissued 1976 by George Godwin Ltd

Second edition published by
Gower Technical,
Gower Publishing Company Limited,
Gower House,
Croft Road,
Aldershot,
Hants GU11 3HR,
England

British Library Cataloguing in Publication Data

Pilborough, Leslie
    Inspection of industrial plant.—2nd ed.
    1. Industrial safety—Great Britain
    I. Title     II. Pilborough, Leslie. Inspection of chemical plant
    363.1′164′0941      T55

    ISBN 0-566-02778-X

Printed and bound in Great Britain by Anchor Press Ltd, Tiptree, Essex

# Contents

# Illustrations

ILLUSTRATIONS

ILLUSTRATIONS

**Tables**

ILLUSTRATIONS

# Foreword

by Sir Frederick Warner, FEng, FIQA, FRS
President of the Institute of Quality Assurance

The many technical developments since the original appearance of this book make it, in effect, a new work. They have also extended the scope beyond the narrow meaning of the title to cover more than up-to-date knowledge of technical requirements which must be met. This basic knowledge is well summarized with necessary references to original documents. It is reinforced by details of new legislation which affects all who are concerned with design, construction, inspection or operation of industrial plant.

For the essential flavour of this book, it is necessary to turn to the last two chapters. These demonstrate the change which has occurred in design from a deterministic to a probabilistic basis. It is now clear that nothing can be free from faults. To live with them requires approaches which will reduce them to a level which can be tolerated, either because they represent a low level of risk or provide an acceptable service or object for the price the customer will pay. This is what total quality assurance adds up to.

Inspection is part of this concept and the book necessarily emphasizes what initial inspection of components or plant as installed should achieve. The case studies selected for examination demonstrate that in-service inspection still presents difficulties. They show how decisions by operators can affect design integrity and nullify the standards achieved by earlier inspection. The Piper Alpha platform tragedy in the North Sea and fire on the moving staircases at King's Cross Underground are too recent for detailed comment in this book, but the reports on these disasters will no doubt reinforce the lessons which the author gives.

This book should help all those who have responsibility for installing and managing complex installations, if only to show their part in meeting requirements of health and safety legislation by ensuring that the organization is staffed at all levels by people who are competent to carry out the tasks with which they are entrusted.

# Preface to the first edition

This book endeavours to cater for all concerned in any way with the inspection of chemical and process plant. In so doing it of necessity deals with principles and techniques of inspection which may be applied in many fields of industrial technology.

As inspection has, in general, to ensure that the designer's requirements are complied with, the work deals with the many specifications, codes and standards (some of an international character) which may be encountered in chemical and process engineering. Consequently it is hoped that it will also be of use to designers, technicians, project engineers, consultants and chemical engineering contractors interested in this important and expanding world wide field.

Inspection arrangements during manufacture, construction, commissioning, maintenance and operation are all covered. Some account is given of the legal framework and of the statutory regulations which may be applicable, particularly in the field of industrial safety, health and welfare where inspection is much in evidence.

Some comment and explanation concerning units and standards, etc., may be necessary. The present time is one of change as regards units; both imperial and metric are in common use in industry. Metric units in the past have been used in English speaking countries for specific purposes or sometimes as alternatives. Now, with the adoption of metric (SI) units for all purposes by the UK and many other countries, new units will come into increasing use to replace the old, but, as the USA still uses the imperial system, both systems will remain in use concurrently for many years. The inspector, however, must be familiar with *any* units which appear in specifications. British Standards are going over increasingly to SI units, and are introducing certain other units which may be used. For instance, in British Standards specifying in metric terms the strength of metallic materials, stress is expressed in hectobars instead of newtons per square metre ($1 \text{ hbar} = 10 \text{ N/m}^2$), this replacing the old familiar pounds per square inch (lbf/in$^2$). Some of these changes are reflected in the text, but, by and large, the units in use at the time of writing predominate.

Specifications, codes and standards are continually being revised and amended in the interests of progress. But in this text the year of issue or revision has not generally been given, and the latest issue or revision with amendments is implied. The fixed designation usually lasts for years, unless cancelled or replaced. Thus BS 229 *Flame-proof enclosure of electrical apparatus* was first issued in 1926; its latest revision is BS 229:1957 to which some six amendments have been made.

Similarly, American Standards are referred to in the text by their fixed designations. Thus the American Society for Testing and Materials issue Standard and Tentative Specifications, Methods of Test, Recommended Practices and Definitions. They are issued under a fixed designation, as, for example, ASTM A 90 *Standard methods of test for weight of coating on zinc coated (galvanized) iron or steel articles*. The initial letter 'A' indicates ferrous metals; B would indicate non-ferrous metals, C cementitious, ceramic, concrete and masonry materials, D miscellaneous materials, E miscellaneous subjects, and F end-use materials. The fixed designation is followed by an indication of the year of adoption or of last revision and, in the case of a tentative, by the letter T. Tentative specifications are used pending their adoption as standards. Thus ASTM E 235-64T is a Tentative Specification for *metal-sheathed corrosion resistant thermocouples for nuclear service*.

A number of ASTM and other standards issued by American organizations have been approved as USA Standards (thus ASTM A 90-53 was approved as ASA (now USAS) No: G8.12-1956. Similarly the Code for Pressure Piping prepared by ASME was approved as ASA (now USAS) B 16. The ASME Boiler and Pressure Vessel Code, whilst not referred to as a USA Standard as such, is recognized internationally, and ASTM material standards have been approved for use with it. Thus ASTM A 263-63 for *chromium steel clad plate* has been approved as ASME Boiler and Pressure Vessel Code Specification No: SA-263.

It is hoped that this present work will fill what appears to be a gap in the literature of industrial technology. It is based on many years of experience in a variety of fields of activity.

Whilst the views expressed are in general my own, they have been coloured by information gleaned over the years, from a number of sources. In particular I would express my thanks to Mr R. W. Dudley, Chief Quality Engineer of the John Thompson Group, and to Mr B. F. Billing of RAE Farnborough, for help and comments received whilst preparing Chapters 3 and 2 respectively, and to many other friends and colleagues who have given assistance, perhaps indirectly. I would also acknowledge the help and guidance obtained from the Journal of the Institution of Engineering Inspection (*The Quality Engineer*) and from the papers read at their course on Professional Education for Inspection in April 1961 (particularly a lecture by Professor F. C. Thompson from which I have quoted).

*Vulcan*, the house journal of the Vulcan Boiler & General Insurance Co. and its successor *Vigilance* of the National and Vulcan Engineering Insurance Group have also been helpful.

Some extracts from, and many references to, British Standards have been made by permission of the British Standards Institution, 2 Park Street, London, W1Y 4AA, from whom copies of the complete standards can be obtained.

Other acknowledgements appear in the text.

L. PILBOROUGH

# Preface to the second edition

This new edition has been given a slight change of title to cover the increased scope of the work, and it has been thoroughly revised to include the latest standards, codes and legislation. Much new material has been added, particularly regarding pressure vessels and systems, environmental hazards and inspection procedures (including in-service inspection).

Since its first publication three important administrative events have revolutionized industrial inspection:

(i) the implementation of the *Health and Safety at Work etc. Act* 1974 (the HSW Act) with its exacting requirements and penalties;

(ii) the introduction and growing use commercially of the Department of Trade and Industry's Register of Quality Assessed UK Companies, entry into which necessitates a company having a Quality Assurance organization complying with the requirements of BS 5750 *Quality systems* – a prerequisite for obtaining contracts from many important and public authorities.

(iii) The growth of consumer safety and protection legislation, culminating in the passing of the Consumer Protection Act 1987, which makes it a criminal offence to supply unsafe consumer goods and implements the European Community directive on product liability which gives people injured by defective products the right to sue for damages.

The Flixborough disaster on Humberside in June 1974 and the subsequent official inquiry, coming as it did around the time of the introduction of the HSW Act, caused a great shock to an industry which was perhaps becoming complacent.

The public was further shocked when much greater disasters occurring abroad at Seveso and Bhopal showed what havoc could arise from inadvertent toxic release from chemical plants, and the Three Mile Island incident showed the great potential threat from ineffective control of nuclear plants—then came Chernobyl! And who could forget 1987's toll: the Space Shuttle explosion, the Zeebrugge ferry disaster and the King's Cross underground fire?

xix

If high technology and hazardous plants are to continue in use then it is essential that the public should be assured that they are not only designed and constructed to high standards of quality and safety, but that their everyday use is adequately supervised.

This has led and is leading to further advances in what may be called total quality (and safety) assurance. However 100 per cent assurance is not humanly possible—but it can and must be approached:

(i) Human behaviour and failings must be taken more into account.

(ii) Clear and correct instructions must be given.

(iii) Rules must not be violated.

(iv) Any changes must be properly approved at high level and documented.

(v) Discipline (which depends largely upon fairness and good morale, backed if necessary by known penalties) must be enforced.

However, much of industry is not greatly involved with highly hazardous plant. Its main object is to produce goods economically and to make a profit. Materials and labour must therefore not be wasted, but the goods produced must be of assured quality and safety if they are to sell and to compete with foreign competition and not result in expensive product liability litigation for the makers.

It is the duty of an inspector (and this includes quality assurance and safety personnel) to work to and interpret standards, codes and legislation etc. He can seek advice, but he must eventually make decisions which it is hoped will be sound and unbiased.

All of the above matters are dealt with to some extent in this book. While any views expressed are in general my own they have been coloured by information and experience gleaned over a lifetime of work in many fields.

Some extracts from, and many references to, British Standards have been made by permission of the British Standards Institution. Complete copies of Standards can be obtained from BSI at Linford Wood, Milton Keynes MK14 6LE. It is essential that the latest issue of a Standard be consulted. Material from the ASME Boiler and Pressure Vessel Code has been reproduced with permission. Other acknowledgements appear in the text.

Summarizing what is said elsewhere in this work, the aims of industrial inspection (including quality assurance) are four-fold:

(i) Traditionally to *prevent the acceptance* of incorrect and unsuitable goods and/or services.

(ii) To *prevent the production* of incorrect goods etc., and thus to prevent loss of materials, time and money.

(iii) To *prevent the infringement* of numerous laws and legislation non-observance of which could at best lead to a fine, or, if followed by an accident—to death and injury, and for the offending *persons* and/or companies—imprisonment, the payment of substantial compensation and maybe even financial ruin.

(iv) To prevent the occurrence of accidents as far as is humanly possible.

If this book can help in the achievement of these aims it will have served its purpose.

L. PILBOROUGH
Farnborough, 1988

# 1 Introductory

## 1.1 Plant quality and safety—the role of inspection and quality assurance

In order that progress may be made with confidence in any branch of technology adequate standards of quality and performance must be available and proper safety rules or codes must be laid down and understood. Such standards and codes should not stultify progress, but should ensure that shoddy and perhaps dangerous designs, materials, articles or practices are not used. The enforcement of such standards and codes is largely the province of inspection.

In the past inspection of industrial plant and equipment was often largely confined to the checking of specified requirements *after* completion.

Consequently the inspector quite often became a rejector. However, in more recent years the practice has gradually evolved of assuring quality by paying particular attention *during* manufacture to the processes employed and to details of the materials and components used. This practice has enabled faulty processes, etc. to be spotted and corrected before much material, time and money has been wasted.

Also, from early Victorian days successive Factories Acts, etc., by the employment of factory inspectors, have striven to safeguard the health and safety of the worker, and of the public, from the worst hazards of the Industrial Revolution and of modern industrial life.

Today advances in the technology and complexity of plant have necessitated designs for operating under a variety of environmental conditions, including the most stringent. But contractors have to secure their business by competitive tender; consequently, although materials and equipment must be selected and specified to withstand the expected environment, their designs must be such as to attain the required objectives with the least possible expenditure. Adequate planning of the work, and of the methods of construction, is thus necessary, while strict adherence to a time scale may be of prime importance.

All these factors may have been adequately taken care of, but they may be of no avail if component parts are incorrect in size or requirements, or if workmanship is poor, or if manufacturing techniques have not been properly applied, or if dangers and perhaps catastrophic failures with possible loss of life and money arise during manufacture and/or operational use. Tests are therefore required to ensure the quality (and safety) both of the raw materials and of the finished product. Consequently it is essential to have a system of surveillance and testing of industrial plant. To be most effective such an inspection and control system should cover not only manufacture but also the preparatory stages before manufacture, the commissioning period, and the period of operational use, until finally the plant is relegated to the scrap heap.

The purchaser of plant may have his own inspection organization, or he may retain an independent inspector or consultant to represent him.

The manufacturer or contractor may have an inspection department to check his work for quality. The plant operator may carry out inspection and tests to check for performance and safety and perhaps as part of a system of planned maintenance.

In addition, various official and other organizations may be required or empowered by legislation to carry out periodic inspections, largely to ensure safety. Thus it will be seen that industrial inspection is directed not only towards quality assurance but to preserving health and safety and preventing unnecessary loss of money.

## 1.2 The Health and Safety at Work Act 1974 (HSW Act)

Before the HSW Act came into force in 1975 the mass of legislation governing health and safety at work in the UK was administered by at least five different government departments and seven inspectorates. This Act, an 'enabling Act' taking over *interalia* the Factories Act 1961, while imposing additional requirements and including penalties under criminal law, put control into the hands of a single independent body, the Health and Safety Commission (whose members are drawn from industry, the Trade Unions and the workers), which through the Health and Safety Executive employs all the necessary official inspectors, scientists, doctors, etc. Under the Act the responsibilities of employers (and workers) are greatly increased, and this includes *all* who design, manufacture, inspect, install, erect, import or supply *anything* for use at work; their duties include ensuring that an article or substance is safe when used in accordance with the information supplied, and extends to the carrying out of any necessary testing, inspection and research.

Section 1 of the Act contains provision for

(i) securing the health, safety and welfare of *all* persons at work;

(ii) protecting persons other than those at work (e.g. the public at large) against risks arising from the activities of those at work;

(iii) controlling the keeping and use of explosives, highly flammable or otherwise dangerous substances:

(iv) controlling the emission into the atmosphere of noxious or offensive substances.

To these ends an employer (under Sections 1 and 2) has the duty to provide and maintain

(a) plant and systems that are, as far as reasonably practicable, safe and without risks to health;

(b) safe methods of handling, storing and transporting materials; and

(c) adequate instruction, training, supervision and information.

Under Sections 7 and 8 employees must co-operate in meeting statutory requirements and they (and others) must not interfere with or misuse anything provided in the interests of health, safety and welfare. Existing Acts of Parliament and legislation (such as most of those given in Table 14.1 and the relevant legislation in Tables 14.3, 14.4 (most), and 14.5) were taken over, and may be amended or replaced and new regulations and codes of practice introduced by the Commission. It should be emphasized however that these Acts and much existing legislation will remain in force in principle for many years (although subject to revision) until gradually repealed or replaced.

Inspectors appointed under the Act may issue to a firm or organization: improvement notices requiring remedial action to be taken within a specified time in order to comply with certain relevant statutory provisions (which the inspector may advise may be done by implementing certain approved codes or standards); and prohibition notices requiring total or partial cessation of operations when there is some serious risk or a danger of personal injury. Cessation may take place immediately, if necessary. There is a right of appeal to an industrial tribunal.

Inspectors may seize, and if necessary destroy, articles or substances which might present an immediate hazard; they are protected from the consequences of civil actions arising from their giving negligent advice or exceeding their powers, etc.

Penalties for failing to comply with requirements, or other offences under the Act, may on conviction in a higher court (e.g. a Crown Court) result in specific cases in imprisonment for up to two years, and/or a heavy fine. It is emphasized that such action may be taken not only against a 'body corporate' but against a person (e.g. a director, manager or operative) who has committed an offence by consent, agreement or neglect.

Thus the HSW Act has teeth which can be used against those responsible for failure to carry out proper inspections or investigations relating to health and safety, or otherwise commit an offence under the Act—irrespective as to whether or not their actions (or non-actions) has led to an accident, non-desirable occurrence, or a disaster. However, should such troubles arise, then additional financial penalties will be incurred, which could include compensation for loss of life and personal earnings, injuries, etc. besides company losses of profits, materials and destruction of plant, etc. and the cost of expensive litigation. The outlook for a company, organization or individual found guilty of negligently failing to comply with any of the requirements of the Act could then, in such a case, indeed be black.

SO BE WARNED—INSPECTION MUST NOT BE NEGLECTED

(A somewhat similar Act (*The Occupational Safety and Health Act* 1970) is in operation in the USA and is enforced by inspectors. Further details on the HSW Act and other legal matters are given elsewhere in this book and particularly in Chapter 14; the implications of the *Consumer Protection Act* 1987 are of great importance in inspection terms.)

### 1.3 The 'package deal' contractor

The rapid growth of chemical and allied process engineering has fostered the development of the large contractor who will undertake the design, procurement, erection, inspection and setting to work of complete industrial projects. Before 1939 most of such work was done by the large chemical, petroleum and other companies for their own particular plants. However the increasing complexity of such work, particularly following the establishment of the petrochemical industry, led first in the USA, and later in the UK, to the establishment of firms who will contract for complete plants and their erection and commissioning at home or overseas. Contractors of this kind do not necessarily themselves manufacture any of the plant required, but in some cases they may be associated with certain established plant manufacturers.

Relying particularly on obtaining 'package deals' for large projects at a lump sum (often known as 'turn-key' contracts), they are peculiarly sensitive to questions of cost. Failure to obtain a specific project may seriously embarrass them, whilst bad estimating or unexpected trouble may increase costs and swallow up profitability. Hence for them a really first class planning, progress and inspection organization is a necessity.

Inspectors from such an organization will not only inspect plant and materials, but will urge deliveries at all stages, anticipating and following up troubles of any kind, including inspection difficulties, so that early remedial action can be taken. In this way, by making use of modern management techniques, the progress of a project can be effectively expedited.

## 1.4 The value and cost of inspection

Each year many hundreds of millions of pounds are spent on new projects. It is of increasing national importance that the plant produced and purchased should have built into it such a measure of quality and reliability as will ensure its safe, satisfactory and economic operation over the life envisaged. It is salutary to consider the heavy capital value of the plant at risk on, say, one location or project, and the cost per hour of a shut-down of its various sections.

Serious failure of only one single item to stand up to its working conditions could well jeopardize the financial or political success of a project. Expensive raw materials or finished products could be wasted, and possibly a situation of great hazard might arise. In spite of a good record, the processing of chemicals, oil, etc., is an extremely dangerous business. Accidents, when they occur, are often catastrophic, and eternal vigilance regarding inspection and safety precautions is essential. Much trouble may arise and heavy compensation become payable following any accident.

In addition the passing of the HSW Act has made the manufacturer, supplier or operator of faulty equipment responsible under criminal law for any accidents due to his negligence. Individual people concerned may now face imprisonment as well as fines.

Hence, expenditure on inspection and quality assurance is an economic necessity.

The amount to be expended depends very much on circumstances. Considerable expenditure will seem justified when difficult or expensive materials have to be processed, or when the operating conditions are onerous, or when questions of safety arise. Again it might be possible to show that such expenditure would lead to an increase in plant availability and reliability and a reduction in maintenance costs.

Inspection is thus much more than an insurance policy.

To give some idea of the cost of inspection it can be stated that one organization considered a figure of 4% of the capital value of the plant as not unreasonable. An electrical manufacturer's analysis showed that his total quality costs were 6·2%.

A government department estimated a figure of 1% as its own costs for inspecting its sophisticated purchases; this did not include the inspection costs its contractors had necessarily to incur. 1% has also been quoted by a firm in the automotive industry as the cost of inspecting its incoming supplies. Some few years ago British industry was spending some £350m p.a. on inspection, control and monitoring, which was some 1% of the Gross National Product. It was losing some £650m p.a. due to rejections, scrap etc. Obviously if inspection with effective quality control could then have cut down the rejections and scrap by something over 50% it could well have paid for itself! This is one of the basic arguments for the adoption of the quality assurance schemes in use (see Chapter 9); it also contributes to the subject of loss prevention (see 9.1.2).

It does not necessarily follow that the cost of inspection can always be based on the cost of the items inspected. To quote an example, a project costing millions of pounds was held up and could have been jeopardized because of what eventually proved to be lack of inspection and quality assurance of certain ancillary items of comparatively little cost. To put the matter right, extensive inspection effort was necessary on these items. The rejection rate approached 100%, new design and manufacturing techniques had to be developed, and costs consequently rose considerably. But, when compared with the cost of the project, the cost of these small items (and of their inspection) was insignificant.*

In many cases trouble which could have been avoided by appropriate prior inspection has developed in service. One particular overseas project failed catastrophically with heavy financial loss; investigation *after the event* showed this to be due to lack of inspection and supervision (see 13.6.5).

The psychological value of inspection is also well known, although it cannot, of course, replace extensive checking and quality control. The mere knowledge that work is subject to inspection, and that any item may be checked, puts an operator on his mettle. Basically, if the design is right, the processes are carefully selected and controlled, and the operators are skilled and are seen to use their skill—then the quality of the product will be right. Sophisticated inspection can be very expensive—but so are delays due, for instance, to the exposure and rectification of a defect at the last moment which it could have found at an earlier stage. Even worse, an unfound defect might cause trouble later in service—with perhaps disastrous results. Other imponderables which a contractor may find difficulty in allowing for in his quotation are the vagaries of different inspectors and the time lags caused by waiting for outside inspectors to arrive—it is an imperfect world!

Some years ago several contractors were asked to quote for certain plant, first, as normally supplied; and second, with stringent inspection to give a really reliable job. Most put a premium of 20% or more on the fully inspected product, but one well known firm quoted exactly the same in both cases!

Today, however, with the increasing use by many purchasers of 'contractors of assessed quality' (e.g. those on the Department of Trade and Industry's Register of Quality Assessed UK Companies and approved generally to BS 5750 *Quality systems* (see Chapter 9)) many of these problems have disappeared. But increased legislation (the HSW Act, Employers Product Liability, etc.) has increased considerably the necessity for effective quality assurance. It is possible to prepare a form of economic

---

*These items were '0' rings, forming part of important seals. Later projects (e.g. the space shuttle) may have been jeopardized by similar trouble (see 13.6.7).

balance sheet regarding the cost and effect of inspection and quality assurance.

With no inspection, complaints from customers would give the firm a bad name and possibly eventually cause bankruptcy. With final inspection only, scrap, rework and repair might leave little good production for sale, and the waste of good material, time and money might possibly bankrupt the firm. With final inspection and quality assurance (QA) the rejects, rework and repairs would drop considerably, as also would customer complaints. The considerable savings made by inspection and QA would be balanced by the increasing costs of this organization. At some perhaps hypothetical point the costs of inspection and QA (although less than the previous costs of rejects, rework etc.) would equal and then surpass the latest, but reduced, costs of rejects, rework and complaints, etc. The question then arises as to how far the cost of more sophisticated inspection should be allowed to rise for perhaps a rapidly diminishing cost of repairs and complaints. But the cost of possible troubles, with unpredictable financial penalties, due to accidents, infringements of legislation, the discovery of unsuspected design faults, product liability, etc., has to be taken into account.

Consequently inspection and QA, as a form of insurance, are costs which modern industry must bear, particularly in high technology, where firms of any standing must have such a QA organization in order to undertake work for most central and local authorities and many public companies. Very often QA gives good value for the money expended (see also BS 6143 *Guide to the determination and use of quality related costs*).

### 1.5 Purposes of inspection

Amongst the purposes for which inspection may be required are:

(i) To ensure that items of plant and stores, or services rendered, etc., comply with the requirements of a contract or order and the relevant specifications, drawings, etc.

(ii) To ensure that such items or services, etc., are suitable for the use required.

(iii) To ensure that various tests are satisfactorily carried out.

(iv) To ensure that certain safety aspects are satisfactorily met.

(v) To investigate some fault, failure or specific matter.

(vi) To investigate and expedite progress of manufacturing processes, etc.

When undertaking the inspection of a contract, etc., the requirements may be sufficiently covered by purpose (i) above. The inspection requirements of a firm inspecting its own products may be sufficiently covered by purpose (ii) only. 'In-use' inspection may however be carried out on plant, equipment and services which have been installed or operated for some time. In such cases one or more of purposes (ii), (iii) and (iv) may be applicable; many routine inspections and periodic statutory tests come into these categories.

The extension of 'inspection' to include *control* of quality during manufacture and the *assurance* of quality in design and operation etc. is considered later, particularly in Chapter 9, and in Chapters 12 and 13.

### 1.6 Inspection and QA personnel

Personnel employed in inspection and QA fall into three main divisions:

(1) *Professionals* (often of chartered engineer status) of such education and experience that they can give authoritative technical advice over a broad field on inspection QA and relevant matters and can direct important tasks in their own branch.

(2) *Technician engineers or specialists* who can apply proven inspection techniques in a responsible manner under general professional/engineering direction.

(3) *Inspection operators* (such as examiners, testers and viewers) who perform inspection and testing operations in accordance with specifications, drawings and other instructions, under the supervision of technicians.

The senior and professional posts in inspection have, in the past, mainly been filled by engineers and/or scientists educated and trained in such fields as mechanical, electrical or chemical engineering. Their transition to the inspection and quality engineering field has been largely by virtue of experience gained, and training given, within the industry. In recent years, advances in techniques and philosophies have required professional QA personnel and inspection engineers to become aware of a range of methods, equipments and subjects far greater than those previously associated with the inspection function; in a properly developed organization their activities extend to embrace the whole field of manufacture and operation, including legislation and safety. They supply the vital services by which variations of quality are continuously observed and assessed. This concept, requiring complete and continuous surveillance and control for quality and reliability, is largely responsible for the efficient and economic operation of plant and of the whole sequence of manufacturing processes.

The nature of an inspector's work demands a high degree of observational skill and the ability to assess the significance of variations in standards of manufacture in relation to design and performance requirements. He must learn to apply constructive criticism to the examination of any design, specification or process, by means of scientific analysis and the exercise of fundamental principles. As the internal economics of a manufacturing plant are related closely to the quality level at which it operates, he should know enough about this subject to appreciate the cost significance of managerial and technical decisions.

The engineering or specialist technician grade of inspection personnel fills an important place in inspection and quality control. Whilst possibly under the direction of a professional inspection engineer, they can become so versed in the application of proven inspection and QA techniques that their detailed knowledge of the intricacies of such techniques, the necessary equipment and the interpretation of results, make them an indispensable link in the chain.

The professional inspection engineer, having technical knowledge over a broad field, may direct several such technicians, each operating in a separate field. The technician's detailed knowledge will however enable the inspection engineer to give executive decisions, etc., with confidence.

The ancillary inspection operators, acting under the supervision of the technicians, carry out routine inspection and testing operations and procedures.

## 1.7 Some basic principles of inspection

When inspecting a contract, if the specifications and drawings have been prepared with sufficient care, then a satisfactory check for compliance with them and the contract conditions should ensure that the items are suitable. This, however, is not always so. For instance, a specialist inspector, or a specialist aiding the normal inspector, may find that although the equipment, etc. complies with contract requirements, it is nevertheless unsuitable for service. The contractor however is not necessarily to blame and must, if he insists, be paid for the work carried out. In such a case the specialist would probably arrange for alterations to the equipment to be carried out in order to make it serviceable, and this would normally be done at extra expense and be authorized by an amendment to the contract, or by other suitable documentary cover. Such a procedure will usually only occur with development work, or with contracts for work where techniques have not yet been sufficiently established.

Should the inspector's terms of reference require him to 'ensure that each and every condition of the contract, specifications and drawings, etc. . . . is complied with', then it would be a poor lawyer who could not find something wrong with most contracts, and a poor inspector who could not find something not exactly complying with specifications and drawings. Satisfaction as to legal conditions is usually obtained by mutual agreement between the parties concerned, but the inspector should know of any major discrepancies on the contractual side, so that he can bring them to the attention of the proper authorities.

Any deviations from specifications and drawings should be known to the inspector. Some he may find himself. Some may be pointed out to him by the contractor (or the contractor's inspection staff, if any). According to the nature of the deviation he may (i) reject the particular item outright, (ii) reject it for rectification, or (iii) arrange for its acceptance.

If the deviation is trivial it may possibly be accepted without further ado (or paperwork). But it should be borne in mind that the amount of discretion which an inspector is allowed to use varies very much with the organization to which he belongs, and his position in that organization. The inspector may refer a deviation to his superior officer, who may accept. Possibly acceptance of the deviation will have to be covered in writing, stating details and the quantity involved. It may well be that the question of a reduction in price due to this deviation will have to be negotiated.

Should the deviation not be detrimental, and one which regularly recurs, action might be taken to amend the specification or drawing concerned.

Sometimes a contractor seeks prior permission to make items which deviate from specification or drawing, possibly because this eases his production problems by enabling him to employ his standard methods of manufacture or to use alternative material. This may be agreed with the inspector (if necessary after he has consulted the designer). Written permission to make items in this manner is termed a *production permit* by some inspection organizations, to distinguish it from a *concession* issued to authorize acceptance of parts already manufactured incorrectly.

*The salient feature of all inspection is that the inspection authority must know of any deviation from specified requirements before the question of acceptance is considered.* For more detailed information see Chapters 9, 12 and 13.

## 1.8  Units and standards of measurement—metrology

It is obviously of importance in inspection, where the inspector's measurements must be capable of precise independent verification, that recognized units and standards of measurement should be employed.

Since 1965 a metric system known as the Système International d'Unités (SI) has been gradually introduced and used in the UK as the principal (and legal) system of measurement for all purposes. It is used widely in most countries except the USA, where imperial units are still the principal units employed. An inspector must be familiar with the units of any system in current use in industry. (For further details see Appendix: Legal metrology)

## 1.9  Specifications, codes and standards

An inspector has to verify that specification requirements have been met and, very often, that compliance with these requirements continues throughout life.

For complex projects and specialized work detailed specifications may have to be prepared. The great majority of work however can be covered by existing standard specifications, and these should be used wherever possible. Detailed plant or project specifications include requirements that materials and components, etc. should comply with certain standard specifications, and they may require that design, construction, inspection and test of major items are in accordance with a code, or codes, of practice.

A standard can be defined as an agreement or authority to follow a certain rule or model, generally when dealing with recurring items.

A code is a system or collection of regulations, often involving safety matters. It usually takes the form of a systematic collection of laws and rules which may be given statutory force by some legislative body.

Standards permit everyday routine recurring work to go on efficiently, whilst releasing the energies of design and development personnel for more advanced and unexplored areas of knowledge. Their use saves the time, energy and manpower which would otherwise be occupied in preparing lengthy, detailed specifications for each and every component and job, when often much of the detail is of a regularly recurring nature.

Standards define such things as screw threads, materials, methods of test, components, etc., and so ensure interchangeability of construction, and familiarity with the subject throughout the world, irrespective of the place of manufacture. Designers, buyers, inspectors and engineers will thus generally be conversant with and understand what is required.

National standards organizations exist in most countries to prepare and issue standards and codes. These are generally prepared by a committee made up of balanced representation from industry, engineering institutions and societies, manufacturers, users, and government bodies.

Thus in the UK the British Standards Institution (BSI), and in the USA the American National Standards Institute (ANSI, previously the USA Standards Institute, formerly the American Standards Association (ASA)), are the principal organizations. In the USA such bodies as the American Society for Testing and Materials (ASTM), the American Society of Mechanical Engineers (ASME), and the American Petroleum Institute (API) also prepare and issue standards and codes, some of which may receive approval as American (ANSI) Standards. Certain of these codes, particularly those applicable to oil and chemical plant, may be widely used, not only in the USA but throughout the world.

In Europe the national standards and codes of the Deutscher Normenausschuss (DIN), and the Association Française de Normalisation (AFNOR) are amongst those commonly encountered. The national standards organizations of some British Commonwealth countries often issue their own standards sometimes based on British Standards, with perhaps local amendments; Canada, however, often follows US practice, besides issuing its own standards.

Committees of the International Standards Organization (ISO) and of the International Electrotechnical Commission (IEC), composed of members from many countries prepare and issue standards, codes and recommendations. National standards organizations often follow such recommendations.

All standards, codes, etc., are dated and are subject to amendment and re-issue. The inspector must ensure that the correct issue is worked to; the contract documents will usually make the matter clear, but in the absence of information the latest issue is implied. Sometimes supplies to an earlier issue are specifically requested, perhaps for replacement purposes.

Increasingly 'harmonization' is taking place between British and International Standards. For instance, certain British Standards may have dual numbering, with the ISO number appearing alongside the BS number on the title page, etc. Sometimes an ISO standard is approved for publication as a British Standard 'without deviation' (but with its own BS number). However, as some conventions terminology and spellings are not identical with British practice, attention is drawn to them in the BS national Foreword. No doubt the most important 'deviation' in these harmonized British Standards is the use of the *comma as the decimal point* (see p. 737).

British (and other) Standards are subject to amendment, replacement or cancellation, often frequently. The latest state of all British Standards is listed in the BSI Catalogue, issued annually. It is now the practice to place the number of any identical or relevant ISO standard alongside the BS standard in the numerical list in the BSI Catalogue.

Important or otherwise relevant US standards, sometimes somewhat equivalent to British Standards, are mentioned in this text and in the tables of standards which follow.

Copies of all British Standards, of the publications of international standards organizations and of most overseas standards can be obtained from BSI Sales Department, Linford Wood, Milton Keynes, MK14 6LE.

### References and further reading

J.M. Juran and others, *Quality Control handbook*, McGraw-Hill, 1974.

*Quality technology handbook*, UKAEA, NDT Centre, Harwell, 4th edition.

Coupland, J. (ed.), *Quality assurance and control; a bibliography of applications*, (contains references aimed at improving quality awareness, training, education, practices, product certification and use and development of British Standards), IEE/Peter Peregrinus, 1983.

Crosby, P. B., *Quality is free*, McGraw-Hill, 1978.

*Quality assurance in industry* (a short illustrated introduction) Soc. Motor Mfrs, 1980.

*Quality control*, Eng. Ind. Training Board, 1978.

*Inspecting and viewing*, Eng. Ind. Training Board, 1969.

*Inspection and measurement*, Eng. Ind. Training Board, 1969.

# 2   Materials testing

## 2.1  Engineering materials

Engineering materials can be classified generally as metallic or non-metallic.

*Metallic* materials may be sub-divided into ferrous and non-ferrous metals and alloys. The *ferrous* group consists of iron containing varying amounts of free or combined carbon, which may be alloyed with, generally, small amounts of other elements which confer special properties on the resulting materials. The *non-ferrous* group consists of all metals and alloys other than iron and its alloys. Occasionally however a non-ferrous alloy may contain a small percentage of iron.

*Non-metallic* materials include many of great importance in industry such as rubber and plastics, ceramics, glass, etc.

Most of the metals, and many non-metals, are of course used in construction, particularly of industrial and chemical plant.

A diagram showing the range of materials available is given in Fig. 2.1.

## 2.2  Selection and inspection of materials

When selecting and inspecting material for a particular purpose several aspects have to be considered:

(i) *Service conditions.* The material must possess the necessary mechanical strength and physical characteristics required by the design or specification, and must be able to withstand the appropriate environmental conditions. Suitable treatment may be required to achieve these ends.

(ii) *Ease of fabrication.* The material must be suitable for the method of fabrication envisaged. For instance, some grades of material are eminently suitable for welding, others may be readily machined and will take a high-quality surface finish, others may be suitable for casting, etc.

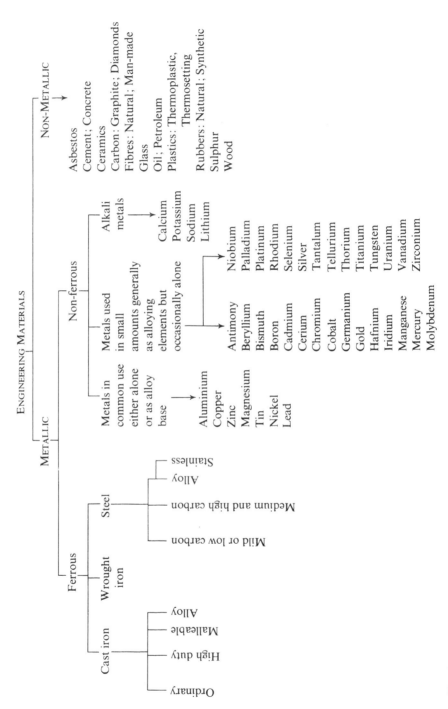

**Fig. 2.1 Principal engineering materials.**

14

(iii) *Economic considerations.* The material costs should be the lowest possible commensurate with satisfying specified requirements. In some instances the use of more expensive material might be economically justifiable if it would secure a longer operational life, *which could be usefully employed.* Scrap values obtainable for expensive materials are high and may even increase, whereas scrap values for some cheaper materials may be negligible.

(iv) *Compatibility.* Particularly for chemical and process plants, the materials selected must be compatible with one another, and must not adversely affect the chemical process in any way.

With regard to (i) above, there are many harsh environments which will attack the materials of construction. Metals may corrode or lose their strength, plastics may crack, craze or otherwise deteriorate. The rate of corrosion of a selected metal should in general be small, but in some cases a measure of corrosion is acceptable if the material will last the life intended under such conditions. A material may often be purposely selected, knowing that corrosion may take place, if it can be replaced during the life of the plant at less total cost than by using a more expensive material initially. However, if contamination by corrosion products is unacceptable then a corrosion resisting (and generally more expensive) material will have to be used.

Thus an inspector will be concerned with carrying out, witnessing or approving tests and examinations of materials to determine their mechanical, physical and chemical properties.

Regarding (iv), compatibility, dissimilar metals in contact or proximity may set up corrosion (see 12.6 and 12.8(8)); some materials and chemicals may not safely be left in proximity or contact for fear of some hazard, such as the evolution of gas or heat (extreme examples are water in contact with calcium or sodium metal, or steam playing on zirconium metal).

Very often, especially with new designs of process plant, laboratory testing of possible materials of construction whilst in contact with the process fluids, materials, etc. *under operating conditions* may be desirable.

Somewhat associated with compatibility is catalysis. A catalyst is a solid, liquid or gas whose presence may cause or accelerate a chemical reaction between other materials but is not itself permanently affected by the process and does not enter into the composition of the product so formed. Thus heating hydrogen and nitrogen at high pressure in the presence of osmium or ruthenium can be used to produce synthetic ammonia.

Many catalysts are widely used in the petroleum industry in catalytic cracking plants for the production of petroleum products. The production of synthetic rubber also depends on the use of suitable catalysts.

However, the inspector should also realize that destructive reactions of materials may be accelerated by the perhaps unsuspected presence of a small quantity of some material or impurity acting as a catalyst; if necessary he should seek specialist advice.

## 2.3 Mechanical properties

Many properties of a material are checked by mechanical tests, generally involving the destruction or deformation of a test specimen. Such mechanical tests can, in general, be classified as:

(i) Design or investigational tests, whose primary purpose is to acquire data. Such tests can be complex and long-term.

(ii) Routine or acceptance tests, whose primary purpose is to see if the material satisfies a specification, etc. Such tests should be simple, cheap and reliable, but it must be realized that they only supply an arbitrary basis for comparison and acceptance.

The principal mechanical tests carried out are those for tensile strength, ductility, hardness, impact and creep. Other mechanical tests deal with strength under compression and shear. It should be mentioned that lack of reliable data on the mechanical and other properties of materials leads to the use of higher factors of safety than necessary. Factors of safety for many metallic materials at temperatures up to the order of 650°F (343°C) have, in the past, varied from 4 to 5 in the UK, but from 3 to 4 in the USA. Detailed information on mechanical testing, the machines used, and the theory of the strength of materials is given in many textbooks (see list of references at the end of this chapter).

### 2.3.1 Some limitations affecting test results

In any form of material testing the specimen selected is supposed to be representative of that material. But it is not always possible to achieve this. That material may not be homogenous; it may contain impurities, inclusions, hidden faults, etc. not present in the test piece. Several specimens may be selected and may give variable results. A specimen may have minute surface or sub-surface cracks or defects.

The effect of temperature is crucial and must be specified and kept constant during a test. A previous high temperature excursion may have seriously affected a specimen. The results of test undertaken in different laboratories, on different machines and with somewhat different test pieces may differ. The method and precision of stress application etc. can affect results. The tensile test data may be of limited design value because they are obtained by a uni-axial test whereas in service there may be multi-axial stresses and concentrations. Similarly the speed of testing may bear little resemblance to conditions in practice.

Nevertheless despite the arbitrary nature of some acceptance tests the inspector has to see that they are carried out exactly to specification, and has to sentence the material on the results obtained. By and large the system works reasonably well as a yardstick, and at least completely incorrect material is rejected.

Perhaps of more practical importance is maintaining the identity of the material with its test piece. This should be ensured by the inspection procedure and documentation (e.g. see 9.1.1(3) and 9.4). But any experienced inspector will know that mistakes can and do occur; for instance important finished components, supposedly made from high tensile steel were found (by inspector's luck) to be made of mild steel. The documentation was in order, to full AID requirements but the system had failed! — there must have been a change of material in store or transit!

## 2.4 Tensile testing

Tensile tests are used for the determination of properties such as yield, proof stress, permanent set stress, tensile strength, percentage elongation and reduction of area, Young's modulus, etc.

Such tests are made by using one of the many designs of testing machine available, the load being applied to the material test piece generally via a lever or screw system or by hydraulic power. Facilities are provided for controlling (and measuring) the amount of load and of the corresponding strain. The load may be applied in increments and the deformation read for each, or it may be continuously and slowly increased at a constant rate; it is sometimes applied until fracture occurs. The extension of the specimen during loading may be measured by some form of extensometer or strain gauge, and can be continuously recorded.

If the speed of testing has any appreciable influence on results it should be stipulated in the material specification. For metals the rate (or range of rates) of straining may be given, a slower rate being specified up to the yield point: an elapsed time for the test may be specified. For textiles particularly, a constant rate of stressing (loading) may be specified; however, the test results for a given fabric obtained by this method will generally differ from those obtained with constant rate of traverse of the driven clamp. Rubber and similar materials are tested using a specified constant rate of traverse of the driven grip or pulley (measured under 'no-load' conditions). The load must be applied axially and the method of gripping the test piece should be specified.

The *tensile testing of metals* at room temperature is covered by BS 18. The latest issue (1987), now dealing with both ferrous and non-ferrous metals, reverts to one part but incorporates Appendices A and B describing proving tests for the verification of permanent set strength and proof strength (see the Appendix of this book, Legal metrology, which also refers to BS 1610 *Methods for the load verification of testing machines*). Included are tensile tests previously given in Section One of Part 1 of British Standard (Aerospace series) 4A4, and some special requirements for aerospace materials which may be referred to as Category 2 requirements (materials tested to other than aerospace requirement may be referred to as Category 1). Specific requirements concerning the rate of straining of the test piece (in line with ISO recommendations), are given; these are particularly important when determining yield strength and proof stress. Non-ferrous metals, however, do not usually exhibit a yield phenomenon. BS 3688 deals with the tensile testing of metals at elevated temperatures. As the detailed definition (and nature) of some of the tensile stress–strain properties required may vary from time to time, and in different organizations, countries, etc., some definitions (generally in accordance with the latest British Standards and ISO 6892) and comments are given below. These apply specifically to metals, but are applicable to non-metals where appropriate. Note that appropriate tensile properties are now referred to as strengths rather than stresses.

### 2.4.1 Tensile testing definitions

*Gauge length* ($L$). Length of the cylindrical or prismatic portion of the test piece defined and used for measurement of elongation or extension.

*Original gauge length* ($L_o$). The test piece gauge length before the application of force (i.e. as marked on the test piece).

*Final gauge length* ($L_u$). The test piece gauge length after rupture, the pieces having been carefully fitted together so that their axes are aligned.

*Extensometer gauge length* ($L_e$). The length of the parallel portion of the test piece used for the measurement of extension by means of an extensometer.

*Yield.* An increase of strain without increase of stress.

*Yield strength* ($R_e$). The stress at the point reached during the test when plastic deformation occurs without any increase in the force (in materials exhibiting a yield phenomenon).

*Upper yield strength* ($R_{eH}$). The value of stress at the moment when the first decrease in force at yield is observed (i.e. when yield begins).

*Lower yield strength* ($R_{eL}$). The lowest value of stress during plastic yielding (i.e. at which it proceeds).

In practice yield strength may be taken as the stress at which a sudden increase occurs in the distance between the gauge points of the test piece, as indicated by direct measurement, a distinct drop of the testing machine lever, or a marked hesitation or fall-back in the movement of the indicating pointer. This corresponds to the upper yield strength. (The terms upper and lower yield point are used in North America.) Yield strength ($R_e$) is not applicable to materials which do not show a clearly defined yield point; for these a determination of proof strength or of permanent set strength may be specified.

*Proof strength* ($R_p$). The stress which produces, *while the load is still applied*, a non-proportional extension equal to a specified percentage of the (original) extensometer gauge length (e.g. 0·2% proof strength, written $R_{p0·2}$). Proof strength as used in British specifications is very similar to the American ASTM *yield strength*—the stress at which a material exhibits a specified limiting permanent set, or deviation from the proportionality of stress to strain. However, the method of test must be stated. ASTM yield strength is customarily determined by (a) an offset method (usually a strain of 0·2%) or (b) total extension under load (usually a strain of 0·5%). The values obtained may differ.

*Elastic limit* and *proportional limit* can be considered as values of the yield strength for which the limiting set is zero. The latter is the more readily obtainable, as it is the stress at which the stress–strain curve departs from linearity, and it may be slightly higher than the elastic limit.

*Permanent set strength* ($R_r$). The stress which, *after removal of the load*, has produced a permanent extension (set) which is a specified percentage of the gauge length. In describing it the specified percentage permanent extension must be quoted (e.g. 0·2% permanent set strength).

*Tensile strength* ($R_m$), previously called ultimate tensile stress (UTS). The maximum load ($F_m$) which the test piece withstands during a test (to fracture) divided by its original cross-sectional area.

*Percentage elongation after fracture* ($A$). The permanent increase in length ($L_u - L_o$) expressed as a percentage of the original gauge length, i.e. $100(L_u - L_o)/L_o$. It is important that the results should detail the test piece used and the gauge length.

*Percentage reduction in area after fracture* ($Z$). The maximum decrease of cross-sectional area ($S_o - S_u$) expressed as a percentage of the original cross-sectional area, i.e. $100(S_o - S_u)/S_o$.

*Young's modulus of elasticity* is the ratio of stress to strain during the elastic behaviour of the test piece.

Various methods of obtaining the properties mentioned above are detailed in the relevant specifications, e.g. BS 18, BS 4 A 4, ASTM E 8, etc. (see Table 2.1).

*Standard tensile test pieces* are of dumb-bell shape and of round or rectangular cross-section. Implicit in these definitions is the knowledge that multi-axial loading and/or the presence of notches can change the value of stress at which yield and rupture may occur.

To ensure that comparable values for percentage elongation are obtained from different forms and sizes of metallic test pieces it is recommended (by the International Standards Organization (ISO) and BS 3894) that such test pieces should have an original gauge length bearing a specified relationship to the cross-sectional area. For these proportional test pieces the recommended relationship is:

$$\text{Gauge length} = 5{\cdot}65\sqrt{\text{original cross-sectional area}}$$

Other non-proportional sizes of test piece may be called for in existing specifications, but to convert the percentage elongation figures obtained from these so that they can be compared with other sizes needs the use of approximate empirical methods.

The actual position in the sample of material from which the test piece is taken may make a considerable difference to the results obtained, especially for some materials. In such cases it should be clearly defined in the material specification. The method of gripping the test piece can affect results and is often specified.

It should also be realized that many materials are anisotropic, i.e. their properties depend upon the direction in which they are measured. Again, manufacturing variations in cooling rates, rolling temperature, chemical composition throughout an ingot, etc. can occasionally cause variations in mechanical properties of as much as 20% in the same batch of material.

It is almost traditional to mark the ends of the gauge length on the test piece by means of centre punch dots, etc. The inspector should realize that for notch-sensitive materials such incised markings may lead to premature failure. In such cases the specimen can be painted with a quick-drying ink and the gauge length marked on this by fine scribed lines.

Tensile test pieces for non-metallic materials are of generally similar form, details being given in the relevant material specification. In some instances shapes other than the dumb-bell pattern may be specified.

Information regarding ductility can be obtained from a tensile test (the material's elongation and reduction in area before fracture providing a measure of it), and also from simple and reverse bend tests, cupping tests, etc. Calibration of test equipment must be traceable directly or indirectly to National Physical Laboratory (NPL) standards, generally through the British Calibration Service.

## 2.5 Hardness testing

Hardness tests, to determine the resistance of a material to indentation, are usually carried out on Brinell, diamond pyramid (Vickers) or Rockwell testing machines, but other machines such as the Herbert pendulum, Shore scleroscope, etc. may be used for particular purposes or materials. The Brinell machine is particularly suitable for testing forgings and castings, and may use a 10 mm diameter hardened steel ball indenter. The indentation produced on an article may sometimes be objectionable, especially on thin or polished surfaces. In such cases smaller diameter balls (with smaller loads) may be permissible, or the Vickers machine with its much smaller square-based pyramid-shaped diamond indenter may be used. It is recommended that the Brinell machine should only be used when the thickness of the material being tested is not less than 8 times the depth of the indentation produced.

The diameter of the ball, $D$ (mm), and the load $P$ (kg) used should be stated in the test results, whilst the value of the ratio $P/D^2$ should be stated in the material specification. Generally a ratio of 30 is used for ferrous materials, 10 for copper and aluminium alloys, 5 for copper and aluminium, and 1 for lead, tin and their alloys.

$$\text{Then Brinell hardness number (HB)} = \frac{P\,(\text{kg})}{\substack{\text{spherical surface area} \\ \text{of indentation (mm}^2)}}$$

The latest revised British Standard (BS 240:1986) introduces a tungsten carbide ball which is harder and should preferably be used for values above 350 HB up to 600 HB (the limit of this standard). For values up to 450 HB either hardened steel or tungsten carbide may be used, but in the range 350 HB to 450 HB the hardness values obtained may differ significantly. Although in this standard the test force (load) is given in newtons, each value of force is such that the same hardness numbers as previously are maintained (and the same four standard values of the ratio $P/D^2$ have been adopted).

When stating a Brinell hardness number the symbol HBS (for steel) or HBW (for tungsten) should be preceded by the hardness value and followed by an index indicating the test conditions, e.g. 226 HBS 10/3000 (where 10 mm is the diameter of the steel ball, and 3000 is the load symbol (corresponding) to a test force of 29·42 kN. This should be followed by the dwell time of full force (in seconds), *if* this is different from the standard dwell time of 10 to 15 seconds. Note that Load symbol = 0·102 × test force (in newtons).

The finite limit of accuracy obtainable from a Brinell hardness test is ±2% HB.

The Brinell machine is unsuitable for use on very hard materials, as the ball will flatten, causing low readings, and the Vickers machine is preferable. When giving readings of Vickers diamond pyramid hardness number (abbreviation HV) the load employed should be stated (e.g. HV/20 = 600).

The accuracy of the results obtained depends upon the microscope used, which in general should be capable of measuring the diagonals of the indentation to better than 1 μm.

The Rockwell machine is widely used in North America. The hardness number (HR) is determined directly by measuring the depth of indentation, rather than from its area divided into the load as with the Brinell and Vickers machines. It may use some 8 different scales, each associated with different loads and indenters (diamond cones or steel balls), although scales A, B and C are the principal scales used for steel. In the UK it is much used for checking the uniformity of hardness of a batch of material, but for accurate numerical results the Brinell (in its own particular sphere) and the Vickers machines may be preferred. Test results must be expressed as a hardness number on the relevant scale (e.g. HR = C20 or B100).

Readings obtained from different types of machine may bear an empirical relationship to one another. For steel (at least) there is also an approximate relationship between hardness and tensile strength:

$$\text{Tensile strength (ton/in}^2) = 0 \cdot 22 \times \text{Brinell hardness number (HB)} \qquad \text{or}$$

$$\text{Tensile strength (N/mm}^2) = 3 \cdot 39 \times \text{Brinell hardness number (HB)}$$

The multiplying factor will vary some $\pm 5\%$ according to the type, condition, etc. of the steel. See also BS 860 *Tables for comparison of hardness scales.* Hardness testing is a valuable guide to the effectiveness of heat treatment.

A rough comparative check with a portable hardness tester enables components for instance made incorrectly in mild steel instead of high tensile steel (see 2.3.1) to be quickly sorted out.

The abbreviations used for hardness number are those given by BSI. Other abbreviations such as BHN, DPN, RHN are widely used both in the USA and UK.

### 2.6 Impact (notched bar) testing

The purpose of impact testing is to determine the resistance of a material to dynamic (shock) loading, and to assess its tendency to brittle fracture. This tendency is increased by the presence of a notch in the test piece, by high rates of loading and by low temperatures. Cold tests involving assessment of a ductile/brittle transition temperature may be required.

Commercial impact tests are usually carried out on notched bar test pieces, which are cantilever in form in the Izod test, and of beam form in the Charpy test.

Such tests give information which tensile or hardness tests alone may not. The results are particularly sensitive to variations in structure due to heat treatment (especially with steel), and to minor changes in composition and manufacturing procedure, as well as to the type of notching. In general the tougher the material the greater the energy required to fracture the test piece.

Toughness can be described as resistance to shock, and expressed in terms of the work required to produce rupture. This work is dependent on the rate of loading and the type of notch. A full evaluation of the 'toughness' of a material and an understanding of its behaviour may be complex; experiments on detailed stress–strain–time relationships and elastic energy absorption may be required.

For example, two steels, of high and low carbon content respectively, may give the same impact values (i.e. absorb the same energy) when tested commercially. A careful experimental test however (Fig. 2.2) may show that the former has a high resistance to deformation and requires a high load to initiate fracture; but it then ruptures abruptly in a typically brittle manner, and the curve may fall to zero immediately, the metal breaking 'like a carrot' with a fracture which is entirely crystalline. The second steel may begin to deform under a relatively low load, but it may not fracture entirely, even when the maximum permissible angle of bend has been attained. The specimens, although absorbing similar energies as evidenced by the area under each curve, and therefore similar when tested commercially, could behave very differently in service.

True impact testing (unnotched) and notched bar testing (i.e. most commercial impact tests) are really quite different. At ordinary temperatures a ductile material may not fracture under impact, but the presence of a notch enhances this possibility. Its tendency to act like a brittle material when notched may be referred to as 'notch sensitivity'.

It is considered that notched tests (especially if complete stress–strain–time curves are obtained) can give an indication of the ability of a material

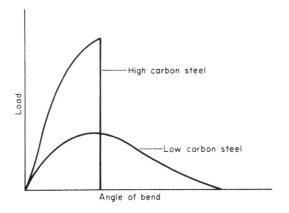

**Fig. 2.2** **Slow bend test on two steel samples possessing similar impact values.**

to resist the spread of a crack (after it has once formed), and of its capacity to resist the effects of stress concentration at a change of section.

However, ASTM Standard A 370 describes the impact test on steel for production purposes as follows:

'... a dynamic test in which a specimen ..., usually notched, is struck and broken by a single blow ... and the energy absorbed is measured. The energy values are qualitative comparisons ... and cannot be converted into energy figures ... for design calculations. ... Minimum impact requirements are generally specified only for ... heat-treated materials ...'

Thus, commercially, impact tests are useful as acceptance tests, tests of identity and checks on heat treatment and changes in manufacturing procedure. They are also useful in testing materials required for service at low temperature in order to obtain an indication as to whether adequate toughness is maintained at such temperatures.

It is customary to record details of any notch and the energy absorbed in breaking the test piece and also the appearance of the fracture. The fractured surface will contain a fibrous (ductile) area and a crystalline (brittle) area. Determination of the percentage crystallinity may be required.

When carrying out any impact test the inspector should note that the results are very sensitive to temperature change even within the normal atmospheric range. Consequently the actual temperature of the test should be reported.

This may be seen from Fig. 2.3 which also shows the ductile to brittle transition of two types of structural steel at descending temperatures. Curves 1, 2 and 3 are for the same material, but with differing heat treatment; curve 4 is for a quenched and tempered carbon steel. The transition temperature may be sharp or diffuse, and may occur well below 0°C for steels required for cryogenic use (see 7.8), at approximately room temperature for many quenched and tempered steels, or well above room temperature for some normalized or as-rolled carbon steels (especially weldments of such material).

The transition temperature rises with an increase in the sharpness of the notch or the speed of striking. Thus a sudden shock at room temperature on a component containing a small defect, such as a minute fatigue crack, would tend to cause it to behave in a manner characteristic of a much lower temperature, and brittle fracture and catastrophic failure might result. Consequently, as service conditions may be more severe than the British Standard impact test at room temperature, many steels for special applications are required to undergo impact tests at say −40°C. The presence of carbon, sulphur, silicon and phosphorus in steel tends to increase its transition temperature, whilst manganese and nickel lower it. It is also increased by exposure to neutron irradiation.

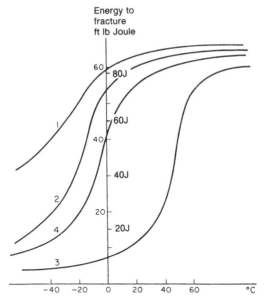

**Fig. 2.3   Impact tests showing ductile/brittle transition of two types of steel at descending temperatures.**
1 Special steel—quenched and tempered      3 Special steel—normalized
2 Special steel—incorrect heat treatment      4 Ordinary carbon steel

No reliable relationship has been found between different types of impact test (and between test pieces differing in size and shape). Conversions from Izod impact test results to Charpy V notch or U notch values are not advisable (although some test data giving approximate guidance on correlating one with the other have been published in the past). In view of the difficulties of carrying out the Izod tests at other than ambient temperatures it is recommended that the Charpy V notch test be used for testing at subambient and elevated temperatures.

## 2.7  Creep testing

Creep tests are carried out to determine the behaviour of a material under constant load (usually tensile) for long periods (especially at high temperatures). The material may gradually deform plastically at stresses below its normal yield point, and eventually fracture at a figure well below its normal strength. This is known as creep. (Figs. 2.4 and 2.5.)

Above a certain temperature and stress, known as the limiting creep stress below which creep is not normally expected to occur, a steadily loaded specimen will extend initially upon application of the load (A–B, Fig. 2.4).

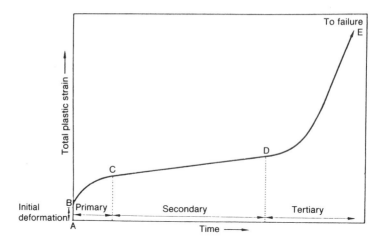

**Fig. 2.4  Tensile creep curve (constant load).**
A–B *Plastic* portion of the loading curve (initial deformation).
B–C *Primary stage* in which rate of strain decreases with time.
C–D *Secondary stage* in which an approximately constant rate of strain occurs until the effect of the applied stress and temperature initiates changes within the material.
D–E *Tertiary stage* in which the rapidly increasing rate of strain terminates in failure.

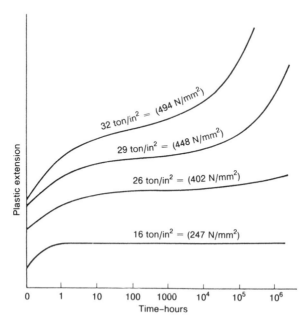

**Fig. 2.5  Creep curves for a material at different loadings.**

Then as time passes the material extends plastically (B–C) at a considerable but gradually diminishing strain rate (primary creep) until a nearly uniform rate is reached. This secondary stage of creep (C–D) may continue for several years until finally the plastic deformation rate increases again and in this tertiary stage (D–E) proceeds to fracture.

The majority of tests are broken off at the end of the secondary stage (i.e. before fracture) and the total elongation measured. The creep rate is then given by the ratio:

$$\frac{\text{Elongation during secondary stage}}{\text{Time of secondary stage}}$$

Short-term creep tests for production batch acceptance purposes require that a certain total extension shall not be exceeded at a certain time and temperature (e.g. see BS 3500: Part 5). Long-term tests up to 100,000 hours (11·4 years) are used in evaluating different types of material, since extrapolation of data, although sometimes necessary, is still uncertain despite recent advances in this field.

Creep must be considered when a material is used at a temperature approaching its recrystallization temperature, for example steel above some 500°C, and when low-melting-point metals (such as lead or tin) are used at room temperatures. However creep tests are usually carried out at elevated temperatures.

*Creep strength* is the stress which, at the specified temperature, produces a minimum specified creep rate (often 0·001% or 0·0001% per hour).

*Rupture strength* is the stress which, at the specified temperature, permits a life prior to rupture of a specified time (perhaps 1000 or 10,000 hours).

Creep data may be presented graphically in many ways, of which perhaps log strain plotted against log creep rate is the most reliable, and appears to allow extrapolation with a fair measure of confidence.

## 2.8 Fatigue testing

If a material is subjected to repeated stresses fluctuating in magnitude and/or direction (including those associated with vibration) it may fail at a figure well below its normal static strength. This is known as a *fatigue failure*, and because of it greater factors of safety must be allowed under dynamic loads than under steady conditions.

A fatigue failure may occur suddenly without any appreciable deformation; it exhibits a characteristic brittle appearance at fracture, even with ductile materials.

A variety of fatigue testing machines are in use which impose a cyclic range of stress (which may be tension, compression or shear, or a combination of these) on a specimen with the object generally of determining its *fatigue limit*. This limit can be defined as the value of the stress condition below which a material may endure an infinite number of stress cycles.

The stress condition is usually designated by the mean value of the fluctuating stress ($S_m$) together with the amplitude of the superimposed alternating stress ($S_a$).

*Fatigue strength* (or endurance limit) is the value of the stress condition under which the test specimen would have a life of $N$ cycles.

If a test is carried out to determine *fatigue life* (or endurance)—the number of stress cycles to failure—then failure can be taken as either the occurrence of a visible fatigue crack or complete failure.

Many fatigue tests employ a number (say 10) of similar test pieces, each of which is subjected to a particular stress amplitude, and the results are expressed in the form of an *S–N* curve of stress amplitude against endurance (in cycles).

Fatigue tests are not meant to be acceptance tests for materials, but rather investigatory tests. They may also be conducted under specific environmental conditions (including corrosive conditions).

Associated with true fatigue is the so-called fatigue fracture in which a creeping crack gradually develops and extends from some minor fault or imperfection until it reduces the available cross-section of the material to such a value that fracture occurs. Fatigue can start from any point of stress concentration, so it is important that the inspector should look out for sharp corners, abrupt changes of section, etc. in any highly stressed parts. In particular, non-metallic inclusions (especially at or near the surface), tool marks, scratches, blemishes, corrosion pitting and surface defects generally should be avoided. Identification markings stamped into the surface (and even inspection stamps!) have been known to set up stress concentrations and small cracks which are self-perpetuating and continue to tear until failure occurs. Polishing, by removing some surface defects, can improve fatigue resistance due to creeping cracks. Surface finish and polishing should be performed in a direction parallel with the principal stress in order to improve fatigue life (may be by some 10% or more of the rough state). Surface coatings which harden the surface may improve matters. So can the use of a tougher and more ductile, rather than a stronger, material. However, the use of a material of higher strength will improve the true fatigue resistance. The importance of achieving a high notched bar value on impact test in retarding crack propagation will be seen. This creeping crack type of fatigue is nothing more than the fracture resulting from such a test carried out on a full-scale component under fluctuating stresses and acting on an accidentally produced notch. Corrosion (especially by oxygen) will reduce fatigue life. The basic effect of irradiation on steels is to increase the tensile and yield strength and decrease ductility. Fatigue properties may be increased, and high-cycle fatigue life may be increased and low-cycle fatigue life reduced. The effect of increased temperature is much the same as with non-irradiated material (the fatigue life of many steels is virtually unaffected by temperatures up to 650°F (343°C), but above the creep range is much reduced). See ASTM STP 463 *Irradiation effects on structural alloys for nuclear reactor application.*

### 2.8.1 Crack opening displacement (COD) testing and fracture mechanics

In tough materials (where a considerable plastic zone is created ahead of a crack) Wells suggested that unstable extension of a crack occurs at a critical value of local displacement near the tip of the crack (termed COD or CTOD) and assumed that this critical value found in a test specimen is the same as that in an actual structure of similar thickness. These critical values of COD are established experimentally by extensometer (or clip gauge) measurements on notched test specimens for particular materials under particular conditions of temperature, etc. (WWP—Wells Wide Plate tests).

In order to avoid failure the material at the crack tip must be able to withstand this value of applied COD.

BS 5762 details the method for COD testing on metallic materials, specifying requirements for test pieces, test equipment, and the analysis of data and the recording of results. See also references at the end of this chapter.

The test method and test specimens are similar to those specified for $K_{Ic}$ testing in BS 5447 *Plane strain fracture toughness ($K_{Ic}$) of metallic materials* (which may be used where there is very little plastic flow at the tip of a crack—see also ASTM E399). For another method of establishing fracture toughness ($K_{Ic}$) see Irvine and Quirk, 1971.

An impact test imposes a high rate of strain on a test sample, whilst a standard tensile and fracture toughness test is carried out at a lower rate. Neither test is necessarily similar to conditions met in practice.

BS 6729 *Determination of the dynamic fracture toughness of metallic materials* deals with intermediate rates of strain but at loading rates greater than those described in BS 5762 and BS 5447, that cause rates of increase in stress intensity factor* between 80 and $10^5$ N.mm$^{-1.5}$.s$^{-1}$ (0·0316 MN.m$^{-1.5}$ = 0·0316 MPa.m$^{0.5}$) and rates of increase of less than 150 mm/s. It describes procedures for assessing the crack opening displacement (COD) and plane strain fracture toughness ($K_{Ic}$) of metallic materials at these higher rates of loading. Such fracture toughness measurements are termed dynamic.

---

*Stress intensity factor ($K_I$) is the elastic stress field intensification at the tip of a crack subjected to an opening mode. It is a function of applied force, crack length and test piece geometry, having units of stress × length$^{0.5}$.

The main method described, although requiring relatively elaborate facilities and a suitable tensile testing machine, is considered to be worthy of adoption as a standard method, although refinements can be expected. A more readily applied method for providing an approximate assessment at higher rates than the standard is given in an appendix to the standard for the guidance of the users.

The principle used involves first the development of a crack at the bottom of a machined notch in the test piece by the application of a cyclic load. This crack is then caused to propagate by applying an increasing tensile or bending force. The displacement (measured by the crack mouth opening clip gauge) and the force at which the fatigue crack begins to extend, or has extended by a specified amount, are then determined and a curve is then plotted. Details of the procedures and the calculations and formulae involved are given in the standard.

Note that plane strain fracture toughness ($K_{Ic}$) is indicative of a material's resistance to crack growth under conditions of high constraint to limited plastic deformation. It is the critical value of $K_I$ at which the first significant extension of the crack occurs (when under the influence of a rising force).

From the results of these fracture toughness tests the maximum size of defect which will not cause brittle fracture can be determined for any material for which the $K_{Ic}$ or COD values are known. See PD 6493 *Guidance on some methods for the derivation of acceptance levels for defects in fusion welded joints*, BSI (1980).

Fracture mechanics may also be used to find out what combination of lowest temperature with operating pressure can be safely used without risking catastrophic failure. With such information it is possible to ensure that any defect in a vessel will develop slowly by plastic yielding and will show itself by slow leaking or by NDT monitoring rather than by sudden catastrophic brittle fracture.

With plant and equipment subject to cyclic stresses fracture mechanics can determine the number of stress reversals required before a crack develops to a size sufficient to cause brittle fracture.

### 2.9 Standards for mechanical testing

The publications of the British Standards Institution and the American Society for Testing and Materials contain a wealth of information and definitions on testing and testing methods of considerable use to the inspector.

A list of British Standards dealing with mechanical testing (mainly applicable to metals), together with some approximately equivalent ASTM Standards is given in Table 2.1. Where an ISO Standard exists it is listed alongside the BS entry in the BSI catalogue.

**TABLE 2.1**

*Some standards for mechanical testing*

| BS No. | Description | Approximate equivalent ASTM No. |
|---|---|---|
| 18 | Methods for tensile testing of metals | E 8 |
| 240 | Method for Brinell hardness test and for verification of Brinell hardness testing machines | E 10 |
| 427 | Method for Vickers hardness test | E 92 |
| | Part 1: Testing of metals | |
| | Part 2: Verification of the testing machine | |
| 891 | Method for Rockwell hardness test | E 18 |
| | Part 1: Testing of metals | |
| | Part 2: Verification of the testing machine | |
| 4175 | Method for Rockwell superficial hardness test (N & T scales) | E 18 |
| 131 | Methods for notched bar tests | E 23, STP 23, 176, 466 |
| | Part 1: The Izod impact test on metals | |
| | Part 2: Charpy V-notch impact test | |
| | Part 3: Charpy U-notch impact test on metals | A 593 |
| | Part 4: Calibration of pendulum impact testing machines for metals | |
| | Part 5: Determination of crystallinity | |
| 1639 | Methods for bend testing of metals | |
| 4 A 4 | Test pieces and test methods for metallic materials for aircraft (includes reverse bend, elevated temperature, uninterrupted creep and rupture tests) | |
| 860 | Table for comparison of hardness scales | E 140 (also ANSI 76.4) |
| 1610 | Methods for the load verification of testing machines | E 4, 74 |
| 3228 | Procedures for obtaining properties of steel at elevated temperatures | |
| | Part 1: Proof stress (superseded by BS 3920) | |
| | Part 2: Rupture strength | |
| | Part 3: Creep strength | |
| 3500 | Methods for creep and rupture testing of metals | E 139 |
| | Part 1: Tensile rupture testing | |
| | Part 3: Tensile creep testing | |
| | Part 5: Production acceptance tests | E150 |
| | Part 6: Tensile stress relaxation testing | |

**TABLE 2.1** *concluded*

| BS No. | Description | Approximate equivalent ASTM No. |
|---|---|---|
| 3518 | Methods of fatigue testing | E 206 |
| | Part 1: General principles | (definitions) |
| | Part 2: Rotating bending fatigue tests | |
| | Part 3: Direct stress fatigue tests | |
| | Part 4: Torsional stress fatigue tests | |
| | Part 5: Guide to the application of statistics | |
| 3688 | Methods for mechanical testing of metals at elevated temperatures | |
| | Part 1: Tensile testing | E 151 |
| 3846 | Methods for calibration and grading of extensometers for testing of metals | E 83 |
| 3855 | Method for modified Erichsen cupping test for sheet and strip metal | A 344 |
| 3894 | Method for converting elongation values for steel | |
| 3920 | Deriving and verifying the minimum elevated temperature proof or yield stress properties of steel products | |
| 4437 | Method for the end-quench hardenability test for steel (Jominy test) | A 255 |
| 4545 | Mechanical testing of steel wire | |
| 4759 | Determination of K-values of a tensile testing system | |
| 5447 | Plane strain fracture toughness ($K_{Ic}$) of metallic materials | |
| 5762 | Methods for crack opening displacement (COD) testing | |
| 6729 | Determination of the dynamic fracture toughness of metallic materials | |
| | Compression testing of metallic materials | E 9 |
| | Effect of high-energy radiation on the tensile and impact properties of metallic materials | E 184 |
| | Methods and definitions for mechanical testing of steel products | A 370 |
| | Drop weight test to determine nil ductility transition temperature of ferritic steels | E 208 |
| | Manual on fatigue testing | STP 91 |
| | Fracture toughness testing at cryogenic temperatures | STP 496 |
| | Charpy V-notch testing requirements for steel plates for pressure vessels | A 593 |

## 2.10 Physical examination of materials

Materials are inspected and tested to determine various physical properties, e.g. thermal, electrical and magnetic characteristics, density, dimensions, etc. Inspection may be necessary to detect any defects or blemishes present in the material which might detract from its serviceability. Many of these defects will be obvious, often in the raw material stage; it should be noted that surface defects often carry the greatest stress. Less obvious defects will require the assistance of non-destructive testing techniques in order to find them (see Chapter 10).

Inspection may be necessary during and after any machining or heat treatment to check that these processes have been carried out satisfactorily and that they have not produced any physical defects such as cracks.

A metallographic examination may be necessary, the primary object of which is to study the structure of a metallic specimen, and so to determine any inherent or processing defects. This can be done by means of a macro-examination (which may be a visual or low-power examination up to say 10 magnifications); if necessary a microscopic examination can be made (up to say 1200 magnifications).

The direction of grain flow may be of importance with many materials and components (such as forgings), as it produces directional strength. This flow can be seen by cutting a sample, polishing its surface and then etching. Examination of this macro-section may reveal other defects, such as segregation of alloying elements, impurities, voids, inclusions, etc. The non-metallic inclusion content of steel, and other metals, is of importance in many applications, and can be determined by macroscopic and microscopic methods. An electrolytic oxalic acid etching test, followed by a microscopic examination, may be carried out on corrosion-resisting steel to check for intergranular disintegration (see 2.13).

Some standards dealing with such matters are given in Table 2.2.

### TABLE 2.2

*Some metallographic standards*

| Specification No. | Description |
| --- | --- |
| BS 4490 | Determination of the austenitic grain size of steel |
| BS 5166 | Method for metallographic replica techniques of surface examination |
| BS 5600 | Power metallurgical materials and products |
| BS 5903 | Method for determination of resistance to intergranular corrosion of austenitic stainless steels: copper sulphate—sulphuric acid method (Moneypenny Strauss test) |
| BS 6285 | Macrographic examination of steel by sulphur print (Baumann method) |

**TABLE 2.2** *concluded*

| Specification No. | Description |
| --- | --- |
| BS 6533 | Macroscopic examination of steel by etching with strong mineral acids |
| ASTM E 2 | Preparation of micrographs of metal and alloys |
| ASTM E 3 | Preparation of metallographic specimens |
| ASTM E 7 | Standard definitions of terms relating to metallography |
| ASTM A 262 | Boiling nitric acid test for corrosion-resisting steels (includes etching test) |
| ASTM A 317 | Macro-etch testing and inspection of steel forgings |
| ASTM E 45 | Determining the inclusion content of steel |
| ASTM E 112 | Estimating average grain size of metals |

### 2.11  Chemical and spectrographic analysis of materials

Changes in chemical composition from the agreed specification can greatly affect quality, and for many years it was customary to control the chemical composition of material by wet chemical analysis methods. Such methods are time-consuming and need skilled personnel, and—what is more—the results are not usually available until *after* the product has been made or partly fabricated. Often in consequence, like a post mortem, it is too late to do anything about the batch or mix in question. In recent years however methods of rapid chemical analysis have been developed which give results in a few minutes or less, so that it is often possible to take rectifying action to bring, say, a particular melt within specification limits before it is cast.

The *optical spectrograph* enables rapid analyses of impurities and alloying elements to be made when they are present in concentrations not exceeding 5%.

The first analysers were those using a light beam derived from a high-tension spark struck on the sample. This beam is concentrated onto a prism, crystal or grating where it is diffracted to produce a spectrum. As all elements have known fixed wavelengths, the constituents of the sample can readily be determined from the presence of peaks at different wavelengths in this spectrum, whilst their relative quantities can be assessed by measuring the heights of these peaks. The spectrum may be recorded on a photographic negative, which can then be compared with a standard spectrum for the material in question to assist quick assessment. Alternatively, by the use of photo-multipliers and electronic counters, an almost instantaneous indication and/or recording of the analysis can be made. Accuracy can be increased by using optical equipment of quartz and enclosing the light path in vacuum to reduce absorption in the ultra-violet region.

For greater accuracy X-ray fluorescence spectrometer analysis is used. The sample being analysed is irradiated by an intense beam of X-rays covering a broad frequency spectrum. Some of this radiation is absorbed, causing secondary or fluorescent radiation to be emitted characteristic of the elements present. Part of this fluorescent beam is collimated and directed onto the surface of an analysing crystal, where it diffracted as a series of lines having wavelengths characteristic of the elements present and intensities comparable with the concentrations of these elements. The X-ray diffraction pattern obtained is recorded; it is then compared with the pattern obtained from carefully analysed reference standards as a basis for determining the composition of the sample.

In most modern instruments, to reduce the absorption of radiation, the sample and the fluorescent path are almost invariably under vacuum. Instruments may be operated manually or can be arranged to print out results automatically.

A further advance in technique is the use of a finely focused electron beam, instead of X-rays, to irradiate the sample. X-rays characteristic of the elements present are emitted and analysed as before. This technique permits fine examination of variations in element concentration across a surface, and the analysis of inclusions in metals; it is particularly satisfactory with the lighter elements.

A spark source spectrometer, in which analysis is carried out using the *mass spectrometer* principle, can be used for both quantitative and qualitative analysis, particularly of impurities, etc. in inorganic solids. One such instrument is capable of detecting elements present in quantities as small as one part in $10^9$ parts of the main constituent of the sample.

A sample of the material under test is used to form the electrodes of a spark gap in an evacuated chamber. When the gap is sparked positive ions are formed from the sample which are representative of the whole range of elements present. These ions are then accelerated in an electric field and focused by an electrostatic field into a parallel beam, which then passes through a strong magnetic field. Here the ions of the different elements (possessing, as they do, different masses) will follow distinctive paths dictated by the influence of the magnetic field on their respective mass. The ions, now sorted out according to their mass, are then allowed to fall on a photographic plate where they produce lines varying in density according to the abundance of each element. This photographic record thus gives the mass spectrum analysis of the sample.

Other types of specially designed mass spectrometer can be used for the analysis of solids, liquids and gases. Instead of positive ions being formed from the sample material by the action of a spark, electron impact or thermionic ionization may be employed. In the first case a high-energy electron beam is directed on to the sample, and in the second the sample is heated thermionically, in both instances under vacuum. The resulting positive ions, representative of the elements present in the sample, are then accelerated electrically and pass into a magnetic field where they are separated magnetically into ions of differing $m/e$ ratio. The ions, and consequently the analysis, can be indicated or recorded electrically, using plate collector or electron multiplier tube techniques.

To secure reliable and reproducible results from any form of spectrometer testing, supervisors and inspectors should realize the importance of standardizing reproducible methods of sampling and sample preparation, and of a routine daily maintenance drill on the equipment.

Some specifications dealing with analysis are given in Table 2.3.

## TABLE 2.3
*Some specifications dealing with analysis*

| Specification No. | Description |
|---|---|
| BS Handbook No. 19 (supersedes BS 1121 and includes BS 1837) | Methods for the sampling of iron and steel and other ferrous metals (see also BS 6200) |
| BS 1427 | Routine control methods of testing water used in industry |
| BS 1747 | Methods for measurement of air pollution |
| BS 2000 | Methods for test for petroleum and its products |
| BS 3156 | Methods for the analysis of fuel gases |
| BS 4314 | Apparatus for physical methods of gas analysis |
| BS 5309 | Methods for sampling chemical products |
| BS 6200 | Methods of sampling and analysis (iron and steel, etc.) |
| ASTM E 137 | Evaluation of mass spectrometers for use in chemical analysis |
| ASTM STP 149 | Mass spectrometric methods of chemical analysis |
| ASTM E 158 | Recommended practices for spectrochemical computations (Deals with analysis by both optical and X-ray fluorescence) |
| ASTM E 168 | General technique of infra-red quantitive analysis |
| ASTM E 169 | General technique of ultra-violet quantitive analysis |
| ASTM E 212 | Spectrochemical analysis methods. Steel, plain carbon and low alloy, by the rod to rod spark technique |
| ASTM E 227 | Method for spectrochemical analysis of aluminium and its alloys by the point-to-plane technique using an optical emission spectrometer |
| ASTM E 282 | Method for spectrochemical analysis of plain carbon and low-alloy steel by the point-to-plane technique |
| ASTM E 311 | Sampling and sample preparation technique in spectrochemical analysis |

## 2.12 Material specifications

The inspector will be concerned with the witnessing of analyses, mechanical tests, heat treatment, etc. to ascertain compliance with specification, and with the checking of documentation such as test certificates, mill sheets, release notes, etc.

Amongst the material specifications he will commonly use are those of the British Standards Institution, American National Standards Institute (formerly ASA), American Society for Testing and Materials, American Iron and Steel Institute (AISI), and perhaps those of the Society of Automotive Engineers (SAE) and of the (German) Deutscher Normenausschuss (DIN); increasingly he will encounter ISO specifications.

Particular reference should be made to BS 970, 1449, 1501, 2, 3, 4 & 6, 3100, 3146 and 4360 which are widely used steel specifications of an omnibus nature; they deal with general requirements, inspection and testing procedures, composition and properties.

In a number of revisions to BS 970 *Wrought steels*, published from 1972 onward, BSI replaced the En numbered series by a new six-symbol method of coding (e.g. 304 S11).

(i)  The first three digits designate the type of steel:

    000 to 199  Carbon and carbon–manganese types, the numbers representing 100 times manganese content.

    200 to 240  Free cutting steel carbon–manganese, the second and third numbers being 100 times the mean sulphur content.

    250        Silicon manganese spring steels (corresponds with AISI numbers).

    300 to 499  Stainless and heat resistant and valve steels (correspond with AISI numbers).

    500 to 999  Alloy steels (correspond with AISI numbers).

(ii) The fourth symbol (a letter) signifies it is supplied to:

    A—chemical composition analysis specification.

    H—hardenability requirements.

    M—mechanical properties specification.

    S (condition)—stainless.

(iii) The fifth and sixth digits correspond to 100 times the mean percentage carbon content, except for stainless steel where numbers within the series 11 to 99 are arbitrarily designated to specific alloys.

Thus 150 M 19 designates a carbon/carbon–manganese steel supplied to a mechanical properties specification having 1·50% manganese and 0·19% carbon.

Likewise 640 M 40 designates an AISI nickel–chromium steel with 1·25% nickel, 0·5% chromium and 0·40% carbon.

Further details can be found in the appropriate specification, including comparisons with steels in previous editions and specific requirements covering chemical composition, mechanical properties, hardenability, heat treatment, sizes and tolerances.*

The American Society of Automotive Engineers (SAE) has a four-symbol numbering code for steels (1000 to 9000). The first two numbers indicate the type of steel and the third and fourth 100 times the percentage of carbon.

BS 4659 for tool steels uses a single-lettered coding based on that of the American Iron and Steel Institute, but prefixed by a B (thus BO is an oil hardening steel for cold working). These code letters are followed by a number designating the steel composition.

Requirements for aluminium and its alloys are covered generally by BS 1470–5,1490 and 4300 and methods for its analysis by BS 1728. The corrosion resistance of aluminium depends mainly on the maintenance of its thin oxide surface film; in the absence of oxygen and moisture it may be subject to 'anhydrous attack', particularly at high temperatures, and rapid corrosion and penetration may occur quite suddenly after a period of apparently normal service in contact with organic materials, etc. The inspector should also be alert to the possibility of electrolytic attack by direct contact of aluminium with heavy metals, including copper, or with solutions containing them. Even the breakage of a mercury thermometer during tests on aluminium plant could cause considerable trouble.

Contact with strong acids, sodium hydroxide and even pure boiling alcohol may result in violent reactions, although aluminium may be used with strongly oxidizing materials such as concentrated nitric acid. Expert advice should be sought.

A 99·0% pure grade of aluminium (BSI designation 1200—similar to ANSI symbol) is generally used for chemical and process plant subject to corrosion. In very severely corrosive conditions a 99·8% pure grade (BSI designation 1080A) may be used. This will be more costly and of lower strength, but this strength may be increased by cold working.

Alloying with small amounts of copper, magnesium, etc. followed by carefully specified heat treatment also increases strength, but at the expense of lower corrosion resistance.

### 2.13 Stainless steel and its inspection

Perhaps the most important of the alloy steels from the chemical plant viewpoint is stainless steel. Although an expensive material it finds increasing use owing to its ability, when properly treated and fabricated, to withstand various forms of severe corrosion. The presence of more than about 12% of

---

*Specifications other than BS 970 generally use this code for stainless and some alloy steels, but for other steels other symbols designating condition, finish, tensile strength, etc. may be used. In the interests of harmonization of European and international standards, new steel designations and different terminology will be adopted; for instance, designations based on yield strength rather than tensile strength will be introduced.

chromium in the steel is said to form a continuous surface film of oxide which resists most oxidizing agents and many chemicals.

Consequently the surface condition and standard of finish achieved are important factors affecting the corrosion resistance of stainless steel to which the inspector should pay great attention. If the surface is rough it is easier for corrosives to penetrate into it and to surround and attack individual molecules. Often a high standard of finish and the elimination of scratches is necessary or desirable for other reasons, but the inspector should realize that a rough surface is the more rapidly attacked. In addition pitting of the surface may be caused by local corrosion set up by galvanic action (see 12.7) due to the presence of embedded contamination such as scale, mild steel, other metals, foreign bodies and abrasives. Hence the inspector should also watch for these things for the presence of cracks and crevices where contamination could collect. It is even possible to get crevice corrosion under rivet heads or gaskets where it is caused by stagnant conditions, giving rise to differential aeration.

In general stainless steels can be divided into three categories—ferritic, martensitic and austenitic. The first two are magnetic but austenitic alloys are not. This provides a rough method of checking for the inspector. He uses a small pocket magnet, which will not attract austenitic alloy (cold working however will produce a small amount of magnetism in this alloy). The first two categories are predominantly chromium steels, whilst austenitic types are chromium–nickel alloys containing 8% or more of nickel and 16% or more chromium.

Within each category there are numerous grades, varying in the proportion of the main elements and of the additives used for special corrosion resisting purposes, etc. Martensitic stainless steels perhaps possess generally superior mechanical properties and can be hardened and tempered.

Ferritic stainless steels have a higher chromium content (not less than 16%) and can be cold-worked and pressed to a greater extent than other stainless steels. They cannot however be hardened to any appreciable extent by heat treatment, and have limitations as regards structural uses and welding.

Austenitic stainless steels are the most widely used and have better welding qualities. They cannot be hardened by quenching, but can be work-hardened to give a variety of combinations of strength and other mechanical properties according to the specific composition. The hardening effects of cold working can be removed by heating in the range 1000–1100°C and then air cooling; in addition to softening the steel, this heat treatment gives the maximum resistance to corrosion. Perhaps the most widely used austenitic stainless steel is the 18/8 variety (18% chromium, 8% nickel).

Stainless steels are listed in such specifications as BS 970 and BS 1449 Part 2, BS 1501 Part 3 and BS 1506. They are often referred to by their American (AISI) notation in the 300 and 400 series, such as 304, 304L, 316, 316L, 321 and 347 which are widely used for austenitic steels.

*2.13.1   Intercrystalline corrosion (weld decay) of stainless steel*

Austenitic stainless steels, having considerable resistance to corrosion, are extensively used for the construction of a wide variety of industrial and chemical plant. However when first put on the market (and occasionally today) 'in-use' inspection soon discovered serious faults developing, generally near welds. Under corroding conditions a form of intercrystalline attack takes place which can reduce the metal into a heap of individual crystals in a relatively short time. The defect is often called 'weld decay', but investigation has shown that it is not always associated with welding. It can occur whenever the material is heated within the temperature range of 450–900°C. This occurs, of course, to the metal on either side of a weld, and also during some forms of heat treatment. Briefly, the defect can be explained as follows. When the stainless steel is heated to the temperature mentioned some of the carbon goes out of 'solution', combines with the chromium, and is precipitated at the boundaries between the crystals of the material. This chromium carbide contains most of the chromium in the material, and hence the edges of the crystals immediately adjacent to the boundaries are denuded of chromium and are immediately susceptible to corrosive attack. When this attack occurs the edges of the crystals are thus weakened, become loose, and the metal rapidly disintegrates.

Considerable research was necessary before methods of combating this intercrystalline corrosion could be developed. One method was to heat-treat after welding (to some 1100°C) and rapidly quench in water, but this presented difficulties, particularly with large fabrications. The method usually employed today is to prevent precipitation of the chromium by 'stabilizing' it by the addition of a small quantity of an element which has a stronger affinity for carbon than has chromium. This element will then combine with the carbon in the steel and the chromium will be left undisturbed. The stabilizing element most widely used is titanium, and the minimum quantity added to the stainless steel to stabilize it is generally four times the carbon content. Such stabilized stainless steels (e.g. BS 970–321 S20 (AISI Type 321)) are proof against disintegration and can be welded and used without any subsequent heat treatment.

Another stabilizing element which is used is niobium (in America known as columbium), and some 8 to 10 times the carbon content is added to the stainless steel (e.g. BS 970 Grade 347 S17, AISI Type 347). Niobium is generally used to stabilize stainless steel welding electrodes, as if titanium is used it is found that a considerable quantity of it is lost in the electric arc.

If stainless steels having a very low carbon content (of the order of 0·03%) are used (e.g. AISI Type 304L (BS 970 304 S12)), then carbide precipitation cannot take place to any appreciable extent, and they are therefore not subject to disintegration attack.

The addition of molybdenum (some 2–4%) to 18/8 austenitic stainless steel (e.g. BS 970 316 S 16) enables it to be used under certain corrosive conditions (e.g. hot acids) in which the normal material is not satisfactory. It is sometimes used without a stabilizing element, as it has a measure of disintegration resistance, but titanium is often added for severe corrosive conditions, or it may have a very low carbon content (AISI Type 316 L–BS Grade 316 S19).

Inspection must of course ensure that austenitic stainless steels are correctly stabilized where necessary (some applications do not necessitate it). To check for this a disintegration test can be carried out. A sample test piece (which may include welding) is boiled in a specified acid solution for a given time, after which it is bent around a given radius and evidence of disintegration is sought (for further details see 9.21.5 and Fig. 9.4). See also ASTM A 262 *Detecting susceptibility to intergranular attack in stainless steels*, and ASTM A 380 *Descaling and cleaning stainless steel surfaces.*

## 2.13.2  Sigma phase formation in stainless steel

If certain stainless steels are subject to prolonged high-temperature service or heat treatment at from say 1050–1700°F (650–900°C), then any ferrite present (which is ductile and magnetic) will be transformed into what is called the 'sigma phase' (which is hard, brittle and non-magnetic). Exposure in the heat-affected zone of a weld is not usually for a long enough period to produce a significant amount of sigma formation. In 18/8 austenitic alloys the amount the ferrite present may be small and sigma formation may occur much more slowly than in higher chromium alloys, and in many cases it may not occur in detrimental amounts. Titanium stabilized alloys contain a small amount of ferrite phase whilst the addition of molybdenum may result in a 50% ferrite content.

The embrittlement resulting from this sigma formation must be allowed for in high-temperature service, but it is most serious when the steel cools from the sigma-forming temperature to atmospheric temperature, or below say 400°F (205°C). It may then become so brittle that it cannot withstand normal usage and manipulation.

Heat treatment above some 1900°F (1040°C) will restore ductility, but the sigma phase will reappear if the temperature conditions, etc. re-occur. Cold deformation of the susceptible stainless steels increases the rate of sigma formation, and consequently any such components should be annealed (above say 1700°F or 900°C) after forming and before high-temperature use. (See also ASTM DS-5-S1 *Report on the elevated temperature properties of stainless steels.*)

## 2.14  Testing of polymers

The inspector will have to apply many of the same exacting types of test to rubbers and plastics as he does to the older established metallic materials of construction. Such tests must be interpreted with great discretion; in addition other special tests will be required. Polymers are of great value in chemical plant and possess considerable resistance to chemical attack. Although some plastics have been developed which possess considerable mechanical strength, they are generally not as strong as metals and do not withstand such high temperatures. However much data concerning their properties and the effect of long-term ageing are now freely available.

Considerable variation in test results can be observed by varying the temperature of test, the details of fabrication or moulding, and the grade of material. Even when these factors are kept constant the results of a mechanical test will depend on the particular way in which it is carried out (especially the rate of loading) and the past history of the test piece. Many plastics, for instance, absorb moisture and could thereby suffer a deterioration in their mechanical properties. In the UK standard laboratory test conditions are usually taken to be $23 \pm 2°C$ with a relative humidity of 50%.

By careful conditioning of the test piece, standardizing test methods, and eliminating defects, variations in performance on test can be minimized.

Care should be taken when fabricating, testing and using most polymers although the finished product may be inert under normal conditions. There may be a dust hazard from powder etc. and smoking should normally be prohibited during fabrication (e.g. PTFE dust on burning tobacco can produce highly toxic fumes). In any case near clinically clean conditions are often desirable and advice should be sought. Many polymers burn readily and give off much dense smoke and toxic fumes. Rubber, PTFE, PVC Polyurethane, etc. when heated to decomposition emit highly toxic fumes and must always be thought of as a major hazard in certain circumstances, and precautions must be taken accordingly.

### 2.14.1 Rubber testing

This subject is dealt with comprehensively in BS 903 *Methods of testing vulcanized rubber*, which has been extensively revised and extended in recent years, and is now issued in a large number of separate parts. These deal with such matters as:

Determination of density, tensile and compression properties, tear strength, hardness, rebound resilience; resistance to abrasion, cracking and low temperatures; rubber-to-fabric adhesion, rubber-to-metal bond strength, creep and stress relaxation, swelling in liquids, permeability to gases, water vapour absorption; accelerated ageing (Parts A 1–50).

Preparation of material, etc., determination of rubber, sulphur, ash, carbon black, antimony, manganese, copper and water content, etc. (Parts B 1–19).

Determination of electric strength, resistivity, permitivity and power factor (Parts C 1–5).

Mechanical testing of ebonite (Parts D 1–7).

*Note:* The results of tests on rubber can be seriously affected by the presence of ozone in the laboratory. Tests should be carried out and precautions taken to ensure that the ozone content of the laboratory atmosphere does not exceed one part in 100 million.

In the determination of tensile stress–strain properties either standard dumb-bell or ring test pieces may be used, but these do not necessarily give the same results. This is mainly because in a stretched ring the stress is not uniform over the cross-section; also dumb-bells may give different values according to whether their length is parallel or perpendicular to the 'grain'. If grain is present to a marked extent, then an average value can be taken, obtained from dumb-bells cut parallel and perpendicular to the grain.

The tensile testing machine must be power-driven, and the rate of traverse of the driven grip or pulley is specified as $20 \pm 2$ in ($50 \pm 5$ cm) per minute. Readings of load and elongation are taken as required during the uninterrupted stretching of the test piece and when it breaks. Automatic recording of the stress–strain curve of a ring test piece is desirable. Test results are usually determined both before and after accelerated ageing (at a temperature of some 70°C).

The scale of British Standard and international rubber hardness degrees is now widely accepted in rubber testing. It corresponds approximately to that obtained on a Shore durometer scale 'A' (see Table 2.4).

**TABLE 2.4**

*Some standard specifications dealing with rubber testing*

| Specification No. | Description |
| --- | --- |
| BS 903 | Methods of testing vulcanized rubber |
| BS 1672 | Methods of testing natural rubber latex |
| BS 1673 | Methods of testing raw rubber and unvulcanized compounded rubber |
| | Some 10 Parts deal with sampling, methods of chemical analysis, physical testing, and measurement of pre-vulcanizing and curing characteristics |
| BS 1674 | Equipment and general procedure for mixing and vulcanizing rubber test mixes |
| BS 2044 | Laboratory tests for resistivity of conductive and anti-static plastics and rubbers |
| BS 2050 | Electrical resistance of conductive and anti-static products made from flexible polymeric material (Method of test described) |
| BS 2719 | Methods of use and calibration of pocket type rubber hardness meters |
| BS 3397 | Methods of testing synthetic rubber latices |
| BS 3424 | Testing coated fabrics |

**TABLE 2.4** *concluded*

| Specification No. | Description |
| --- | --- |
| BS 3502 | Schedule of common names and abbreviations for plastics and rubbers |
| BS 3558 | Glossary of rubber terms (Includes those dealing with rubber properties and testing) |
| BS 3574 | Recommendations for the storage of vulcanized rubber |
| BS 3734 | Dimensional tolerances of solid moulded and extruded rubber products |
| BS 4396 | Raw natural rubber |
| BS 4370 | Methods of test for rigid cellular materials |
| BS 4398 | Compounding ingredients for rubber test mixes |
| BS 4443 | Methods of test for flexible cellular materials |
| BS 5214 | Testing machines for rubbers and plastics |
| BS 5293 | Methods for sampling and testing carbon black for use in the rubber industry |
| BS 5294 | Method of test. Determination of crystallization effects in rubbers by hardness measurements |
| BS 5324 | Guide to application of statistics to rubber testing |
| BS 5421 | Methods of test for elastomeric threads |
| BS 5738 | Methods of test for evaluation of vulcanization characteristics of raw natural rubber |
| BS 5923 | Methods for chemical analysis of rubber |
| BS 6315 | Methods for sampling and sample preparation of raw rubber |
| BS 6442 | Limits of surface imperfection on elastomeric toroidal sealing rings ('O'-rings) |
| BS 6882 | Guide for storage of raw solid natural & synthetic rubber |
| ASTM D 15 | Sample preparation for physical testing of rubber products (ANSI approved) |
| ASTM D 412 | Tension testing of vulcanized rubber (ANSI approved) |
| ASTM D 2240 | Test for indentation hardness of rubber and plastics by means of a durometer (calibrated in Shore hardness) |

The British Standard hardness test (see BS 903: Part A 26) consists in measuring the difference between depths of penetration of a 2·44 mm ball into the rubber under a small initial load (30 g) and a large final load (570 g). This difference is the same as that defined in BS 903:1940 as British Standard hardness number. From this difference, the hardness in BS or International rubber hardness degrees is derived by using either tables or a graph, or is read directly from a scale calibrated in BS degrees.

The measured hardness depends to some extent on the thickness of the test piece, which should be stated in any test report, together with the temperature of test, if other than $20 \pm 2°C$. The standard test piece should be 8–10 mm thick in order to give true hardness.

Many specifications for rubber, etc. particularly American, will refer to Shore hardness, in which case the particular scale should be mentioned (it is usually Scale A). Shore hardness is a measure of the depth of indentation, varying from 100 at zero indentation to 0 at an indentation of 0·1 in, and is automatically indicated on the scale. Various scales are used depending on the material to be tested (e.g. Scale D for hard rubber and plastics). Results obtained on one cannot be correlated with those obtained on another.

A tolerance of ±5 should be allowed when reading the portable instruments much used by inspectors.

BS 903: Part A 26 also deals with the *Determination of hardness (micro-test)* using a 'micro' instrument, scaled down one-sixth from the normal or 'macro' instrument. The results obtained by these two instruments can differ substantially, especially if test pieces smaller than those prescribed are used, or if the tests are carried out on a curved surface (also dealt with in BS 903: Part A 26 *Determination of apparent hardness on curved surfaces*).

Consequently, such tests should only be used for comparative purposes, and when accurate results are required a bench type 'macro' instrument should be used under the prescribed conditions.

See also *Hardness testing of rubber compounds and components (with particular reference to the use of the micro instrument)*, Information Leaflet FSAC/148, Federation of British Rubber and Allied Manufacturers, London 1962.

*Note.* Most types of rubber are often subject to considerable changes in properties with time and the action of light, temperature, humidity, oxygen (and ozone), oil and other chemicals. Consequently rubber components may become unserviceable, perhaps even dangerous, because of hardening, softening or other forms of degradation.

Such changes may be minimized by suitable storage and environmental conditions (e.g. 15–25°C and the absence of condensation), but must always be borne in mind particularly in environments where hazards may arise.

## 2.14.2 Testing of plastics

BS 2782 *Methods of testing plastics* covers in some detail the various methods employed. It is divided up into some 11 parts, Parts 1–8 dealing with thermal, electrical, mechanical, chemical, optical, dimensional, rheological and other properties. Parts 9–11 deal with sampling and test specimens, glass reinforced plastics and thermoplastics, pipes, fittings and valves. Part 0 (1982) is an introduction to this revised new loose-leaf series which will eventually replace the bound volume of methods published in 1970. Each method is given a specific method number, but the new edition does not use the same method numbers as the 1970 edition and many additional numbered methods have been and will be added. An appendix in the new Part 0 lists the 1970 methods and their appropriate replacement method numbers. A further appendix lists the current standards with their method numbers together, where appropriate, with their equivalent method number in the 1970 edition and any equivalent ISO standard or other document. For standards dealing with testing plastics, see Table 2.5.

**TABLE 2.5**

*Some standards dealing with plastics and their testing*

| Specification No. | Description |
|---|---|
| BS 1755 | Glossary of terms used in the plastics industry |
| | Part 1: Polymer and plastics technology |
| | Part 2: Manufacturing processes |
| BS 2782 | Methods of testing plastics (see 2.14.2) |
| BS 3502 | Schedule of common names and abbreviations for plastics and rubbers |
| BS 4370 | Methods of test for rigid cellular materials. |
| BS 4549 | Guide to quality control requirements for reinforced plastics mouldings |
| BS 4618 | Recommendations for presentation of plastics design data |
| BS 4735 | Test for assessment of horizontal burning characteristics of cellular plastics, etc. (not used to assess potential fire hazard) |
| BS 4893 | Veneered PTFE tape. Acceptance criteria for Grade A and A(e) electrical |
| BS 5111 | Test for determination of smoke generation characteristics of cellular plastics, etc. |
| BS 6564 | PTFE materials and products |
| ASTM D 543 | Standard method of test for resistance of plastics to chemical reagents |
| ASTM D 648 | Vicat softening point test (see also BS 2782 Part 1. Methods 120A-E-Vicat softening temperature) |
| ASTM D 1248 | Polyethylene plastics moulding and extruding material |
| ASTM D 1927 | Rigid PVC sheet |
| ASTM D 1693 | Comparative resistance of polyethylene to environmental stress cracking—bent strip |

Particular attention is drawn to BS 4618: *Recommendations for the presentation of plastics design data* which besides dealing with design matters gives details of relevant tests. Some 5 parts divided into separate sections deal with mechanical, electrical, thermal, chemical and other properties; an introduction explains the system adopted.

All plastics gradually extend or creep when subjected to sustained loads for long periods even at normal temperatures; consequently data obtained from rapidly loaded stress–strain tests (as used for metals) are not as such suitable for purposes of design.

Their *creep behaviour* can be characterized by a continuously changing deformation (*excessive deformation*) with increasing time which is strongly affected by temperature, humidity and other environmental conditions and by the processing to which the material has been subjected.

Plastics may recover, perhaps almost completely, when the load is removed even after a long period of creep, but visible defects such as cracking, necking and crazing may have occurred which might prevent complete recovery and may have led to failure (or rupture).

Most plastics are prone to *notch sensitivity*. The notch may be external and deliberately made for the test, or it may be external or internal and accidentally present, caused by irregularities, voids or other inhomogeneities. The notch creates a stress concentration, making the test piece more susceptible to fracture. Impact strength tests on plastics by the Izod method use a moulded square test piece of ½ in side (12·7 mm), the notch being centrally placed; the strength may be given as the energy absorbed or this figure divided by a specified cross-sectional area of the test piece.

*Impact behaviour* (the ability of a material to resist knocks and drops) can be impaired by any internal or surface imperfections which might act as stress raisers during impact and so initiate failure. Consequently the surface finish of an article can have an important effect on its impact strength. With brittle failure a crack starts and quickly (perhaps immediately) extends to rupture with little or no yielding (deformation) of the material, but with ductile failure considerable yielding takes place before rupture.

Internal imperfections include crazing (the characteristic appearance of which can be seen in transparent materials) which are not really cracks but perhaps plastically deformed material and voids often associated with stripes, ripples and changes in colour. The presence of a hostile environment, high temperature, or may be inadequate processing can encourage crazing, and under stress real cracks may appear (environmental stress cracking). But, unless unduly stressed, crazing can still support a load, and with due precautions affected material may be allowed to continue in service.

Impact tests have been devised for measuring the temperature at which polythene, and other plastics, become brittle; a rectangular specimen can be bent rapidly to some defined extent. The test is carried out on a number of specimens at different temperatures, and that temperature at which half the specimens break is quoted as the *brittleness temperature*. This measured temperature has been shown by ICI (Hoff and Turner, *ASTM Bull.* 58.225) to depend very markedly on the degree of perfection with which specimens are prepared, e.g. a razor-cut specimen of polythene gave a value of $-69°C$, whereas one roughly stamped out gave only −15°C. Evidently then it is really the low-temperature notch sensitivity of the material that is being measured, and quoted figures must be treated with caution.

Tests such as the Izod (pendulum) to Method 350 and the falling weight (drop) test to Method 352 D, using either notched or un-notched specimens, may be called for to the relevant test methods described in BS 2782: Part 3 (or in equivalent ASTM standards).

The degree of ability of a plastic material to withstand an applied force without failure is termed its *strength*. BS 2782: Part 3: Methods 320 A–F *Determination of tensile strength, elongation, etc.* describes some relevant tests of a stress/strain character.

*Static fatigue failure.* For a particular plastic material or component the relationship between a long period constantly applied stress and the time before failure can be established experimentally for various environmental conditions and displayed as a graph. Such methods of predicting life (of beyond some 50 years) are used in specifications for plastic tube such as BS 6437 & 6572 (see 4.8). *Normal fatigue failure* in plastics (as with metals) occurs with the repeated application of a relatively low stress.

Some stress–strain test curves for polythene are given in Fig. 2.6, which show the decrease in tensile strength with increasing temperature, and the increase in strength observed with increasing density or with speed of testing. The region from O to the yield point A covers the range of stress and strain usefully employed in service; the slope at the origin (a measure of elastic modulus) increases with density and rate of test and decreases with increasing temperature. Fig. 2.7 illustrates how the speed of separation of the clamps of the testing machine can influence the value obtained for

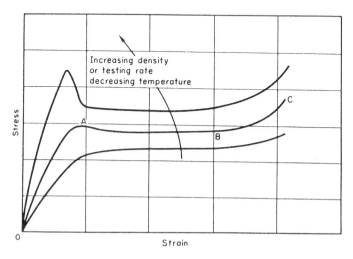

**Fig. 2.6 Schematic stress–strain curves for polythene.** (ICI Ltd.).

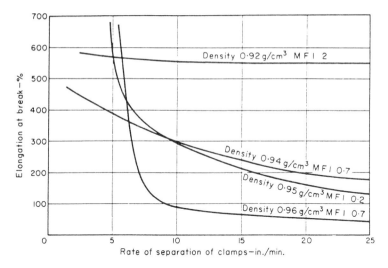

**Fig. 2.7   Dependence of elongation at break on the rate of straining of polythene specimens of 1 in gauge length.** (ICI Ltd.).

percentage elongation. Note the rapid drop in elongation as the rate of separation rises in the case of the higher density polymers; this indicates their susceptibility to notch-impact failure.

The arbitrary nature of mechanical tests on plastics when used for inspection and acceptance purposes, as distinct from design purposes, is thus emphasized; extreme care should be taken when interpreting results.

Investigations made by various workers (including Vincent (ICI) — see particularly his 'Strength of plastics', *Plastics*, Oct. 1961–Aug. 1962) show generally that:

(a) Increasing the speed of testing increases yield strength (and maybe brittle strength), and over a narrow range of speeds the fracture changes from tough to brittle, and the energy and elongation to break drop.

(b) Lowering the temperature is equivalent to increasing the straining rate, and is the best way to study brittle fracture.

(c) Impact tests are merely high-speed tests, and their only important function is to test for shock brittleness.

(d) Tests on notched specimens tend to measure crack propagation energy, whereas tests on unnotched specimens measure crack initiation energy.

(e) Pendulum impact tests can be in error by as much as 300%; falling weight tests are considered better.

By carrying out a visual inspection of polymeric samples or test specimens, to ensure close adherence to specified conditions and dimensions, during preparation and testing (and after fracture) for surface finish, laminations, inclusions, blowholes, etc. and any indications of foreign matter, poor mixing, or variations in colour, transparency or cure, information may be gleaned which may help to forecast behaviour or to explain premature test failures. However it should be emphasized that tests on even carefully prepared samples, although useful for purposes of acceptance and comparison, do not necessarily reproduce the results obtainable in practice, and there may be no substitute for practical experience and tests on actual components.

It has been found that all mechanical test results can vary widely according to the position of the test piece during moulding. This is due to the differing strains set up by shrinkage after moulding. In the direct line of flow of the material the shrinkage (for PVC) may be some 0·015 inch per inch, but only some 0·006 inch per inch at right-angles to this line of flow. Consequently two groups of test pieces, at right angles to each other, may be cut, and extreme care should be taken when interpreting the results of any arbitrary tests. A factor of safety of at least 5 is usually allowed in design calculations, and this may rise to 10 when threaded fittings (as on pipes) are involved, owing to the extreme notch sensitivity of plastics.

The properties of thermoplastics are much dependent upon temperature. Polyvinylchloride (PVC), acrylonitrile-butadiene-styrene (ABS) and polyethylene) (PE—but often called polythene) may be used up to some 60–80°C. At the other end of the scale the fluoropolymers can be used at temperatures up to the order of 80–120°C (with PTFE at the top).

Their performance at high temperatures can be compared by means of softening or heat (BS 2782: Part 1 Methods 121/2 or ASTM 648). The Vicat test (Methods 12A–E) gives a measure of the temperature at which a material begins to lose its form and stability: for polyethylene this varies from 81–124°C depending upon density). Heat distortion temperature tests provide measures of the temperatures at which materials lose their load-bearing capacity. The BS softening point test (Method 102C) and the Marten's test involve the bending under load of samples held at one end while subject to a temperature rise. Melting points are determined by Methods 123. Thermosetting resins such as phenol formaldehyde (Bakelite) can be used up to about 160°C, after which they will char. In powder form they can be moulded by standard techniques but, unlike thermoplastics, cannot subsequently be further manipulated by heating. Liquid type resins are rather brittle and are often reinforced by natural or man-made fibres (see Chapters 4 and 5).

Polythene can be produced in many different grades depending on its molecular weight and density. To distinguish between them use can be made of a test to determine the *melt flow index* (MFI) laid down in BS 2782: Part 1 Method 105C, (now Part 7 Method 720A–Determination of *melt flow rate* of thermoplastic. ASTM D 1238 calls the flow of the material (grammes) extruded in 10 minutes at 190°C under specified conditions the 'melt index' of the sample.) A low MFI corresponds to a high melt viscosity and high molecular weight. This latter in turn is related to its mechanical properties. In general, a decrease in MFI increases toughness, whilst an increase in MFI decreases the material's low-temperature properties and usually its tensile strength and elongation at break (Fig. 2.8).

Polythene, when stressed and in contact with liquids such as alcohols and detergents, may be subject to *environmental stress cracking*. A grade of high molecular weight (and of low MFI) gives improved resistance to cracking. The incorporation of some 5–10% of butyl rubber also reduces the risk.

A 'high-density' polythene is available which has appreciably different properties from that of the conventional 'low-density' material; in particular it is more rigid and has a higher softening temperature.

When the higher-density polythenes are subjected to stress they may fail similarly by stress cracking without the presence of a hostile environment. For a given MFI the likelihood of failure increases with both temperature and density. At constant density the likelihood of failure increases with increasing MFI (decreasing molecular weight).

The incidence of both types of failure may depend upon the method of fabrication. Any residual strain present is of major importance in determining the crack initiation period. Strain viewing, and stress relieving by heat treatment, may be specified.

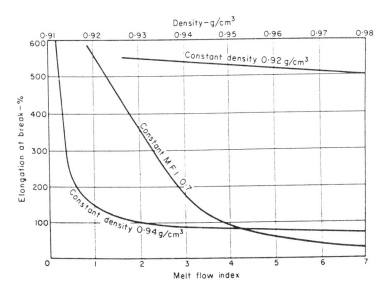

**Fig. 2.8    Dependence of elongation at break at 20°C on density and melt flow index. (Rate of clamp separation 18 in/min on a specimen of 1 in gauge length.) (ICI Ltd.)**

Polyvinyl chloride (PVC) can be compounded with appropriate fillers, plasticizers and stabilizers to give flexibilities ranging from hard and rigid to soft and pliable. Rigid PVC can be used for pipes, guttering and tanks etc. PVC has good strength and toughness, chemical and abrasian resistance, and can be fabricated by welding and sealing. By itself PVC is a rather hard, rigid and brittle material, difficult to mould and manipulate. The addition of specific amounts of plasticizers and other materials can make it flexible and materially change its properties and suitability for many applications, so where flexibility is needed plasticized PVC is used, while rigid articles use unplasticized PVC (UPVC).

## 2.14.3 Polymethyl methacrylate (PMMA) and its inspection

This material, often known by one of its trade names as 'Perspex', besides standing up well to chemical attack, particularly from alkalis and foodstuffs, is more transparent than glass and thus has advantages in certain plant applications where it is desired to watch a process. It is however somewhat expensive. Like PVC, when softened by heat it can be shaped or formed by a variety of processes, and can be sawn, drilled and machined on standard machinery (taking care to cool the material adequately).

Also like PVC it can be welded by hot gas, but more usually it is cemented by solvent welding processes, and the strength of a good welded joint can approach that of the original material. However polymethyl methacrylate is very subject to 'crazing', i.e. fine cracks which may gradually extend in a network over or under the surface, particularly at joints and after shaping. This crazing, if it develops, can spread through the material (particularly if it is under chemical attack) and disintegration may occur. It can develop over an extended period, or sometimes within seconds of an attack. It may be initiated by stress and/or exposure to solvents or their vapours.

Inspectors should be aware of the problem, and on the alert to detect the incidence of crazing, and to minimize this risk should insist on the correct heat treatment being carried out on the material after forming, cementing or fabrication. Details of cementing, fabrication, heat treatment etc., are given in ICI Publications, and in Specifications DTD 925 (MOD), but are summarized here.

Panels which do not require forming or cementing should be annealed after cutting, polishing, etc., for 3 hours at a temperature of 90–96°C followed by cooling to room temperature under draught-free conditions. Panels for forming should be heated in a clean oven to 135–170°C, shaped quickly, trimmed, polished and then annealed for 3 hours at 84–89°C followed by cooling.

Annealing, or heat treatment shaping and annealing of components, should be carried out before cementing them together.

Assemblies may be cemented using Tensol No. 3 Cement (an ICI product) or other approved monomer/polymer cement.

Partial curing is then effected either by:

(i) Exposure to ultra-violet light for not less than 3 hours, or

(ii) Heat treatment at 55°C for not less than 2 hours followed by cooling to room temperature under draught-free conditions.

Alternatively Tensol No. 6 Cement, or other approved solvent/polymer cement, may be used, in which case the cemented assembly must be allowed to stand at room temperature for at least 3 hours.

During the cementing of double-skinned components the interspaces should be purged of solvent vapours by means of clean, dry air at the same temperature as that of the component.

After any trimming and polishing and fitting of metal components, etc. (and/or after being fitted in a 'slave' frame corresponding to the final required shape), annealing for 3 hours should be carried out, followed by cooling.

Although heat treatment will reduce the possibility of crazing it does not entirely eliminate it. Consequently the inspector should be on the alert to avoid the imposition of unknown stresses during assembly, or contact of the Perspex with, or even proximity to, materials known to cause crazing (such as rubbers compounded with plasticizers; solvent-containing paints, compounds and cleaning agents; many hydrocarbons, alcohols and phenols, ethers, chlorinated compounds; and ammonia).

Perspex panels, etc., should be examined for unacceptable defects by placing them over a suitable illuminated screen. For items for which the greatest possible acuity of vision is required, special tests for distortion, transparency, etc., are laid down, and the maximum size and distribution of surface faults, foreign matter or fibres are specified. Sheets for other purposes should originally contain no fibres longer than 5 mm, foreign matter larger than $1 \cdot 5$ mm$^2$, or surface faults larger than 4 mm$^2$. Any scratches must in general be polished out, and crazing is a cause for rejection.

A fire-resisting grade is also available.

## 2.14.4 *Polytetrafluoroethylene (PTFE) and its inspection*

PTFE possesses remarkable properties. For all practical purposes it is insoluble in all solvents and is not attacked appreciably (when below its melting point) by any of the common corrosive agents except molten alkali metals. On prolonged contact with fluorine at atmospheric pressure it is merely bleached, but at greater pressures the fluorine attacks it, the product of the reaction being carbon tetrafluoride. The presence of contaminants such as water or grease greatly aids the attack. PTFE will withstand temperatures approaching 300°C for long periods without serious degradation and it is not brittle at low temperatures, retaining its flexibility at temperatures down to some −190°C.

The material possesses outstanding electrical properties. Its dielectric strength is high, and after an arc is formed the material does not 'track'. It has an extremely low coefficient of friction.

The principal uses of PTFE are:

(1) For making valve seats, gaskets, packing, pipes and tubing, pump pistons and diaphragms, etc., in equipment handling corrosive fluids.

(2) As a protective coating applied to other materials.

(3) As an electrical insulator, particularly at high temperatures and high frequencies.

(4) As a self-lubricating bearing (the material has a slippery surface).

(5) To provide a 'non-stick' surface on vessels, rollers, etc.

It is produced as a powder for moulding, etc. principally by the American firm of E. I. du Pont de Nemours who market the material under the trade name Teflon, and Imperial Chemical Industries Ltd, who market the material under the name of Fluon.

It can be supplied in the form of sheet, rod, tubes, tapes and coated wires, or as simple shapes and mouldings.

PTFE is difficult to fabricate by conventional methods owing to its resistance to heat and its high viscosity in the molten state. Although it is a thermoplastic, its melting point is ill-defined. Special methods of fabrication have therefore to be employed and extreme cleanliness is necessary.

One method is to cold-press the powdered material into a cake using normal moulding pressures, and then to sinter it at something over 327°C in a thermostatically controlled oven. Suitable sintering techniques and schedules have been developed and should be followed by the moulder and checked by the inspector.

The bonding achieved after sintering should be checked by scraping with a blunt instrument. If satisfactory this will slide over the surface, but if insufficient it will bring up a powder.

Machining of PTFE is carried out with sharp standard tools. Care should be taken to see that the material does not move in the chuck, owing to its slippery surface. Ragged edges and poor finish may be caused by blunt tools.

Extrusion of PTFE is possible by using special techniques.

Components should be visually examined for finish. Surfaces should be smooth and have a waxy appearance. Components should be clean and also appear clean and white. Fabricated components sometimes show a brown or greyish colour, and exhibit speckles, discoloration or blemishes. This may be due to slight contamination, of either the powder or the moulds. A close watch should be kept for any possibility of contamination, and it should be eliminated as far as possible. Discoloration and blemishes can often be removed by heating in clean air under laboratory conditions to about 327°C, when the material becomes translucent or transparent, but cools down to its waxy white colour. In many cases the discoloration is not in itself necessarily harmful, and efforts to remove it may not be warranted; it depends very much on the use for which the material is required and on the source of contamination—a slight trace will readily spread itself over a wide area during moulding. Inclusions of foreign matter can be extremely harmful. If on the surface they may be attacked by corrosive process fluids, and voids will appear. If this were to occur on the surface of a valve seat, for instance, the valve would develop a leak and cause trouble. Normally no inclusions on or near the surface are permissible, but it is sometimes necessary to reconsider components rejected for inclusions. The guiding principle to be followed in such cases is to imagine all the inclusions to be burnt out, and by the aid of general arrangement drawings determine whether the component would then satisfactorily perform its function. Obviously inclusions on valve seat faces must be rejected. The material is easily dented and scratched, so care must be taken during handling. Dents and scratches on working surfaces of valves, etc. must obviously be rejected.

Finished components must be free from grease.

Dimensions, however, call for special mention, owing to the peculiar properties of the material. Besides the normal, to be expected, increase of dimensions with temperature, the volume of PTFE changes abruptly at around 20°C and to a lesser extent around 30°C. The volume–temperature relationship also varies according to whether the temperature is increasing or decreasing, and with the rate of temperature increase.

Some strange dimensional occurrences have been observed, particularly where material has perhaps been formed or extruded to shape. It seems to have a memory and tends to return to something approaching its previous state. Careful attention to fabrication techniques and heat treatment may be the answer to this problem.

Clinically clean conditions are essential for work of the highest quality. Smoking must be prohibited and tobacco indeed can become contaminated and cause personal harm if smoked. The fumes from over-heated PTFE (over say 327°C) are toxic and contain oxidized products of carbon and fluorine and should not be breathed (they may be carcinogenic).

Considerable time is needed after moulding or machining for the structure of the material to settle down. Although the thermal conductance of the material is small, this 'settling-down' period is much longer than would be needed for the attainment of thermal equilibrium; hence dimensional measurements are not conclusive until after this period has elapsed. The temperature at which these are taken should be recorded. A temperature of 18°C is recommended. The length of this settling-down period depends on various factors, but the following information is given as a general guide:

After machining: 2–4 days          depending on the size
After moulding: up to 5–6 days    of the components

When PTFE powder is obtained it should be examined before use to see that it is free from any foreign matter. Dirt, grease, pieces of packing material, such as paper and sacking fibres, etc. have been known to get into it, with harmful results. Lumps should be removed, as they lead to air pockets in the finished mouldings.

Much trouble was experienced and many rejections were made when moulding from some early consignments of PTFE powder. Investigation eventually tracked down the fact that the then very expensive powder had been transferred into sacks which had once contained sugar!

Owing to its good electrical insulating properties and its non-hygroscopic nature PTFE powder, when in motion, readily acquires an electrostatic charge due to friction. It will therefore attract to itself any dust particles, etc. in the vicinity. Consequently, nothing less than laboratory conditions of cleanliness are permissible when handling it.

As components may easily become dented or scratched if allowed to knock against one another, the method of packing adopted should ensure that this cannot occur. Clinical cleanliness in handling and packing will pay dividends.

The peculiarities of PTFE were little known when it was first introduced and specifications were unknown or vague. In 1985/6 BSI co-ordinated and revised their standards, issuing BS 6564  *PTFE materials and products* (in three parts):

Part 1   PTFE powders for moulding and extrusion.
         Specification and method of specifying.
Part 2   Specification for fabricated unfilled PTFE products.
Part 3   Specification for fabricated glass fibre filled PTFE products.

Up to five *grades* of product are specified, designated grade A1, grade A and grade B, with grade A1E and AE having specified electrical properties. Also there are two *types* of product: type 1 having a degree of dimensional stability (maximum change not exceeding 0·5%); type 2 (designated as 'fabricated') not necessarily so dimensionally stable.

Reprocessed material may be added during manufacture (provided that the finished product meets the specified requirements) but its use is not recommended for work of the highest quality (e.g. for valve seats), as contamination and inclusions will generally be introduced.

Products are coded as follows:

(i) A letter denoting the filler material and content (G for glass fibre, U for unfilled PTFE).

(ii) The grade of product, i.e. A1, A, B, A1E or AE.

(iii) The type of product, i.e. types 1 or 2.

Examples:   UA1/1, UA/1 GB/2.

Specified pigments, usually for colouring, may be added but are undesirable for many technical requirements. Tests for tensile strength, elongation at break, density, resistance to heat (at 300°C), and dimensional stability are laid down.

For thin-walled tube extruded from coagulated dispersion powder (code UA/2 only) a simple leakage test, using air at 3·5 bar pressure and looking for air bubbles under water, is applied; also a proof pressure test, at a pressure decreasing as the nominal bore of the tube increases, has to be withstood for some 2 minutes without leakage or bursting.

Electrical tests have to be carried out on a specified or agreed number of test pieces of grades A1E and AE products to determine their ability to withstand a proof voltage of 24 kV/mm.

A special electrical test is laid down for thin veneered tape up to and including 0·25 mm in thickness to determine the number of conducting paths per m² using a power source giving a voltage gradient of 18 kV/mm across each test piece.

Fluorinated thermoplastics other than PTFE have been developed and can be more readily fabricated. Generally, however, they do not possess quite such outstanding properties as PTFE. These materials include polychlorofluoroethylene (PCTFE) and fluorinated ethylene propylene (FEP) (see ASTM D 1430 and D 2116); also polyvinylidene fluoride (PVDF) and perfluoroalkoxethylene (PFA). Such materials have the advantage that they can be extruded, injection moulded and fabricated by similar techniques to those used for other thermoplastics.

### 2.14.5 Some other plastics

A vast number of plastics are available for industrial use, and many can be tailored for certain applications. Details may be found in the reference books quoted but mention of a few particular points may be made here. Nylon 66 has considerable strength and toughness (a tensile strength of some 66 MPa), polycarbonate, a glass like material, is rigid and tough — possibly susceptible to embrittlement perhaps due to 'moulded in' stresses and notches.

Polypropylene is light but relatively strong and has good fatigue resistance.

All of these (and many other plastics) can be reinforced with such materials as glass and carbon fibres to increase their strength and stiffness by some 2–4 times.

See *Fibre reinforced composites* (I. Mech. E. conference papers), Mech. Eng. Publications.

### 2.14.6 Some recent developments in thermoplastics

Polyetheretherketone (PEEK) has very good flame and chemical resistance, being suitable for continuous service at temperatures of up to 90°C, and if reinforced with glass (30%), up to some 180°C; carbon fibre reinforcement can enhance its performance still further, its tensile strength then being some 255 MPa. It has obvious applications in wire and cable insulation, being at least comparable with the best of the rubber insulants, silicone, which has a continuous service temperature of up to 225°C.

A technique has been developed (by ERA Technology) which by the destructive examination of a very small used sample of many of the common thermoplastics, permits the maximum temperature which that material has reached in service to be determined retrospectively.

### References and further reading

*Materials*

Anno, J.N., *Notes on radiation effects on materials*, Hemisphere, Washington and Springer-Verlag, Berlin, 1984.

Atkins, A.G. and Mai, Y.W., (eds.), *Elastic and plastic fracture: metals, polymers, ceramics, composites, biological materials,* Ellis Horwood, Chichester, 1985.

*Behaviour of short fatigue cracks* (I. Mech. E.), Mech. Eng. Pub., 1986.

Bradley, A.N. (ed.), *Materials Engineering*, (Conf. I. Mech. E.), 1985.

Davis, H.E., Troxell, G.C. and Hanck, G.E., *The Testing of Engineering Materials*, McGraw-Hill, 1982.

*Fatigue and crack growth of off-shore structures* (Conf. I. Mech. E.), 1986.

*Fatigue of Engineering Materials and Structures* (Symp. I. Mech. E.), 1986.

*Guidance notes on the safe use of stainless steel in chemical plant*, I. Chem. Eng., Rugby, 1978.

Kanninen, M.F. and Popelar, C.H., *Advanced fracture mechanics*, Oxford University Press, 1985.

Marshall, P., *Austenitic stainless steels: microstructure and mechanical properties*, Elsevier Applied Science, 1984.

*Materials for the Process Industries* (I. Mech. E.), Mech. Eng. Pub., 1982.

*Materials Handbook*, McGraw-Hill, 1986.

*Metals Handbook*, American Soc. of Metals, Ohio, USA, 1975.

Peapell, P.N. and Belk, J.A., *Basic Materials Studies*, Butterworths, 1985.

Pomeroy, C.D. (ed.), *Creep of Engineering Materials* (I. Mech. E.), Mech. Eng. Pub., 1978.

Pomeroy, C.D. (ed.), *Materials Handbook*, McGraw-Hill, 1977.

Ross, C.T.F., *Applied Stress Analysis*, Ellis Horwood, Chichester, 1986.

Stephens, R.I. (ed.), *Fatigue and low temperatures* (STP 857), ASTM Philadelphia Pa., 1985.

*Fracture mechanics*

'A general introduction to fracture mechanics,' (Mech. Eng. Pub., I. Mech. E., 1978) in *Fracture mechanics in design and service: 'Living with defects'* (Royal Soc. Phil. Transactions, Series A, Vol. 299), No. 1446, pp. 1–239, 1981.

*Dynamic Fracture Toughness*, The Welding Institute, 1977.

Egan, G.R., *Weld defects and fitness for purpose—brittle fracture*, Welding Research Council Vol. XVIII, No. 3, November, 1972.

Irvine, W.H. and Quirk, A., *The application of the stress-concentration theory of fracture mechanics to the assessment of the fast structure characteristics of thick walled nuclear reactor pressure vessels*, UKAEA, Risley, 1971.

Valluri, S.R. and others (eds.), *Advances in fracture research*, Procs. of international Congress, Pergamon, Oxford, 1986.

Wells, A.A., *Unstable crack propagation in metals—cleavage and fast fracture*, Symp. Vol. 1, Royal College of Aeronautics, Cranfield Institution of Technology, Cranfield, Beds., September, 1961.

See also the following ASTM publications:
STP 513 Stress analysis and growth of cracks
STP 514 Fracture toughness
STP 556 Fatigue and fracture toughness—cryogenic behaviour
STP 559 Fracture toughness and slow stable cracking
STP 560 Fracture analysis

*Plastics*

Clegg, D.V. and Collyer, A.A. (eds.), *Mechanical properties of reinforced thermoplastics.* Elsevier Applied Science 1986.

Crawford, R., I. Mech. E. Mech. Eng. Pub., *Plastics and rubbers, engineering design and applications* 1985.

*Design with Composite Materials*, I. Mech. E. 1983.

Fenner, O.G., *Plastics Testing, Chemical Engineering Deskbook*, 1970, p. 53–59.

Johnston, A.F., *Engineering Design Properties of GRP*, HMSO 1979.

Lansley, M. (ed.), *Carbon fibres in engineering*, McGraw-Hill, 1971.

*Modern Plastics Encyclopedia*, McGraw-Hill (annually).

Turner, S., *Mechanical Testing of Plastics*, Geo., Godwin, 1984.

West, G.H., *Quality Control for the Plastics Industry*, Plastics and Rubber Institute, 1987.

West, G.H. *Engineering design in plastics-data and applications*, (Plastics and Rubber Institute, 1987).

*PMMA*

Marshall, G.P., Culver L.E. and Williams J.G., *Craze growth in PMMA: a fracture mechanics approach* (Proc. Royal Soc.), London, 1970, A319, 165.

Williams, J.G. and Marshall, G.P., *Environmental crack and craze growth phenomena in polymers* (Proc. Royal Soc.), London 1975, A342, 55.

Williams, J.G. and Marshall, G.P., *Thermal and environmental effect in craze growth and fracture'* in *Deformation and fracture of high polymers* (ed. H.H. Kauschy), Plenum Press, 1974.

*Fluorinated plastics*

*ASME Design Manual*, PTFE Seals in reciprocating compressors, 1975.

British Fluoropolymer Processors' Association, *Code of practice for machining tolerances for components machined from PTFE*, No. 284/1.

British Fluoropolymer Processors' Association, *Industrial Health and Safety for PTFE polymers*, No. 254/1.

Wall, L.A. (ed.), *Fluoropolymers*, New York, Wiley Interscience, 1972.

# 3 Boilers and pressure vessels

## Part 1   Unfired pressure vessels

### 3.1 Introduction

A pressure vessel is one which is subject to either internal or external pressure, the term including both fired boilers and unfired vessels.

The application of pressure to a vessel creates a hazard; hence in order to ensure safety of operation the design must be such that the materials used are not stressed beyond a safe value, whilst the methods of construction must be sound. It is the function of inspection to ensure all this by adequate control and testing procedures, and to see that contract, drawing and specification requirements are complied with.

Generally speaking the design of all pressure vessels is based on the stress expected in service, but it should be mentioned that the practice of assuming a uniform elastic stress distribution and using a factor of safety (or ignorance) can result in the use of greater thicknesses of material than are really necessary.

Early pressure vessels were constructed by bending sections of metal plate and riveting them together. Leakages at these joints proved troublesome, and a process of caulking them by hammering, both during manufacture and in service, was necessary. Today riveted construction is seldom used in its entirety, although some riveted vessels are still in service.

Most modern pressure vessels are of fusion-welded construction; this has made it possible to meet demands for higher (and lower) pressures and temperatures. Today boilers and pressure vessels operating at up to 3–5000 lbf/in$^2$ (21–35 MPa) and at temperatures of some 650°C are not unusual, and they may have shell thicknesses of the order of 6 in (150 mm). Large pressure vessels may have a length of some 90 ft (27 m) and a diameter of 10 ft (3m); others may operate with very corrosive or toxic substances, or under high-vacuum conditions, or at the lowest temperatures; wall thickness may be up to some 18 in (450 mm); special methods of construction may be utilized.

In order to operate safely and satisfactorily under such onerous conditions inspection and testing must be carried out strictly and methodically. In particular, satisfactory fusion-welded joints depend largely on adequate control of the process and the skill of the operator, and testing them calls for far more than the eye can see. Consequently radiography and other methods of non-destructive testing (NDT) come into their own.

Today semi-automatic and automatic methods of welding are also widely used. Properly controlled (and tested) they can give very consistent results.

In what follows reference should also be made to the subjects of fusion welding and its inspection (See 9.7), and of non-destructive testing (Chapter 10).

## 3.2  Inspection and legislation

Owing to the many fatal boiler explosions which occured in the mid-nineteenth century, periodic inspections associated with insurance were introduced around 1859. Government legislation followed (the *Boiler Explosions Act* of 1882), enabling the Board of Trade to conduct investigations. Later legislation, including the various Factories Acts, made the owners of plant responsible for its safety, and laid down certain compulsory fittings, and the period between thorough inspections. However few detailed requirements were given, but responsibility for examination and certifying as to safety was put into the hands of a 'competent person', which meant in effect an inspector independent of the owners. (See 12.4 and 12.5)

Owing to these developments, to progress in design and construction and to the efforts of the inspector, boiler and steam pressure vessel explosions and fatalities have diminished over the years, fatalities falling from some 100 in 1860 to almost nil a hundred years later. The total killed in the period 1822–1967 has been given as 1265, with 3421 people injured.

## 3.3  Regulations and codes

The inspections and investigations of the various insurance societies and of other workers led to the accumulation of data which enabled design rules to be formulated and used. In the last decade of the nineteenth century the Board of Trade published rules for machinery for sea-going vessels, and these proved invaluable to the certifying organizations concerned with land plant. Around this time the various British engineering insurance and inspection organizations co-operated to form the Associated Offices Technical Committee (AOTC). This committee now examines the designs of boilers and pressure vessels, and of machinery, submitted to it by manufacturers for approval, and publishes its own regulations and rules relating to the design and safe operation of engineering plant. It also arranges inspection of materials, components and plant generally, and operates a scheme for the certification of qualified welders.

In 1901 an Engineering Standards Committee was formed by the leading British Engineering Institutions and eventually became the British Standards Institution. Various committees of the BSI, on which the manufacturers, engineering institutions, users and AOTC are represented, are responsible for the preparation, issue and revision of the appropriate British Standard Specifications for pressure vessels, plant and associated equipment, which are now widely used.

Similarly in the USA, after a number of boiler explosions and a particularly disastrous one which killed 58 persons, the state of Massachusetts enacted the first legal code of rules for the construction of steam boilers in 1907. Thereafter other states followed suit, and in 1911 after an appeal the American Society of Mechanical Engineers (ASME) set up a committee to formulate standard specifications for the design, construction and inspection of steam boilers and other pressure vessels, and for their care in service. As a result the first (1914) edition of the ASME Code for Stationary Boilers was adopted in the spring of 1915. The first issue of the ASME Unfired Pressure Vessel Code followed in 1925.

The use of the various regulations, codes and specifications for pressure vessels, etc. which have been introduced has largely become obligatory today in most countries. In general each manufacturing country has its own requirements, often legally enforceable. Some countries, such as Belgium, Israel, Norway, Turkey and the British Commonwealth and South Africa, will or may accept British, American and perhaps Swedish codes. The majority of these codes cover design, manufacture, inspection and testing, and require both destructive and non-destructive tests on the parent metal and on any weld deposit. The destructive tests usually include tensile strength, yield, elongation and reduction of area, bend tests, notched bar impact tests, micro- and macro-examination. The non-destructive tests include radiographic, ultrasonic magnetic and other methods (see Chapter 10).

Normally, for plant to be operated in the UK, the various British inspection organizations and engineering insurance societies rely on the relevant British Standard codes and specifications, unless otherwise required. But there is no legal compulsion to do so, and any certifying organization is free to use its own judgement if it considers that regulations from other sources are more appropriate. Again, the Health and Safety at Work (HSW) Act 1974 makes inspection during manufacture in effect mandatory in that, if British Standards or equivalent codes which require comprehensive inspection at works were not followed, the certifying inspection engineer would be in a difficult position, in the event of an accident, to prove that he had not been negligent.

The rules of Lloyd's Register of Shipping are often followed in the British Commonwealth, as are the codes of Imperial Chemical Industries and the Institute of Petroleum.

For plant installed in North America the National Board of Boiler and Pressure Vessel Inspectors, composed of chief inspectors of states and municipalities in the USA and of provinces in the Dominion of Canada, administers and legally enforces the rules of the ASME Boiler and Pressure Vessel Code.

Under an agreement negotiated by the BSI with the Canadian Standards Association and the Chief Provincial Boiler Inspectors in Canada, UK manufacturers of boilers, pressure vessels, air receivers, etc. can obtain the necessary certification of their equipment before it is shipped from their works.*

The chemicals industry undoubtedly makes the greatest use of pressure vessels and also of course uses many steam boilers. Many allied industrial plants also use a variety of pressure vessels such as heat exchangers, impregnators (which may be subject to both pressure and vacuum), vacuum drying stills, etc. Prior to the Second World War practically all the requirements of the petroleum and petrochemical branches of the chemical industry were met by the USA. Since then, however, British and other firms have entered this expanding market, and it is only natural that much American design and procedure has been adopted. Consequently various American specifications, and particularly the codes of the American Society of Mechanical Engineers and of the American Petroleum Institute, are widely used internationally in this field.

For many years a code for the design, construction, inspection and repair of unfired pressure vessels for petroleum liquids and gases was issued jointly by the API and ASME. However, with the increasing comprehensiveness of later issues of the ASME Boiler and Pressure Vessel Code, the Joint API-ASME Code was replaced by Section VIII of this ASME Code, which now qualifies as an American National Standard.

The complete ASME Code (see Table 3.1) has addenda and revisions published twice a year and a new edition is published every three years. In keeping with American practice the code has been written using English units but later editions have included reference to SI units. However starting from October 1983 a separate SI edition has also become available.

A list of some of the more important national regulations and codes for boilers and pressure vessels is given in Table 3.1. Further details concerning UK and foreign regulations and legislation will be found in 14.8 and 14.9.

Following the Ministry of Technology *Report of the Committee of Enquiry on Pressure Vessels* (HMSO, 1969), 1981 saw the setting up in the UK of the Pressure Vessel Quality Assurance Board (PVQAB) to provide a scheme of recognized assurance that pressure vessels and the components of

*Further details can be obtained from the BSI/CSA Agency.

## TABLE 3.1

*Principal regulations and codes governing construction of boilers and pressure vessels (for some other standards see Table 3.5 in Part 2 of this chapter). (When consulting a standard or code, make sure that it is the most recent issue, including any later amendments.)*

| | |
|---|---|
| Australia | Standards Association of Australia Boiler Code, Parts I–V (Standard No. CB1) AS 1200, 1210, 1228, 1797.<br>SAA Boiler Welding Certification Code (CB 14). |
| Austria | Dampfkesselverordnung (DKV) BGBI No. 83 and Werkstoff und Bauvorschriften (WBV) BGBI No. 264. |
| Canada | CSA Standard B51—Canadian Regulations for the Construction and Inspection of Boilers and Pressure Vessels (refers to ASME Code). |
| EEC | General Directive on Pressure Vessels 76/767/EEC |
| Finland | Finlands Forfattningssamling No. 573/575.<br>Numerous Finnish Codes e.g. SFS 2862-4. Suomen Standardisoimislitto r.y. 2223—Welding of pressure vessels. |
| France | Code de construction des récipients sous pressions non soumis à l'action de la flamme (CODAP 80), SNCT No. 1 Boiler Code NF E32-101/7. |
| West Germany | Technische Regeln für Dampfkessel (TRD)—Boiler Code of Practice Pressure Vessels (TRB) AD-Merkblätter and Unfallverhütungsvorschriften (UVV): Druckbehölter (VBG 17, 18)—Data sheets and Safety Regulations: Also DIN Standards. |
| Holland | Grondslagen waarop de beoordeling van de constructien en het materiaal van stoomtoestellen, damptoestellen en drukhouders-berust. Rules for Pressure Vessels. |
| India | Indian Boiler Regulations. Code for Unfired Pressure Vessels IS 2825. Foreign codes acceptable if Indian legislation satisfied. |
| International Standards Organization | ISO Boiler Code R831—Rules for Construction of Stationary Boilers ISO/DIS 2694—Pressure Vessels. |
| Italy | 1. Controllo della Combustione e Apparecchi a Pressione, ANCC N 775 and other ANCC Codes.<br>2. Specifiche per la constriziore Saldater di Apparecchi a Pressione Sogetto al Control Co deii ANCC, N4. |
| Japan | Ministry of Labour Safety Regulations and Construction Codes for Boilers and Pressure Vessels. Japan Industrial Standards (e.g. B8201 (Boilers) and B8243 (Pressure Vessels). |

**TABLE 3.1** *continued*

| | | |
|---|---|---|
| New Zealand | New Zealand Boiler Code<br>New Zealand Fusion Welded Pressure<br>Vessel Code | } BS or<br>ASME<br>by arrangement |
| Norway | Forskrifter for Kjeler, beholdere og Røredninger som er Utsatt for Damptrykk. General rules for Pressure Vessels. | |
| Sweden | Normer for Hallfastetsberakning av Tryckkarl (Swedish Boiler and Pressure Vessel Codes)<br>Normer for Svetsning av Tryckkarl (Pannsvetsnormer)<br>Normer for Ångpanners Urfordande Registrering, Besikting, m.m. | |
| Switzerland | Schweizerischer Verein von Dampfkessel-Besitzern (SVDB Code), Berechnungs–Vorschriften (Zürich) | |
| UK and Northern Ireland | BS 1113—Water-tube steam generating plant (including superheaters, reheaters and steel tube economizers)<br>BS 4994 Vessels and tanks in reinforced plastics<br>BS 5276 Pressure vessel details (dimensions)<br>BS 5500 Unfired fusion welded pressure vessels<br>Associated Offices Technical Committee—Rules for the construction, testing and scantlings of metal arc welded steel boilers and other pressure vessels.<br>Lloyd's Register of Shipping—Rules for the construction and classification of steel ships<br>Lloyd's Register of Shipping—Requirements for design, manufacture and testing of pressure components—land based nuclear installations<br>Institute of Petroleum—Model Code of Safe Practice Part 12. Pressure vessel Inspection | |
| USA | ASME Boiler and Pressure Vessel Code | |

ASME Boiler and Pressure Vessel Code (USA):

| Section I | Power boilers |
|---|---|
| Section II | Material specifications |
| Section III | Nuclear vessels |
| Section IV | Heating boilers |
| Section V | Non-destructive examinations |
| Section VI | Recommended rules for care and operation of heating boilers |
| Section VII | Recommended rules for care of power boilers |
| Section VIII | Pressure Vessels—Division 1<br>Alternative rules for pressure vessels—Division 2 |
| Section IX | Welding and brazing qualifications |
| Section X | Fibreglass Reinforced Plastic Pressure Vessels |
| Section XI | Rules for in-service inspection of Nuclear Power Plant Components |

**TABLE 3.1** *concluded*

| USA cont. | Standards of Tubular Exchanger Manufacturers' Association American Petroleum Institute—Guide for inspection of refinery equipment. Chapter 6 Unfired pressure vessels. Chapter 7 Heat exchangers, etc. Chapter 8 Direct fired boilers. RP510 Inspection, rating and repair of pressure vessels in refinery service.<br>National Board Inspection Code (National Board of Boiler and Pressure Vessel Inspectors) |
|---|---|

pressurized systems are manufactured in conformity with British Standards etc. Commercial inspection organizations can be approved under the scheme (including those run by insurance groups, and also a manufacturer's own organization if it is truly independent.)

### 3.4 Definitions, standards, materials and design

*3.4.1 Some definitions*
The term *pressure vessel* is taken to include any branches up to the point of connection to the piping (and may itself be constructed of standard pipes and tubes).

*Safe working pressure* means the maximum gauge pressure permitted in operation.

*Design pressure* is the value used in design formulae to determine minimum thicknesses and must be not less than the safe working pressure.

*Weld joint factor* (joint efficiency) is the ratio of the arbitrary strength of the welded joint to the strength of the plates welded.

*Stress relief* refers to heat treatment, at predetermined temperatures to relieve a structure or part of residual stresses. In particular it may refer to *post-weld heat treatment.*

*3.4.2 Standards and codes*
(a) The British Standards Institution have rationalized their require-ments for pressure vessels in recent years and have issued a new comprehen-sive specification:

BS 5500 *Unfired Fusion Welded Pressure Vessels\**

This replaces the following standards:

---

\* The 1988 edition of BS 5500 comprises some 400 loose-leaf pages in a binder and costs £475 including an updating service.

BS 1500    *Fusion welded pressure vessels for general purposes*
Part 1 Carbons low alloy steels (Part 2 was never issued)
Part 3 Aluminium

BS 1515    *Fusion welded pressure vessels for use in the chemical, petro-leum and allied industries*
Part 1 Carbon and ferritic alloy steel
Part 2 Austenitic stainless steel

As many vessels to these earlier standards are in use some mention of them will be made later. Fired pressure vessels (i.e. boilers) and similar items of plant are dealt with in 3.23 et seq.

BS 5500 may eventually include other types of pressure vessels for some of which British Standards currently exist and it is intended to cover all requirements for design, manufacture, testing and inspection. Strengths assumed for design purposes of materials covered by current British Standards are tabulated for steels and for aluminium and its alloys. The derivation of these design tables and the formulae upon which they are based are described in appendices to the standard (see also 3.4.5).

A significant departure in BS 5500 is that design strengths in the creep range are given in the tables for a range of design lifetimes (up to 250,000 hours—over 25 years) that may be extended on expiry on the basis of periodic 'fitness-for-continued-service-reviews' based on inspection and consideration of actual load-temperature history. Details of these reviews will be covered by other standards, etc. for the periodic inspection of pressure vessels (see BS PD6510—also 13.9).

This standard applies only to pressure vessels manufactured under the survey of a competent engineering inspecting authority or organization and made only by manufacturers who can satisfy the inspecting authority that they are competent and suitably equipped to fulfil the appropriate specified requirements. A scheme to provide such assurance is operated by the Pressure Vessels Quality Assurance Board (PVQAB) (see 3.3) under the direction of the Institution of Mechanical Engineers. Manufacturers holding a valid PVQAB Certificate (or nationally accredited product certification) for the relevant construction category may also be deemed to be competent. This will assure the required degree of surveillance by an independent inspecting authority and will avoid the necessity for the purchaser to commission his own (see 9.4).

Attention is drawn to Chapter 9 of this book dealing with Inspection procedures (particularly 9.4) which describes the arrangements necessary for a manufacturer to set up and obtain approval of his own Quality Assurance system and for its entry in the Department of Trade and Industry's register of Quality Assessed Companies (see 9.4.8). A manufacturer without such a Quality Assurance system would not satisfy an Inspecting Authority (such as PVQAB) of their competence to manufacture pressure vessels to fulfil the specified requirements. BS 5500 is included in the Health and Safety Executive's list of standards significant to health and safety at work and is referred to in HSE guidance publications.

Construction categories are designated in BS 5500 by the amount of non-destructive testing required and are related to the type and thickness of material being welded as indicated in Table 3.2. Three categories are laid down (Categories 1, 2 and 3). Any additional requirements to cover special risks should be specified by the purchaser taking into account any relevant statutory requirements.

(b) *The ASME Boiler and Pressure Vessel Code* at present consists of 11 sections (see Table 3.1). Section VIII, dealing specifically with pressure vessels, is divided into two parts: *Division 1*, evolved from the original Section VIII, covers requirements for the vast majority of pressure vessels and is implied generally in this chapter.

*Division 2* deals with alternative rules which are more restrictive in the choice of materials, but permit higher design stress-intensity values in the range of temperatures over which these values are controlled by ultimate strength or yield strength; more precise design and fabrication procedures are required and more exacting examination, testing and inspection requirements are necessary.

It should be noted that the ASME Code, besides dealing with the requirements for welded vessels, also deals with those fabricated or partially fabricated by forging and brazing.

Like BS 5500 the ASME Code requires that pressure vessels be made under the survey of an independent authorized inspection agency. The manufacturer must also have a competent quality control system in operation (See Code Section VIII Appendix 10, 'Quality Control Systems'), and be capable of designing and fabricating pressure vessels to the Code's requirements. A survey of the manufacturer's capabilities is carried out jointly by the authorized inspection agency and the state's legal jurisdictional authority and/or the National Board of Boiler and Pressure Vessel Inspectors. Some further details are given in 3.23.

Both BSI and ASME operate a system of Enquiry or Code Cases for Boilers and Pressure Vessels. Any ambiguity or doubt arising as to the meaning or interpretation of any clause or part of the specification can be referred to a technical committee who after due consideration publish their findings or interpretation as a Enquiry or Code Case.

### 3.4.3 Materials

(a) BS 5500. In general only approved materials are permitted, and these are subject to inspection and test at the maker's works and to the maintenance of identity throughout manufacture. Amongst the permissible materials (listed in BS 5500 Tables 2, 3 (a)–2A3 which give their

**TABLE 3.2**
*Construction categories—BS 5500*

| Construction category | NDT requirement | Permissible materials† (see also 3.4.3) | Maximum thickness (mm) | Temperature limits | |
|---|---|---|---|---|---|
| | | | | Upper | Lower |
| 1 | 100% | All in BS 5500 Table 2.3 (steel) and Table 2.A3 (aluminium) | None, except where limited by NDT method | As agreed | Some limitations (except for austenitic steel and aluminium alloys which can go down to −196°C) |
| 2 | Partial NDT (generally at least 10%) including selected locations. 100% of main seams welded on-site* | See BS 5500, Table 2.3 Carbon Steel (MO and MI) — 40; C Mn Steel (M2) — 30; Austenitic steel / Aluminium alloys — 40 | 40 / 30 / 40 | As agreed | Some limitations None down to −196°C |
| 3 | Visual only (but visual aids including magnetic particle and penetrant methods may be used) | C and C Mn steel; Austenitic steel | 16 / 25 | 300°C | Some limitations None down to −196°C |

*This applies specifically to steel
†Design stresses not to exceed the nominal value given in the tables quoted at the design temperature.

*(Based on BS 5500, Table 3.4 with acknowledgement to British Standards Institution)*

70

appropriate nominal design strengths at various temperatures) are those covered by:

| BS 1501: | Pt 1–3 | Steel plates |
| 1502 | | Steel sections and bars |
| 1503 | | Steel forgings |
| 1504 | | Steel castings |
| 3059 | Pts 1 & 2 | Steel pipes and tubes |
| 3601 | | Steel pipes and tubes |
| 3602 | Pts 1 & 2 | Steel pipes and tubes |
| 3603 | | Steel pipes and tubes |
| 3604 | | Steel pipes and tubes |
| 3605 | | Steel pipes and tubes |
| 3606 | | Steel pipes and tubes |

and for aluminium and its alloys:

| BS 1470 | Wrought aluminium, etc. plate, sheet and strip |
| 1475 | Wrought aluminium wire |
| 4300 | Wrought aluminium and alloys (supplementary series) |

For category 3 construction additional steels selected from BS 1449 and 4360 may be used (BS 5500, Table 2.4).

In practice representative samples of plates and tubes may be selected for destructive tests at the mills, but good results on these do not necessarily guarantee the bulk quantity which they represent, and faults in the bulk (particularly in tubes) may show up later during manufacture. Non-destructive testing on the bulk may be called for (see Chapter 10).

For vessels designed to operate below 0°C special consideration should be given to the choice of materials and their heat treatment (e.g. impact tested steels to BS 1510 (now in BS 1506) may be specified). Appendix D of BS 5500 gives some guidance. Consideration should be given to the possibility of fatigue cracking during service because of cyclic stresses due to variations in temperature, pressure and loading, and to forced vibrations. Here again Appendix C of BS 5500 gives guidance and this is similar to that proposed in the draft international standard for pressure vessels ISO/DIS 2694 which in turn was based on the philosophy adopted in the ASME codes.

Inspection should help to eliminate fatigue cracking by appropriate testing of the materials, and by vigilance during construction. For instance, welds and irregularities should be dressed smooth and sharp edges should be radiused.

*Note:* Neutron irradiation of steel may induce damage; fast neutrons may displace its atomic structure, thermal neutrons may transmute trace impurities and so change the properties of the material, and may lead to its swelling or distortion and may be embrittlement or fracture. Hence specifications must eliminate harmful impurities.

(b) *The ASME Code Section VIII* deals with pressure vessels, constructed of carbon and low alloy steels, non-ferrous metals, high alloy steels, cast iron, integrally clad plate, pipe, *corrosion-resistant linings* and cast nodular iron.

Requirements are given for ferritic vessels with tensile properties enhanced by heat treatment, and for those of materials having higher allowable stresses at low temperatures (notch-tough materials).

It is the policy of ASME to adopt ASTM material specifications, and these are quoted in their Code (with prefix S, etc, in front of their ASTM number) and detailed particularly in Section II, Parts A and B. Besides the traditional metallic materials, pressure vessels of prestressed concrete (see ASME Section III Division 2), plastics and fibreglass (see Section X) are sometimes employed. Polythene vessels have been constructed to withstand very high pressures.

Prestressed concrete pressure vessels (PCV) containing hot media must be protected from temperatures above 150°F (65°C) by suitable insulation and a steel liner. Cooling coils adjacent to this liner may be required. The concrete is kept in compression under all loading conditions by high tensile steel wire embedded in the concrete and prestressed by a suitable method. A PC pressure vessel has an advantage over steel in that it is not restricted by size limitations as it may be fabricated on site. Strict control and inspection of fabrication is essential. For reinforced plastics pressure vessels see 3.22.

### 3.4.4 Corrosion

In cases where corrosion (including erosion) may occur, additional metal thicknesses over and above that required by design calculations should be provided, equal to the loss expected from corrosion during the vessel's life.

Protective linings may be provided, usually on a mild steel basis metal, to prevent (or restrict) corrosion; clad materials may be used (see 5.1–5.7). In such cases it may not be necessary to increase the thickness by the usual corrosion allowance on, for example, the mild steel side.

Alloy steels (e.g. austenitic stainless steel) may be used to restrict corrosion. Aluminium, particularly in the pure state, has excellent corrosion resistance and, not being subject to brittle fracture, is very suitable for low-temperature applications. Some aluminium–magnesium alloys of relatively high magnesium content may become susceptible to stress corrosion cracking after use for long periods above 65°C (150°F). If the magnesium content is reduced weld cracking may occur during solidification. This can be obviated by the use of the correct filler material and welding technique, and the inspector should ensure that these are employed.

Consideration should be given to the effect which corrosion (and corrosion cracking) may have on the life of the vessel. Corrosion tests on the metal (and weld metal) can be carried out (see 12.6). Where severe conditions of erosion and abrasion arise, or are likely to arise, locally, it should be ensured that suitable renewable 'wear' plates are fitted in the path of the impinging fluid or material.

*3.4.5 Design*

(i) BS 5500 does not cover pressure vessels designed in general for the storage of liquids at or near atmospheric pressure (e.g. tanks not exceeding 140 mbar above or 6 mbar below atmospheric pressure (additional to the hydrostatic head, for which see Part 2 of this chapter, Table 3.5 and 7.11.1). No upper limit of pressure is specified. The rules in the ASME Code Section VIII Division 1 have been formulated on the basis of design principles for pressure vessels up to 3000 lb/in$^2$ (20,670 kPa).

Division 2 does not specify any limitations on pressure and for pressures above 3000 lb/in$^2$ design deviations and additions may be necessary including electroslag multi-welding, strip (or wire) wound and multi-layer vessels (see 3.11(ix)).

*Pressure loading*

Methods of calculating plate thicknesses for different materials under various conditions of pressure and temperature, and design details of certain components, are given in most codes and specifications.

The inspector, or his supervising engineer, may have to check all design calculations (for thickness, working pressure, etc.) using the formulae given in the respective code. This process is greatly facilitated if the manufacturer supplies a stereotyped calculation sheet containing all the necessary design data (see Fig. 3.1).

The design stresses to be used in such formulae are often tabulated for different materials, temperatures, etc. in the respective codes. They are based in general on the use of a 'factor of safety' by which the appropriate property (such as tensile strength) is divided, but this factor of safety has not always been stated in the past.

Until comparatively recently the nominal material design strength for pressure vessel materials used in most codes and standards was of the order of one quarter of the minimum tensile strength of that material at the temperature concerned (which is the same as a 'dividing' factor of safety of 4). This factor could be deduced from the tables of design stress given in BS 1500 (now obsolete).

Somewhat similarly ASME in their pressure vessel code Section VIII (in what is now known as Division 1) use as the basis for calculating the allowable design stresses for steels the lesser value of:

(i) $\frac{1}{4} \times$ minimum specified tensile strength at room temperature

(ii) $\frac{5}{8} \times$ minimum specified yield strength at room temperature

(iii) $\frac{1}{4} \times$ tensile strength at design temperature

(iv) $\frac{5}{8} \times$ yield strength at design temperature

(v) Stress required to produce 1% creep in 100,000 hours at design temperature.

(vi) 80% of stress required to produce rupture at the end of 100,000 hours at design temperature.

But progress in the knowledge of the behaviour of the materials under difficult environmental conditions has enabled economical designs to be made using lesser thicknesses of material which could safely withstand extremes of temperature, pressure, impact and fatigue as well as hazardous environments.

This led to the use of lower ('dividing') factors of safety in pressure vessel codes.

For example the International Standards Organization's *Recommendations for Stationary Boilers* (R831), which is also applicable to pressure vessels, laid down that design stresses should be based primarily on the lowest of four criteria, namely:

(i) The tensile strength at room temperature divided by 2·7.

(ii) The yield or proof stress at the operating temperature divided by 1·6.

(iii) The mean stress to produce rupture in 100,000 hours at the operating temperature divided by 1·6.

(iv) The stress to produce 1% creep in 100,000 hours at the operating temperature.

Elevated temperature yield or proof stress properties also have to be certified or otherwise suitably verified.

In general these ISO recommendations were in due course incorporated in specific national standards.

ASME, Section VIII, Division 2 at present allows stress intensity values up to one-third of the tensile strength or two-thirds of the yield strength at room or operating temperature whichever is the less (i.e., the dividing factors are 3 and 1·5 respectively).

Similarly, the factor given in BS 1515* *Fusion welded pressure vessels for use in the chemical, petroleum and allied industries* Part 1 Carbon and ferritic alloy steels for minimum tensile strength ($R_m$) at room temperature was 2·35.[†] Alternatively, the yield stress ($R_e$) could be divided by 1·5. The least value of design stress obtained by considering each criterion separately was used. The safe use of the resulting higher design stresses was ensured by the more exacting inspection and non-destructive testing specified. All these factors were incorporated in the new BS 5500.

---

* First issued in 1965. Withdrawn May 1978 and superseded by BS 5500.
[†] In BS 1515 Part 2 for austenitic stainless steel this factor was 2·5.

(ii) *Nominal material design strengths for BS 5500 category 1 and 2 vessels.*

The nominal design strengths given in Table 2.3 of BS 5500 for category 1 and 2 vessels are in general related to the relevant mechanical property values given in the therein specified British Standards (i.e. the BS 1501–4 and 3601–6 series plus BS 3059). These standards include and specify minimum elevated temperature yield/proof stress values (derived generally in accordance with the procedures given in BS 3920). In most cases the values of nominal (time-independent) design strength ($f$) given in Table 2.3 are based on a relationship derived using a similar factor to that which was given in BS 1515.

For carbon, carbon manganese and low alloy steels

(i)  for temperatures up to and including 50°C:

$$f = \frac{R_e}{1\cdot5} \quad \text{or} \quad \frac{R_m}{2\cdot35} \quad \text{whichever is the lower}$$

(ii)  for temperatures 150°C and above:

$$f = \frac{R_{e\,(T)}}{1\cdot5} \quad \text{or} \quad \frac{R_m}{2\cdot35} \quad \text{whichever is the lower}$$

(iii) for temperatures between 50°C and 150°C the values of $f$ have been obtained by linear interpolation.

For austenitic stainless steels

(i)  for temperatures up to and including 50°C:

$$f = \frac{R_e}{1\cdot5} \quad \text{or} \quad \frac{R_m}{2\cdot5} \quad \text{whichever is the lower}$$

(ii)  for temperatures 150°C and above:

$$f = \frac{R_{e\,(T)}}{1\cdot35} \quad \text{or} \quad \frac{R_m}{2\cdot35} \quad \text{whichever is the lower}$$

(iii) for temperatures between 50°C and 150°C the values of $f$ have been obtained by linear interpolation.

For aluminium and aluminium alloys

$$f = R_{p0\cdot2}/1\cdot5$$

Time-dependent values of $f$ are given in Table 2.3 (of BS 5500) for design life times ($t$) of 100,000, 150,000, 200,000 and 250,000 hours.

In general these values are related by:

$$f = S_{Rt}/1\cdot3$$

where $S_{Rt}$ is the stress required to produce rupture in time $t$ (at temperature $T$).

(iii) *Calculation of plate thicknesses.* Formulae are given in BS 5500 and other codes to determine the minimum plate thickness or dimensions to ensure safety of the vessel against the risk of gross plastic deformation and/or collapse. Recommendations are also given to safeguard the vessel against fatigue and against brittle fracture (for vessels operating below 0°C Charpy V-notch impact tests may be required). In general the design stresses for each category may not exceed the tabulated and specified values for the design temperature.

The nominal design stress ($f$), as derived above, for the particular specified material is used in the various formulae given in the standard (or any other relevant code) in order to calculate the minimum thickness of pressure parts (or any other relevant quantity). For example to calculate the minimum plate thickness of a cylindrical shell, for pressure loading only, the basic equations given are:

| BS 5500 | ASME Division 1 | ASME Division 2 |
|---|---|---|
| $e = \dfrac{pD_i}{2f - p}$ | $t = \dfrac{pR_i}{SE - 0\cdot6p}$ | $t = \dfrac{PR_i}{S - 0\cdot5P}$ |

For a spherical shell:

| | | |
|---|---|---|
| $e = \dfrac{pD_i}{4f - 1\cdot2p}$ | $t = \dfrac{PR_i}{2SE - 0\cdot2P}$ | $t = \dfrac{0\cdot5PR_i}{S - 0\cdot25P}$ |

where thickness $e$ (mm) or $t$ (in)
design pressure $p$ (N/mm$^2$) or $P$ (lb/in$^2$)
Inner diameter of shell $D_i$ (mm) or inner radius $R_i$ (in)
design stress $f$ (N/mm$^2$) or $S$ (lb/in$^2$)
$E$ is joint efficiency

In all cases a corrosion allowance may have to be made. Provision must be made for any additional loadings (such as external pressure; weight of vessel and contents, fixtures etc.; impact, wind and earthquake loads, etc.) which may be present or could reasonably be expected. These loadings may apply a bending moment (e.g. due to wind), an axial force and/or a torque.

Plate thicknesses are therefore generally based on the stress expected in service. However, recent advances in stress analysis (which allow stresses to be estimated more accurately) have enabled design methods to be developed which utilize strain as the criterion, instead of tensile strength or yield stress as in conventional design practice. Such new methods have been used to form the basis of the graph of shape factor for various 'depth ratios' of dished ends which has also been included in ISO/R831 and in other specifications (including BS 1515), and in consequence can result in a more economic and effective use of material. (See S.E. Mitchell, *National Engineering Laboratory Report No. 171.*)*

By agreement between purchaser and manufacturer designs (and thickness, etc.) based on other than BS rules (such as ASME Section VIII Division 1 Appendix Y (for bolted flanged connections)) may in general be used, but in no case shall the minimum thickness for pressure loading only be less than that required by BS 5500, paras. 3.5.1, 2 and 3.

(iv) *Combined loadings, etc.*

Much design information is given in BS 5500 combined loadings, etc. and in the ASME Code with appendices and tables giving details and recommendations for such matters as combined loadings (including wind and earthquakes), fatigue, low-temperature operation, welded connections, calculations, alternative design methods, heat treatment, etc.

The inspecting authority may be required to independently check the design of the vessel, carrying out all necessary calculations, and has to certify that it complies with all design requirements, as well as certifying that it has been constructed and tested under their surveillance to the particular Code requirements. (A typical calculation sheet for the ASME Code (for pressure loading only) is given in Fig. 3.1.)

It is impossible to give a realistic equation for shell thickness, etc., under any possible combination of loadings and some trial and error may be necessary. Calculations can be made for any loadings expected in service, bearing in mind that these will not necessarily occur simultaneously. Wind and earthquake loadings (particularly the latter) are difficult to predict and depend so much on geographical and topographical location, statistics, etc.

It can be assumed (perhaps incorrectly) that wind and earthquake loadings will not act simultaneously. However, when all these allowable stress intensities have been considered and/or calculated they may, by agreement, be increased by a factor of 1·2 (see BS 5500 Appendices A3.6 and B6.6) to cater for earthquake loading.

The ASME Code Section VIII Division 2 requires that wind loads, snow loads and earthquake loads be considered during design, operation and test.

---

*See also BS PD 6433 Guide to the application of stress analysis to design which discusses the subject with particular reference to its application in BS 1515 and the ASME Code, Section III.

| CUSTOMER'S NAME | | | | | | ORDER NO. | | |
|---|---|---|---|---|---|---|---|---|
| Design pressure | | Material specification | Stress | Radiography | | Postweld heat treat | Joint efficiency | |
| Design temperature | | Shell | | None | | Yes | percent | |
| Corrosion allowance | | Heads | | Spot | | No | percent | |
| Inside diameter | | Bolts | | Complete | | | | |
| Head radius | | Nuts | | | | | | |

**Shell thickness**

$$t = \frac{PR}{SE - 0\cdot6P} = \underline{\hspace{3cm}} = \underline{\hspace{1cm}}$$

| | | |
|---|---|---|
| $SE$ | | |
| $0\cdot6P$ | | |
| $SE - 0\cdot6P$ | | Code Par. UG-27 |

+ _____ Corrosion allowance
_____ Thickness required
_____ Thickness used

**Torispherical head thickness**

$$t = \frac{0\cdot885PL}{SE - 0\cdot1P} = \underline{\hspace{3cm}} = \underline{\hspace{1cm}}$$

| | | |
|---|---|---|
| $SE$ | | |
| $0\cdot1P$ | | |
| $SE - 0\cdot1P$ | | Code Par. UG-32 |

+ _____ Corrosion allowance
_____ Thickness required after forming
_____ Thickness used

**Ellipsoidal head thickness**

$$t = \frac{PD}{2SE - 0\cdot2P} = \underline{\hspace{3cm}} = \underline{\hspace{1cm}}$$

| | | |
|---|---|---|
| $2SE$ | | |
| $0\cdot2P$ | | |
| $2SE - 0\cdot2P$ | | Code Par. UG-32 |

+ _____ Corrosion allowance
_____ Thickness required after forming
_____ Thickness used

**Flat head thickness**

$$t = d\sqrt{\frac{CP}{S}} = \sqrt{\underline{\hspace{3cm}}} = \underline{\hspace{1cm}}$$

Code Par. UG-34

+ _____ Corrosion allowance
_____ Thickness required
_____ Thickness used

Maximum Allowable Working Pressure for New and Cold Vessels (see Code Par. UG-99)

**Shell**

| $R$ | |
|---|---|
| $0\cdot6t$ | |
| $R + 0\cdot6t$ | |

$$p = \frac{SEt}{R + 0\cdot6t} = \underline{\hspace{3cm}} = \underline{\hspace{1cm}} \text{ psi}$$

**Torispherical head**

| $0\cdot885L$ | |
|---|---|
| $0\cdot1t$ | |
| $0\cdot885L + 0\cdot1t$ | |

$$p = \frac{SEt}{0\cdot885L + 0\cdot1t} = \underline{\hspace{3cm}} = \underline{\hspace{1cm}} \text{ psi}$$

**Ellipsoidal head**

| $D$ | |
|---|---|
| $0\cdot2t$ | |
| $D + 0\cdot6t$ | |

$$p = \frac{2SEt}{D + 0\cdot2t} = \underline{\hspace{3cm}} = \underline{\hspace{1cm}} \text{ psi}$$

**Flat head**

$$p = \frac{st^2}{d^2C} = \underline{\hspace{3cm}} = \underline{\hspace{1cm}} \text{ psi}$$

Maximum allowable working pressure = _____ pd (limited by _____ )
Hydrostatic heat pressure = _____ × _____ psi = _____ psi

**Fig. 3.1   Calculation sheet for ASME pressure vessels (Sect. VIII, Division 1).** (Courtesy of ASME).

The thickness of vessel parts and attached supports must be determined by the applicable formula using the most severe combination of loadings and allowable stress intensities expected to occur simultaneously. The stress intensity due to this combination of loadings (design pressure and mechanical loadings etc.) has to be multiplied by a $k$ factor which for an earthquake *or* wind load is 1·2. For hydrostatic testing the $k$ factor is 1·25 and for pneumatic testing it is 1·15.

The primary bending stress due to any simultaneous combination should not exceed 1·5 times the average primary stress intensity. During operational use the actual loading conditions have to be considered and a vessel fatigue life evaluation may be necessary (for further information see ASME Division 2 AD100-160 and Appendix 5—Mandatory design based on Fatigue Analysis).

The following British Standard documents on pressure vessel design methods and codes may be of assistance:

PD 6437   A review of design methods given in present standards and codes and design proposals for nozzles and openings in pressure vessels.
PD 6438   A review of present methods for design of bolted flanges for pressure vessels (refers to ASME Code, Sect VIII, App.Y (now incorporated in BS 5500, Sect. 3.8).
PD 6439   A review of methods of calculating stresses due to local loads and local attachments of pressure vessels.

See also

*The Journal of Pressure Vessel Technology* (published quarterly by ASME)
IEEE Standard 344 (NY, 1975), *Recommended Practices for Seismic Qualification. Class IE Equipment for Nuclear Power Generating Stations* (qualifications must be demonstrated by stress analysis, testing and documentation of past performance).
ASCE, *Guidelines for the Seismic Design of Oil and Gas Pipeline Systems, (NY, 1984).*

It would be unwise to build nuclear or chemical plants on a known geological fault, or anywhere nearby without taking extra precautions. Fortunately in the UK such active faults are rare (but not unknown) and major earthquakes have been few over recorded centuries. But this is not the case for instance in China and Japan (or the USA). Japan, in particular, has carried out much research since 1978, aided by the passing of the *Large Scale Earthquake Countermeasures Act.* It seems that many seismographs, strainmeters and other sensors (including one which detects the release of hydrogen from a fault a few days before an earthquake) *may* help to predict an earthquake. In Japan, under the Act, specific countermeasures have to be taken when an earthquake of magnitude 8 or more (Richter scale) is predicted. Of course in earthquake zones, some buildings etc. are constructed with earthquakes in mind. But such precautions, if any, did not prevent the reputed loss of 242,000 lives in the Tangshan (China) earthquake of 1976, although it was said it had been predicted two years before! However some other Chinese predictions and precautions seem to have been more effective.

Obviously in earthquake zones many industrial, chemical and nuclear plants should be constructed with earthquake protection incorporated into their design. In the UK (not in any sense an earthquake zone) such is the case with the latest *designs* of nuclear plant; possibly in earlier designs relevant factors of safety have been *increased* by 20% (as already indicated). Clearly a much larger increase in the factor of safety is desirable in Japan.

But what about the older UK stations? One point to remember is that at the time of their construction the factor of safety for tensile strength in pressure vessel materials was around 4, but later specifications (relying *inter alia* on advanced design and better non-destructive testing) *decreased* this to 2·35 (see 3.4.5). It would seem that the inspector of nuclear plant, especially when certifying design or undertaking 'in-service' inspection is expected to be well 'genned' up (see 3.30). (For further information on seismic qualification see 3.30.)

### 3.4.6 Weld design and welded seams

Vessels should be designed with the minimum practical number of seams with adequate access for the deposition and inspection of weld metal to meet specified manufacturing and inspection requirements. Where practicable, the cylindrical portion of a vessel should be made from a single plate. As far as possible seams should be positioned clear of supports so that they can be made readily visible for inspection in service. Where more than two weld seams meet consideration should be given to the desirability of intermediate stress relief (not applicable to aluminium). Where any part of a vessel is made in two or more courses (plates) the longitudinal seams shall be completed before commencing the adjoining circumferential seam(s). Full penetration butt welds shall be used for any radial joints. The soundness of all such welds shall be demonstrated on completion by appropriate radiographic or ultrasonic inspection. Typical forms of weld preparation for the principal seams, and for other than principal seams, of vessels covered by BS 5500 are illustrated and detailed in Appendix E of that standard. (Figs. 3.3–3.5 have been selected from BS 5500 Appendix E and will be referred to again later.)

Where plates of different thicknesses are joined by means of butt welding a tapered transition shall be provided.

The design of principal seams where the deposited weld metal will have a yield strength (or proof stress) less than either of the materials being joined should be the subject of special consideration. It is important to note that the intention of Appendix E of BS 5500 (and of Figs 3.3–3.5 in this book) is to exemplify sound and commonly accepted practice which has given satisfactory results. It is not intended to be mandatory or to restrict development in any way. In general the joints or weld preparations are also permitted by ASME.

*3.4.7 Welded joints–location and type*

In the ASME Code Section VIII welded joints are defined according to location (see Fig. 3.2). In general categories A and B include all longitudinal and circumferential joints respectively, and categories C and D various

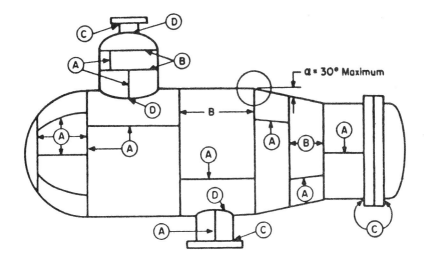

Category A   Longitudinal joints; any welded joint within a sphere; circumferential joints connecting hemispherical heads to main shell or communicating chambers, etc.
Category B   Circumferential joints; circumferential joints connecting formed heads other than hemispherical (e.g. torispherical or ellipsoidal) to main shell, etc; angle joints (not exceeding 30°) connecting transitions in diameter.
Category C   Flange joints, tube sheets, Van Stone laps, or flat heads to main shell etc.
Category D   Joints connecting communications chambers, nozzles, spheres, heads, flat-sided vessels to main shells.

**Fig. 3.2   Welded joint locations typical of ASME Categories A, B, C and D.**
*Source: ASME.*

other joints connecting flanges or communicating chambers. When vessels are to contain lethal substances all category A joints must be type 1 (double butt weld without any backing strip remaining in place), and all joints of categories B and C of either type 1 or type 2, (which is a single butt weld with backing strip). All butt-welded joints must be fully radiographed and post-weld heat treatment must be carried out on carbon or low-alloy steel.

Similarly, for vessels designed for steam at pressures exceeding 50 lb/in$^2$ (except that the type of joint for category C is not specified) and for vessels designed to operate below $-20°F$ ($-29°C$) (when impact tests are required for the material or weld metal). Category C and D joints must be full penetration welds.

BS 5500 (in an amendment dated April 1987) introduced a somewhat similar diagram to Fig. 3.2 defining locations and types of welded joints. The main differences between the ASME and BS 5500 descriptions are:

ASME categories A and B correspond generally to what is called type A in BS 5500.

ASME categories C and D correspond generally to what is called type B in BS 5500.

The non-destructive testing requirements of BS 5500 for these joints are dealt with in 3.15.1 and 3.15.8.

## 3.5 General inspection procedure

Some detailed information on the procedure for the inspection of pressure vessels culled from the various codes and specifications and the practice of industrial organizations will now be given. Refer also to Table 3.3 (adapted by permission from BS 5500) which summarizes the various inspection stages.

## 3.6 Inspection and identification of materials

(i) Where the specification or order requires inspection at the works of the material suppliers, the inspector at these works will issue a report of his findings, together with the results of any tests carried out and/or witnessed, and relevant test certificates and any chemical analyses for the material supplied.

(ii) The inspector will also check and/or arrange identification markings, such as cast number, quality of plate, tensile strength, manufacturer's mark, inspection stamps (including marking of any materials required for test plates). Where necessary these markings should be transferred under supervision if they are, or are likely to become, obliterated during manufacture.

**TABLE 3.3**

*Checklist of inspection stages for pressure vessels*

| Stage | Inspection | Remarks |
|---|---|---|
| *At sub-contractor's works* | | |
| Examine material at product makers works, select test pieces and witness tests | MI and/or AIB | AIB will inspect if required by purchaser, or MI will carry out inspection/surveillance at sub-contractors subject to approval of AIB |
| Correlate material Test Certificates and chemical analyses with materials and specifications | MI and AIB | Test certificates to be sent to AIB for independent checking |
| Identify material/and witness transfer of identification marks at maker's works. Examine for size and flaws, etc. | MI and/or AIB | Identity of material to be traced back to its origin from records. MI and/or AIB to witness and examine if desired |
| *At manufacturer's works* | | |
| Examine cut edges of material and heat-affected zones | MI and AIB* | AIB inspection optional for categories 1 and 2 |
| Approve weld procedures and welding consumables | AIB | AIB to witness unless procedures already approved |
| Approve welders and operators | AIB | AIB to witness unless welders etc. already approved |
| Witness production weld tests | AIB | AIB to witness if tests specified |
| Examine plates, etc. after forming | MI and/or AIB | AIB inspection optional |
| Examine set-up of seams and weld preparations, etc. Dimensional check | MI and AIB* | AIB inspection optional for categories 1 and 2 |
| Inspect second side after first side weld is completed and root cleaned | MI and AIB* | AIB inspection optional for categories 1 and 2 |

**TABLE 3.3** *concluded*

| Stage | Inspection | Remarks |
|---|---|---|
| Examine NDT reports and any heat treatment records and check acceptability | MI and AIB | AIB to carry out independent check |
| Check all main dimensions | MI and AIB | |
| Witness pressure test and record any permanent set | MI and AIB | |
| Examine completed vessel before despatch. Check marking | MI and AIB | |
| Correlate documentation, etc. Certify Form X-Certificate of Compliance | MI and AIB | AIB to countersign |

*Notes:*

AIB—Authorised inspection body, an independent engineering inspectorate usually commissioned or maintained by the purchaser, and/or assessed by the Pressure Vessels Quality Assurance Board.
MI—The manufacturer's own inspection organization.
*AIB are required to carry out this examination independently on all category 3 components. Except where specifically indicated in the table the degree of AIB's participation in inspection/surveillance is at their discretion.

*(Source: Adapted from BS 5500, Tables 5.1, 5.2 and 5A8.1.)*

(iii) The inspector should particularly check that these markings are not so deeply stamped, and are not in such positions, as to cause incipient cracks. In the case of vessels intended for low-temperature service marking by hard stamping should be avoided.

(iv) All materials should be examined at the fabricator's works prior to assembly to ensure that they are the materials identified and/or released from the supplier's works, and that they comply with order requirements. Attention should be paid to such features as freedom from laminations, surface cracks, flaws and other defects. Hammer dressing, patching, welding or other forms of repair to plates, etc. is generally not permitted without the express approval of the inspector. Plates, components, etc. will be checked for dimensions and thickness, and curved surfaces may be checked by templates of wood or metal.

(v) If material is taken from stock, or cannot otherwise be identified, it may at the inspector's discretion be examined and any relevant specification tests carried out by a recognized test house or authority.

(vi) Any discrepancies or doubts as to the quality of materials, etc. which cannot be immediately resolved must be referred to higher authority, and the material must not be used until the doubt has been resolved.

(vii) Inspection should check that any plates welded prior to forming are welded to the standard applicable to the appropriate classification.

(viii) Any approved arc welding process whereby the arc and the deposited metal are protected from atmospheric corrosion may be used (subject to agreement). Welding consumables (e.g. wire, electrodes, flux, shielding gas) must be of the same type or brand as those used in the welding procedure (see 3.9) or any alternatives permissible (e.g. by BS 4870 Part 1) if agreed with the inspector. Evidence must be available that the deposited weld metal is suitable for the intended duty, and has tensile properties not less than those specified for the parent material.

(ix) Plate specifications, etc. may or may not give details of the extent of any faults which could be acceptable.

Attention is drawn to the following standards which may be used in conjunction with, or otherwise called up by, a pressure vessel specification or order:

(a) BS 6512 *Limits of repair of surface discontinuities of hot-rolled steel plates and wide flats* which specifies limits for surface discontinuities (in terms of depth, surface area and nature) and requirements and limits for repair of plates, etc. of thickness from 3 mm up to 150 mm.

Surface discontinuities are classified as *imperfections* (which do not generally require repair and may be acceptable) or *defects* (which require repair perhaps by grinding alone, or by chipping and/or grinding followed by welding to an approved procedure).

Such discontinuities are identified by the letters A to E, the depth, extent and nature of each being tabulated. Type E defects (the worst–which could contain cracks, etc.) may even if repaired, impair the use of a pressure vessel.

(b) BS 5996 *Methods of ultrasonic testing and quality grading of ferritic steel plates* recognises some four quality grades of internal discontinuities or defects (for details see 10.6.5–Assessing for quality).

When either of the above standards are used then the maximum grade or type of acceptable defect must be specified by the purchaser.

## 3.7 Constructional details

(i) Before manufacture commences the manufacturer must submit to the inspecting authority for approval a dimensioned drawing giving the following information:

(a) Standard or Code and category, etc. applicable.

(b) Material specifications (plate thicknesses, etc.)

(c) Welding processes to be used for all parts of the vessel.

(d) Dimensional details of the weld grooves for the longitudinal and circumferential seams.

(e) Position and details of joints for branch pipes, seatings, etc.

(f) Design pressure and temperature.

(g) Test pressure.

(h) Amount and location of any corrosion allowance.

(i) Any other relevant information on the product or substance to be handled, service conditions, classification, radiography, heat treatment, etc.

(j) Non-destructive testing requirements.

(k) Any test plate requirements.

(ii) The type or types of welding electrodes to be used must be approved, and any change reported to the inspector.

(iii) By agreement between purchaser and manufacturer work on individual parts may be commenced before final approval of the drawings. No modifications to the approved design may be made without prior agreement.

(iv) The possible requirement for manholes, access and inspection openings (see BS 470) in accordance with Sect. 30 of the *Factories Act* must be borne in mind.

## 3.8 Supervision of fabrication

### *3.8.1 Plate cutting*

Plates will generally be cut to size by flame cutting and/or machining, or—for mild steel not exceeding a thickness of 1 in (25 mm)—by cold shearing. The severely cold-worked material produced by the shearing operation must be removed by grinding, machining or chipping to a depth of not less than one-quarter of the plate thickness, with a minimum of $\frac{1}{8}$ in (3 mm) to provide a suitable surface for examination prior to welding. A similar allowance is required on edges flame-cut by hand to ensure the removal of burnt metal, etc.

Plates less than 10 mm (0·4 in) thick (in steel or aluminium) which are cold-sheared need not be dressed where the cut edges are to be subsequently welded.

Austenitic stainless steel is preferably cut by machining, but flame cutting (by flux injection or metal arc) and cold shearing are permitted provided that the affected metal is removed and, in the case of flame cutting, at least 0·02 in (0·5 mm) of additional metal.

Inspection should check for the presence of cracks, laminations, slag inclusions, etc. at cut surfaces and heat-affected zones particularly in flame-cut alloy or high carbon steels; preheating may be required to ensure satisfactory results. An independent examination by the authorized inspecting authority is required for all BS 5500 Category 3 components.

### 3.8.2 Preparation for welding

(a) No welding of any kind should be attempted when the temperature of the base metal is below 0°F (−18°C). Between that temperature and 32°F (0°) local heating may be applied to warm the areas to be welded. Protection from the weather is desirable. Preheating to a specified temperature may be required for some materials.

(b) Welding grooves for butt welds are usually prepared to the correct profile by machining; welding edges or grooves for various attachments are also prepared by hand or by machine flame cutting followed by chipping and grinding to a clean surface.

(c) The inspector should check groove profiles, plate edges, etc. and should thoroughly examine them for any evidence of flaws, cracks, slag inclusions or laminations. Non-destructive testing methods may be used.

(d) Plates are formed to shape by either hot or cold working. If austenitic stainless steels are hot-worked, attention should be paid to the somewhat limited temperature range permitted by the specification; they must be heated in a neutral or an oxidizing atmosphere and must not come into contact with flame.

(e) Head plates and ends, where practicable, shall be made from one plate. Dishing and peripheral flanging of end plates shall be done by machine; flanging should preferably be done in one operation. After forming all plates etc. shall be examined visually (and by suitable NDT methods if required) and checked for thickness.

(f) Plates and components should be assembled in stages and checked for alignment of matching edges. They can be retained in position for welding by any suitable method, such as tack welding. Any tack welds must be examined to ensure that they are sound and of such size and shape that they can satisfactorily be fused into the main run; if not they must be cut out.

(g) Tolerances on misalignment, circumference, out of roundness, thickness, etc. should be checked to drawing and specification requirements, making sure that maximum permitted gaps between components are not exceeded.

(h) Particular attention should be paid to the assembly of branches, etc.; they must not be hammered into alignment (except when heated to forging temperature).

### 3.9  Welded joints and their inspection

Each welder must have passed a qualifying test and be approved for the type of work in hand. In addition it is sometimes required that his work should be identifiable later, either by marking it or by a record system. The welding procedure may also be subject to a qualification test (see 9.21 and BS 4870, 4871 and 4872). Where stipulated by the purchaser, production control test plates (see 3.14) may be required.

Before commencing work it should be remembered that for Category 3 components (BS 5500) the inspecting authority must see and approve the assembly and the preparation of the second side.

Butt-welds only are used for the main longitudinal seams of pressure vessels. They are also in general use for the main circumferential seams, except that lap welds are permitted on the circumferential seams of certain BS 5500 Category 3 vessels (not exceeding $\frac{5}{8}$ in (16 mm) plate).

Butt-weld preparations in accordance with Fig. 3.3 (a, b and c) are made where both sides of the plate are accessible for welding.

For small diameter vessels the single V should be on the inside. The inspection procedure is generally as follows.

### 3.9.1  Stage 1—preparation

(i)  Examine weld preparation for cleanliness and freedom from defects—all places where weld metal is to be deposited must be free from rust, scale, oil and foreign matter.

(ii)  Check the dimensions of the weld preparations with the appropriate drawing—using a profile gauge or template.

(iii)  Check the alignment of the plates with each other—a maximum error of $\frac{1}{8}$ in (3 mm) or 10% of their thickness is usual.

### 3.9.2  Stage 2—welding of first side

(i)  The welding of the first side is then carried out, first checking any pre-heat temperatures that may be specified.

(ii)  Each run of weld metal must be thoroughly cleaned and all slag, cracks, blowholes, etc. removed before the next run is deposited.

Maintenance of the correct clearance during, and critical inspection after, the first run is of particular importance, as incipient cracks can readily develop here. A root gap of $\frac{1}{16}$ (2 mm) in may be specified for aluminium.

(iii)  All welding shall be carried out in the down-hand position, wherever practicable.

(iv)  If welding is stopped for any reason, care must be taken when restarting to ensure proper fusion and penetration between the plates, the

| Fig. | Joint | Name | Application |
|---|---|---|---|
| (a) | (1) 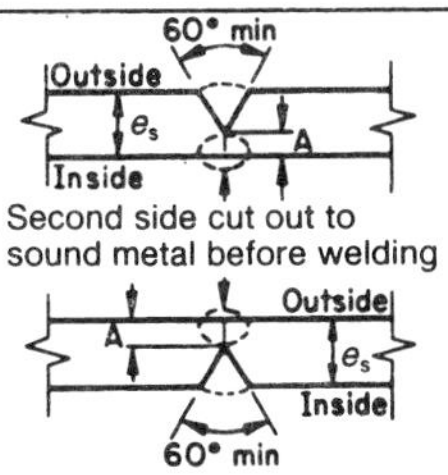 <br> 60° min <br> Outside <br> $e_s$ A <br> Inside <br> Second side cut out to sound metal before welding <br><br> (2) For small diameter vessels <br> Outside <br> A $e_s$ Inside <br> 60° min | Double-welded butt joint with single 'V' | Longitudinal and circumferential butt welds in plates not more than 20 mm thick <br> The 'V' should be on the inside of small diameter vessels as shown in (2) opposite <br><br> A = 3 mm where $e_s$ is 10 mm or over |
| (b) | 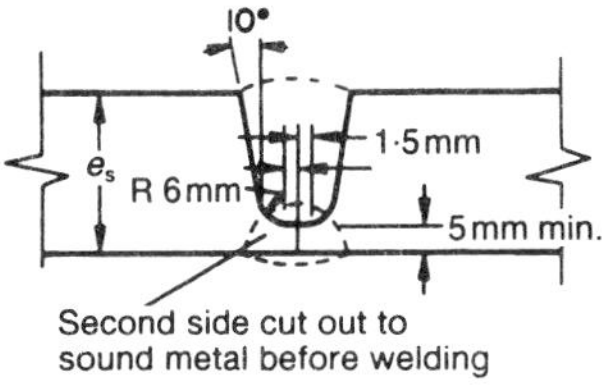 10° <br> $e_s$ <br> R 6mm <br> 1·5mm <br> 5mm min. <br> Second side cut out to sound metal before welding | Double-welded butt joint with single 'U' | Longitudinal and circumferential butt welds in plates where the thickness is greater than 20 mm |
| (c) | 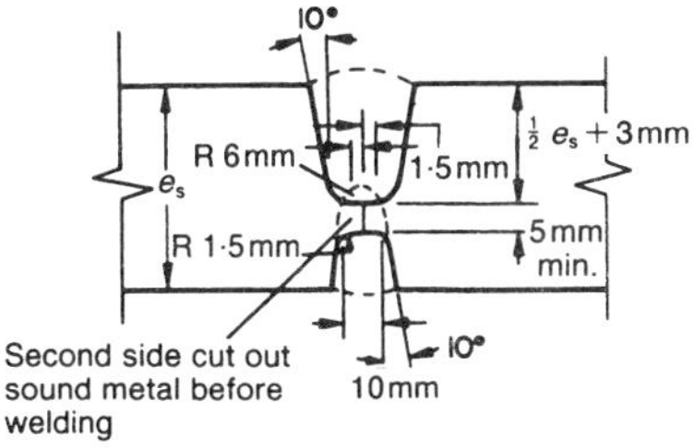 10° <br> R 6mm <br> $e_s$ <br> R 1·5mm <br> 1·5mm <br> $\frac{1}{2}e_s + 3mm$ <br> 5mm min. <br> Second side cut out sound metal before welding <br> 10° <br> 10mm | Double-welded butt joint with double 'U' | Longitudinal and circumferential butt welds where the thickness is greater than 20 mm |
| (d) | 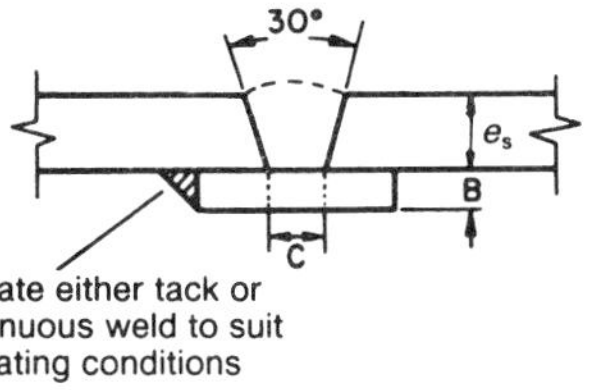 30° <br> $e_s$ <br> B <br> C <br> Indicate either tack or continuous weld to suit operating conditions <br><br> Weld dimensions are minima. <br><br> (see table below) | Single-welded butt joint with backing strip | Longitudinal and circumferential butt welds Backing strip to be removed after welding except where otherwise permitted |

| Plate thickness $e_s$ | B | C |
|---|---|---|
| Up to 7·5 mm | 4·5 mm | 7·5 mm |
| Over 7·5 mm to 12 mm | 6 mm | 9 mm |
| Over 12 mm | 9 mm | 9 mm |

**Fig. 3.3  Typical weld preparations for butt welds using the manual metal arc process.**
*(Reproduced by permission from Fig. E1(1), BS 5500: 1988).*

weld metal and the previously deposited weld metal, which must be cleaned and freed from slag.

(v) The arc should be struck only on those parts of the parent metal where weld metal is to be deposited. The inspector should watch this point particularly, as the indiscriminate striking of the arc can cause damage and local residual stresses of some magnitude.

### 3.9.3 Stage 3—preparation of second side

(i) Before the second side of the plate is welded, the metal at the bottom of the weld on the first side must be removed by grinding, chipping, machining or other approved methods to such a depth as to ensure that all unsound metal at the root of the weld has been removed.

(ii) The inspector should make a careful visual examination of this second side groove and check its depth throughout its length. This examination may prove difficult, but significant unsoundness can be detected by examining the final chippings as they are produced. Where the preparation has not been taken to a sufficient depth to remove unwelded edges of the parent plate this will be indicated by the splitting of the chippings as the cut is made. This examination of chipping is particularly essential when the main seams are not examined by radiography.

(iii) The contour of the finished groove should be smooth, and it should be clean and free from defects.

### 3.9.4 Stage 4

The welding of the second side can then be carried out, watching the same details as given for the first side.

### 3.9.5 Stage 5

(i) Examine the entire length of the completed weld. Magnifiers, gauges and liquid penetrants can be used.

(ii) The welding grooves should be completely filled with weld metal and the weld surface should be smooth and free from defects such as cracks, blowholes, cavities and any marked irregularities, groove and depressions. The adjacent parent metal must be free from undercut.

### 3.10 Welded joints—second side inaccessible

(i) Where the 'second side' is inaccessible for welding, longitudinal and circumferential butt welds may be made (usually subject to agreement) using a backing strip. The weld preparation is shown in Fig. 3.3 (d). The es-

| Figure | Joint | Name | Application |
|---|---|---|---|
| (a) | 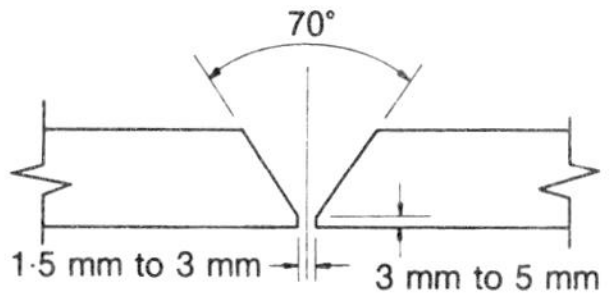 70°<br>1·5 mm to 3 mm — 3 mm to 5 mm | Single-welded butt joint with 'V' groove, without backing strip | Butt welds in plates having a thickness not greater than 16 mm |
| (b) | 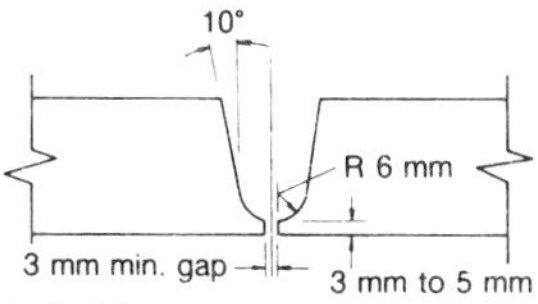 10°<br>R 6 mm<br>3 mm min. gap — 3 mm to 5 mm | Single-welded butt joint with 'U' groove, without backing strip | Butt welds in plates having a thickness greater than 16 mm |
| (c) | 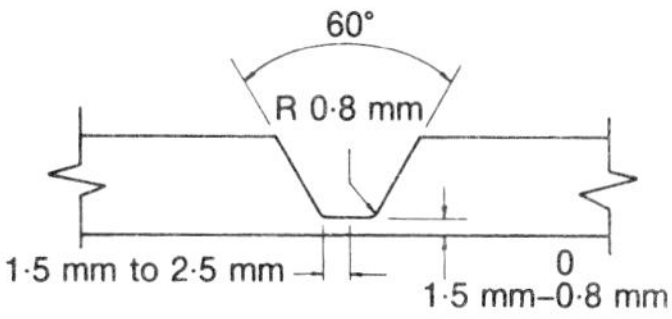 60°<br>R 0·8 mm<br>1·5 mm to 2·5 mm — 0<br>1·5 mm–0·8 mm | Single-welded butt joint with 'U' groove, without backing strip | Butt welds in plates up to 20 mm thick where the second side is inaccessible for welding. Initial pass to be made by the TIG process with inert gas backing |
| (d) | 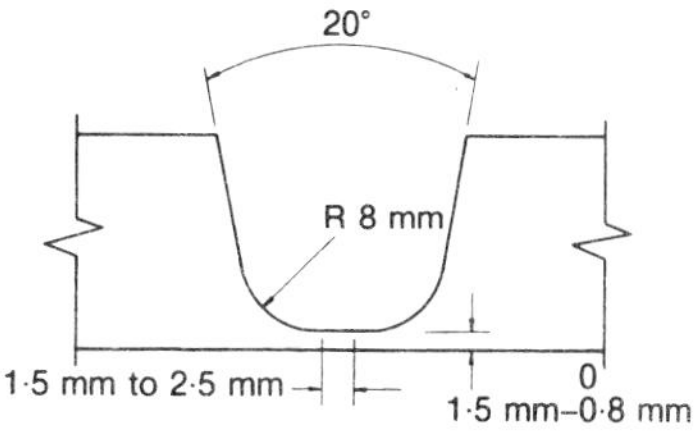 20°<br>R 8 mm<br>1·5 mm to 2·5 mm — 0<br>1·5 mm–0·8 mm | Single-welded butt joint with 'U' groove, without backing strip | Butt welds in plates over 20 mm thick where the second side is inaccessible for welding. Initial pass to be made by the TIG process with inert gas backing |
| (e) | 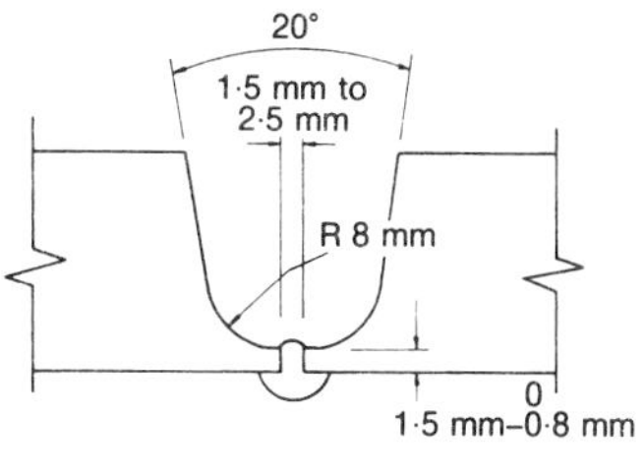 20°<br>1·5 mm to 2·5 mm<br>R 8 mm<br>0<br>1·5 mm–0·8 mm | Single-welded butt joint with 'U' groove, with consumable root insert | Butt welds in plates over 20 mm thick where the second side is inaccessible for welding. Initial pass to be made by the TIG process with inert gas backing |
| (f) | $90°\,{}^{+10}_{0}$<br>10 mm max.<br>1·5 mm min. gap — 1·5 mm | Single-welded butt joint with 'V' groove, without backing strip | Butt welds in plates not exceeding 10 mm thickness |
| (g) | 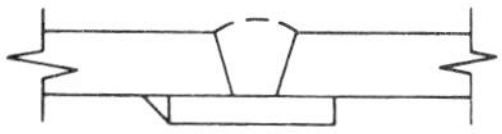 See Fig. 3.3(d) | Single-welded butt joint with backing strip | Butt welds in all thicknesses of plate |

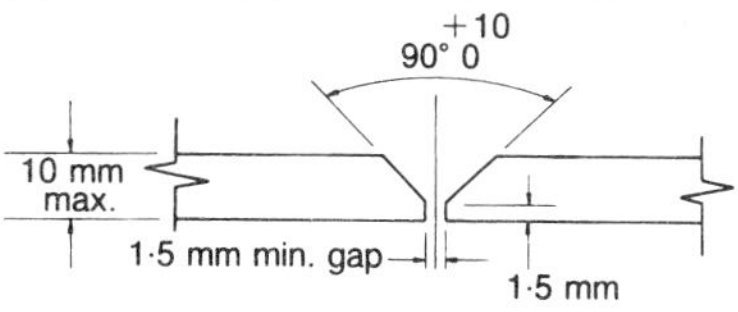

**Fig. 3.4   Typical weld preparations for circumferential welds where the second side is inaccessible for welding.**

*(Reproduced by permission from Fig. E.1(2), BS 5500: 1988).*

sential feature of this is that the gap at the root of the weld must be wide enough to permit unrestricted manipulation of the welding electrodes at the bottom of the groove, so enabling a sound weld to be produced having adequate fusion with the backing material.

The inspection procedure will follow generally that already given, as far as it is applicable. However, particular attention should be paid to ensuring that the gap is nowhere less than the minimum specified, and that during welding it is prevented from closing to a width less than this. A check should also be made that the backing strip or ring is a good, close fit. After welding, the backing strip has usually to be removed unless otherwise permitted.

(ii) Where the 'second side' is inaccessible for welding, circumferential butt welds can be made without a backing strip. The weld preparations for single V and U types are shown in Fig. 3.4 a–f. Fig. 3.4 g shows the use of a backing strip.

Producing a good weld from one side only requires careful assembly and alignment and correct preparation, and particular skill on the part of the operator. Consequently it is as well to assess this skill and establish a suitable technique by examining and testing typical samples. Fig. 3.5 shows joint preparations for aluminium and its alloys.

Inspection procedure will again follow that already given, as far as it is applicable. When examining the completed weld this should include the unwelded side if this is possible. If it is not, then it is highly desirable that a typical sample should be prepared and examined. The weld metal must penetrate through the full wall thickness, but penetration must not be excessive and must be regular in appearance on the inside.

*Note:* Permanent backing strips are not permitted for longitudinal welds or for construction category 1 (this applies to both steel and aluminium).

### 3.11  Further points regarding welded joints

(i) *Automatic (machine) welding.* Inspection will follow similar lines if continuously covered electrodes are used. With processes such as the submerged arc, in which the arc is maintained under a powder flux, the weld preparation may be different: for instance a double V may be used. Each case of machine welding must consequently be treated on its merits.

Where an automatic welding process has been employed, the 'second side' weld preparation to remove unsoundness at the root should if possible be inspected. If this is not possible then radiographs of the whole or part of the seams will usually be required.

(ii) *Lap welds* such as may be used on circumferential joints on certain category 3 vessels are shown in Fig. 3.6. Inspection follows the same general lines, care being taken to examine the contour and dimensions of the fillet welds.

| Material thickness | Edge preparation | Remarks |
|---|---|---|
| Up to 3 mm | 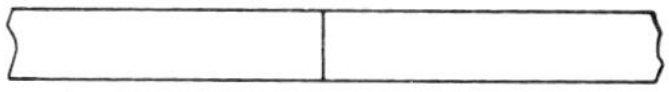 | Suitable for a.c., argon, TIG, d.c. helium TIG and pulsed MIG. Penetration from one side only during welding can be achieved. (Manual or mechanized). |
| 3 mm to 6·3 mm | 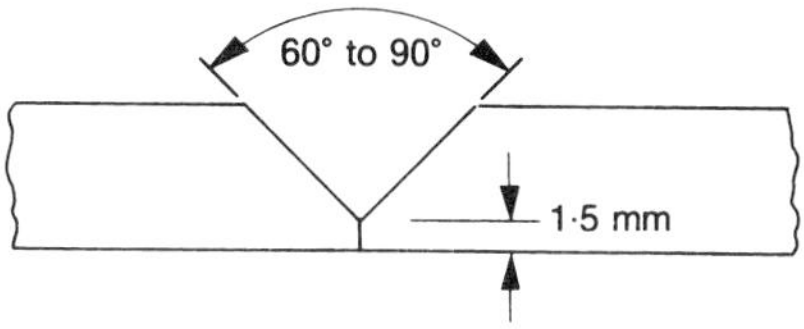 60° to 90°   1·5 mm | Suitable for a.c. TIG and pulsed MIG. Controlled penetration possible (Manual or mechanized). |
| 3 mm to 4 mm | 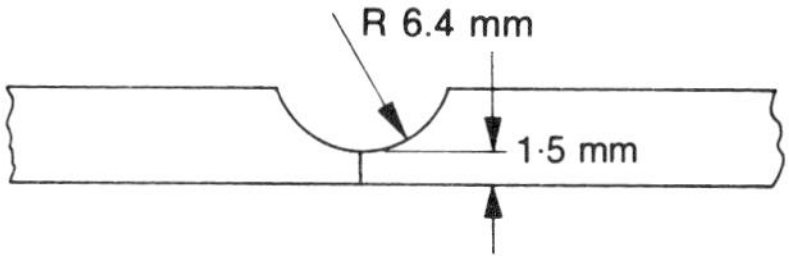 R 6.4 mm   1·5 mm | Suitable for rolled or positional fixed pipes using a.c. TIG. Controlled penetration possible (Manual) |
| 4 mm upwards | 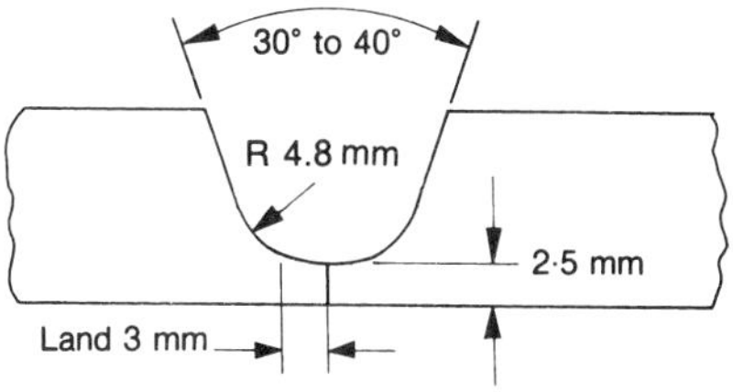 30° to 40°   R 4.8 mm   2·5 mm   Land 3 mm | Suitable for rolled or positional fixed pipes using a.c. argon TIG Controlled penetration possible (Manual) |
| 6·3 mm to 9·5 mm | 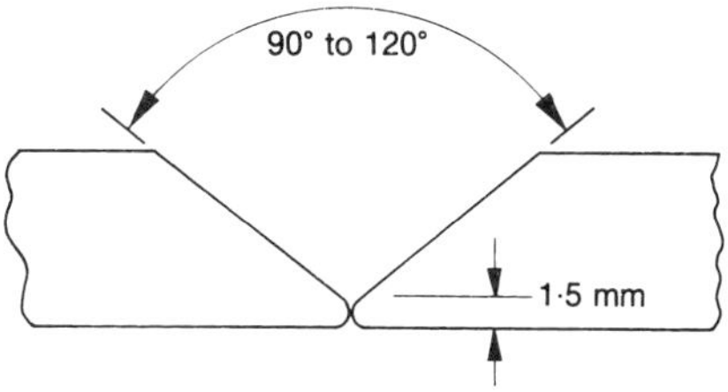 90° to 120°   1·5 mm | Suitable for rolled pipes with a.c. TIG or pulsed MIG. Controlled penetration possible Root faces radiused slightly. |

Note: These joint preparations are designed to permit a controlled penetration bead to be achieved on one-sided joints where accessibility to the underside is restricted.

Pipe joints preparations are also included.

**Fig. 3.5 Typical full penetration joint preparations for one-sided welding only; aluminium and its alloys.**
*(Reproduced by permission from fig. E.1(6), BS 5500: 1988).*

| Joint | Name | Application | |
|---|---|---|---|
| | | Longitudinal | Circumferential |
| 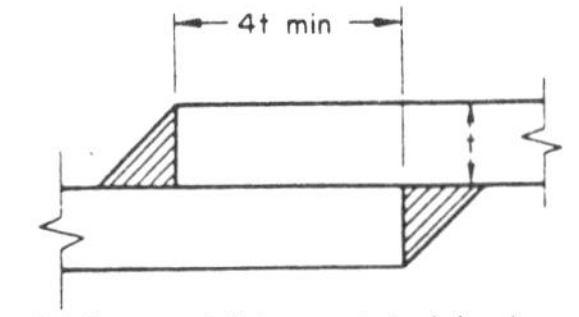 4t min<br>t=thickness of thinner plate joined | Double full-fillet lap joint | Not allowed* | Not exceeding $\frac{5}{8}$in. (16mm) plate for Category 3 vessels only |
| 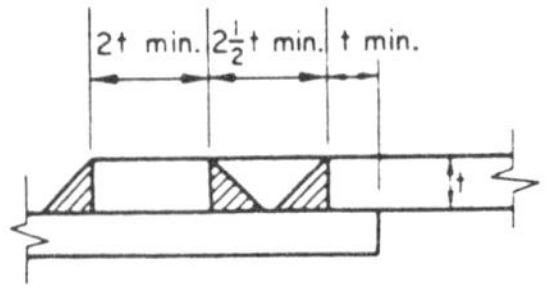 2t min. $2\frac{1}{2}$t min. t min.<br>t=thickness of thinner plate joined | Single full-fillet lap joint with plug weld | Not allowed | Not exceeding $\frac{9}{16}$in. (14mm) plate. Plugs shall be proportioned to take 20 per cent of total load. For Category 3 vessels only |

*Allowed by ASME Code for plate not exceeding $\frac{3}{8}$in.

**Fig. 3.6   Typical lap-welded circumferential joints.**
*(Adapted by permission from Fig. E.1(5), BS 5500).*

(iii)  When *alloy clad steels* are used the weld may be made from the mild steel side, using a V or U preparation; the reverse clad side is then chipped out, inspected, and then welded with suitable alloy electrodes. Alternatively the cladding is cut back from the joint, V or U preparation made and the mild steel completely welded from both sides. The cladding surface is then built up with alloy electrodes (see 5.7 and Fig. 5.1 (a) and (b)).

(iv)  The types of weld used for the attachment of flanges, branches, tubes to tube plates and shell plates, jackets, etc., will vary widely, but the approved detail drawings and the general inspection procedure will be followed.

(v)  Fig. 3.7 shows some types of welded joint which are not allowed.

(vi)  It is desirable that main welded seams should be readily visible for inspection when the vessel is in service (after the removal of any insulation, etc.).

(vii)  The attachment of a jacket to a pressure vessel (see Fig. 3.8) calls for some comment. The pressure in the jacket space will tend to separate the jacket from the 'blocking' ring, and this is resisted by the circumferential butt weld. It is difficult to assess the quality of this weld by radiographic examination, and in consequence reliance must largely be placed on the production of a good weld by paying careful attention to weld preparation, a correct groove, and the employment of such a welding technique and operator as would be appropriate to a main circumferential butt-welded seam of a category 1 pressure vessel. An additional inspection of the jacket to blocking ring welding after the first run of metal has been deposited may be desirable. Fig. 3.8 (a) shows one recommended form of construction. Fillet or fillet-plus-groove welds are used to attach the blocking ring to the body of

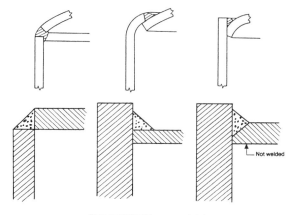

Non-permissible corner joints

**Fig. 3.7   Prohibited end connections and corner joints.**
*Source: ASME.*

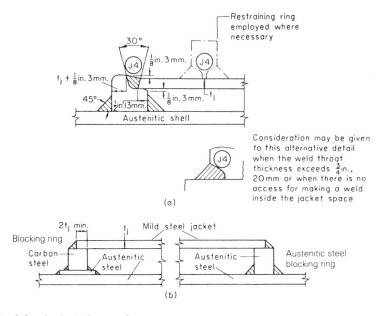

**Fig. 3.8   Jacketed vessels.**
*(Based on BS 1515: Part 2: by permission).*

the vessel. These welds are examined and gauged. The final machining of the recess in the blocking ring to permit the accommodation of the jacket is then carried out and gauged.

If a restraining flange or support ring is specified, this is then welded to the jacket, usually by two fillet-plus-groove welds.

The assembly of the jacket on the blocking ring is next examined to ensure correct positioning, and then welding in the groove is carefully carried out, followed by final examination of the completed weld.

(viii) Where a mild steel jacket is employed with an austenitic steel inner vessel the jacket must not be welded directly to the shell of this inner vessel but to an intermediate belt of austenitic steel of suitable composition of the same curvature as the inner vessel. Fig. 3.8 (b) shows two suitable forms of construction using blocking rings. Consideration must be given to the effect of any stresses set up as a result of differential expansion between the jacket and the inner vessel. (See also ASME Sect. VIII, Div.1, Appendix 9.)

(ix) Both Divisions 1 and 2 of ASME Section VIII cover the design, construction, welding and non-destructive testing of pressure vessels fabricated using layered construction. A layered vessel is one having a shell and/or heads made up of two or more separate layers. Such construction, much used in the petroleum and chemical industries, permits an inner layer of material compatible with the contents of the vessel and provides a means of prestressing the vessel wall, the layers acting as arrestors of running cracks due perhaps to brittle fracture. Layered vessels can conveniently be used for higher pressures. They can also be designed to avoid hydrogen embrittlement attack by venting each layer to prevent the build up of pressure by hydrogen diffusing through the material (see 5.7 and 6.14). The layers may be held in place by various means, including welding. Large calibre guns, with wire wound barrels or barrels having concentric cylinders forced upon them may be considered as layered vessels subject to intense internal pressure on discharge.

Some acceptable welded joints of layered-to-layered and layered-to-solid pressure vessel sections are shown in Fig. 3.9. Note that layered, strip wound, compound or other special designs of vessels appropriate for very high pressures are not covered by BS 5500.

(x) Where more than two weld seams meet, consideration might be given to the desirability of intermediate heat treatment at this point. The attachment of parts by welds which cross or are in the immediate vicinity of existing main weld seams should be avoided, or care should be taken to minimize local stress concentrations. Special inspection should be given to such areas, and to openings, etc. in welds or within ½ (12 mm) in of main seams. The use of non-destructive testing methods may be considered, w'.ilst the presence of s'-arp corners, sudden changes of section and other stress raisers must be avoided.

## 3.12 Riveted construction

Should any riveted construction be employed, then the inspector must ensure that all rivets before use are free from injurious defects and are of

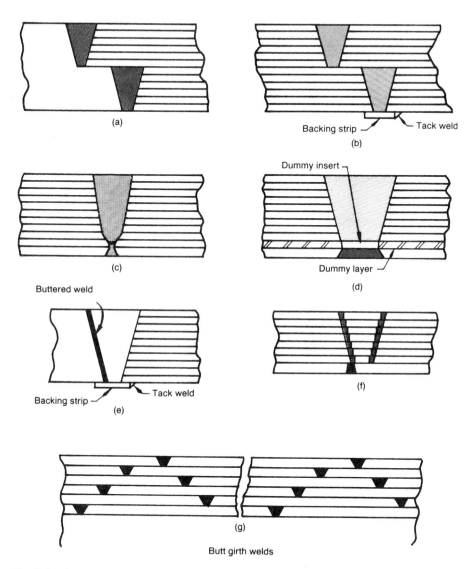

**Fig. 3.9   Some acceptable welded joints of layered-to-layered and layered-to-solids sections**
*Reproduced with permission from ASME Code Sect VIII ULW-17.6*
*\*'Buttered weld' means build-up overlay welding.*

sufficient length to fill the rivet hole and to give a full head. All mill scale must be removed from them, and those over $\frac{5}{8}$ in diameter must be driven hot. When rivet holes are required to be drilled this operation should be seen. All burrs and chips around holes and between plates must be removed, and holes after reaming must be chamfered and clear. Shell plates, butt straps, etc., should be examined for proper curvature and fit, and plates laid up tightly together and held by sufficient bolts before riveting is started.

No driven rivet head shall have an eccentricity of more than 10% of the nominal diameter of the rivet. The tightness of rivets in their holes shall be tested by tapping the heads with a hammer whilst holding a finger against one side of the rivet head next to the plate. Any loose, cracked or burned rivets must be replaced.

In general the riveted longitudinal joints of a shell exceeding $\frac{1}{2}$ in thickness must be of double-strap butt-type construction, and the strength of a circumferential joint must be at least one-half of that of the longitudinal joint.

Fusion welding may be used to seal the caulking edges of circumferential riveted lap joints and other joints provided the carbon content of the steel plate does not exceed 0·35%. This seal welding should be done after the vessel has passed a preliminary hydrostatic test.

### 3.13 Stress relief by heat treatment

(a) *Preheat requirements.* To avoid hard zone cracking in the heat affected zones of welds in ferritic steels, and to assist in achieving adequate fusion of welds in aluminium and its alloys, it may be necessary to preheat the parent metal before welding.

Recommendations for preheat temperatures are given in specifications, but as a general guide temperatures in excess of 200°C should not be necessary. Austenitic steels do not require preheat for welding. For steels no welding should be carried out when the temperature of the parent metal within 150 mm of the joint is less than 5°C. Hot formed parts of ferritic steel vessels may require a normalizing or grain refining heat treatment either before or after welding.

(b) *Post-weld heat treatment* of carbon and low-alloy steel vessels after completion of all welding may be specified or required:

(i) On category 1 and similar type vessels.

(ii) On vessels exceeding some 25 mm wall thickness at any welded connection.

(iii) On vessels for service where stress corrosion cracking may occur.

(iv) On vessels intended for service at low temperatures below say 0°C (unless the material is exempt from the ASME impact test or BS 5500 Appendix D does not require it).

Post-weld heat treatment is not usually required with non-ferrous materials or high alloy steels. (In special cases some welding may be permitted after heat treatment, e.g. layered vessels subject to certain conditions—see ASME Section VIII Div. 1 ULW-26).

It is desirable to stress-relieve a vessel in one operation by completely enclosing it in a furnace. Where this is impracticable it may be heated in overlapping sections when completed, or in complete sections plus heat treatment of the closing circumferential joints. Alternatively it may be heated internally.

The inspector should examine the furnace or other heat treatment arrangements and check their suitability, and the adequacy of temperature measurement and control, which must be continously and automatically recorded. Heat treatment should be carried out within the specified temperature range (e.g. some 600-650°C for carbon and low-alloy steels) and for a period in hours approximately equal to the maximum plate thickness in inches. The heating up and cooling periods should be controlled. Special work may require temperatures up to some 950°C.

The inspector should check and sign the temperature control charts and see that any weld test pieces (see 3.14) are placed inside the vessel for heat treatment at the same time. AOTC rules, however, permit the test pieces 'to be placed inside any other vessel of comparable dimensions which is to be heat-treated in accordance with the specification'.

When post-weld heat treatment has to be carried out in more than one stage, or in overlapping sections, it should be ensured that the heat gradient between these sections or stages is checked and is within the allowable limits. This will also apply to local stress relieving of closing circumferential joints.

Should repairs to welds have been carried out on a vessel which has been heat-treated, then this heat treatment must be carried out again. It is advisable to check the dimensions of a vesssel for accuracy before heat treatment, so that any corrections required can then be carried out, and not involve later reheat treatment.

### 3.14 Approval of welding and of test plates representing welded seams
(see also 9.21)

(i) *Approval of weld procedures* is required generally to BS 4870: Part 1 Steel, or Part 2 Aluminium (TIG or MIG).

The manufacturer has to make and test a welded joint or joints, representative of those to be used in production, in order to prove the feasibility of a documented welding procedure. A specific number of test pieces are cut from the welded joint and subjected to specified physical tests. A report is then prepared describing the results and the types of defects found. These defects are assessed in accordance with permitted acceptance levels and a statement as to whether or not the particular welding procedure is satisfactory to the required standard is prepared and signed.

(ii) *Approval of welders and operators* is required (generally to BS 4871: Part 1 Steel and/or Part 2 Aluminium). All welders and operators engaged in the welding of pressure parts of vessels must pass the welder approval tests to demonstrate their competence to make sound welds of the types to be employed. A welder who successfully welds all the test pieces required for a weld procedure test to BS 4870 will not normally be required to undertake separate tests. If a welder has not carried out welding of the type and procedure required for a period of more than six months, or if there is some reasonable doubt of his ability, then he may be required to retake the whole or part of the approval test. A welder approved by one inspecting authority may by agreement be accepted as approved by another inspecting authority. A list of approved welders/operators, with their records, should be retained by the manufacturer (see also 9.21).

(iii) *Production control test plates.* Some codes and standards require welded test plates to represent the longitudinal seams of pressure vessels (particularly the now obsolete BS 1500 which required test plates for all such seams on Class 1 vessels). BS 5500 now states that production control test plates are not required for most steel vessels unless specified by the purchaser (except for those vessels manufactured in 9% Nickel steel, where owing to the special nature of this material they must be provided until such time as the manufacturer has demonstrated that production welding produces satisfactory results).

However BS 5500 requires production control test plates for pressure vessels manufactured in aluminium or its alloys.

These test plates are tack-welded to the shell and suitably supported and reinforced to prevent distortion during welding. The weld in the test piece must be made at the same time and as a continuation of the longitudinal weld. On completion the surfaces of the weld are dressed and the weld in the test plate is radiographed with the seam.

The test plate must be stamped and its outer surface identified before removal from the shell. The inspector must check on the identity of the test plate material to ensure that it has been cut from the material forming the shell or, in certain cases, is otherwise similar and acceptable. If any identification markings are likely to be removed during subsequent preparation he must ensure that they are restamped on a surface not likely to be thus affected.

The test plate is then marked out for cutting into the required separate test specimens, each one being stamped so that its identity and original position can be ascertained. Before cutting, the marked test plate should be compared with its radiograph in order to exclude and reject any test specimens which contain weld defects which if present in the seam of the vessel would have been rejected. A typical method of marking out, identifying and cutting up the test plate to form the requisite number of test specimens is illustrated in Fig. 3.10 (a).

The results from one set of specimens are generally required for each weld, and typical details of the tests and identification markings (as on Fig. 3.10 (a)) are tabulated in Table 3.4. The test plate should be large enough to provide material for retests if need be, and perhaps for the fabricator's own private preliminary tests if required. The test plate must be

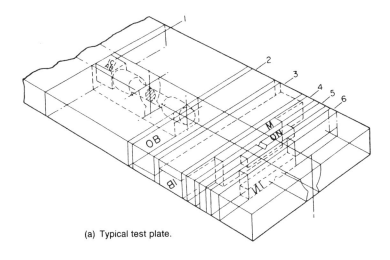

(a) Typical test plate.

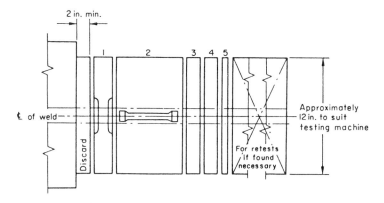

(b)  1 Reduced section tensile test piece (welded seam)
     2 All weld metal tensile test piece
     3 Transverse (direct) or side bend specimen
     4 Transverse (reverse) or side bend specimen
     5 Macro and hardness test specimen

**Fig. 3.10   Typical test plates representing welded seams.**

**TABLE 3.4**

*Identification marking for test specimens*
(See Fig. 3.10(a))

| Test specimen | | Identification | |
|---|---|---|---|
| No. in Fig. 3.10(a) | Type | Stamp marks to be included | Position of marks |
| 1 | All-weld-metal tensile test specimen (may include elevated temperature testing | AB | Serial number to be marked in weld metal on stub provided |
| 2 | Bond test specimens<br>(i) Outer surface in tension | OB | In plate material on the outer surface of the test plate |
| 3 | (ii) Inner surface in tension | IB | In plate material on the inner surface of the test plate |
| 4 | Macro-specimen and hardness survey | M | In plate material on the outer surface of the test plate |
| 5 | Notched bar test specimens<br>(i) Notch at outer surface of weld | ON | In plate material on the outer surface of the test plate |
| 6 | (ii) Notch at inner surface of weld | IN | In plate material on the inner surface of the test plate |

cut into specimens by machining, and not by flame cutting. The mechanical test requirements are listed in the appropriate application specification, details of these tests are given in BS 709 *Methods of destructive testing fusion welded joints and weld metal in steel* (see 9.21 and BS 4870, 4871 and 5169); and BS 131 *Methods for notched bar tests*. An all-weld-metal test and a tensile test on the welded joint on a specimen cut transversely to it may be required. In both cases the tensile strength obtained on test shall not be less than that of the parent metal. The inspector should examine the macro-etched ends of the all-weld-metal specimen cut longitudinally from the seam, to ensure that no parent metal has been included in the gauge length, and see that it is machined to the largest possible standard diameter. It is permissible to build up the ends of the test specimen with weld metal in order to provide sufficient material for gripping in the tensile testing machine. For aluminium, BS 5500 calls for mechanical tests generally in accordance with the appropriate requirements of BS 3451 *Methods of testing fusion welds in aluminium and aluminium alloys,* specifying two transverse tensile tests on plates up to 10 mm thick, with the alternative of one transverse and one side bend test above this thickness (the two specimens being at least 150 mm apart). Macro-tests are also required.

Although BS 5500 does not specifically require production control test plates for most steels (i.e for each welded seam) unless requested by the purchaser, this same type of test plate is required for welder procedure and performance qualification.

The layout of such a test plate is shown in Fig. 3.10 (b).

The various mechanical tests on weld specimens cut from test plates should be witnessed by the inspector and a report issued. Impact tests and tests at elevated temperatures may be required.

### 3.15 Non-destructive testing of pressure vessels

NDT methods (including visual and visual aided inspection) are used in much of the preliminary work of pressure vessel construction. In particular, BS 5500 category 3 vessels basically require only visual examination. When NDT of parent materials is required the procedures adopted can be in accordance with appropriate British Standards for NDT (e.g. Castings—BS 4080; Forgings—BS 4124; Pipes and tubes—BS 3889; Plate—BS 5996; other products—BS 6072). Some details regarding NDT techniques are given in Chapter 10. Non-destructive testing of welded joints (particularly by high technology methods) is required by most codes and standards for pressure vessels during construction, maintenance and operation.

The ASME Code deals with Non-destructive Examination in Section V and defines the specific methods required by reference to ASTM standards and recommended practices. The standards, etc adopted are prefixed by the letter S in front of the ASTM designation (i.e. SE 109) and may be subject to any modifications, additions or restrictions required by the Code.

### 3.15.1 *Radiographic examination methods* (see also 10.2–10.5)

Radiographic examination provides information on the quality of the welds, and the presence or absence of discontinuities such as cracks, porosity, cavities and slag inclusions, and of lack of fusion or penetration.

Radiographs, often obtained by X-ray techniques, may be required of the entire length of the main seams and of the corresponding test plates for many pressure vessels, including BS 5500 category 1 vessels. (BS 5500 category 2 vessels require examination of at least 10% of the length.)

Until recently the then current BS 1500 and many organizations did not permit the use of other than X-rays for first class work, it being stated generally that they gave a better definition than gamma rays. Gamma ray sources however are permitted by the ASME Code. The now obsolete BS 1515 required full radiography of all main seams, etc. without specifying X-rays or gamma rays. The examination of welds in plates of over some $2\frac{1}{2}$ in (63 mm) thickness presents difficulties, as at this thickness a 400kV X-ray set may begin to lose its definition. The new BS 5500 permits the examination of welds by radiographic and/or ultrasonic methods.

The ASME Code, Section VIII refers to Section V of the Code and specifies that the weld shall be radiographed with a technique which will have sufficient sensitivity to indicate the features of the penetrameter described (generally as Fig. 10.5), using a penetrameter of the specified thickness for the thickness of the weld being examined. Penetrameter thicknesses ranging up to 0·2 in for welds up to 20 in thick are designated. The holes will ordinarily be $2T$, $3T$ and $4T$ in diameter (where $T$ is the penetrameter thickness), but not less than $\frac{1}{16}$ in. A slot is to be provided for weld thicknesses less than $\frac{1}{2}$ in. A number identifying the thickness (e.g. 40 represents 0·040 in) shall be marked in symbols at least $\frac{3}{32}$ in high. All these images shall appear clearly on the radiograph.

For vessels constructed of clad plate or having corrosion-resistant linings the ASME Code requires radiographic examination to the normal rules, plus examination of the joints between adjacent liner sheets or stainless steel cladding for the purpose of detecting possible cracks. According to circumstances this examination may be a full length radiographic examination, a spot radiographic examination or any other method which will disclose cracks.

The ASME Boiler and Pressure Vessel Code Section VIII lays down various maximum welded joint efficiencies to be used in the design formulae in the Code depending on the degree of radiographic examination and the type of joint. These range from 100% of the plate material's strength for a fully radiographed double-welded butt joint (joint type 1) to 45% for a single full-fillet lap joint without plug welds (joint type 6) which has not been spot examined radiographically (for ASME joint types see Fig. 3.2).

A joint type 1 which has been spot radiographed with satisfactory results is allowed a joint efficiency not greater than 85% but not greater than 75% if it has had no radiological examination. Single welded butt joints with backing strip (joint type 2) if fully radiographed are allowed a maximum joint efficiency of 90%, and if spot radiographed 80%. Without radiological examination the joint efficiency is reduced to a maximum of 65%. Other types of welds are assessed for joint efficiency without radiological examination and reduce gradually to 45/50%. For assessment of weld radiographs see 3.16.

ASME Code Section VIII Division 1 (para. UW-18) specifies the allowable load on fillet welds connecting non-pressure parts to vessel pressure parts as being equal to the product of the weld area based on the minimum leg dimension (see Fig. 9.3) and the allowable stress in tension of the material (Sa) times a joint efficiency of 55% (3.4.1).

ASME Code Division 2 requires all pressure shell welds to have a full radiographic examination (for 100% joint efficiency—AF221 and 2). All welds joining non-pressure parts to pressure parts (AD-920) must be continuous. For fillet welds the nominal weld area is the minimum throat area (see Fig. 9.3) and this is used in load calculations. The joint efficiency (reduction factor) can be from 0·5 for a fillet weld, 0·75 for partial penetration to 1·0 for full penetration welds.

### 3.15.2 Preparation

Before radiography is commenced the surfaces of the welds should be examined to see that any excess weld metal has been removed and that the surface finish is smooth and approximately level with, but not below, the adjoining parent material. Surfaces shall be dressed only where weld ripples or weld surface irregularities will interfere with interpretation of the radiographs.

### 3.15.3 Identification marking

Each portion of welded seam radiographed must be positively identifiable with its completed radiograph.

This is usually done by stamping or marking a series of numbers on the vessel at intervals along the length of the weld, and placing similar lead ciphers beneath these numbers and below the weld. Each radiograph must overlap its neighbour. Letter L indicates a longitudinal and C a circumferential seam.

In addition to checking this identification the inspector should ensure that:

(a) The width of the weld is indicated by lead arrows or wires.

(b) A suitable penetrameter (image quality indicator), possibly of the BWRA step type, Fig. 10.4, the ASME type, Fig. 10.5, or of the wire type, Fig. 10.6, of similar material to that of the vessel and of appropriate thickness range is placed parallel with and close to the weld.

(c) A small lead marker is pointed to indicate, for instance, the penetrameter step, having a thickness equal to or just below a value of 2% of the thickness of the parent plate at the weld. This difference in thickness must be discernible on the completed radiograph (see 10.3).

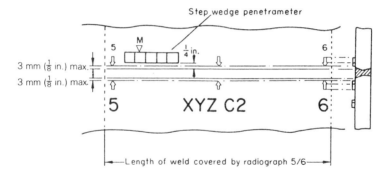

**Fig. 3.11 Typical arrangement of penetrameter, lead markers and stamp marks.** Part of second circumferential seam (C2).
The upper figures (5 and 6) indicate stamp marks.
The lower figures represent lead markers.
The lead marker (M) is provided to indicate the penetrameter step nearest 2% of the plate thickness.
XYZ is the Job Number, etc.

A typical arrangement showing the identification markings and a penetrameter placed along the length of a welded seam to be radiographed is shown in Fig. 3.11.

### 3.15.4 Radiographic technique

The inspector should check the radiographic technique employed. Some details are given in 10.5.

Radiographic examination of steel (as laid down in BS 5500) shall be in accordance with BS 2600: Part 1 or Part 2 or BS 2910 as appropriate. For aluminium it shall be in accordance with BS 3451. Radiographic sensitivity may be determined by image quality indicators (penetrameters) in accordance with BS 3971 (see 10.3). Because several techniques with differing sensitivities are detailed in these standards it is necessary to specify for each particular application which technique is required. For thicknesses up to 50 mm X-ray techniques are normally used.

Other techniques may be used provided that adequate sensitivity can be demonstrated.

### 3.15.5 Examination of radiographs

All radiographs of the welded seams and of the test plates should be submitted to the inspector for examination. Any radiograph which is not itself of the proper standard of radiographic quality (as seen for instance by an examination of the penetrameter image or otherwise (see 10.3))should be rejected, and a further radiograph taken of that particular length of weld.

The examination and interpretation of any defects revealed by a good quality radiograph is the responsibility of the inspector and is dealt with to some extent in 3.16 and 10.4.

### 3.15.6 Repairs

Should this examination show that certain welds or portions of welds are of an unacceptable standard, then repairs or rewelding must be carried out, generally by cutting out and rewelding the defective portions or, if thought necessary, the whole of the seam. All repairs will be subject to examination and test in the same manner as the original work; for instance new test plates may be required if a whole seam is rewelded. If practicable the same welding process as the original shall be used for repairs, but another process may be approved in certain cases.

When a spot radiograph reveals a defect, then either the whole seam represented may be cut out and rewelded, or it may be radiographed throughout its entire length and any defects then revealed repaired.

Stereoscopic radiography is sometimes used as an effective method of showing exactly the location and nature of weld defects, and can help in deciding on repair techniques, such as the best side of the weld from which to carry out the repair.

On completion of repairs the rewelded portions must again be radiographed. These portions should be identified radiographically as a repair by placing a lead letter R alongside.

### 3.15.7 Reports

The inspector should normally issue a report of his examination of the radiographs, giving details of his findings and of reference numbers of films, identification markings, contract or job number, etc., and details of the radiographic technique employed. The actual radiographs should be stored for a period of 10 years. (The ASME Code requires at least 5 years.)

### 3.15.8 Non-destructive testing of welded joints

BS 5500 requires examination of welds by radiographic and/or ultrasonic methods after completion of any required post-weld heat treatment.

The distinction between the different categories of pressure vessel in this standard is based largely on the extent of the required non-destructive testing of welds. In the older BS 1500, to which many pressure vessels now in service were made, the distinction between classes was based largely on weld joint factor, Class I vessels having a weld joint factor of 0·95 ensured by full radiographic examination of the main seams; Class II or III vessels for which less exacting test requirements were specified were allotted lower weld joint factors of 0·70 (0·80 stress relieved) and 0·60 respectively.

For construction category 1 BS 5500 requires examination for internal flaws and states:

The full length of *all* full penetration butt welds including the welds of forged butt welded nozzles (now called type A)* shall be examined by radiographic or ultrasonic methods. Unless otherwise agreed the full length of all other welds (e.g. nozzles and branches (now called type B)) in or on pressure parts shall be examined by ultrasonic and/or radiographic methods where the thickness of the thinnest part to be welded exceeds 40 mm for aluminium (and 10 to 40 mm according to the grade of steel).

For the examination of surface flaws the standard requires:

The full length of *all* Type B welds shall be examined by magnetic particle or penetrant methods. Full penetration butt (i.e. Type A) welds shall be examined by these methods when agreed between the manufacturer, the purchaser and the Inspecting Authority.

For construction category 2 BS 5500 requires:

Construction to be subjected to partial non-destructive testing . . . but (for steel) in those cases where main seams are required to be welded on site they shall be 100% examined by radiographic and/or ultrasonic methods . . . At least 10% of the length of all full penetration butt welds (i.e., of Type A), including the welds of forged butt welded nozzles (and branches) shall be examined by radiographic and/or ultrasonic methods. Such examination shall include each intersection of longitudinal and circumferential seams. Preferably for each longitudinal and circumferential seam and for each forged butt welded nozzle there should be at least one radiograph. Where ultrasonic testing is specified, at least a 200 mm length shall be examined. At least 10% of the length of all welds other than main longitudinal and circumferential seams shall be examined for surface flaws by magnetic particle or penetrant methods. Also for steel such methods should be used for the full length of all welds attaching nozzles, branches and compensating plates to shell and end plates. In addition to the above when openings occur in, or within, 12 mm of welded seams, such seams shall be examined each side of the opening for a distance of not less than the diameter of the opening.

For vessels in category 3 BS 5500 states:

Non-destructive testing for internal flaws is not required. However insofar as magnetic particle or penetrant methods are aids to visual

---

*See 3.4.7 and Fig. 3.2 for details of ASME and BS 5500 categories and types A and B.

examination, which is required, they may be used subject to agreement between the manufacturer and the purchaser, or the Inspecting Authority (see 9.21.3 and BS 5289).

The requirements for non-destructive examination of welded joints in layered vessels (See 3.11(ix)) laid down by ASME (ULW–50 to 57) are stringent. In general category A and B joints in the inner shells and heads require 100% radiography, as do full thickness welds of solid to layered sections. Category A joints in layers generally require 100% magnetic particle plus 10% ultrasonic examination, or 100% ultrasonic for the thicker sections. Category B joints in layers require either 10% or 100% magnetic particle examination according to thickness, plus random spot ultrasonic, or 100% ultrasonic only for the thicker welds. (See Fig.3.2 for ASME categories and Fig.3.9.)

### 3.16 Assessment of welds — acceptance criteria and standards

For some 50 years the question of acceptance standards for welding has been the subject of much thought. Frequently the inspector has demanded 'clear' radiographs, and costly repairs have been necessary to satisfy his requirements. In some cases the repair has put worse features into the weld than previously, and further repairs have been needed. Perfectly clear radiographs are of course the ideal, but they are not always necessary, and many an inspector is unwilling to accept responsibility for deciding what can be tolerated. For nuclear installations, where there is an additional hazard and failure may have far-reaching consequences, caution is understandable, and because of this what could be called a 'Class I plus standard' was created for nuclear work. However, there is a tendency for some inspectors to apply this standard unnecessarily to conventional work, and to request the removal of minor defects which in the past have been tolerated and accepted as being safe.

Investigations by such bodies as the British Welding Research Association (now the Welding Institute) and various American organizations have shown that a limited amount of porosity and of small slag inclusions can be tolerated in certain welds, as they seem to have very little influence on fatigue strength. This was taken into consideration in relation to service conditions by certain codes for pressure vessels (notably the ASME and the Swedish Codes) when assessing radiographs. British Standards now also give some guidance (e.g. BS 5500). The ASME Code provided charts which showed the maximum amount of weld porosity which could be accepted for each of five weld thicknesses, a table showing numbers, sizes and maximum areas for permitted porosity. This method has now been superseded. The ASME Code now states:

The following types of imperfection are also unacceptable:

(1) Any crack or zone of incomplete fusion or penetration.

(2) Any elongated slag inclusion which has a length greater than:

$\frac{1}{4}$ in for thicknesses ($t$)up to $\frac{3}{4}$ in.

$\frac{1}{3}t$ for thicknesses ($t$) from $\frac{3}{4}$–$2\frac{1}{4}$ in.

$\frac{3}{4}$ in for thicknesses ($t$) over $2\frac{1}{4}$ in.

(3) Any group of slag inclusions in line that have an aggregate length greater than $T$ in a length of $12T$ (except where the distance between imperfections exceeds $6L$ where $L$ is the length of the longest imperfection).

(4) In addition, for welds which have to be fully radiographed (and this includes all welds in Section VIII Division 2), 'rounded indications' in excess of that specified by the acceptances standards given in an appendix.

This mandatory appendix (Appendix 4 of Division I) defines 'rounded indications' appearing from any source in the weld, such as porosity, slag or tungsten, as those with a maximum length of three times the width or less on the radiograph. These indications may be circular, elliptical, conical or irregular in shape and may have tails. (It should be noted that rounded indications are only considered as a factor in the acceptability of welds which have to be *fully* radiographed, and this includes all welds in Section VIII, Division 2. Spot radiography ignores them). The maximum permissible size of any rounded indication is $\frac{1}{4}t$ or $\frac{5}{32}$ in (4 mm) whichever is the smaller (where $t$ is the thickness of the weld); except that an isolated indication (separated by at least 1 in. (25 mm) may be $\frac{1}{3}t$ or $\frac{1}{4}$ in (6 mm) whichever is the less. For thicknesses ($t$) greater than 2 in (51 mm) the maximum permissible size of an indication is increased up to $\frac{3}{8}$ in (10 mm). (The Code gives a table of examples.) For aligned indications (a sequence of four or more touching a line parallel to the length of the weld), see Figs. 3.12 and 3.13.

The Code also gives charts illustrating the maximum acceptable concentration limits for various random, isolated and clustered indications for several ranges of weld thicknesses (see Fig. 3.14).

An assessment of radiographs listing similar unacceptable imperfections and permitted porosity is given in the Boiler Code prepared by the International Organization for Standardization (ISO R 831).

An assessment of welds is permitted in the Swedish Boiler Code by using reference radiographs under the heading *Radiographic Inspections:*

'If the result of the visual inspection is satisfactory, the weld shall be subjected to radiographic inspection. The radiograph is evaluated according to the five number system where five (black) is the highest and one (red) the lowest number. As a basis for evaluation the *Collection of Reference Radiographs of Welds,* issued by the International Institute of Welding, shall be used. For approval, at least Number 4 is required. (See Table 10.3.)'

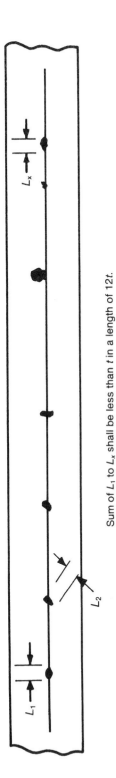

Sum of $L_1$ to $L_x$ shall be less than $t$ in a length of $12t$.

**Fig. 3.12 Aligned rounded indications.**

The sum of the group lengths shall be less than $t$ in a length of $12t$.

Maximum group length

$L = 1/4$ in for $t$ less than 3/4 in
$L = 1/3t$ for $t$ 3/4 in to 2-1/4 in
$L = 3/4$ in for $t$ greater than 2-1/4 in

Minimum group spacing

$3L$ where $L$ is the length of the longest adjacent group being evaluated

**Fig. 3.13 Groups of aligned rounded indications.**
*Reproduced with permission from the ASME Boiler and Pressure Vessel Code, Section VIII.*

**Appendix 4—mandatory**

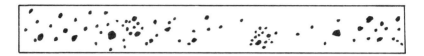

**Random rounded indications**

Typical concentration and size permitted in any 6 in length of weld

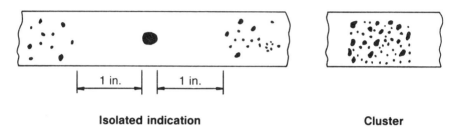

**Isolated indication**                                    **Cluster**

**Fig. 3.14   Charts for *t* over $\frac{3}{8}$–$\frac{3}{4}$ in inclusive.**

*Reproduced with permission from the ASME Boiler and Pressure Vessel Code, Section VIII.*

This collection of radiographs is an excellent guide and offers much useful information. Although the radiographs are intended for reference only and not as a standard of acceptance, the Swedish Code regards them as a basis of approval. The radiographs in No.4, Blue Group (Table 10.3) illustrate the maximum amount of defect of any kind which can be tolerated. These reference radiographs permit the designer and engineer to specify an acceptance level.

*3.16.1 Acceptance criteria for weld defects revealed by visual examination and NDT (BS 5500)*

Like the ASME method, although different in detail, the method adopted by BS 5500 for assessing weld defects leading to rejection is somewhat complex and needs experience before consistent results can be achieved.

The following defects are generally not permitted for category 1 and category 2 constructions:

| | |
|---|---|
| Planar defects | Lack of roof fusion, side fusion, inter-run fusion and of root penetration, cracks and lamellar tears. |
| Cavities | Linear porosity, wormholes aligned (if associated |

| | |
|---|---|
| | with lack of fusion or penetration); surface cavities, crater pipes (in aluminium). |
| Solid inclusions | Copper; linear oxide inclusions (in aluminium); tungsten—if accompanied by oxide inclusions (in aluminium); otherwise permitted up to some 3 mm diameter. |
| Profile and visible surface defects: | Overlap; insufficient weld size; shrinkage grooves and root concavity (in aluminium) |

Tables are given in the standard specifying the acceptance levels of permitted defects (Tables 5.7 (1) and (2) for steel and 5.A.7 for aluminium). For all practical purposes (with the exception of inclusions) these levels are the same as those adopted for welder approval and procedure approval in BS 4870 and BS 4871. In fact welds accepted to these two standards could have a smaller level of inclusions than those permitted in BS 5500 Table 5.7 (1). When inclusions are greater than those permitted in BS 4870 and 4871 but less than those permitted by BS 5500 (i.e. they are acceptable) the reason for this should be investigated in order to improve future welding performance.

Some latitude is possible in the acceptance of defects in excess of those permitted (e.g. see BS PD 6493) where for particular applications, suitably documented, they have been agreed.

Other defects, such as cavities (including pores and porosity and wormholes), solid and slag inclusions, profile defects (including undercut, excess penetration, reinforcement shape, overlap and misalignment) may be permitted up to specified maximum levels.

For category 2 construction using steel a greater level of porosity, slag and tungsten inclusion is permitted (in Table 5.7 (2)). Also if any 'not permitted' defects are present in the sample examined the total length of the seam shall be examined by the same NDT method (s) and re-assessed in accordance with the relaxed Table 5.7(2).

Alternatively, if no 'not permitted' defects are present but defects in excess of the maximum permitted by Table 5.7(1) are present then two further random representative checks of the relevant weld length shall be made and assessed against Table 5.7(1). If these two additional areas are acceptable, then the original area inspected shall be re-assessed against the relaxed Table 5.7(2). If still unacceptable repairs should be carried out, examined by the same NDT method(s) and re-assessed.

For category 2 construction using aluminium the defects shall be assessed against Table 5.A.7 in which for category 2 such cavities as isolated pores (or individual pores in a group) and uniformly distributed or localized porosity may be accepted without limit provided representative mechanical tests from production test plates meet requirements.

### 3.17 Spot radiographic examination

Guidance is given in the ASME Code on the assessment of spot radio-graphy. The minimum requirements are in general that one spot shall be examined in the first 50 ft (15 m) of welding and for each additional 50 ft or fraction thereof. Additional spots as may be required shall be selected so that the work of each welder is checked. The minimum length of spot radiography and hence length of film is 6 in (150 mm).

Welds of which the radiographs show any type of crack or incomplete penetration are unacceptable.

Slag inclusions or cavities are unacceptable if their length is greater than two-thirds of the thickness of the thinner plate welded ($T$). If several imperfections (within these limitations) exist in line, the welds may be acceptable if the sum of their longest imperfection is not more than $T$ in a length of $6T$ (or proportionally), and if the longest imperfections considered are separated by at least $3L$ of good weld metal, where $L$ is the length of the longest imperfection (which must not exceed $\frac{3}{4}$ in (19 mm)).

When a spot radiographed as above does not meet the minimum requirements stated, two additional spots selected by the inspector may be examined. If these meet the requirements then the entire weld unit represented is acceptable, but the defective welding disclosed may be removed and repaired at the inspector's discretion. If either of the additional spots discloses defects then the weld unit represented shall be rejected. This may then be rewelded entirely, or radiographed fully and all defective welding corrected.

It will be realized that spot radiography, although a useful method of quality control, does not ensure the elimination of all defects.

### 3.18 Ultrasonics and other non-destructive testing methods

(i) There has been an impressive growth in recent years in the application of ultrasonics (and other methods of NDT) as a means of examining a wide variety of materials. Such methods are widely used in the examination of plates, forgings, castings and welds for pressure vessels.

Defective plate due to poor steel cleanliness was a major cause of complaint for years. UK steelmakers have in the past charged a 20% premium for defect-free plate selected by full ultrasonic testing, but the increasing use of vacuum-degassed steel plate and more sophisticated ultrasonics has improved matters.

By using ultrasonics for the examination of pressure vessel plates it is possible to select with confidence those which when prepared at the edges will be virtually defect-free. (See BS 5596 and 10.6.5.) The ASME Code Division 2 requires ultrasonic examination of all plates and forgings of 4 in and over in thickness.

A further development is the use of automatic ultrasonic testing and recording, in which a record of the examination is provided. This method is generally accepted as complementary and also as an alternative to radiography, sometimes as the normal method, X-ray plant being used only occasionally for special cases.

The ASME Code permits the use of ultrasonics in specific cases. Testing, generally to Code Section V, Article 5, must be carried out by a suitably qualified and certified examiner who can determine (by ultrasonic reflection) the shape, identity and location of defects and evaluate them generally in accordance with the acceptance standards already given in 3.16 (1) and (2). See Code Section VIII Appendix 12.3.

It has been established that ultrasonics, intelligently applied and interpreted, will find defects in the thicker welds and materials which may be missed by even the best radiographic techniques. For example the Central Electricity Generating Board obtained 'clear' radiographs of the butt welds on a boiler drum, whereas ultrasonic examination revealed serious cracking, which was confirmed by cutting out the welds.

Ultrasonics may be used for the detection of defects in castings, etc., either specifically or in lieu of radiography. BS 3923 deals with methods for ultrasonic examination of welds; acceptance levels may be given in an appropriate application standard.

(ii) Other methods of non-destructive testing (NDT) may be used in pressure vessel inspection, and some details are specified in particular in the ASME Code. For instance, liquid penetrant inspection or magnetic particle inspection (in the case of ferrous metals) may be specifically called for, or may be used as an alternative or additional to radiographic examination, for checking such items as the welding on forged vessels after heat treatment; the brazing on brazed vessels; the cut edges and weld preparation of specified plate; the surface examination of castings, machined gasket seatings, etc.; and repairs to welds. Liquid penetrant inspection is required on all austenitic chromium-nickel alloy steel welds having a shell thickness over $\frac{3}{4}$ in (19 mm) and all 36% nickel steel welds (see also 10.10).

### 3.18.1 Choice of NDT methods for weld examination

BS 5500 and the ASME Code permit the use of both ultrasonics and radiography in the detection of internal flaws in welds. Both methods have advantages and disadvantages as far as flaw detection, identification and sizing are concerned. Radiography is particularly suitable for the detection and identification of defects having volume, such as cavities, solid inclusions and incomplete penetration (where a gap exists). Ultrasonics is suitable for the detection and sizing of defects in one plane (planar) such as cracks and lack of fusion. The two techniques may be considered as complementary; both may be used on the one component—the choice being a matter for agreement between purchaser, manufacturer and inspecting authority. However, ultrasonics in certain circumstances may indicate lengths of flaws apparently in excess of those given by radiography, and the inspector should be on his guard.

Both magnetic particle and liquid penetrant testing methods can detect surface defects on welds, etc. but they do not indicate their depth. Magnetic methods are quicker and more economic with ferritic steels, but penetrant methods must be used for austenitic steels and aluminium and its alloys. Alternative methods of NDT (including newly developed techniques) may be used by agreement (see 10.10).

Ultrasonic examination may be in accordance with the general principles of BS 3923 (Part 1 *Manual examination of fusion welded butt joints in ferritic steel* and Part 3 (nozzles)) as appropriate, provided due allowance is made for different calibration tests due to the changed sound velocity.

Before carrying out ultrasonic examination of welds the adjacent parent metal should be ultrasonically examined to establish the thickness of the material and to locate any flaws which may prevent effective examination of the weld. Dressing of the weld area may be necessary so that satisfactory contact and coupling with the probe is achieved.

It should be noted that certain difficulties may arise with the ultrasonic examination of welds in austenitic steels (see 10.6.2).

Magnetic particle techniques should comply with BS 4397 or 6072 and should be limited to applications where surface flaws are being sought. Care should be taken to avoid any damage to component surfaces by misuse of the magnetic equipment employed. The surface must be free of any foreign matter and may be dressed to permit accurate interpretation of indications. A suitable contrast medium (e.g. BS 5044, Contrast aid paints, used in magnetic flaw detection,) may, if necessary, be applied after cleaning and prior to magnetization.

Dye or fluorescent penetrant techniques in accordance with BS 4416 or 6443 should be used for the surface examination of welds. The surface should be free of any foreign matter which would interfere with the application and interpretation of the tests. Care should be taken to avoid masking flaws by distortion of surface layers due to any dressing process necessary.

### 3.19 Final inspection

Before pressure testing, the finished vessel must be checked for dimensional accuracy, including any departure from circularity, and for flatness and alignment of flange faces, openings, etc.

Any attachments, fittings, protective devices, etc. required should be checked for position and correctness.

Every pressure vessel must be protected by one or more pressure-relieving devices, except, in general, where it is connected without an isolating valve to a system which is protected, or where an external source of pressure is so controlled that the pressure in the vessel cannot exceed its design pressure.

Relief valves and fittings may be in accordance with:

BS 759    Valves, gauges and other safety fittings for application to boilers and to piping installations for and in connection with boilers

          Part 1 Specification for valves, mountings and fittings

BS 2915  Bursting discs and bursting disc assemblies

BS 3463  Observation and gauge glasses for pressure vessels

BS 6759  Safety valves

          Part 1 Safety valves for steam and hot water (replaces BS 759 Part 2)

          Part 2 Safety valves for compressed air or inert gases

          Part 3 Safety valves for process fluids

The total capacity of the relief valve or valves must be sufficient to discharge the fluid without permitting a rise in the pressure of the vessel under maximum operating conditions of more than 10% above the safe working pressure. If more than one valve is provided, then one may be set to operate at the safe working pressure, and the remainder at not more than 5% above this pressure.

The use of a bursting disc (generally to BS 2915) may be preferable where a rapid pressure rise analogous to an explosion or combustion may occur, of if service conditions are such that gumming up or other reasons may render a relief valve inoperative or unreliable. Bursting discs may be fitted in place of, in series or in parallel with relief valves.

In general no stop valves are permitted on either side of a pressure-relieving valve. If, in order to comply with a periodic inspection require-ment, a relief valve requires to be isolated from the vessel which it protects, then it is recommended that a duplicate valve be provided, with the stop valves so interlocked that one relief valve is always connected to the vessel.

## 3.20 Pressure tests

(i) It is a general requirement that pressure tests be carried out on all pres-sure vessels in the presence of the inspector to demonstrate the integrity of the finished product.

Such pressure tests will include one or more of the following:

(a) A standard hydraulic test, for vessels where design calculations have been made of the required thicknesses of pressure parts.

(b) Proof hydraulic tests, for vessels where thicknesses cannot be satisfactorily calculated, and in consequence the working pressure must be based on the pressure at which distortion or yielding occurs.

(c) Pneumatic tests.

(d) Combined hydraulic/pneumatic tests.

(e) Vacuum tests. For tests required at sub-atmospheric pressures see 8.16 and 11.7.

(ii) The *standard hydraulic pressure* is generally some 1·5 times the design safe working pressure, and it is applied to the vessel for a minimum period of 30 minutes, during which all seams and joints, etc. are carefully examined for leaks and any other defects (for more rigorous leak testing see Chapter 11). If necessary any defections from the previously checked dimensions should be measured so that any permanent set remaining after the test pressure has been removed can be ascertained.

For vessels manufactured from cast iron ASME requires (under paragraph UCI-99) that the standard hydrostatic test should be twice the maximum allowable working pressure for working pressures greater than 30 psi (207 kPa), and 2½ times the maximum allowable working pressure for pressures of 30 psi and under.

In the interests of safety the inspector should ensure, by proper venting, etc. that no air is trapped in pockets where it could be compressed with disastrous results.

A coated or lined vessel may be tested at the standard hydraulic pressure before coating, and again after coating at the designed safe working pressure.

Vessels with expanded tube connections may have the standard hydraulic test made before the tube holes are drilled, followed by a further test on the completed vessel (at $(1·25 \times \text{design pressure} + 100)$ lb/in$^2$).

Single-wall vessels subject to vacuum may be given an internal hydraulic test at 25 lb/in$^2$ ($1\frac{3}{4}$ bar), before any vacuum tests which may be required.

Where a vessel consists of more than one chamber, each must be given the standard hydraulic test without pressure in the others, except that where a jacketed vessel has an inner vessel designed to operate at atmospheric pressure or under vacuum then the jacket space need only be tested at a pressure not less than 1½ times the maximum differential pressure for which the inner vessel is designed.

Hydraulic tests are normally carried out using water, but other fluids may be used if necessary. The water (or fluid) should be at approximately room temperature, but not below, in order to prevent moisture condensation on the outside surfaces. Warm de-ionized water may be preferred.

It is advisable to have two pressure gauges in circuit, in case one fails or is incorrect and leads to damage through over-pressurizing.

A standard hydraulic test, or any pressure test, should be performed *after* any stress relief required, and *after* general dimensional checking.

During hydraulic testing the inspector should be on the look-out for possible causes of trouble. For instance, a vessel left under test for some time may be subject to a temperature increase which can materially increase the pressure, and so cause overstressing and possibly an accidental failure. As an example a vessel left under a water pressure of 50 lb/in$^2$ at 70°F may rise to some 100 lb/in$^2$ if the temperature rises 10°F. A liquid relief valve set to some 1⅓ times the test pressure would obviate this trouble.

The provision of suitable vents when filling and emptying vessels to permit the escape and entry of air is important. Should air be trapped under pressure and failure occur, the results may be fatal. Conversely, should a vacuum be formed when emptying an unvented vessel which has not been designed to withstand vacuum, it may collapse.

Checks should be made to ascertain that all filling lines and other equipment not intended for high pressure are disconnected before the test pressure is applied.

The presence, or development, of small cracks at or adjacent to welds, especially in the heat-affected zone or between different components or materials, may initiate failure and has been known to do so hydraulic test, particularly with materials prone to *brittle fracture.* Correct heat treatment usually prevents such trouble, but as a precaution care should be taken to ensure that the hydraulic test is carried out at a temperature above the ductile/brittle transition temperature of the material used, which in some cases can approach room temperature. (Impact tests to determine transition temperatures may be made on the material—see 2.6.)

In fact, experiments have demonstrated that a structure (or vessel) loaded (or pressure-tested) in the same manner as in service, but to a greater magnitude, and at a temperature well above the material's transition temperature, *will be immune from brittle fracture at the working pressure even at temperatures below the transition temperature.* Such test pressures should be not less than 10% nor more than some 20% above the working pressure; higher pressures could result in plastic deformation in regions of stress concentration.

(iii) *Standard test pressure.* For hydraulic, pneumatic and combined hydraulic/pneumatic tests the test pressure for acceptance to BS 5500 must be, except 'if otherwise stated', the standard test pressure $p_1$ determined as follows:

$$p_1 = 1 \cdot 25 \left[ p \frac{f_a}{f_t} \times \frac{t}{t-c} \right]$$

For category 3 construction the same formula is used or $p_1 = 1 \cdot 5p$ whichever is the higher

where $p$ is the design pressure

$f_a$ is the nominal design strength for the material at test temperature

$f_t$ is the (time independent) strength for the material at design temperature

$t$ is the thickness of the section under consideration

$c$ is the corrosion allowance.

If a liquid other than water is used any appropriate precautions should be observed

(iv) *Proof hydraulic test.* The design pressure of vessels for which the strength cannot be satisfactorily calculated can be determined with suitable strain measuring equipment (see Appendix A.7 and A.8) and the results of a proof test carried out in the presence of the inspector. After adequate precautions have been made pressure is applied gradually until either the standard test pressure for the expected design pressure is reached (this standard test pressure may often be taken as 1·5 times the expected design pressure) or significant yielding of any part of the vessel occurs.

When either of these points is reached the pressure shall not be further increased. The highest pressure applied shall be maintained for sufficient time to permit inspection.

BS 5500 requires that strain readings shall be taken as the pressure is increased gradually by steps of approximately 10% and unloaded between steps, until the standard test pressure $p_1$ is reached or until significant general yielding occurs.

Strain readings shall be repeated during unloading. Should the plot of strain versus pressure during the application of pressure and unloading show evidence of non-linearity the pressure reached may be re-applied not more than five times until the loading and unloading curves corresponding to two successive pressure cycles substantially coincide. Should coincidence not be attained $p_y$ shall be taken as the pressure range corresponding to the linear portion of the curve obtained during the final unloading.

If the standard test pressure $p_t$ is reached and a linear pressure/strain relationship is obtained the expected design pressure shall be considered as confirmed.

If the final test pressure is limited to a value less than the standard test pressure $p_t$ or the pressure range corresponding to the linear portion of the pressure/strain record is less than $p_t$, the design pressure $p$ shall be calculated from

$$p = \frac{1}{1\cdot25}\left[p_y \frac{(t-c)}{t}\frac{f_t}{f_a}\right]$$

where $p_y$ is the pressure at which significant yielding occurs or the pressure range corresponding to linear pressure/strain behaviour of the most highly strained part of the vessel during final unloading; $t, c, f_t$ and $f_a$ are defined in 3.20 (iii) (standard test pressure).

As an alternative to the above method a strain indicating coating technique may be used (see Appendix A.8). If the standard test pressure is reached without significant yielding being observed on the outside surfaces the expected design pressure can be confirmed. If significant yielding occurs at a pressure less than the standard test pressure then the design pressure can be calculated from the same formula as used for the strain gauge technique.

(v) *Pneumatic tests.* Pressure testing with air or gas is sometimes required. As this presents a considerable safety hazard the inspector must approach all such tests with extreme caution, and satisfy himself that all reasonable precautions have been taken. Water under pressure is to all intents and purposes incompressible, and should a vessel fracture under hydraulic test little damage, if any, will result. With air or gas, however, should fracture occur, the air or gas will expand with explosive violence, taking with it any broken parts, and perhaps causing damage to property and injury to people in its path.

Remember, compressed air and gases may be lethal. It is good practice to carry out crack detection by magnetic (10.7) or dye penetrant (10.8) methods on certain welds on vessels before any pneumatic testing; indeed BS 5500 requires that all welded seams etc be subjected to 100% radio-graphic or other equivalent NDT inspection before such testing.

Should a standard hydraulic test have been first satisfactorily carried out on a pressure vessel, it can be pneumatically tested at the designed working pressure. Pneumatic leak testing (see Chapter 11) is sometimes desirable before the application of a hydraulic test. Provided the pneumatic test pressure does not exceed 10% of the equivalent design pressure the requirements for 100% radiography or its equivalent of welded seams do not apply. Pneumatic testing is normally carried out using air as the test gas, but other gases may be used or specified, suitable precautions being taken. Leak testing particularly makes use of gases such as the halogen compounds (see 11.5).

It may not be practicable or permissible to carry out a hydraulic test on some designs of pressure vessel. Possibly the weight of water may impose an undue strain on the structure, or perhaps even small traces of water, which may be impracticable to remove, cannot be tolerated in crevices, etc. during operational use. In such cases pneumatic testing in lieu of hydraulic testing may be specified. Adequate safety precautions, such as blast walls or pits, means for remote observation (if necessary by closed-circuit television) and testing above the transition temperature, etc. are essential.

When such precautions have been arranged the pneumatic pressure inside the vessel is gradually increased to a value of half of its designed safe working pressure. Then the pressure is increased in steps of about 10% until the standard test pressure is reached,* when it must be reduced to the

---

*A maximum of up to 125% is specified by the ASME Code under certain conditions, whilst BS 5500 may permit up to 150% of the equivalent design pressure.

designed safe working pressure, and held at this during the inspection of the vessel.

ASME requires (under Paragraph UW-50) that before pneumatically testing a welded pressure vessel the full length of the following welds must be non-destructively examined (usually by magnetic particle or by liquid penetrant as appropriate) for the purpose of detecting possible cracks:

(a) all welds around openings

(b) all attachments welds, including welds attaching non-pressure parts to pressure parts, having a throat thickness greater than $\frac{1}{4}$ in (6 mm).

It should be noted that if the test gas is passed down into the vessel under test from high-pressure storage its temperature will fall. Arrangements must be made so that the temperature of the gas entering, and hence in the vessel, is not lower than the agreed test temperature. The possibility of condensation occuring within the vessel should also be borne in mind.

Single-walled vessels designed for vacuum conditions only may be tested internally by a pneumatic pressure not less than 75% of the safe working pressure.

Where a jacketed vessel has an inner vessel designed to operate at substantially less than the jacket pressure, the jacket space only need be tested pneumatically at a pressure not less than 125% of the designed external pressure of the inner vessel and not greater than 100% of the safe working pressure of the jacket.

(vi) *Combined hydraulic/pneumatic test.* If it is required to test a vessel partially filled with liquid then a pneumatic test as above is applied to the space above the liquid, minus the pressure due to the static head of the liquid.

This test pressure must not cause the general membrane stress in any part of the vessel to exceed 90% of the yield or proof stress of the material.

(vii) *Repairs.* If during or subsequent to any pressure test repairs are found to be necessary, they must be carried out under supervision; after satisfactory completion and any stress relieving necessary, the vessel must again be subjected to the required pressure test.

*Note:* it is becoming common to use acoustic emission monitoring during proof testing of vesels; this will show deformation under stress (see 10.4 and ASTM STP 571 and E596).

### 3.21 Final acceptance and marking (see Table 3.3)

An internal and external examination must be made by the inspector after the hydraulic test, and he should also check that the finished dimensions have not been altered by it. Any out-of-roundness should be noted and checked to see that it is within tolerance.

Every pressure vessel must be distinctly marked under the supervision of the inspector with such details as the number and classification or category of the standard or code to which it has been built, the weld joint factor, the manufacturer's name and serial number, the year built, the safe working pressure and maximum temperature coincident with it, and the inspector's reference and stamp. Pressure test details should be included.

These markings can be stamped on some conspicuous portion of the vessel (taking care not to cause any damage or incipient cracks) or a separate nameplate can be used. A separate nameplate is regarded as essential on vessels to be used at low temperatures or less than $\frac{1}{4}$ in (6 mm) thick, and any stamping is done prior to fixing it to the vessel.

Vessels inspected in accordance with the ASME Code must be marked with an official U symbol, with additional lettering beneath it signifying the type of construction used for the longitudinal and circumferential joints, e.g. W (welded), B (brazed), and whether fully or partially radiographed or heat-treated (RT1, RT2, HT, PHT). Data reports on the prescribed form must be made out and signed by the manufacturer and the inspector.

Before final acceptance the inspector must check that all specified requirements have been met, including any cleaning, protective treatment and finishes, painting, signwriting, special identification markings, etc. With some vessels, particularly those for vacuum service or exacting chemical processes, it is as well to blank off all openings to prevent the ingress of foreign matter, moisture, etc.

BS 5500 requires that upon satisfactory completion of the vessel the organization(s) responsible for design, construction and inspection should certify jointly (on form X) that the design satisfies the requirements of this standard and that the vessel has been so constructed and tested.

The appropriate authorized inspecting authority will countersign that they have checked the design and carried out surveillance of construction and testing. The manufacturer will supply full documentation, including drawings, information, list of materials, details of heat treatment, welding and NDT, etc. Should deviations or concessions have been authorized then the suffix 'XX' will be added to the vessel's serial number and details of deviations, etc. supplied.

Similarly the ASME Code requires that the data reports and certificates of inspection, signed by the manufacturer and the competent inspector, must certify that the vessel's design, material, construction and workmanship conform to the Code.

## 3.22 Pressure vessels in glass reinforced plastics (GRP)

Many vessels and tanks are fabricated from plastics, often suitably reinforced. BS 4994 deals with the design, construction, inspection and testing of such vessels in reinforced plastics, consisting of a polyester, epoxy or other resin system reinforced with glass fibres, manufactured by the wet lay-up process.

As with BS 5500 and the ASME Code for fusion welded metallic pressure vessels:

(i) The manufacturer is required to demonstrate his ability to design and/or produce a satisfactory vessel, either by documentation of past experience or by producing and testing a prototype.

(ii) All vessels designed for pressure and/or vacuum and as indicated below (and those designed to contain hazardous substances) must be manufactured under the survey of a competent and independent engineering inspection organization. Such vessels are designated as Category 1.

A category I vessel would be designed for a pressure and/or vacuum equal to or greater than $\pm 5$ mbar above the static head, at temperatures generally above the heat distortion temperature (HDT) of the fully cured resin system used for the reinforced laminate minus 40°C (i.e. $>$ HDT $-40$°C), and equal or less than HDT $= -20$°C, and for a volume greater than 50 m$^3$.

Vessels and tanks of small volume, low pressure, temperature or hazard are designated Category II or III.

Category III vessels include those subject only to the hydrostatic head of the contents, temperatures generally below 60°C, of volume less than 10m$^3$, and of little or no hazard.

Category II vessels are of an intermediate class generally between 10–50 m$^3$ capacity; below $\pm 5$ mbar pressure and/or vacuum; between 60°C and (HDT $-40$°C)

The principal stages of inspection required include:

(i) inspection of workshop conditions (cleanliness, etc).
(ii) records, including identification, of materials, resin, mixing, etc.
(iii) approval and tests of laminating and welding procedures.
(iv) examination during construction, curing and any repair necessary.
(v) witnessing of spark and pressure testing.

Polyester or epoxy resins (to BS 3532 or 3534) are used together with a suitable hardener, catalyst, accelerator, etc. to prepare laminates reinforced with a form of fibre glass (to BS 3396, 3496, 3691 or 3749). The type and number of layers of laminate applied must be recorded, and the lay-up examined by the inspector. Air bubbles, pits and inclusions must be avoided as far as possible and should not exceed an amount agreed by the inspector.

BS 4994 deals with design matters for GRP laminates, the methods being different from those used for metals—see BS 6464 in 4.20.

If required thermoplastic linings (of PVC or polypropylene) must be shaped and welded and then bonded to the laminate. Approval of weld procedures and welders is required and mechanical tests of welds and laminates are specified. All production welds must be examined visually and tested by a high frequency spark tester giving a minimum peak voltage to earth of 20 kV (see 5.2 and 5.17). These tests should be witnessed by the inspector, who should also see a hydraulic test of not less than 1.3 times the design pressure, or an agreed vacuum test if applicable.

The pressure should be gradually increased to the test value and maintained for at least one hour during which no sign of leakage, distortion, etc. should be apparent. When specified, vessels intended for use at temperatures of 70°C or higher may be subjected to a boilout test at 85°C for 8 hours. After completion of tests the vessel should be thoroughly examined internally and externally. Any indication of cracking, crazing or excessive strain may be a cause for rejection, perhaps for repair. Thermoplastic linings should again be spark tested and examined for signs of weld defects, blisters, etc. After completion of any necessary repairs the appropriate tests should be repeated in the presence of the inspector. Exceptionally, pneumatic testing may be agreed, provided that adequate safety precautions are taken.

It should be noted that the full procedure and testing outlined above only applies to category 1 inspection. Tanks not designed to contain hazardous substances and subject only to hydrostatic head are not required to have an independent inspection. The manufacturer's own inspection may be considered adequate. This is known as category 2 inspection. Certification of inspection and testing must be fully documented. The organizations responsible for design and construction, where appropriate (particularly for category 1), must also certify that the vessel complies with the requirements of the standard.

Pressure vessels constructed in other forms of plastics, not covered by particular standards, may be inspected along similar lines to those outlined above, but although methods of test (of welds, laminates, etc.) are given in specifications (as in Appendix C of BS 4994) much may depend upon the skill and know how of the manufacturer (not given in specifications) to ensure that a satisfactory vessel is produced.

The ASME Boiler and Pressure Vessel Code, in Section X—Fibreglass-Reinforced Plastic Pressure Vessels, may be referred to for additional information.

Although specifications such as BS 4994 do give some design information there is a tendency to treat GRP material and components as if they behave in the same way as metallic structures—which they do not. Considerable research is being directed towards obtaining meaningful information for use in the design of GRP vessels and pipes, particularly of bends, and the bending stresses due to thermal expansion. Fatigue and creep rupture tests have been carried out. In due course relevant information may appear in new specifications. Failures of GRP storage tanks have occurred in service due perhaps to poor fabrication or misuse. However, the introduction of acoustic emission testing techniques (see 10.14) for acceptance and in service testing has enabled flaws to be detected before they have a chance to develop to dangerous proportions. See *GRP vessels and Pipework for the chemical and process industries*, (I. Mech. E.), Mech. Eng. Pub. 1983. Also see BS PD 6480 for the philosophy behind BS 4994.

The 1987 revision of BS 4994 takes account of the factors mentioned above and of the explanatory supplement PD 6480 and as a result this has helped to reduce environmental stress cracking of the laminates in aqueous environments as a source of failure.

### References and further reading

Bednar, H.H., *Pressure vessel design handbook*, Van Nostrand Reinhold, N.Y. and Wokingham, 1986.

Chuse, R., *Pressure vessels: The ASME Code simplified*, McGraw-Hill, 1984.

Gupta, J.P., *Fundamentals of heat exchanger and pressure vessel technology*, (Hemisphere, Washington DC, Springer-Verlag, Berlin, 1986.)

Harvey, J.F., *Theory and design of pressure vessels*, Van Nostrand Reinhold, N.Y. and Wokingham, 1986.

Nichols, R.W. and Day, G.J. (eds.) *Non-destructive examination for pressurized components* (proceedings of 3rd international seminar at Monterey, Calif., Elsevier Applied Science, London, 1984, Elsevier Applied Science Pub. 1976.

Nichols, R.W. (ed.), *Developments in Pressure vessel technology*, 3 vols., Applied Science Pub, 1979–80.

International conferences on Pressure Vessel Technology, organized by ASME, New York.

G.R.P. vessels and pipework for the chemical and process industries. I. Mech. Eng. Pub. 1984.

High temperature design data for ferritic pressure vessel steels (presents creep strain data and hot tensile data not previously published) I. Mech. Eng. Pub. 1983

Periodic inspection of pressure vessels I. Mech. Eng. Pub. 1972

Problems and needs in the analysis, design and manufacture of pressure vessels. I. Mech. Eng. Pub. 1969

ASME, Applications of materials for pressure vessels and piping. MPC-10 (3rd. National Congress, San Francisco)                                              1979

Welding Institute, Joint preparation for fusion welding of steel        1966

# 3 Boilers and pressure vessels

## Part 2   Boilers, storage and reactor pressure vessels

### 3.23  Inspection of boilers and similar items of plant

Many of the general principles of pressure vessel inspection dealt with in Part 1 of this chapter apply equally to the inspection and QA of boilers and similar items of plant, and in particular to those pressure vessels and components forming part of a nuclear installation. Table 3.1 includes some codes and standards from various countries which deal with boilers as well as pressure vessels and includes some for nuclear installations. A selection of British Standards dealing specifically with boilers, their design, construction, inspection, testing and acceptance, and with air receivers, heat exchangers, nuclear vessels, tanks, etc. is given in Table 3.5.

The somewhat similar inspection and QA arrangements made for pressure vessels and boilers both by BSI and ASME should be noted.

As defined by ASME Boiler and Pressure Vessel Code (Sections I, III and VIII) the inspector means the authorized inspector employed by a state, an insurance or inspection company, etc. properly qualified by a written examination and regularly making inspections of pressure vessels. He must be independent and *not* in the employ of the manufacturer. He corresponds to the UK official or insurance company inspector authorized by the Pressure Vessel Quality Assurance Board (PVQAB) (see 3.3).

ASME requires the manufacturer to have a certificate of authorization from the ASME Boiler and Pressure Vessel Committee authorizing him to fabricate the class of vessel being constructed, and *inter alia* to have an effective inspection and quality control system to ensure that the detailed examinations and tests required are performed satisfactorily. This corresponds in the UK to the assessment of the competence of the manufacturer by the PVQAB etc. and of his inspection and QA system to the requirements of BS 5750 by the authorized inspection body and PVQAB (see 9.4).

**TABLE 3.5**

*British standards dealing with boilers, heat exchangers, nuclear plant, air receivers, etc.*

| BS No. | Description | Comments |
|---|---|---|
| **Boilers** | | |
| 843 | Thermal-storage electric water heaters | |
| 853 | Calorifiers and storage vessels for central heating and hot-water supply | |
| 855 | Welded steel boilers for central heating and hot-water supply | Deals with design, inspection and testing |
| 1113 | Water-tube steam generating plant (including superheaters, reheaters and steel tube economizers) | Deals with design rules, inspection and testing, and incorporates relevant recommendations from BS 5500 |
| 1894 | Electrode boilers of riveted, seamless, welded and cast iron construction for water heating and steam generating | Deals with design rules, inspection, testing and safety and applies to design temperatures up to 650°F where the water is heated by its resistance to the passage of alternating electric current |
| 2790 | Shell boilers of welded construction | Deals with design rules, inspection and testing for three classes of boiler. Incorporates ISO recommendations |
| **Testing and acceptance** | | |
| 526 | Definitions of the calorific value of fuels | Also gives information for calculating values from experimentally determined data |
| 845 | Assessing thermal performance of boilers for steam, hot water and high temperature heat transfer fluids. | Deals with simple efficiency tests, etc. by (i) concise and (ii) comprehensive procedures. Not for power station type boilers |
| 1374 | Recommendations on use of BS Log-sheets for steam and hot-water boiler plants | For recording boiler plant performance |
| 1756 | Methods for sampling and analysis of flue gases | |
| 2455 | Methods of sampling and testing boiler water deposits | |

**TABLE 3.5** *continued*

| BS No. | Description | Comments |
|---|---|---|
| 2486 | Treatment of water for land boilers | |
| 2740 | Simple smoke alarms and alarm metering devices | |
| 2741 | Construction of simple smoke viewers | These are dealt with in Chapter 14 |
| 2742 | Notes on use of Ringelmann and miniature smoke charts | |
| 2885 | Code for acceptance tests for steam-generators of the power station type | Covers the determination of thermal efficiency, etc. Gives a standard form of test report with explanatory notes |

**Heat exchangers, tanks, etc.**

| | | |
|---|---|---|
| 2594 | Horizontal mild steel welded storage tanks | Deals with design, construction, inspection and pressure testing |
| 2654 | Vertical steel welded storage tanks with butt-welded shells for the petroleum industry | Pressure and non-pressure type tanks for erection above ground for temperatures down to $-10°C$ (see 7.11) |
| 3274 | Tubular heat exchangers for general purposes | Specifies design, construction, inspection and testing |
| 4741 | Vertical cylindrical welded steel storage tanks for low temperature service down to $-50°C$ | (see 7.11) |
| 5387 | Vertical cylindrical welded steel storage tanks for low temperature service down to $-196°C$ | (see 7.11) |

**Air receivers**

| | | |
|---|---|---|
| 5169 | Fusion-welded steel air receivers | Design rules, inspection and testing requirements for three classes of receiver: Class I (unlimited pressure) Class II (35 bar) Class III (17·5 bar) |

**Nuclear installations**

| | | |
|---|---|---|
| 3915 | Carbon and low alloy steel | |

**TABLE 3.5** *concluded*

| BS No. | Description | Comments |
|--------|-------------|----------|
| | pressure vessels for primary circuits of nuclear reactors | (see 3.28) |
| 4208 | Steel containment structures for nuclear reactors | (see 3.28) |
| 4975 | Prestressed concrete pressure vessels for nuclear reactors | |
| 5882 | Total quality assurance programme for nuclear installations | (see also 9.4.5, 12.10.4 and 13.10) |

The mandatory quality system required of a manufacturer by ASME corresponds very much in detail with that of BS 5750, the additional requirements for ASME Section VIII Division 2 relating to design, the complexity of the work and its possibly high level of technology (perhaps beyond the 'state of the art') corresponding very much to that of BS 5750 Part 1 (compare for instance Table 9.1 with ASME Section VIII Division 1 Appendix 10, 10.1–10.15 (or Div. 2. Appendix 18, 18.109–18.123)).

A very similar general correspondence will be found to exist between the requirements for boiler inspection and QA found in ASME Section I and that laid down by BSI in for instance BS 1113 and BS 2790. In technical and design matters also there is often general correspondence, although not in detail, for both pressure vessels and boilers.

In the case of nuclear components the requirements of BS 5750 Part 1 for QA correspond generally with the relevant articles and clauses dealing with QA in ASME Section III (particularly Divisions 1 and 2 Sub-Section NCA General Requirements, Articles NA 3360-3769, NA 4000, NA 5000, NA 6000) but ASME's requirements are more detailed.

As with pressure vessels, a boiler manufacturer wishing for approval applies to the PVQAB for recognition of his capability to manufacture to nominated British standards (in this case the boiler standards embraced by the scheme at present are BS 1113 and 2790, and also air receivers (BS 5169), transportable gas containers (BS 5045: Part 2), pipework (BS 806) and certain valves). The manufacturer has to demonstrate to the satisfaction of the board that he has the technical ability and resources and a quality management system consistent with BS 5750 and that he can comply fully with Part 1 of that document, or to Part 2 supplemented by certain design and planning requirements from Part 1 (in the list of approved firms issued by PVQAB those authorized only to Part 3 are so indicated).

It is further required that manufacturers shall have engaged one of the inspectorates on PVQAB's list of Authorized Inspection Bodies (AIB) which have themselves been assessed by PVQAB (against criteria listed by the EEC). The AIB will undertake surveillance of the manufacturer's quality system and carry out such independent checking as necessary. The PVQAB when satisfied will issue a certificate of authorization to a manufacturer. This is valid for three years and confirmed (or otherwise) by an annual audit carried out by the AIB, who may, at its discretion, permit certain inspection activities required by the relevant standards to be undertaken by the manufacturer's in-house inspectorate.

Similarly in North America the ASME *Boiler and Pressure Vessel Code Section 1, Power Boilers* includes rules for the construction and inspection of boilers in which steam or other vapour is generated at a pressure more than 15 lb/in$^2$ (psig) and high temperature water boilers operating at pressures exceeding 160 psig and/or temperatures exceeding 250°F. Pressure parts connected directly to the boiler without intervening valves come within the scope of Section 1; the intervening piping must be fabricated in accordance with ANSI B31.1 *Code for pressure piping.* Quality control arrangements, welding procedures, etc. are similar to those required for pressure vessels.

### 3.24 Water-tube boilers—design, manufacture and inspection

The 1985 edition of *BS 1113   Design and manufacture of water-tube steam generating plant* incorporates a number of developments from BS 5500 (see 3.4.2 etc.). Design stress values (steel), material specifications, 'continued service reviews', manufacture under the survey of a competent inspecting authority, the manufacturer's mandatory QA system and approval by PVQAB are the same or similar to those laid down in BS 5500. Again approval of welding procedures, operatives and production control test plates, inspection of welding and standards of acceptance, and NDT techniques are basically the same.

(i) *Design matters.* The inspecting authority (AIB) is responsible for checking that design, materials and construction comply with the standard. Other inspectors, where relevant, should also be able to check the calculations. The derivation of nominal design stresses for different materials, temperatures and conditions are generally the same as with pressure vessels (see 3.4) except that temperatures above 250°C are catered for with a resulting reduction in stress (generally to $f = \dfrac{R_{\mathrm{m}}}{2.7}$).

Using the design stress (calculated or derived from tables) the basic calculation for the minimum thickness $t$ (in/mm) of a boiler shell can be determined from $t = \dfrac{pD}{2f}$ which is re-arranged in BS 1113 as: $t = \dfrac{pD_{\mathrm{o}}}{2f\eta + p}$ or

$$t = \frac{pD_{\mathrm{i}}}{2f\eta - p}$$

where $p$ is the calculation pressure (N/mm$^2$)

$D_o$ is the outside diameter of the shell (mm) and $D_i$ the inner diameter
$f$ is the design stress (N/mm$^2$)

$\eta$ is the ligament efficiency (the ratio of an arbitrary strength of a ligament to the strength of the unpierced plate, expressed as a decimal), a complex calculated factor due to the arrangement and pattern of holes drilled or otherwise in the boiler drum (it may be of the order of 0·5 and would be unity if there were no holes—see BS 1113 Clause 3.3.3. Holes obviously weaken a plate but the presence of tubes in them gives some strengthening. The ligament is the material between the holes).

Some increase in thickness may be necessary (due to corrosion, etc.) if the shell is exposed to flue gases and will depend upon any agreed design life. An absolute minimum thickness of 9·5 mm is specified.

The same equation can be used to determine the minimum thickness of straight tubes and integral pipes, but in this case the ligament efficiency is inapplicable and will be omitted.

(ii)*Materials*. Tubes will be supplied to types/grades specified in, and examined in accordance with BS 3059 (for boilers and superheaters) and BS 3601, 3602, 3604 and 3605 for general pressure purposes. They must be fitted to drums or headers by welding or some approved method of expanding and/or belling.

Plates will be supplied to types/grades specified in BS 1501. All drum plates must be ultrasonically examined in accordance with BS 5996. The minimum acceptable quality grade is LC2 (see 10.6.5). The visual examination of plate edge weld preparation must, in general, be supplemented by a 100% magnetic particle examination; any indications exceeding 30 mm in length should be investigated ultrasonically and if necessary cleared by dressing or welding.

Steel castings to specified types/grades in BS 1504 must be examined by NDT methods in accordance with category I or II of Appendix B of BS 1504. For ultrasonic examination the acceptance level specified in BS 6208 Table 1 quality level 1 and Table 2 quality level 1 shall be applied (10.6). For radiographic examination the maximum acceptable severity levels for defects are those specified in ASME Boiler and Pressure Vessel Code Section VIII Division 1, Appendix 7, paragraph 7–3(a)(1). (These are based on comparisons with standard reference radiographs in ASTM Spec SE-446 and 186-81.) Similarly magnetic particle examination acceptance levels are those specified in paragraph 7–3(a)(3) of the same ASME Code, and are based on reference photographs in ASTM Spec. E–125.

(iii) *Design Lifetime*. Where the nominal design stress for a material (or for instance a tube) as given in the series of tables (Table 2.1.2 of BS 1113) is time-dependent for the particular design temperature, a design lifetime

(100,000, 150,000, 200,000 or 250,000 hours) related to the creep-rupture properties of that material has to be agreed between the manufacturer and the purchaser. Replaceable components may be designed for shorter lifetimes than the life expectancy of the boiler, and in general should be replaced before their design life is exceeded. However, 'continued service reviews', i.e. procedures for assessing whether the life of a component, etc. could be extended, may be carried out using the techniques outlined in BS publication PD6510 *A review of the present state of the art of assessing remnant life of pressure vessels and pressurized systems designed for high temperature service* (see also 13.9), and should be instituted at not later than two-thirds of the design lifetime.

(iv) *Weld inspection.* Inspection and non-destructive examination of welds is carried out in a somewhat similar manner to that laid down for pressure vessels (see 3.4.6). Welding procedures and welders have to be approved to the appropriate standards. Production control test plates for the welded main seams, etc. of boiler drums have to be tested to destruction, generally to the requirements of BS 4870: Part 1, BS 709, BS 3688: Part 1, BS 131: Part 2, etc.

*All* longitudinal and circumferential butt welds in drums and headers, and butt welds generally in piping, etc., must be examined over their full length by either radiographic or ultrasonic methods, and all branches, nozzles, etc. by ultrasonic methods in the case of ferritic steels, and by dye penetrant methods in the case of austenitic steels. Surface flaw detection methods (e.g. magnetic particle and dye penetrant) are used over the full length of main seams, and over 10% of the length of attachments, and on 10% of welds attaching branches, nozzles and stubs.

(v) *Official inspection.* The inspecting authority will make examinations at appropriate stages, identifying material, test plates, etc. witnessing forming of ends and setting up ready for welding, checking radiographs and the records of ultrasonic testing and of heat treatment. Where agreed a reduction in the percentage rate of NDT of welds to a minimum of a 5% rate will be permitted by the inspecting authority when it has been demonstrated that welds consistently comply with the standards of acceptance tabulated in BS 1113 Table 5.9 (which are very similar to those given in para. 3.16 of this book). Conversely should results show that flaws are in excess of the standards of acceptance the percentage rate of examination can be increased by the inspecting authority until such time as a satisfactory quality of weld is established.

The authorized inspector will also witness hydraulic tests and carry out final examinations, marking and certification of documents.

The hydraulic test pressure on completely assembled boilers is in general 1·5 times the maximum permissible working pressure or 1·25 times the highest calculation pressure, whichever is the greater.

### 3.25 Shell boilers of welded construction

Shell boilers, mostly of traditional design such as fire tube horizontal cylindrical boilers basically of the Lancashire and Cornish types but extending to vertical types and intended for industrial steam raising or hot water supply, form the largest class in common use. In these days of fuel conservation they may be intended to make use of waste heat perhaps from some industrial process. They may be fired by coal, oil, gas or even heated by electricity; coal may be fed in by automatic stoker or by hand. The traditional riveted construction has been almost entirely superseded by welding.

Recent demands for increased efficiency and higher specific output from shell boilers, coupled with the need for safe and reliable operation, have resulted in improved design standards in many countries.

BS 2790   *Design and manufacture of shell boilers of welded construction* has been completely revised, and is now included in the list of 'Standards significant to health and safety at work' published by the Health and Safety Executive; it is also one of the standards which come under the aegis of the PVQAB. This standard specifies the various grades of carbon or carbon-manganese steels which may be used. It recognizes three classes:

| *Classification* | *Limits of application* |
|---|---|
| Class I | (a) Design pressure greater than $0·725$ N/mm$^2$ and/or (b) Design pressure (N/mm$^2$) $\times$ mean diameter of boiler shell (mm) is greater than 920 |
| Class II | If neither (a) or (b) above apply |
| Class III | If (a) above is not greater than $0·38$ N/mm$^2$ and (b) above is not greater than 480. |

($1$ N/mm$^2$ $= 1$ MPa $= 10$ bar (or $145$ lbf/in$^2$))

The maximum permissible design stress ($f$) for the selected shell material is the lower of:

Elevated temperature yield stress or $0·2\%$ proof stress at design temperature divided by $1·5$; and tensile strength at room temperature divided by $2·4$

This stress ($f$) is used in the formulae quoted in the standard for the calculation of pressure parts. For example, to calculate minimum thickness of shell ($e$) for pressure loading only:

$$\frac{e}{\text{(mm)}} = \frac{pR_i}{fZ-0·5p} + C \qquad \text{(Note: } e \text{ must not be less than 6 mm)}$$

where $p$ = design pressure (N/mm$^2$)

$\quad R_i$ = inner radius of shell (mm)

$\quad f$ = design stress (N/mm$^2$)

$\quad C$ = corrosion allowance (usually taken as 0.75 mm)

and $Z$ = 1·0 for class I boilers or seamless shells

$\qquad\qquad$ 0·85 for class II boilers

$\qquad\qquad$ 0·65 for class III boilers

Amongst the definitive requirements of the standard the following items have to be agreed and documented by the purchaser:

(i) A specification of working conditions of the boiler, including any transient or adverse conditions, and any operational (in-service) inspection requirements.

(ii) The name of the inspection authority being commissioned by the purchaser.

(iii) Any special statutory regulations, etc. (e.g. foreign legislation) with which the finished boiler must comply.

(iv) The name of any regulating authority (e.g. one charged with the enforcement of the boiler regulations of the country of installation).

Reference to other parts of the standard shows that the appointment of an independent authorized inspection body is essential, and that it will act on behalf of the purchaser (or owner) and/or the regulating authority to check and certify that design, materials and construction comply with requirements.

Also the inspecting authorities must be recognized in the country of manufacture and/or installation. Consequently much of what has been said elsewhere in this chapter on pressure vessels applies to the inspection of shell boilers to this standard.

In particular, inspection during construction by persons nominated by the inspecting authority follows similar lines to those laid down in Table 3.3. Non-destructive testing is required on class I and class II, but not for class III boilers.

Pressure tests, applied hydraulically for at least 30 minutes at 1·5 times the design pressure without any sign of defect, have to be witnessed by the inspector. Such tests are carried out after completion of welding and any heat treatment which may be required. Non-destructive testing for the parent metal plates is specified for set-on end plates (generally 100% ultra-sonic) and to ensure compliance with the requirements of quality grades L4 and C4 and edge discontinuity grade ES of BS 5996. For all other plates grades L1 and C1 (normal commercial quality) is appropriate, and edge discontinuity grade E should be used as a guide to acceptability (see 10.10). Welder procedure/approval is required generally in accordance with BS4870 and 4871; production test plates are required to represent all butt-welded main seams (the relevant details being similar to 3.14–3.16 and Fig. 3.10).

Butt-welded seams should be subjected to radiographic or ultrasonic testing (Class I and II boilers only) to an extent laid down in a comprehensive table, etc. given in the standard. Generally speaking the requirements are somewhat similar to those in BS 1113 (see 3.24). Class I boilers require 100% radiographic or ultrasonic testing on longitudinal welds and on circumferential shell welds between shell sections and set-on end plates, with 25% on other welds. 100% testing on circumferential welds between shell sections and set-on end plates and 10% on longitudinal and other circumferential shell welds is necessary on class II boilers.

Most other butt welds (class I or II) require 10% (or for T-butt furnace welds 25%) of the total length of weld to be tested, each length selected at random. Certain attachment welds should be examined over their full length by ultrasonic means and/or by magnetic particle or penetrant methods for surface flaws. Other fillet welds, etc., should be examined for surface flaws (25% for class I and 10% for class II). All welds (including those on Class III boilers) must be examined visually for defects. Acceptance criteria for weld defects (observed by visual examination and NDT) are generally the same or similar to those given in Part 1 of BS 4870 and 4871 for welder/procedure approval, and are detailed in Table 5.7 of the standard (a truncated table similar to Table 5.7.1 of BS 5500 (see 3.16). Acceptance limits for inclusions and other details may be seen in the standard. Welds repaired in accordance with the requirements of the inspection authority are subject to the same acceptance criteria as the original welds.

Boilers not continuously supervised in service must be fitted with suitable automatic water level and firing controls.

### 3.26  Acceptance testing of boilers

BS 1113 and similar construction codes do not themselves contain detailed clauses regarding testing facilities and acceptance tests on the completed boiler, although these may be incorporated in a contract. BS 1113 Appendix G—Inspection and testing facilities, however, does state that 'failing facilities at his own works for making the prescribed tests, the manufacturer should make arrangements for carrying out the tests elsewhere'.

A standard code for tabulating the results of a comprehensive trial of a boiler plant was included in the Heat Engines Trials Code of the Institution of Civil Engineers (1927). BS 845 *Acceptance Tests for Industrial Type Boilers* was first issued in 1939 and revised in 1987 (see Table 3.5) and *Acceptance Tests on Stationary steam generators of the Power Station Type* (BS 2885) in 1957 (revised 1974). Based to some extent on the ICE Code, and the latter on ISO Recommendations ISO/R889, the latest issues are expressed in SI units. These British Standards establish procedures for conducting and reporting acceptance tests and for determining thermal efficiency. However, they do *not* follow the ICE recommendation of using the gross (or higher) calorific value of the fuel when computing thermal efficiency; either the net (lower) or the gross (higher) calorific value of the fuel may be used, provided that the basis is clearly stated.

Should the gross calorific value be used this means that if the fuel contains hydrogen, then water will be one of the products of combustion and will be evolved in the form of steam. In practice this steam will be lost, but when the calorific value of a fuel is being measured by means of a calorimeter this steam condenses and adds its heat to the experimentally determined gross calorific value. Thus, in such a case, the overall thermal efficiency obtainable when using the gross value would be lower than if the net value had been used.

$$\text{Thermal efficiency} = \frac{\text{heat output}}{\text{heat input}}$$

$$= \frac{\text{total heat output of complete boiler plant}}{\text{total heat input of fuel}}$$

$$= \frac{\text{quantity of steam produced (kg/s)} \times \text{heat imparted to steam (kJ/kg)}}{\text{rate of firing (kg/s)} \times \text{calorific value of fuel (kJ/kg)}}$$

Alternatively, it may be convenient or more accurate to measure all losses. Then

$$\text{thermal efficiency} = \frac{\text{heat input} - \text{losses}}{\text{heat input}} \quad \text{or} \quad \frac{\text{heat output}}{\text{heat output} + \text{losses}}$$

*Note 1:* Either the gross or the net calorific value should be used, whichever is specified.

*Note 2:* Care should be taken to ensure that the heat imparted by such items as reheaters, superheaters, feed water heaters, etc. where these are fitted, is included in the total heat output of the complete plant.

*Note 3:* The power used by auxiliaries is to be separately recorded (and not deducted from the output to give a net thermal efficiency).

*Note 4:* Thermal efficiency ($\eta$) is usually expressed as a percentage. Consequently the fractional quantity above should be multiplied by 100.

Before any acceptance test the plant should be thoroughly inspected to check for completeness, cleanliness and to ascertain that there are no abnormal leaks, particularly air leaks in the boiler casing and passages. A preliminary steaming run should be carried out to check the proper operation of instruments and to establish proper combustion conditions. Thereafter the plant should be run for a sufficient time to attain temperature equilibrium under test load conditions; this may take a minimum of 12 hours or up to three days if there is much brickwork etc. to warm up.

Before the actual test the plant should be run and checked under steady test conditions for one hour; a similar run of one hour after the test is generally required. The actual duration of the test, during which conditions must be maintained as constant as possible at the specified output, may be from four to 24 hours according to the type of plant installed.

The test reports specified by British Standards are lengthy and comprehensive documents giving details of the plant, the fuel used, and test and corrected measurements of the many factors involved, together with a diagram of the installation. They finish up with a heat balance account, together with details of losses, from which the thermal efficiency can be calculated. SI units are used throughout (although the bar is used for pressure). If other units are required by the contract, etc. the necessary observations/conversions must be made.

The 1987 issue of BS 845 for industrial boiler performance is divided into two parts. BS 845, *Assessing thermal performance of boilers for steam, hot water and high temperature heat transfer fluids*, describes the methods for assessing performance of boilers of output generally greater than 44 kW using either the net or the gross calorific value of the fuel.

Part 1   provides a *concise procedure* for simple types of boiler using the indirect (losses) method.

Part 2   provides a *comprehensive procedure* for all boilers including complex types such as those with multiple flows to and from the boiler and using any type of fuel, fluidized bed combustion, etc. Either the direct method (all heat flows in and out being separately determined), or the indirect (losses) method of procedure being employed.

The testing of steam generators for power stations is covered by BS 2885. ASME publish a similar *Power Test Code for Steam Generating Units* (PTC 4.1). General practice in the USA is to use English units (e.g. lb/hr, °F, etc.), but mention is being made of the equivalent SI units.

### 3.27 Fusion welded steel air receivers

The design, materials and methods of construction, inspection and testing of fusion welded steel air receivers follow similar lines to those already laid down for pressure vessels in such standards as BS 5500. Three classes of receiver are specified in BS 5169:

Class I   No limit is placed upon size or design pressure, but non-destructive testing (NDT) of all welded seams is required.

Class II   Design pressure is limited to 35 bar. The product of design pressure (bars) and internal diameter (mm) must not exceed 37,000.

Class III   The design pressure is limited to 17.5 bar and the product of design pressure (bars) and internal diameter (mm) must not exceed 8800.

The materials of construction are selected from specific grades of steel to BS 1501, 1502, 1503, 970, 3601 and 3602, or, for class III receivers only, to BS 1449.

Tensile and bend tests are required on plate and sheet material, and impact tests may be required if the design temperature is below 0°C or if agreed by the purchaser, manufacturer and inspecting authority (see Appendix D of BS 5500).

Where practicable shells and end plates should be made from a single plate; if not practicable butt-welded plates may be used subject to agreement by the inspecting authority. For class I receivers welded on end plates must be outwardly dished (concave to pressure).

Forming, preparation for welding, types of welded joints, welding procedure and inspection are largely similar to those detailed in 3.5. In general receivers should be fabricated with double sided butt welds, however certain types of full penetration butt welds, deposited from one side against a temporary backing strip may be regarded as equivalent. For class I receivers a weld joint factor (weld efficiency) of 0·95 is used in the formula for calculating plate thickness; for class II receivers the weld joint factor is 0·75 and for class III receivers it is 0·65, or 0·40 if the welding is from one side only and without a backing strip.

Welding procedure tests and approval of welders must be carried out in a similar manner to pressure vessels etc. supplemented by non-destructive testing of production welds in the case of class I receivers.

Test plates (similar to Fig. 3.10) have to be prepared for each longitudinal welded seam (see 3.14) and for class I receivers may be attached at one end only. For class I receivers the tests are indicated in Fig. 3.10 and Table 3.3. For class II receivers a lesser number of tests are required (transverse tensile, bend and nick bend). For class III receivers tests are not specifically required except for mechanized welding.

Class I receivers have also to be radiographically tested on all butt-welded seams in the shell and end plates to the general recommendations of BS 2600 and BS 2910 and similar to those covered in 3.15.

Radiographs have to be examined for imperfections and any of the following are unacceptable:

(a)  Any crack or zone of incomplete fusion or penetration

(b)  Any elongated slag inclusion of greater length than 3 mm for $t$ up to 10 mm, 6 mm for $t$ from 10–19 mm, $\frac{1}{3}T$ for $t$ from 19–57 mm, 19 mm for $t$ over 57 mm.

(c)  Any group of slag inclusions in line that have an aggregated length greater than $t$ in a length of $12t$.

(d)  A total area of porosity exceeding 6 mm$^2$ per 25 mm of wall thickness in any 645 mm$^2$ of projected weld area.

The thickness of the cylindrical shell plate may be calculated from the formula:

$$\frac{t}{(mm)} = \frac{pd}{20fJ - p} + 0.75$$

where $p$ = design pressure (bar)
  $d$ = inside diameter (mm)
  $f$ = design stress (N/mm$^2$)
    (as given in the appropriate table)
  $J$ = joint factor

Each completed receiver, after any necessary heat treatment has to satisfactorily withstand a hydraulic test of 1·5 times the design pressure maintained for not less than 15 minutes. A signed and detailed certificate of construction and test must be supplied.

### 3.28  Inspection of nuclear vessels and power plant components

Something has been said elsewhere regarding the beginning of atomic energy in the UK and the role played by the Ministry of Supply Inspectorates (nominally by the Inspectorate of Electrical and Mechanical Equipment but staffed and headed largely by a nucleus of engineers transferred from AID or with AID experience). (see 13.11). Obviously they made use of their established system and expertise when dealing with their new problems. Work started in 1946 but in 1954 the bulk of the inspection staff were transferred to the UK Atomic Energy Authority on its formation. Shortly after they were combined with others to form an Inspection and Progress Division, apart from some members of IEME staff working on other atomic work. A somewhat similar military organization operated in the USA dealing with the massive nuclear submarine programme under the control of the redoubtable Admiral Hyman Rickover. Both organizations did sterling work, often under great pressure.

Following the Windscale incident of 1957 (see 13.11.1) and the resulting enquiries, the Nuclear Installations Inspectorate was established under an Act of 1959 and the Nuclear Safety Advisory Committee was set up in 1960. The UKAEA itself set up a Health and Safety Branch. A Radiological Protection Service run by the Medical Research Council, and a Radioactive Substances Advisory Committee were combined and together with other activities were taken over in 1970 to form the National Radiological Protection Board. This board now advises, *inter alia*, on maximum levels of radioactivity, etc. (see 6.17.2).

After the Atomic Energy Authority Act 1971 was passed, certain reorganizations took place. The UKAEA Production Group, (in part located at Risley and Windscale (Sellafield)) together with the Radiochemical Centre, Amersham, became a public limited company known as British Nuclear Fuels plc (BNFL). The Authority Health and Safety Branch was reorganized and renamed the Safety and Reliability Directorate, and in conjunction with the Health and Safety Executive formed the National Centre of Systems Reliability, situated at Culcheth, Warrington.

As regards the construction and inspection of nuclear installations, the American Society of Mechanical Engineers (ASME) was early in the field, issuing Section III of its Boiler and Pressure Vessel Code in 1963 dealing with nuclear vessels and components, and design, inspection and safety matters relating to their construction. It is now divided into sub-sections as follows:

Sub-section NCA: General requirements for Division 1 and 2
Division 1
Sub-section NB    Class 1 components
Sub-section NC    Class 2 components
Sub-section ND    Class 3 components
Sub-section NE    Class MC components
Sub-section NF    Components supports
Sub-section NG    Core support structures
Appendices
Division 2    Code for concrete reactor vessels and containments
Sub-section CB    Concrete reactor vessels
Sub-section CC    Concrete containments
Appendices

The requirements laid down for QA are exacting, but are based on those for Section VIII Division 2 (Pressure Vessels) but more so. A registered professional engineer has to clear and certify certain matters. Portions of Sub-section NCA, Code Article 4000, were deleted (in 1980) and replaced by ANSI/ASME NQA-1, *Quality Assurance Requirements for Nuclear Power Plants*. Many of the administrative QA requirements have their very similar counterpart in BS 5750   Part 1 (as had been noted already in 3.23).

BS 5882 *Total Quality Assurance Programme for Nuclear Installations* (see 13.10) invokes BS 5750, *Quality Systems*, in a somewhat similar manner.

The various sub-sections of the ASME Nuclear Code apply to the classification of pressure retaining or containing components and their supporting structures.

Class 1 components include reactor and primary circuit vessels containing coolant for the core that cannot be separated from the core and its radioactivity. Class 2 components are those which are not part of (e.g. within) the reactor coolant boundary but are used to remove the heat from the reactor coolant pressure boundary. Class 3 components provide support for Class 2 components without being part of them. Class MC deals with metal containment structures.

Class 1, Class 2 and Class MC components require that a complete stress analysis of pressure parts be prepared by the manufacturer and certified by a registered professional engineer. Copies of the certified stress report (with supporting documents and design calculations) must be made available to the authorized inspector and to the enforcement authority of the area in which the installation is carried out.

Some details and diagrams of basic nuclear reactors are given in Fig. 3.15, showing the arrangement of components. The primary and secondary circuits are indicated, but notice that the boiling water reactor (BWR) has no secondary circuit. The primary circuit components are subject to a high level of radioactivity and are termed Class 1 by ASME for design and inspection purposes, secondary circuit components being designated Class 2. The electrical generating plant is basically of conventional design.

The sub-sections of the ASME Nuclear Code contain articles and paragraphs dealing with specific requirements applicable to components for different reactor types e.g. water-cooled (PWR and BWR), and gas-cooled (HTGR and AGR) etc.

By complying with the procedures outlined specifically in this chapter and in Chapters 9, 12, and 13 and elsewhere in this book (in particular those of BS 5750 (note particularly Figs. 9.1 and 9.2), BS 5882, the ASME codes, PVQAB and the various atomic energy and legislative authorities) with special reference to nuclear matters a manufacturer/inspector should be well on the way to an understanding of the rigorous standards of fabrication and QA necessary to ensure satisfactory and safe construction and operation of nuclear components and plant.

Some British Standards have been issued dealing with nuclear power plants and installations:

BS 3915 *Carbon and low alloy steel pressure vessels for primary circuits of nuclear reactors*
BS 4208 *Carbon and low alloy steel containment structures for stationary nuclear power reactors*
BS 4975 *Pre-stressed concrete pressure vessels for nuclear reactors.*

These give information on material and nominal design stresses, design and manufacture, and inspection and test. Much of the information is similar to that available in pressure vessel specifications and other British Standards. Testing of materials and welds, radiography and other methods of non-destructive testing, leak testing and pressure tests are laid down, but generally standards of acceptance, instrumentation, and certain material requirements, etc. have to be agreed between the purchaser and the manufacturer.

In BS 4975 appendices give information on concrete and the effects of nuclear radiation on it, and design and the methods of stress analysis.

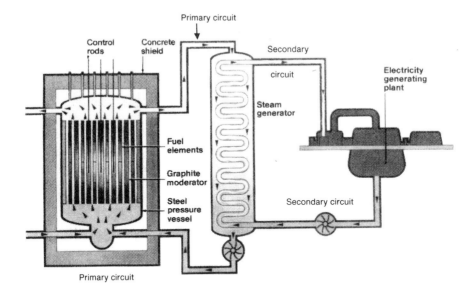

**Magnox Thermal Reactor — Graphite Moderated (UK)**

**Fuel**   Uranium metal. To conserve neutrons and allow natural uranium to be used, the fuel is clad in a magnesium alloy (Magnox) with low neutron absorption.

**Moderator**   Graphite.

**Heat extraction**   Carbon dioxide gas is heated by passing it over the fuel in the core and transfers its heat to water in a steam generator; the steam drives a turbine coupled to an electric generator.

**Indicative data for a reactor of 600 MW(E) size**

Uranium enrichment (% U.235)      0·7% (natural)
Coolant outlet temperature       360–400°C
Coolant pressure                 300 psia
Steam cycle efficiency           31%
Core dimensions                  14 m dia. × 8 m high

Reprocessing   Necessary within one year since fuel cladding corrodes under water

Refuelling   Can be carried out on-load

**Fig. 3.15   Some nuclear reactors showing primary and secondary circuit components** (adapted by courtesy of UKAEA).

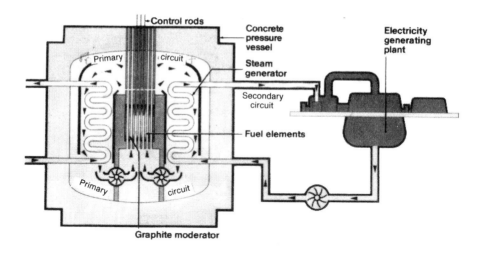

Graphite moderator

**Advanced Gas-cooled Reactor (AGR)**
**Thermal Reactor — Graphite Moderated (UK)**

**Fuel**  Uranium dioxide in stainless steel cladding. The fuel can operate at higher temperatures and heat output rates than Magnox reactor fuel, giving a smaller size of reactor core and a more efficient steam cycle. To achieve these advantages and a greater heat rating, the proportion of U.235 in the fuel has to be increased (enriched uranium).
**Moderator**  Graphite.
**Core layout**  Clusters of fuel elements are joined together end-to-end in a stringer, placed in vertical holes in the graphite.
**Heat extraction**  Carbon dioxide gas is heated by passing over the fuel in the core and transfers its heat to water in a steam generator; the steam drives a turbine coupled to an electric generator.
**Indicative data for a reactor of 600 MW(E) size**
    Uranium enrichment (% U.235)        2.3%
    Coolant outlet temperature          650°C
    Coolant pressure                    600 psia
    Steam cycle efficiency              42%
    Core dimensions                     9.1 m dia. × 8.5 m high
Reprocessing   Necessary within 10 years if stored under water
Refuelling   Can be carried out on-load

**Fig. 3.15** *continued*

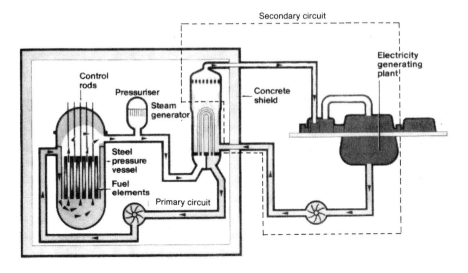

**Pressurised Water Reactor (PWR) Thermal**
**Reactor — Water Moderated (USA basic design, used world-wide)**


**Fuel**   Uranium dioxide clad in an alloy of zirconium (Zircaloy).
**Moderator**   Light water (ordinary water, $H_2O$).
**Core layout**   Fuel pins, arranged in clusters, are placed inside a pressure vessel containing the light water moderator, which also is the coolant.
**Heat extraction**   The light water in the pressure vessel at high pressure is heated by the core. It is pumped to a steam generator where it boils water in a separate circuit; the steam drives a turbine coupled to an electric generator.
**Indicative data for a reactor of 700 MW(E) size**

| | |
|---|---|
| Uranium enrichment (% U.235) | 3·2% |
| Coolant outlet temperature | 317°C |
| Coolant pressure | 2235 psia |
| Steam cycle efficiency | 32% |
| Core dimensions | 3·0 m dia. × 3·7 m high |

Reprocessing   Fuel can be stored under water for long periods,
Refuelling   Must be carried out off-load.


**Fig. 3.15** *continued*

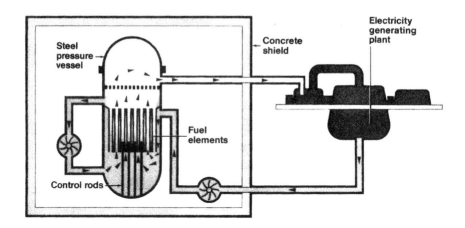

**Boiling Water Reactor (BWR) Thermal**
**Reactor — Water moderated (USA; used world-wide. Its simple construction**
**favours its use for nuclear submarine propulsion)**

**Fuel**  Uranium dioxide in Zircaloy cans.
**Moderator**  Light water (ordinary water, $H_2O$).
**Core layout**  Fuel pins, arrangement in clusters, are placed inside a pressure
vessel containing the light water moderator, which also is the coolant.
**Heat extraction**  The light water in the pressure vessel is heated by the core
and allowed to boil at pressure. The steam from the boiling coolant drives a
turbine coupled to an electric generator.
**Indicative data for a reactor of 600 MW(E) size**

| | |
|---|---|
| Uranium enrichment (% U.235) | 2·6% |
| Coolant outlet temperature | 286°C |
| Coolant pressure | 1050 psia |
| Steam cycle efficiency | 32% |
| Core dimensions | 3·7 m dia. × 3.7 m high |

**Refuelling**  Must be carried out off-load
**Reprocessing**  Fuel can be stored under water for long periods

**Fig. 3.15**  *concluded*

Methods of testing concrete are covered in BS 1881, and non-destructive methods in BS 4408 (Part 1: Electromagnetic — to measure the 'cover' over the reinforcement. Part 2: Strain gauges and Part 3: Gamma radiography — to locate and identify grouting voids and steel reinforcement bars).

The first two of the above reactor standards are now regarded as obsolescent, possibly owing to the advent of BS 5500 and 5882 and customers' detailed specifications. BS 5882 *A total quality assurance programme for nuclear installations* is discussed in Chapter 12. But, as yet, no further detailed technical British Standards concerning nuclear installations have been issued.

The ASME Code Section III is the most comprehensive yet available, but even so many of the technical details are subject to agreement between the respective parties. In fact the ASME Nuclear Code requires that the 'owner' (the organization which has obtained authority to construct a nuclear installation) has to provide, or cause to be provided, design specifications for components (establishing their class), appurtenances and supports and these specifications must be certified as being correct and complete and in compliance with the relevant requirements of the Code by one or more registered professional engineers.

In addition QA programmes, quality manuals, etc. have to be prepared by the manufacturer for the various components, etc. they seek approval to produce, and these documents have to be evaluated initially by ASME who will, if satisfied, issue a certificate of authorization detailing the scope and any limitations of the activities covered. Further, the manufacturer seeking approval must have an agreement with an authorized inspection agency to provide inspection and audit services. And, of course, the certificate holder must have his own QA organization, complying with all the requirements detailed in the ASME Code and in ANSI/ASME NQA-1 (which replaced part of the Code), to work in conjunction with and to the requirements of the authorized inspection agency and the appropriate legal authority.

The arrangement is very similar in organizational principles to that practised in the UK; the manufacturer has to be approved for technical competence by the PVQAB; he must have appointed an authorized inspection body, and he must have a QA organization approved by that body and/or the PVQAB.

Amendments to the ASME Code are made from time to time, perhaps at the behest of the US Nuclear Regulatory Commission through the issue of Regulatory Guides, Inspection and Enforcement (IE) Bulletins and other documents.

For further information on in-service inspection (ISI) of nuclear plants see Section XI of the ASME Code Rules for Inservice Inspection of Nuclear Power Plant Components and 12.10.3.

### 3.29 Reactor pressure vessel integrity

The integrity of a reactor pressure vessel (RPV) is of fundamental importance to safety. An explosive failure, however remote, could lead to a large uncontrolled release of radioactive materials with dire results.

Even a non-explosive failure (e.g. a tube failure) could for instance cause coolant to be lost, and if this coolant could not be replaced by an emergency core cooling system, then the reactor core would melt, again possibly leading to a disastrous uncontrolled release.

In an endeavour to prevent such failures:

(a) methods of design, manufacture, inspection, testing and operation are applied which should ensure that the possibility of a major failure without forewarning is extremely remote;

(b) an analysis may be carried out to determine the sizes of defect which might cause a failure (see 2.8 and PD 6493); then it must be ensured that the methods of NDT used (perhaps ultrasonic) will readily and reliably detect faults present in the vessel some degree smaller than these sizes;

(c) as an additional precaution two independent inspection organizations may carry out the NDT tests (perhaps using different techniques).

See also Marshall, *An assessment of the integrity of PW Reactor pressure vessels* (UKAEA/HMSO 1976).

The design and inspection will be generally at least to the requirements of the relevant parts of the ASME code or BS 5500 plus specific additions. The inspection arrangements will involve QA organizations as previously discussed, often checked over or audited by a further independent organization, such as PVQAB.

Regarding the RPV for the Sizewell B PWR, arrangements have been made for design material and information to be supplied by Westinghouse of the USA (the experienced original designers of the system), for manufacture to be undertaken by Frematone of France (the very experienced and only ASME approved company in Europe making this type of vessel) from steel supplied by Japan (which apparently is the only country with a proven capability to make it to the required specification).

The inspection arrangements are complex and go beyond the outline given above. CEGB has its own QA organization; as do most of its sub-contractors, and they have a contract with Lloyds to act as an independent assessment authority. In addition, Frematone's ASME qualified inspectors are checked and their work certified by UKAEA whilst special inspection equipment has been manufactured by Babcock and Wilcox Ltd. For further details see the Sizewell B Report, HMSO 1987.

### 3.30  Seismic qualification of nuclear plant

Some design requirements and calculations for pressure vessels subject to loadings due to earthquakes are given in BS 5500 and ASME Code Sect VIII (see 3.4.5). An earthquake produces simultaneous ground movements having horizontal and vertical components. One of magnitude 6 or higher on the Richter scale may produce a horizontal ground acceleration of from 0·1 to 0·6 times gravity, and may last from 15–30 seconds the major energy being imparted in, say, the first 5–10 seconds. The motion may be magnified by the building characteristics, etc. and equipment mounted on, say, upper floors may be subjected to an acceleration much greater tha.. that at ground level. Some building codes empirically assess the horizontal force on a building as a function of the building's weight times various factors (which collectively may be less than one).

Although many buildings and industrial plants have in the past been designed (and strengthened) to withstand earthquake shocks, using often 'rule of thumb' methods, it was not until the planning of the Heysham II AGR nuclear power station that the Nuclear Installations Inspectorate (NII) made it a requirement that the safety related components incorporated in it should be formally seismically qualified. It was their intention that in the event of an earthquake a reactor must be capable of being safely shut down and maintained in that condition indefinitely (a safe shutdown earthquake—SSE).

Some of the basic documents which the designers (including the CEGB and the National Nuclear Corporation, NNC) had to guide them included: ANSI/IEEE Standard 344   Recommended practices for seismic qualification of Class 1E equipment for nuclear power generating stations (first published in New York in 1971 and subsequently updated). This required that qualification must be demonstrated by stress analysis, testing and documentation of past performance. See also:

IEEE Standard 382   Qualification of safety-related valve actuators (NY, 1980).
ANSI B16.41 Standard for Functional qualification of power operated active valve actuators for nuclear power plants.
ASCE   Guidelines for the seismic design of oil and gas pipeline systems (New York, 1984)
ASME Boiler and Pressure Vessel Code, Section III.

After much work involving consultants, research into history, hazard analyses, mathematical modelling and computer programming it was eventually decided that a seismic design level (SSE) involving withstanding a peak ground level acceleration (pga) of 0·25 times gravity with a probability of occurrence of 1 in 10,000 years should be the target for UK nuclear power stations. (This corresponds to the ASME Code Section III, level D.)

In addition equipment qualified to ANSI/IEEE 344 must be capable of understanding a number of operational basis earthquake (OBE) shocks at peak ground accelerations of 0·125, prior to SSE. (Should a component be required to function (be active) *after* an earthquake the limits appropriate to ASME Code Section III Level A or B must be used.)

Many type tests of selected items of plant (such as valves, actuators and transformers) have been carried out at establishments such as the National Engineering Laboratory at the instigation of CEGB and NNC etc.

As a result of implementing the seismic requirements Heysham II (and later stations) has more massive foundations, significantly stiffer steelwork, stronger reinforced concrete supports for the reactor building and Reactor pressure vessel (RPV), stronger fuelling machine structure and strengthened component supports than its predecessors. At the Sizewell B inquiry the CEGB agreed to design the projected PWR nuclear power station and its RPVs to withstand simultaneously an exceedance level earthquake (which occurs in the UK about once in 10,000 years and would have a magnitude of 7 on the Richter scale with its focus 25 km from Sizewell) and a large loss-of-coolant accident. An earthquake of this magnitude would cause a maximum peak ground acceleration in the UK of 0·25 g, but this figure (0·25g) would be used in calculations. In earthquake zones such as Japan and California ground accelerations had exceeded 0·25 g but no plant so far had suffered significant damage.

CEGB's seismic studies also conclude that the early Magnox stations (with a few plant modifications) can be safely shut down and cooled following an earthquake with a peak horizontal ground acceleration of 0·1 g, although not initially designed with earthquakes in mind. The probability of such an earthquake in the UK is assessed as once in 2000 years, and CEGB further predict that the reactors would be capable of withstanding shocks nearer 0·2 g before damage would occur sufficient to prevent them being controlled safely (see Bradwell Nuclear Power Station—the findings of NII's assessment of the CEGB's long-term safety review (HSE-1987); NII, whilst agreeing that the plant has substantial resistance to earthquakes, reserved final judgement pending further consultations,* before agreeing to extend the life of the Bradwell Station by 5 years to 30 years: see p. 612).

---

*In July 1988 it was agreed (subject to the usual monitoring) that Bradwell could continue in operation until 1992. A similar safety review of Berkeley Magnox station (which was already operating on somewhat reduced power and not refuelling on-load) disclosed no unsafe features, but CEGB decided that the costs of complying with NII's requirements were not economically justifiable for so short a life extension. Consequently an expensive de-commissioning programme will have to be undertaken.

All this precautionary work costs money, which adds to the cost of nuclear power, and seemingly has to be done to guard against something which may not happen to the station for 10,000 years. But if an earthquake did occur and the strengthening had not been done, then there would be a massive public outcry (and no doubt heavy litigation expenses). See also *Seismic qualification of safety related nuclear plant and equipment* (I. Mech. E. Seminar), Mech. Eng. Pub., 1984.

### 3.31 Pressure vessel failures

For an analysis of defects found in pressure vessels whilst in operational use see 13.7 and Table 13.15.

### References and further reading

H.S.E. I. Mech. E. *Berkeley Nuclear Power Station – The finding of NII's assessment of the CEGB's long term safety review (HMSO 1988)*

I. Mech. E. *Performance testing of boilers*. Mech. Eng. Pub. 1988.

*Tolerance of flaws in pressurised components.* Mech. Eng. Pub. 1978.

Int. Atomic Energy Agency, *Quality Assurance for Nuclear power plants*, HMSO, 1982.

Int. Atomic Energy Agency, *Quality Assurance in the manufacture of items for nuclear power plants*, HMSO, 1981.

Int. Atomic Energy Agency, *Source term evaluation for accident conditions* (symposium Vienna 1986).

Marshall, W. (editor), *Nuclear potter technology*, 3 vols, Oxford UniPress, 1984.

Matfield, (editor), *Quality assurance in nuclear power plants*, Harwood Acad. Pub., 1985.

Openshaw, S., *Nuclear power: sitting and safety*, Routledge & Kegan Paul, 1986.

Technical Help to Exporters: *Boilers and pressure vessels: an international survey of design and approval requirements*, BSI, Milton Keynes, 1987.

Welding Institute, *Failures in pressure vessels*, 1966–75.

Wylie, R.D. and McGonnagle, W.J., *Quality control in the fabrication of nuclear pressure vessels*, Rowman and Littlefield, New York, 1964.

# 4    Pipes, pipework and valves

## 4.1 Pipes and tubes—design considerations

Traditionally, tubes produced in accordance with the sizes standardized by the various pipe specifications (particularly American) have been called pipe. All other tubes not produced in standard pipe sizes may be called tubes or tubing. A further distinction is that a pipe has as its *primary* purpose the *conveying* of a fluid, whilst with a tube this is not necessarily so; its primary purpose may be, for example, heating a fluid or supporting a structure. However, British Standards now state, for their purposes, that no difference in meaning between pipes and tubes is intended. So either term may be used.

Pipes and specials (a fitting made from fabricated pipe) are now generally designated by their outside diameters which (together with thickness) should always be quoted when ordering. The nominal size may be used as a convenient round number for reference purposes (generally common to all components of a system) and is only loosely related to manufacturing dimensions, being less than the outside diameter.

### 4.1.1 Design stress, pressure and thickness

The following simplified relationships between pipe wall thickness and internal pressure (using SI units) may be of use:

$$t = \frac{pD}{2fe} + c \quad \text{or} \quad p = \frac{2tfe}{D}$$

where $t$ = pipe wall thickness (mm)
  $p$ = maximum internal pressure during operation or test (N/mm$^2$)
  $D$ = external pipe diameter (mm)

$f$ = minimum permissible design stress in material (N/mm$^2$) divided by an appropriate factor of safety

$e$ = efficiency of any longitudinally welded joint (weld joint factor)

$c$ = allowance for reduction in wall thickness due to manufacturing tolerances and corrosion (mm)

The permissible design stress may be taken from a table in a relevant specification, or from test results, etc. In the past, when designing on the basis of tensile strength (at an appropriate temperature) a factor of safety of the order of 4 might have been used. Today design may be based also on yield stress, proof stress etc. (see 2.4).

American standards however generally specify a relationship based on yield strength. Thus API Standard 5LX for high-test line pipe gives:

$$p = 2st/D \text{ (or 3000 whichever is the smaller)}$$

where $p$ = hydrostatic test pressure (lb/in$^2$),

$s$ = allowable fibre stress (lb/in$^2$), which increases with pipe size from 60–90% of the minimum yield strength,

$t$ = pipe wall thickness (in),

$D$ = *outside* diameter of pipe (in)

A similar formula is specified by American Waterworks Association (AWWA) Specification C 201-60T for Fabricated Electrically Welded Steel Water Pipe of large diameter, except that in this case $D$ is the *inside* diameter, and the allowable fibre stress is some 85% of the yield strength, instead of the 90% quoted for large diameter pipes by the API Specification.

If required, a supplementary hydrostatic test may be made on sample lengths of API Standard 5LX line pipe in order to determine actual yield strength properties, etc. Such tests must be carried out by using accurate strain gauges, or may be continued to destruction.

The appropriate formula etc. should be used when designing or testing to a particular standard. Details and units will vary.

American practice is further considered in 4.6.2.


## 4.2 Tube manufacture

Some knowledge of the methods of manufacture of the various types of pipes and tubes is desirable before carrying out their inspection and testing. A good product depends on adequate control checks being undertaken during manufacture. Some types of fault to be expected, for instance, in lap-welded pipe, would not be present in seamless tube.

For *lap-welded pipe*, plate or strip material is heated and bent into circular section with overlapping edges which are then joined by hot-rolling; the material can be said to be wrapped round a 'hole' leaving a seam of possible weakness.

For *seamless tube* the 'hole' is made by punching or piercing it hydraulically into a suitable hot *billet*, which then takes the shape of a short thick tube closed at its lower end (known as a *bloom*). Seamless tube is then produced by elongating this bloom by feeding it on to a long rod or mandrel and pushing it through dies on a suitable *push bench* or mill to form a longer thick-walled tube known as a *hollow*. For stainless steel and some non-ferrous metals the 'hole' is generally bored into the billet rather than punched or pierced, and the bloom is then raised to a suitable temperature for extruding through a press. The extrusion process can also be used for heavy wall pipe and hard to pierce alloys, but is limited to small diameters up to some 4 in. The hole may be pierced by a mandrel which advances through the hot billet in front of the extrusion stem, which later forces the pierced billet through a die.

The 'hollow' obtained is formed into seamless tube by a variety of detailed methods involving rolling and drawing, including the push bench (for diameters up to some 6 in (150 mm)), the rotary forge and the Pilger mill. For the larger diameters (up to some 18 in (450 mm)), blooms obtained from cast ingots are normally used. If, with steel, the processing and finishing are carried out at a temperature of the order of 900°C the resulting product is known as 'hot finished' tube. Its surface will be rough and covered with mill scale and it will be impracticable to work to fine dimensional limits. In general the tube will be in the normalized condition, owing to its finishing temperature of around 900°C, but special steels, etc., which harden on air cooling will need subsequent special arrangements for heat treatment.

When a better finished tube is required, having a smoother surface and/or closer dimensional tolerances, it is produced by cold working, usually by cold drawing. Smaller diameter tubes, and those possessing higher mechanical strength, are also produced by this method. For instance it is estimated that by securing a 25% reduction of cross-sectional area of a softened mild steel tube by means of cold drawing and consequent work hardening, its tensile strength is increased by some 50%. By suitable adjustment of the reduction in area of the final draw, and of any heat treatment given before it, alloy steel tubes having tensile strengths up to around 60 ton/in$^2$ (930 N/mm$^2$) can be produced. Higher strengths than this (up to around 100 ton/in$^2$ (1560 N/mm$^2$)) can be obtained after the final draw by suitable heat treatment, quenching and/or tempering. A fully hardened carbon steel should of course be tempered to remove any resulting extreme brittleness.

*Welded pipe.* When welding pipe material formed into cylindrical shape, the edges can either overlap one another—*lap weld*—or can butt squarely against each other—*butt weld*. The only appreciable use today of lap welding is in the making of hydraulic lap weld pipes of large diameter (from about 18 in to 6 ft (450–1800 mm)), in which process the overlapping edges are heated to welding temperature and then squeezed together by hydraulically operated rollers.

*Butt-welded* pipe (BW) is produced from steel plate (*skelp*) of the correct size which has had its edges bevelled. It is heated to welding temperature and then drawn through dies of funnel shape. The dies form the plate into circular shape and the bevelled edges then meet squarely, are forced together and become welded. Finishing is carried out by a series of rolling operations to produce the required dimensions. The process may be continuous. Pipe up to some 6 in (150 mm) outside diameter and 36 ft (11 m) long can be produced.

*Electric resistance welded* (ERW) pipe and tubing of up to some 18 in (450 mm) diameter is made from steel strip which is formed cold on a number of pairs of forming rolls which gradually shape it into circular cross-section. It then passes between two circular welding electrodes connected to a supply of alternating current (at a frequency of some 120–350 Hz). The edges of the strip are forced together by a pressure roll and current flows across the seam, heating it to welding temperature, so making a continuous joint. Subsequent rolling and finishing operations remove any 'flash' and secure the required dimensions, possibly by cold drawing.

Modern developments include *high-frequency resistance welding* at some 450,000 Hz, and *induction welding* at some 10,000 Hz where the seam is heated by an inductor close to but not touching it.

The *electric fusion welding* (EFW) process is used to make pipe of from some 6 in to 48 in (150–1200 mm) diameter. The skelp is trimmed and rolled into cylindrical form with abutting edges, or large individual plates are pressed into circular shape; the longitudinal seam is then usually welded automatically by some method such as the submerged arc process (see 9.12). For thick plate a bead of welding may be run both outside and inside the pipe. Stainless steel EFW tubes are usually made using the tungsten inert-gas (TIG) process (see 9.13).

The *spiral weld* process of electric fusion welding (SFW) is now increasingly used for pipe over some 12 in (300 mm) diameter. Long, and if necessary continuous, lengths of steel strip are wound helically so that their edges abut along a spiral line. These edges then pass under a fixed welding head where they are continuously welded by any of the accepted methods. As diameters are not limited by the width of the available skelp, practically any size of pipe can be manufactured by this process.

## 4.3 Inspection and control during tube manufacture

An adequate inspection and control system must be in operation throughout the mills, etc. to ensure the effectiveness of manufacturing processes.

(a) Firstly it must be possible to ensure that the raw material selected for a particular type of tube is that actually used, and, in certain cases, that the identity of particular batches of material is maintained throughout the works. The various billets, blooms and hollows should be identified by stamped markings and tally cards from which details of material, batch number, release note, specification and condition, etc. are obtainable.

(b) The control system employed should check manufacturing operations, dimensions and identity of material. A simple control sometimes used as a rough check on steel tubes passing through the works is to *spark* test them by holding the end against a revolving grinding wheel. From an examination of the shape, size and colour of these sparks it is possible for a skilled operator to give an approximate estimate of the carbon content of the steel.

A further control employing spark testing, which is carried out on each length of tube, if required, is to check for the presence of various alloying elements. One comparatively simple method of doing this is to use an instrument (such as a Spekker steeloscope), which gives an immediate qualitative (not quantitative) indication of the presence of chromium, cobalt, copper, cadmium, manganese, molybdenum, nickel, tin, titanium, tungsten and vanadium, and can be used by a semi-skilled operator.

Briefly, an electric arc or spark is drawn from the tube under test, and an optical system inside the instrument spreads out this light into its constituent radiations. These spectral lines, the position of which are indicative of the materials present, are seen through the eyepiece. By previously checking the position of the lines of the constituents of a check piece of the alloy under examination, and comparing these with the results from the tube under test, the presence or otherwise of these constituents can be ascertained (see also 2.11).

Periodic laboratory tests of selected samples and of the effectiveness of the spark testing should be made, using normal wet analysis methods, or maybe a mass spectrometer method.

(c) An effective control of all heat treatment, hardening and tempering operations should exist, as it is of the utmost importance to the customer in ensuring the subsequent satisfactory usage of the tube. Regular checks should be made of the correct reading of thermocouples and other temperature measuring and recording instruments used in conjunction with the various furnaces. An error of less than 5°C can mean a ruined batch.

*Annealing* is carried out in order to bring steel to a very soft condition for subsequent severe manipulation. The process may take place in an open furnace, followed by slow cooling, or in sealed containers. Bright annealing is applied to tubes, possibly as a final operation in a furnace containing an inert atmosphere; a bright finish free from scale is then obtained. Annealing temperatures vary from around 750–1100°F (400–600°C) according to requirements.

*Normalizing* aims at restoring the normal structure of the material after it has been disturbed during, for instance, hot manipulative working. It relieves internal stresses and promotes uniform refinement of the grain. It is usually carried out at about 50–100°C above the upper critical temperature (i.e. at around 800–900°C for steel), followed by cooling in still air. If cooled quickly from this temperature, perhaps by quenching in oil or water, steel becomes *hardened* (or rather retains its hardness). This is due to the forcible retention of carbon in a martensitic structure, the transformation from austenite occurring during rapid cooling at temperatures well below the upper critical temperature.

Low-temperature *tempering* or *stress relieving* can be carried out after cold drawing, thus relieving 'work hardening' by increasing ductility without materially affecting tensile strength. Again, if hardened 'right out' the steel becomes much too brittle for practical purposes, and tempering is necessary; the steel is heated, allowed to cool to some specific temperature, and then quenched, so 'letting down' the extreme brittleness and degree of hardness to some suitable value.

(d) When inspecting seamless tube and the processes involved in its manufacture care must be taken to ensure that faults such as cavities, laminations, etc., which may be present in the base or centre of a cast ingot, are not allowed to spread into the wall of the bloom or into the finished tube. In general static, as distinct from rotary, piercing of cast ingots, combined with cropping off of the closed end of the bloom or hollow, reduces the incidence of such faults. However, insufficient cropping of the pipe end, or other reasons, may allow these faults to get through undetected. Concentric laminations will not show up during hydrostatic testing, and they may cause welding defects. Reliance for their detection may have to be placed on non-destructive testing methods.

## 4.4 Tests on tube during and after manufacture

Many different tests may be carried out both during and/or after manufacture, according to the requirements of the relevant specification and/or order. These tests can be performed on a small percentage of samples, or on all tubes; they may be either destructive tests on the samples or non-destructive tests on some or all of the tubes.

The destructive tests may include the usual mechanical tests for tensile strength, yield strength, percentage elongation and reduction of area, and also proof stress and Young's modulus of elasticity ($E$) if required (see 2.4).

The *tensile test* is a means of proving that the tensile strength on which working stresses have been calculated is adequate, and that ductility in the longitudinal direction is satisfactory. When a tube is made by drawing (in the longitudinal direction), all defects would not necessarily show up when tested in the longitudinal direction. Consequently a *flaring* or *expanding* test on the end of a tube is often specified. This causes elongation in a circumferential direction and illustrates the capacity of the tube to undergo expansion in a tube plate. Any critical longitudinal lines of weakness would also be shown up. In larger diameter tubes bend tests are carried out to show this property.

Flattening tests and proof bend tests are regularly carried out on tube samples. The flattening test enables a check to be kept on the degree of ductility of the material used, the flattened sample being examined to ascertain whether it satisfies the agreed standard. A typical flattening test on electric resistance welded tube is to flatten a sample to three times its nominal wall thickness with the weld at 90° to the direction of the applied force. Should any cracks or flaws appear they will cause rejection.

The proof bend test enables the permanent set of a tube to be determined, after it has been deflected by a calculated load applied at a point on the tube whilst it is supported as a beam at two other points.

The permanent set is generally measured by an attachment to the testing machine consisting of a plunger which moves downwards when the tube deflects. Attached to this plunger is a cord which moves a pointer over a graduated dial.

*Hardness tests* should be regularly carried out on the material as it passes through the various stages of manufacture and heat treatment, and also on the final product, to the requirements of the relevant specification. The indentation produced by the specified load under the specified conditions is measured and converted into the appropriate hardness number. Amongst the hardness testing machines regularly used are the Brinell, Vickers diamond pyramid, Rockwell and Firth's hardometer (see 2.5).

The hardness of small thin-walled tubes can be ascertained with reasonable accuracy by the use of Brinell pliers, a hand-operated instrument.

Hardness tests to check for localized areas of differing hardness may help to detect possible sources of trouble.

A Charpy V-notch impact test is sometimes required (see 2.6)

### 4.4.1 Detection of tube defects—non-destructive testing (NDT)

Defects such as cracks, laminations, seams, laps, tears, slivers and scabs will occur. Such defects, when parallel to the surface, are not so serious as those which are perpendicular or at a diagonal to it. Certain specifications lay down limits of acceptability for surface defects. For instance, such defects deeper than 5% of the nominal wall thickness may have to be removed by machining or grinding. Surface defects can be detected visually, or with the aid of non-destructive testing techniques. Defects hidden below the surface require the use of NDT techniques.

These techniques may be applied at various stages of tube manufacture, and are dealt with briefly here. Further information on NDT is given in Chapter 10.

### 4.4.2 Crack detection—magnetic materials

For tubes made of magnetic materials electromagnetic methods can be applied as a means of detecting cracks, flaws and other surface and slightly sub-surface defects (see 10.7).

In one method the tube under test is magnetized by placing it between the poles of an electromagnet so that the magnetic flux passes through it. Should any crack or discontinuity be present then a magnetic pole will be set up on both sides of it. The tube is then dipped into a detecting fluid consisting basically of paraffin containing finely divided iron filings. The magnetic flux between the two poles of any crack or flaw will then attract and retain some of the iron particles, and the paraffin, being of low viscosity, will ensure their penetration into the defect. On removal of the tube defects will be indicated by a line of iron particles.

After magnetic testing it is usually necessary to demagnetize the tube or component. This can be accomplished by inserting and withdrawing it into a coil of wire through which an alternating current is passed. A check with a compass needle will show the success of the operation. Demagnetization is most effectively carried out when the axis of the coil lies in an east-west direction.

### 4.4.3 Crack detection by dye penetrant

This method of detecting cracks and surface imperfections can be carried out on both magnetic and non-magnetic materials, and has come into increasing use owing to the development of penetrants more effective than the hot oil and chalk method on which it is based.

The tube is first thoroughly cleaned and degreased, allowing time for the solvent to evaporate from any cavities, etc. Then it is dipped or coated with a penetrating dye solution (which is coloured red). After an interval the surplus dye penetrant is wiped off the tube, and a developer fluid containing white absorbents is applied. The surface is now white, but any of the dye penetrant which has penetrated into cracks or imperfections is now gradually drawn out by the white absorbent by capillary action and leaves a red stain, precisely indicating the defect.

### 4.4.4 Crack detection by fluorescent compound

This method is somewhat similar to the one previously described. After adequate cleaning and/or degreasing the tube is suitably coated with a chemical compound, containing a fluorescent material, which is able to penetrate any surface imperfections. After an interval the compound is wiped from the tube, which is then taken to a screened booth or a dark room and viewed under an ultra-violet lamp (a 'black-light' filter is used). Any of the fluorescent compound which has been retained in any surface cracks or defects will then show up brilliantly. As with the dye penetrant method, a developer can be used to enhance the effect. For further information on liquid penetrant inspection see 10.8.

### 4.4.5  Radiographic inspection

Radiography, using either X-rays or gamma rays, may be used to detect defects beneath the surface of a tube, and is sometimes called for by a particular specification or order. The result can be recorded on a photographic film, or seen momentarily on a screen. The techniques employed, the interpretation of radiographs and acceptance standards are described in more detail in 10.2–10.5. In particular the welding of pipe joints often requires radiographic examination. General recommendations concerning this are given in BS 2600 and in BS 2910 in connection with circumferential butt joints in steel pipes.

### 4.4.6  Eddy current testing

Sometimes hidden defects will occur in tubes, and as they do not create an immediate leak the hydraulic pressure test may not find them. Fig. 4.1 is representative of a bad fault in the inside wall of a non-ferrous tube which would pass the normal hydraulic test, but could lead to early failure in service.

One method of finding such faults is by *eddy current testing* (see Fig. 4.2 for a defect so found), and this can if necessary be used for continuous inspection on a production line. The tube is arranged so that it passes through a pair of solenoids forming part of an a.c. bridge circuit. Induced eddy currents will flow circumferentially around the tube wall. Initially the bridge is balanced with a good tube in position, the current then being the same in each coil. The passage of a discontinuous fault through one of the coils will then reduce the current flowing through it and unbalance the bridge. This can be arranged to sound an alarm or even to reject the tube (or section) automatically. Alternatively the defect can be displayed on a cathode-ray tube. It should be noted that continuous defects (such as die lines) will not unbalance the bridge, but these, if on the surface, can readily be seen by visual inspection. Also a high-frequency current will tend to restrict its flow to the outer surface of the tube wall, so a frequency to ensure adequate penetration must be chosen.

Even so the sensitivity of the test gradually decreases with the depth of

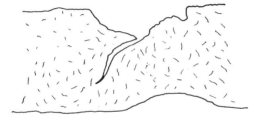

Fig. 4.1   Defect in copper tube wall which passed 500 lb/in² hydraulic test.

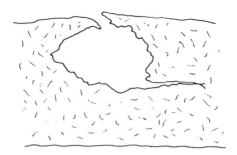

Fig. 4.2   Defect in brass tube wall which passed 1000 lb/in² hydraulic test, found by eddy current test.

the defect from the outer surface, and consequently the size of the defect which can be detected depends on tube diameter and thickness, and also its metallurgical condition. The test can however be adapted to automation and rapid and continuous testing arrangements can be developed. Testing speeds of at least 3 ft/s (1 m/s) can now be reached.

*4.4.7 Ultrasonic testing*

In addition to the methods already described, cracks, laminations and other defects in tubes can be found by ultrasonic methods. Ultrasonics are particularly useful in detecting faults in thick-walled tubes which are hidden below the surface, and which might be difficult to find by, say, the eddy current method. The speed of testing is however rather slower than the eddy current method, and the equipment required is perhaps more complex and temperamental; in some cases it can be used in lieu of expensive radiographic tests. Further information will be found in 10.6 but, briefly, ultrasonic waves (of a frequency above that of sound waves and therefore inaudible) are generated by suitable means and propagated through the material under test. When they strike the natural boundary surface of the material an echoing wave is reflected back and can be received and displayed on a cathode ray tube. Since the speed of the wave in a given material is constant it follows that the time interval between the transmission and echo signals is a measure of the distance travelled, and hence, for instance, of the thickness of the tube. *An echo is also reflected back if the wave strikes any discontinuity or fault within the material.* Hence, by watching the cathode-ray tube display whilst a probe is moved along the tube, any signal received between the transmission and boundary echo will indicate the presence and location of a fault, and can if required be arranged to operate a warning system.

It may be convenient to carry out this method of flaw detection by immersing the tube in a tank of water and applying the instrument through this.

It will be evident that ultrasonics can be used to measure the thickness of tube, and that if desired this can be done on a continuous flow basis. This is particularly useful where tubes of constant outside diameter may have, either intentionally or otherwise, a wall thickness which is tapered or stepped or variable. Thickness testing is not usually carried out by immersing the tube but by transmitting the ultrasonic waves directly into the material, through a thin layer of oil for contact purposes.

### 4.4.8 Reference standards for non-destructive testing of tubes

BS 3889 and BS 6072 deal with methods for non-destructive testing of pipes and tubes especially those suitable for automated processes. Reference standards for ultrasonic and eddy current testing are laid down against which actual tube defects can be compared and calibrated. Such standards, prepared from a length of the particular tube to be inspected, have notches (on both inner and outer surfaces) and/or holes machined in them, and the test equipment is adjusted so that readily distinguishable individual indications are obtained from each. Indications equal to or greater than the smallest of these are considered to represent rejectionable imperfections.

The equipment should be checked against the appropriate standard immediately prior to the commencement of inspection, and at intervals generally not exceeding two hours during continuous operation, and recalibrated whenever the type of tube is changed or any adjustment is made.

BS 3889: Part 1 gives four methods of automatic ultrasonic testing of wrought steel tubes which are now widely used. Any one or a combination of more than one method may be employed. It is necessary to relate the signals received from any imperfections in the tube passing through under examination to the signals from the reference standards that indicate the level of acceptance. Any suspect portion of tube may set off an audio or visual alarm, or perhaps operate a marking sorting or recording device. Any suspect length may be re-checked, investigated and perhaps dressed to see if it can be considered acceptable.

Artificial calibration standards, in general, are unsatisfactory for penetrant and magnetic particle testing; it is necessary to distinguish between relevant indications from imperfections and non-relevant indications arising from other causes.

### 4.4.9 Pressure testing of pipework

A pressure test proves a tube to be capable of withstanding high pressures, and should detect any wall thinning, leakage or manufacturing defects.

Hydraulic pressure tests are normally carried out on many types of pipe or tube to meet the requirements of the relevant British Standard or other specification. In some cases representative samples are tested; in others each pipe must be so checked. The pressure specified is usually some $1\frac{1}{2}$–2 times the normal working pressure and the test is, generally speaking, adequate for most purposes, although small leaks are difficult to observe. If it is important to eliminate existing small leaks than some more refined testing technique should be adopted (see Chapter 11).

Leakage of the test rig sealing arrangements at the tube ends may mask a defect here, and should be watched. The design of an efficient and effective leak-tight fitting for sealing the ends, especially at very high pressures, is somewhat difficult. In fact for some high-pressure tests a screwed joint between the tube under test and the test equipment may be necessary in order to make a satisfactory joint. This of course is undesirable and time-consuming, and very expensive if a hydraulic test is required on all tubes.

End fittings which expand inside the tube and seal the joints by means of a neoprene or other suitable sealing ring are shown in Fig. 4.3. They are quickly and easily applied and removed, and have given good results at pressures up to some 10,000 lb/in$^2$ (70 N/mm$^2$). Make-shift sealing arrangements are a source of considerable trouble and waste valuable inspection time; they should be avoided.

Hydrostatic tests are required at the mill on every length of API pipe, etc., the pressure being held for a minimum of 5–10 seconds. Welded pipe is generally required to be struck near the weld while under pressure, using a 2 lb hammer—any leaks being noted. Threaded pipe made up 'power-tight' should not leak, but if made up 'handling-tight' minor leakage at the joint may be disregarded.

Occasionally a specification or order may require a hydraulic strength test to be carried out to destruction in order to calculate or assess the strength of the pipe material. The tube or pipe is connected up to a hydraulic pressure system in a suitable location and the pressure is gradually increased until bursting occurs. This pressure is noted, and the strength of the pipe may be calculated from an appropriate formula.

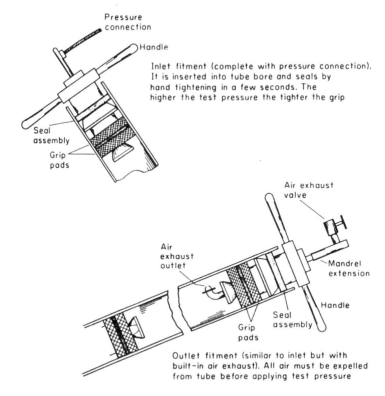

**Fig. 4.3 Hydrostatic test equipment for tube pressure testing.** (*High Pressure Components Ltd.*)

Air pressure tests are sometimes specified for tubes. In such cases the safety aspect should receive full consideration, and the practices and procedures described in 3.20 (v), for pressure vessels would be generally applicable.

Pressure and bursting tests and apparatus somewhat similar in principle to that described above are given in BS 4728 for thermoplastics pipe and in BS 486 for asbestos-cement pipe.

### 4.4.10 Final inspection of tubes

If all the various checks and tests previously described have been systematically carried out then the final inspection can proceed with confidence.

This consists essentially of a close and critical visual examination and dimensional check of the tubes together with a check that any special requirements particular to the order have been satisfactorily dealt with. Any surface defects not detected, or detectable, by the methods in use may become apparent, and will have to be dealt with appropriately. An intrascope examination of the bore may be necessary. Identification markings, stamping, etc., and any colour banding required to identify the material should be checked and correlated with any documentation. In some cases metal die stamping of the tubes may set up incipient cracks or damage and should be avoided; stencil marking or etching by electric pencil may be used in lieu. Alternatively, stamping can be carried out prior to hot-forming or final heat treatment.

Should any protective treatment have been specified, then this must be checked, and will probably involve the checking of process controls. Finally it might be necessary to check packing arrangements, and any oiling and wrapping of the tubes which may be required.

### 4.5 Tube failures

In spite of the inspection and testing procedures carried out, tubes do occasionally fail in service, usually on account of some inherent defect in the material principally of a metallurgical origin. The cause would appear to lie in some faulty or inadequate processing somewhere along the line, and points the way to more effective process control. Some illustrations of tube defects leading to failure are given in Figs. 4.4–4.8 by courtesy of the National and Vulcan Engineering Insurance Group.

Some modes of failure applicable to tubes and weldments are mentioned in 13.4.

Considerable controversy exists as to the best type of tube. Seamless tube is generally considered to be superior to the corresponding size of jointed tube. However, it should be borne in mind that the longitudinal weld, when properly made and subject to rigorous quality control, inspection and testing techniques, is not necessarily a source of weakness. The wall thickness of welded pipe can be more carefully controlled, and freedom from surface defects on the inside can be more readily assured by inspection and the method of manufacture than is the case with seamless tube. Consequently for some hazardous plants, such as nuclear power instal-lations, some authorities, after experience, have expressed a preference for welded tube. For instance, faults like those shown in Figs. 4.1, 4.2 and 4.5 should not occur in welded tube.

### 4.6 Piping codes and standards

A large number of organizations, British, American and foreign, issue codes and specifications applicable to pipes and pipework, tubes, fittings, etc.

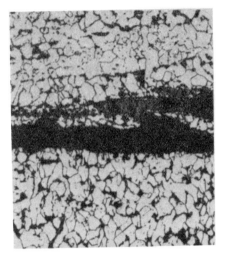

**Fig. 4.4 Photomicrograph of a lamination in the apparently sound part of a boiler tube which failed in service.** Such a defect may extend for some distance along a tube, and may or may not break out into the surface of the bore. In this case local overheating due to the insulative effect of corrosion products along the lamination caused a break-out (× 250).
(*National and Vulcan Engineering Insurance Group.*)

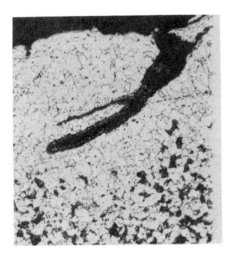

**Fig. 4.5 Photomicrograph of a lap defect within a decarburized zone in a 16 in alloy steel seamless pipe, sectioned at the surface within the decarburized zone.** The surfaces of the crack have been oxidized by subsequent heat treatment (× 250). This fault was found on the bend test, but could easily have been missed. Eddy current testing would have found it.
(*National and Vulcan Engineering Insurance Group.*)

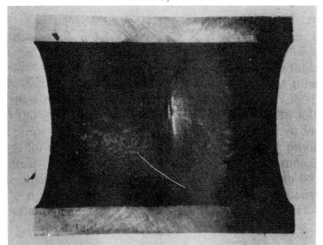

**Fig. 4.6   Photograph of a 'wrinkle' in a boiler tube bore, which failed when the final pressure test was being applied.** This test was a prolonged one—the normal test would not have found it.
(*National and Vulcan Engineering Insurance Group.*)

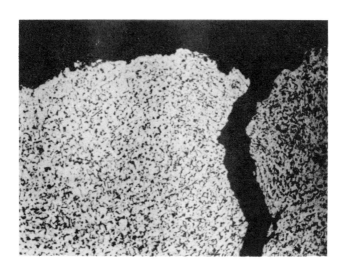

**Fig. 4.7   Photomicrograph of the crack section of Fig. 4.6, showing the 'kink' on the banded structure of the tube wall, indicating the action of some high external forces exerted on the tube** ($\times$ 250).
(*National and Vulcan Engineering Insurance Group.*)

**Fig. 4.8 Microstructure of the bore of a 16 in steel tube, showing the line of oxide inclusions in a band of purer iron running along the lap weld junction** (failed in service) ($\times$ 50).
(*National and Vulcan Engineering Insurance Group.*)

British requirements are generally covered by British Standards and Codes of Practice, supplemented if necessary by the specifications of the ordering authority or classification society, and sometimes by American specifications, particularly for petroleum applications.

American requirements are covered in part by specifications and codes issued by the American National Standards Institute (ANSI, formerly ASA), usually after being sponsored by such bodies as ASME and ASTM. In addition other specifications (not approved as ANSI Standards) published by these two bodies, and by other organizations such as the American Waterworks Association (AWWA), the American Petroleum Institute (API), the American Gas Association (AGA), the Society of Automotive Engineers (SAE), the Pipe Fabrication Institute (PFI), the Manufacturers Standardization Society of the Valve and Fittings Industry (MSS), the Instrument Society of America (ISA), the General Services Administration (GSA), Department of Commerce and military departments of the Federal Government are widely used. In Europe, and internationally, ISO Standards may be used.

Increasingly British standards are being issued based on, similar to, or identical with ISO standards. In the latter case they are published with dual-numbering.

Where an ISO standard exists agreeing to some extent with a British standard it is listed in the BSI catalogue against the appropriate BS entry with a symbol indicating the extent of agreement (see also 1.9).

Many of these standards, codes, etc. will be encountered by the inspector and contain details regarding inspection and testing.

British Standards applicable to ferrous pipework and ferrous and steel alloy tubes are listed in Tables 4.1 and 4.2. Some pipe and tube specifications for other materials are included in Table 4.3. In some cases an *approximately* similar American or ISO specification has been given. A selection of American piping standards is given in Table 4.4.

**TABLE 4.1**

*British standard pipe and tube specifications (steel)*

| BS No. | Description | Similar American specification |
|---|---|---|
| 10 | Flanges and bolting for pipes, valves and fittings (obsolescent)<br>(Tables of working pressures (and temperatures), materials, dimensions, tests, etc., for use up to 2800 lb/in$^2$ and temperatures from $-200°C$ to $524°C$ ($-328°F$ to $975°F$))<br>Also covers cast iron and copper alloys | ANSI B 16.5 |
| 21 | Pipe threads for tubes and fittings where pressure-tight joints are made on the threads<br>(Deals with sizes from $\frac{1}{16}$ to 6 in and their gauging; applies to all materials) | |
| 534 | Steel pipes and specials for water, and sewage (seamless and welded from some 60·3 to 2820 mm<br>Hydraulic tests and coating and lining requirements included) | ANSI B 36.10 |
| 778 | Steel pipes and joints for hydraulic purposes<br>(Up to 1500, 1500–2500 and 2500–5000 lb/in$^2$; up to 6000 lb/in$^2$ for seamless pipes with welding neck flanges) (obsolescent) | |
| 806 | Ferrous pipes and piping installations for and in connection with land boilers: Design and construction for<br>(a) Pressures exceeding 3·5 bar<br>(b) Over (250 mm) bore up to 3·5 bar | |
| 879 | Steel tubes for water-well casing | |
| 1387 | Steel tubes and tubulars suitable for screwing to BS 21 pipe threads<br>(Three thicknesses: light (brown); medium (blue); heavy (red)) | |

**TABLE 4.1** *continued*

| BS No. | Description | Similar American specification |
|---|---|---|
| 1560 | Part 1: Steel pipe flanges and flanged fittings (nominal sizes $\frac{1}{2}$ in to 24 in) for the petroleum industry (Classes 150–2500) <br> Part 2: Metric units | ANSI B 16.5 |
| 1600 | Dimensions of steel pipe for the petroleum industry <br> Part 1: Imperial units <br> Part 2: Metric units | Maintains identity with ANSI B 36.10 and B 36.19. Screw threads to API Std 5B or ANSI B 2.1 |
| 1864 | Stainless steel milk pipes and fittings (recessed ring joint type) | |
| 3059 | Steel boiler and superheater tubes | |
| 3063 | Dimensions of gaskets for pipe flanges (Used with BS 10, 1770 and 2035) | |
| 3293 | Carbon steel pipe flanges (over 24 in) for the petroleum industry (for Classes 150, 300, 400 and 600) | ANSI B 16 |
| 3351 | Piping systems for petroleum refineries and petrochemical plants (A design installation and testing standard) | ANSI B31.3–4 |
| 3581 | Stainless steel cone joint pipe fittings | |
| 3600 | Dimensions and masses per unit length of welded and seamless steel pipes and tubes for pressure purposes | |
| 3601 | Steel pipes and tubes for pressure purposes. Carbon steel: with specified room temperature properties | ASTM A 53 |
| 3602 | Steel pipes and tubes for pressure purposes. Carbon and carbon manganese steel: elevated temperature properties | ASTM A 106, 155, 520 |
| 3603 | Steel pipes and tubes for pressure purposes. Carbon and alloy steel: low-temperature duties | ASTM A 333 |
| 3604 | Steel pipes and tubes for pressure purposes ferric-alloy steel: elevated temperature properties | |
| 3605 | Steel pipes and tubes for pressure purposes. <br><br> Austenitic stainless steel | ASTM A 358, 376, 420 <br> ANSI B 36.19 |
| 3606 | Steel tubes for heat exchangers | |
| 3889 | Methods for non-destructive testing of pipes and tubes | |
| 3974 | Pipe supports | |

**TABLE 4.1** *concluded*

| BS No. | Description | Similar American specification |
|---|---|---|
| 4368 | Carbon and stainless steel compression couplings for tubes | |
| 4504 | Flanges and bolting for pipes, valves and fittings. Metric Series | Based on European ISA/DIN details |
| 4515 | Process welding of steel pipelines on land and offshore | API 1104 |
| 4534 | Weldable chromium–nickel centrifugally cast steel tubes (for high-temperature and pressure applications) | ASTM A 296, 297, 251, 451 |
| 4882 | Bolting for flanges and pressure containing purposes (for temperatures from $-250°$ to $1750°C$) | ANSI B 31.3 Appendix C |
| 6129 | Code of Practice: Selection and application of bellows expansion joints for use in pressure systems. Part 1. Metallic | |
| 6323 | Seamless and welded steel tubes for mechanical automobile and general engineering purposes | |
| | (8 parts cover chemical composition, mechanical properties including drift expanding test for all types of tube) | |
| CP 2010 | (now BS 8010) Code of practice for pipelines: — Part 2 steel | ANSI B 31 |
| BS Aircraft Series T (for Tubes) includes: | | |
| 3 T100 | Inspection and testing procedure for steel tubes | |

**TABLE 4.2**
*British standard cast and wrought iron pipes*

| BS No. | Description | Similar American specification |
|---|---|---|
| 78 | Cast iron spigot and socket pipes (vertically cast) and spigot and socket fittings | ANSI A21.23 |
| |    Part 1: Pipes (withdrawn) ⎫ See BS 4622 for | |
| |    Part 2: Fittings       ⎬ metric version | |
| | (Covers pipe 3–48 in diameter in Grades A, B, C and D; details dimensions and weights, test | |

**TABLE 4.2** *concluded*

| BS No. | Description | Similar American specification |
|---|---|---|
| | and coating requirements and test facilities) | |
| 437 | Cast iron spigot and socket drain pipes | |
| 1211 | Centrifugally cast (spun) iron pressure pipes for water, gas and sewage (Details 3 classes:     B—400 ft head test pressure     C—600 ft head test pressure     D—800 ft head test pressure Corresponds to BS 78) | ANSI A 21.6–9 ASTM A 377 |
| 2035 | Cast iron flanged pipes and flanged fittings (Covers sizes 2–48 in diameter conforming to BS 10 and details quality, tolerances, hydraulic testing and inspection) | ANSI B 16.1, B 16.2 |
| 4622 | Grey iron pipes and fittings | |
| 4772 | Ductile iron pipes and fittings | |
| 8010 | Code of Practice for Pipelines: Part 2 Sect. 2.1/Ductile iron | |

**TABLE 4.3**

*Some pipe and tube specifications in materials other than steel*

| BS No. | Description | Similar American specification |
|---|---|---|
| 65 | Vitrified clay pipes fittings | ASTM C13 |
| 486 | Asbestos-cement pressure pipe | ASTM C296 |
| 864 | Capillary and compression tube fittings of copper and copper alloy. (Gives requirements for satisfactory installation) | |
| 1306 | Copper and copper alloy pressure piping systems | |
| 1471 | Wrought aluminium and aluminium alloys for general engineering purposes. Drawn tube (Details chemical composition, mechanical properties, tolerances, methods of test, and gives notes on heat treatment) | ASTM B 210 |

**TABLE 4.3** *concluded*

| BS No. | Description | Similar American specification |
|---|---|---|
| 1474 | Wrought aluminium and aluminium alloys for general engineering purposes. Extruded round tube and hollow sections | ASTM B 221, 241 |
| 2598 | Glass plant pipeline and fittings | |
| 2760 | Pitch-impregnated fibre pipes and fittings for below and above ground drainage | ASTM D 1861 |
| 2871 | Copper and copper alloys. Tubes | |
| 2997 | Aluminium rainwater goods | |
| 3656 | Asbestos-cement pipes and fittings for sewerage and drainage | |
| 4625 | Prestressed concrete pressure pipes (including fittings) | |
| 5222 | Aluminium piping systems | ASTM B 345 |
| 5911 | Precast concrete pipes and fittings for drainage and sewerage. | ASTM C 76, 361 |
| 5927 | Guide for laying asbestos-cement pipelines | |
| 8010 (formerly CP 2010) | Pipelines  Part 4 Asbestos-cement  Part 5 Prestressed concrete | |

## 4.6.1 Steel tubes

Details of sizes (diameters, thicknesses and mass per unit length) for steel tubes for pressure purposes are tabulated in BS 3600 (now only in metric sizes) and have been selected from ISO specifications. Certain of these (known by ISO as series I diameters) are those for which all components and accessories have been standardized and apply to the BS 3601–3605 series and as far as possible to other fully metricated standards.

Details of manufacture, steel grades and mechanical and chemical properties, inspection and test etc. are given in BS 3601. The method of manufacture is designated as follows: butt welded (BW), electric resistance and induction welded (ERW), seamless (S) and submerged arc welded (SAW). Other methods of manufacture, e.g. hot finished seamless (HFS), cold finished seamless (CFS) and cold finished electric resistance welded and induction welded (CEW) are included in the series BS 3602–6. Dimensions for butt-welded tubes and for tubes suitable for screwing to BS 21 pipe threads are given in BS 1387. The requirements for butt welded tubes in BS 3601 are comparable to those for plain end tubes given in BS 1387. Tubes complying with the requirements of BS 3601/2 may be supplied to the dimensions given in BS 1600 Part 2. BS 3601 specifies mechanical properties only at room temperature. BS 3602, 4, 5 and 6 cover tubes suitable for use at elevated temperatures and specify proof stress and long-term stress-rupture values at these temperatures. Amongst the tests required are: visual inspection, hydraulic test, tensile test to BS 18 (tensile strength $R_m$, upper/lower yield stress $R_{eH}/R_{eL}$ or proof stress $R_p$ and elongation A), and bend test. BS 3603, dealing with steel tubes for use at low temperatures, gives details of impact properties and tests.

Other standards to which BS 3601 can apply are BS 534, 806, 879 and 3351. BS 3602 introduced two categories of test, category 1 requiring non-destructive acceptance testing (normally ultrasonic), whilst category 2 can use eddy current testing as an alternative to hydraulic testing. These two categories are included in BS 3059 Part 2, whilst Part 1 also permits the use of eddy current testing as an alternative to the hydraulic test for leak tightness. Part 2 includes proof stress values at elevated temperatures for the various grades of steels specified, and methods of verifying them (e.g. testing to BS 3920). Stress-rupture values of stress for various rupture times at various elevated temperatures up to 760°C are also given. All this necessitates comprehensive testing and inspection work and supervision of manufacture, heat treatment and installation.

*Boiler and superheater tubes* are normally manufactured to BS 3059 which contains requirements for a series of tubes of different methods of manufacture and material, Part 1 covering carbon (up to 400°C), and Part 2 for carbon manganese, alloy and austenitic steels, the latter available for use at temperatures up to as high as some 700°C. The relevant design aspects are covered by BS 1113.

*Steam pipework* is generally supplied to BS 3602, 3604 and 3605 and feed pipes to BS 3601 and 3602 and heat exchangers to BS 3606, the design aspects being covered by BS 806, 1113 or 5500 as relevant. Temperatures up to some 720°C are catered for. Piping to American Standards may be used subject to certain provisos, e.g. documentary or test evidence of suitability. Pipes for the chemical and petroleum industries may also be supplied to these British Standards (or the equivalent American Standards) although the design standard may be BS 3351. Pressures up to 3000 atmospheres may be used, but, unlike steam pipework, high-pressure and high-temperature properties are rarely required simultaneously.

Pressure-temperature design stress ratings for each class of pipe, fitting, material, etc. may be tabulated in specifications (e.g. BS 3351 and 5500).

*BS 534 for steel pipes and specials* for water and sewage (but not now for gas) covers seamless and welded pipes from 60·3 mm to 2220 mm outside diameter and includes protection against the corrosive action of the surrounding medium or conveyed fluid. Sizes, etc. are selected from the Table in BS 3600 and are given in an appendix together with the hydraulic test pressures required. The grades of steel to be used are specified in BS 3601. Jointing can be by butt welding, welded sleeve joints, couplings or flanges, or bitumen lined pipes with screwed and coupled joints. Other forms of protection include internal concrete and mortar, external coal tar and plastics (see Chapter 5).

Hydraulic testing is specified to be in accordance with BS 3601 and all welds which have not previously been hydraulically tested must be tested by a penetrant oil or other NDT method (see Chapter 10) to ensure leak tightness.

The hydraulic test pressures stated in BS 534 are works inspection test pressures in accordance with BS 3601 and are not intended as a basis for design and do not necessarily have any direct relationship with working pressures (pipework etc. should withstand $1\frac{1}{2}$ times the maximum working pressure). BS 3601 states that for butt-welded tubes the test pressure should be 50 bar. For other forms of welding (ERW, S and SAW) it should be calculated from the following formula (except it should not normally exceed 70 bar, or for BS 3602 pipe 140 bar).

$$P = \frac{20Sa}{D}$$

where $P$ = test pressure (bar)

$D$ = outside pipe diam. (mm)

$a$ = pipe thickness (mm)

$S$ = stress (N/mm$^2$) in material (taken as 80% of specified minimum yield strength at room temperature)

This test pressure should be maintained sufficiently long for proof and inspection. The same formula is used to calculate the hydraulic leak tightness test required by BS 3059 (except that the maximum test pressure applied should not normally exceed 70 bar or 140 bar for Part 1 and Part 2 of the specification respectively). An eddy current test can be applied in lieu of this hydraulic test.

*BS 806 Ferrous piping installations for and in connection with land boilers* deals with the design and construction, inspection and testing of ferrous pipework connecting land boilers to engines, turbines or industrial plant and any auxiliary pipework and fittings in connection therewith. It deals with carbon steel pipework designed for use up to 480°C, alloy steels up to some 600°C, and austenitic steels up to some 700°C. It does not apply to boilers, superheaters, etc. and their integral piping, the design standards for which are BS 1113 and BS 2790. It applies to pipes, etc. of any bore at pressures exceeding 3·5 bar (0·35 N/mm² or 50 psig), and to pipes over 250 mm (10 in) bore for steam pressures up to and including 3·5 bar. The materials and standard sizes of steel pipe applicable to this standard are covered by BS 1503 and BS 1504, and flanges and bolting by BS 10, 1560, 4504 and 4882. The temperature and pressure limits within which pipes, etc. of various grades of steel may be used and their maximum design stress values (N/mm²) are tabulated, together with details of the derivation of these design stress values (in a somewhat similar manner to that given in BS 1113 and 5500) (see 3.4). Similarly the minimum thickness of straight pipes can be calculated from the formula

$$ t = \frac{pD}{2fe + p} $$

where $e$ is a factor depending upon the method of manufacture of the pipe, being 1·0 for seamless pipe and 1·0, 0·95 or 0·9 for various types of welded and NDT tested pipe. Where the tabulated design stress values ($f$) are time-dependent a design lifetime (from 100,000 to 250,000 hours) must be agreed. No component should remain in service after its operational hours have exceeded its design lifetime unless a 'fitness-for-continued-service' assessment has been carried out (see PD 6510 and 3.4.2(a); also 13.9).

When handling and manipulating alloy steel pipes cold it is essential to ensure that they are not subject to impact or hammer blows likely to cause local damage. Inspection or identification marks *must not* be stamped on the body of the pipe. They may be stamped on end faces of plain end pipes or rims of flanges, but preferably on identification plates attached to the pipes. Alternatively they may be vibro-etched or painted on with suitable paint.

Similarly during fabrication care should be taken to avoid the formation of notches or other sharp changes of contour on the pipes as these are likely to cause stress concentrations. Contamination of the surface of pipes by corrosive substances, etc. and particularly by sulphur and non-ferrous metals should be avoided.

Subject to certain exceptions class I welding (to BS 1821, BS 2633 and BS 4677) must be used for steam services exceeding 17 bar or 220°C, and class II welding (to BS 2640 and BS 2971) for services below. Welding procedures are somewhat similar to those described in 3.4.6–3.9).

Jointing of pipes may be carried out by flanges and bolting to BS 4504 or BS 1560: Part 2, or to BS 10 (for flanges with inch dimensions). Screwed joints should not be used where severe erosion, corrosion, shock or fatigue is expected. In other cases they may be permitted, but the specification gives limitations including those on temperature and pressure; tapered threads may have to be used.

*Hydraulic testing.* Unless previously tested to an equal or greater pressure (and subject to certain other provisos) all pipework and fittings must be tested before or after erection by a hydraulic pressure sustained for some 10–25 minutes. This pressure ($p$) is calculated from the equation

$$p = \frac{0.83 p R_e}{f}$$

where $p$ is the design pressure (N/mm$^2$), $R_e$ is the specified minimum yield stress (N/mm$^2$) and $f$ is the maximum permissible design stress (N/mm$^2$). Where this test has been carried out before erection and the welded joints are of class II (BS 2640 and 2971) construction, the erected system should be tested hydraulically at a pressure of 1.5 times the design pressure, or the pressure calculated as above, whichever is the less.

Alternatively if all butt and branch-welded joints (class II) have been tested by NDT methods (radiographic, ultrasonic as appropriate) the final hydraulic test may be waived.

In general all class I welded joints must additionally be tested by NDT methods, either 100% for diameters of over 170 mm and thicknesses of and over 25 mm or 10% tested below these figures.

### 4.6.2 American pipe standards and their relationship to UK practice

In American practice pipes and fittings etc. (see Table 4.4) are made in seven different pressure classes: 150, 300, 400, 600, 900, 1500 and 2500 pound (lb/in$^2$) generally in accordance with the American Steel Flange Standard (ANSI B 16.5). The temperature-pressure ratings conform to the tables listed in ANSI B.16.5 and the American Petroleum Institute Standard API No. 600. Thus a Class 600 carbon steel fitting may be used at 600 lb/in$^2$ gauge at a temperature of up to 850°F, and at lower pressures up to 1000°F (when the permitted pressure is 170 lb/in$^2$), and at higher pressures at lower temperatures (e.g. at 1440 lb/in$^2$ at 100°F).

For temperatures from 100°F down to $-20$°F the pressure ratings are the same as that for 100°F. Below $-20$°F steels with suitable impact strengths must be used.

It seems that in the USA pipe and tubing are not necessarily the same (see 4.1). Tubing is specified by its outside diameter. Thus 4 in tubing is 4 in outside diameter whilst 4 in pipe is 4.5 in outside diameter. Pipes of all wall thicknesses are designated by their nominal pipe size. For pipe sizes 14 in and larger the outside diameter corresponds with the nominal pipe size. For pipe sizes 12 in and smaller the nominal pipe size approximates to, but does not equal, the inside diameter of the standard weight size. Over many years wall thicknesses (and therefore weights) of pipe have been known as standard (S), extra strong (XS) and double extra strong (XXS). These wall

**TABLE 4.4**

*Some American pipe standards*

| Specification No. | Description |
|---|---|
| ANSI A 21 series | Cast iron pipe and fittings |
| A 40 series | Soil pipe |
| (includes A 40.8) | Plumbing code |
| B 16 series | Pipe flanges and fittings |
| B 31 series | Code for pressure piping (see 4.6.2) |
| B 36 series | Steel pipe |
| API Std 5A | Casing, tubing and drill pipe |
| 5AC | Grade C-75 casing and tubing |
| 5AX | High-strength casing and tubing |
| 5B | Threading, gauging and thread inspection of casing, tubing and line pipe threads |
| 5L | Line pipe |
| 5LS | Spiral weld line pipe |
| 5LX | High test line pipe |
| 1104 | Field welding of pipelines |
| RP 1102 | Recommended practice for liquid petroleum pipelines crossing railroad and highways |
| RP 1107 | Recommended pipeline maintenance welding practices |
| RP 1109 | Recommended practice for marking liquid petroleum pipeline facilities |
| RP 1110 | Recommended practice for pressure testing of liquid petroleum pipelines |
| AWWA C 201 | Fabricated electrically welded steel water pipe |
| PFI ES 1–11 | A series of specifications dealing with preparation, machining, welding, testing, identification, etc. of piping |
| ES(M)8–12 | |
| ASTM various Nos. (including A 53, 106, 134, 155, 161, 199, 200, 203, 312, 333–5, 358, 423 and 450) | Steel piping and tube specifications in a variety of materials and methods of manufacture, many of which have been adopted as ANSI Standards in the B 36 series |
| A 72 | Wrought iron pipe (welded) |
| A 419 | Wrought iron pipe (electric fusion welded) (16 in and over) |
| A 377 | Cast iron pressure pipe (refers to ANSI A 21 series) |

TABLE 4.4 *concluded*

| Specification No. | Description |
|---|---|
| **ASTM plastic pipe standards** | |
| D 1180 | Bursting strength of round rigid plastic tubing |
| D 1503 | CAB pipe—iron pipe size (IPS) |
| D 1527 | Extruded ABS plastic pipe, dimensions of (IPS) |
| D 1598 | Time-to-failure of plastic pipe under long-term hydrostatic pressure |
| D 1599 | Short-time rupture strength of thermoplastic pipe, tubing and fittings |
| D 1785 | Rigid PVC plastic pipe, schedules 40, 80 and 120 |
| D 2104 | Polyethylene plastic pipe |
| D 2282 | ABS plastic pipe |
| D 2846 | Chlorinated PVC pipe (for use up to 82°C) |
| D 2855 | Recommended practice for making solvent cemented joints with PVC pipes and fittings |
| **Society of Automotive Engineers tube specifications** | |
| J 524 | Seamless low-carbon steel tubing for bending and flaring |
| J 525 | ERW low-carbon steel tubing, annealed for bending and flaring (pressure tube for hydraulic line service) |

thicknesses have been used for low, medium and high pressure applications respectively, and their designations are still specified for some pipe sizes. However, it has been common practice for many years to use a Schedule number when specifying pipe. Thus in pipe sizes $\frac{1}{8}$ in to 10 in nominal ANSI Schedule 40 thicknesses are identical to standard weight (S) pipe; in pipe sizes $\frac{1}{8}$ in to 8 in nominal Schedule 80 is identical to XS; and Schedule 160 falls between XS and XXS. In larger sizes the actual thickness may be given. There is no fixed relationship between ANSI B 16.5 pressure classes and pipe schedules.

*Derivation of Schedule Numbers.* Originally the schedule number system was developed solely for the purpose of determining a rational set of wall thicknesses reasonably consistent with design principles and formulae. Given here for record purposes only the formula used by the original drafting committee was:

$$t = \left( \frac{p}{S} \times \frac{D}{1 \cdot 75} \right) + 0 \cdot 1$$

where $p$ = internal pressure (lb/in$^2$)
  $S$ = allowable fibre stress (lb/in$^2$)
  $D$ = outside diameter (in)
  $t$ = wall thickness (in)

and $1000 \times \dfrac{p}{S}$ represented the schedule number

Analysis showed that up to 12 in size common usage was largely centred on wall thicknesses corresponding to definite pressure–stress ratios which could be expressed simply as 40, 80, 120 and 160.

For pipes larger than 12 in wall thicknesses were selected with schedules equalling 60, 100 and 140.

From the light wall outside diameter sizes and from certain 8, 10 and 12 in standard pipes used in larger quantities three additional schedules were set up for lower pressures. The formula was not applied to sizes smaller than 1 in.

Calculations of wall thickness, strength etc. for design purposes *must* however be made using the formulae given in the relevant application code or standard, such as ANSI B.16 or B31, and a suitable pipe selected from the tables referred to therein.

Perhaps the most used American piping standard is the Code for Pressure Piping (ANSI B 31) sponsored and published by ASME. It is divided into associated standards as follows:

Section 1  B 31.1  Power piping.
     2  B 31.2  Fuel gas piping.
     3  B 31.3  Petroleum refinery piping.
     4  B 31.4  Liquid petroleum transportation piping.
     5  B 31.5  Refrigeration piping systems.
     6  B 31.6  Chemical process piping.
     7  B 31.7  Nuclear power piping.
     8  B 31.8  Gas transmission and distribution piping systems.

This Code prescribes minimum requirements for selection of materials, design, fabrication and assembly, inspection and testing, and constitutes a series of safety standards.

It is generally accepted in the USA and on most American and many other projects elsewhere.

As with pressure vessels, formulae for design calculations on such matters as minimum wall thickness for a specified service pressure, taking into account maximum allowable stress at maximum anticipated operating temperature for a specified material, corrosion allowance, welded joint efficiency, etc. are given.

Calculations of strength and wall thickness of cast iron pipe may be made in accordance with a Manual ANSI A 21.1, whilst dimensions, tolerances, ratings and details of fittings are given in the A 21 series. The use of cast iron pipe is limited generally (with some variations) to temperatures not exceeding 250°F and to pressures of 100 lb/in$^2$ gauge (above ground) and 400 lb/in$^2$ gauge (underground).

Centrifugally cast (spun) pipe is generally used in process work as it is stronger than vertical (pit) cast pipe.

Tubes to British or American standards may (subject to any necessary agreement) be offered in various alternative equivalent material specifications, including those of the BSI, ASTM, American Iron and Steel Institute (AISI) and continental bodies.

API Standards are available for a variety of casing, tubing, drill pipe and line pipe for oilfield and pipeline use. For successful and economical operations they are largely dependent on the use of high-strength steels whilst effective quality control during manufacture is essential. Steels with yield strengths of up to some 105/110,000 lb/in$^2$ are used for tubing and casing, up to 75,000 lb/in$^2$ for drill pipe and up to 60,000 lb/in$^2$ for line pipe.

The API specifications for pipe cover a number of grades of material and permit generally a variety of manufacturing methods. Thus either seamless or welded pipe can be supplied to API Standards 5L and 5LX, but ASTM and other specifications may call for pipe made by one particular process only. Again API specifications permit a thinner wall for a given pipe diameter than the minimum ASTM requirement. There are differences in manufacturing and testing methods and procedures between API and other similar pipe specifications which the inspector should watch carefully. Thus API defines yield strength only on the basis of 0·5% *total* extension, whilst ASTM permits the total extension or the permanent extension, measured at 0·2% offset, or the yield point determined by the drop of the beam, etc., to be used. API requires 100% inspection of the full length of welded seams by a non-destructive method, and generally requires close control of chemical constituents, and a specified amount of tensile, flattening and bend testing, etc. (see also 4.1 and 4.25). For linepipe, acceptance limits for the maximum size and distribution of slag inclusions and/or gas pocket discontinuities are laid down in tables and diagrams in a similar manner to that of the ASME Boiler and Pressure Vessel Code (see 3.16 and Fig. 3.14). With circular inclusions the sum of their diameters in any 6 in length must not exceed $\frac{1}{4}$ in.

In BS 1600 *Dimensions of steel pipe for the petroleum industry* identity has been maintained with ANSI B36.10 Wrought steel and wrought iron pipe, and B36.19 Stainless steel pipe, to ensure interchangeability of pipes used in the petroleum industry irrespective of origin. The designation of pipe thicknesses is by schedule numbers, a traditional practice widely used in the petroleum industry, pending any other agreement by ISO. Schedule numbers carrying the additional designation 'S' (5S, 10S, 40S, 80S) apply only to austenitic chromium-nickel stainless steel pipes.

Except where noted in the specification 'standard' (S), 'extra strong' (XS) and 'double extra strong' (XXS) wall thicknesses have pipes of corresponding wall thickness listed under one of the schedule numbers (e.g. Schedules 40, 80 and 160 respectively).

Schedule numbers are given approximately by the formula $p/S \times 1000$ (in inch units). However, BS 1600 states that for design purposes the calculation of wall thicknesses should be made in accordance with the relevant provisions of BS 3351, which states:

$$t = \frac{pD}{20S + p}$$

where $t$ = wall thickness (mm)
     $p$ = design pressure (bar)
     $S$ = design stress (N/mm$^2$)
     $D$ = outside diameter of pipe (mm)

The value of $S$ to be used should be obtained from the relevant British design standard (e.g. BS 5500, BS 1306, BS 5222 or BS 3351) or, for materials supplied to API or ASTM standards, from ANSI 31.3 for the design temperatures indicated therein.

Should nominal pipe sizes greater than 36 inches be required then API Standard 5LS  *Spiral weld line pipe* may be used. The screw threads of any threaded pipes and couplings should be gauged and inspected to check compliance with ANSI B2.1 or API Standard 5B.

BS 1600 Part 2 is similar to Part 1 except that the nominal pipes sizes (expressed in inches) have their outside diameters and wall thicknesses expressed in millimetres.

BS 3351  *Piping systems for petroleum refineries and petrochemical plants*. First issued in 1961, it was basically similar to ANSI B31.3, but some differences, such as the requirements for quality control and inspection of fusion welding, have since been introduced. However, in some respects identity with the ANSI Code has been maintained, particularly regarding the treatment of piping flexibility (see BS 3351 para. 5.6). A list of British Standards for materials and components, which may be used in the construction of piping systems, is included, together with tables of pressure/temperature rating for materials/components made to relevant British and equivalent ASTM standards, and an appendix on piping stress analysis.

### 4.6.3 Stability of pipework

All pipework installations are subject to forces and moments which may tend to destabilize or upset them. Consequently anchors, supports, hangers etc. have to be designed, inspected and maintained to ensure that there is no slipping, undue stressing or twisting of pipe, which must be so arranged that the system is sufficiently flexible under all operating conditions. Any expansion joints must be fitted correctly (and not out of line as was done at Flixborough (see 13.6.3)). Some guidance on installation etc. is given in BS 6129 Part 1. A flexibility analysis may be carried out, details of which are given in BS 3351 sect. 5.6 and also in BS 806, including (in Appendix E) recommended proof and rupture stress values which may be used in connection therewith. See also BS 3974 *Pipe supports* and BS 5500, Appendices A and G.

'In-service' inspection and maintenance must see that any corrosion which develops in the installation is kept under control.

## 4.7 Inspection of cast iron pipes

BS 4622 *Grey iron pipes and fittings* is the metric version of BS 78, BS 1211 and BS 2035 and is based on ISO recommendations. The external diameters, wall thicknesses and standard lengths of three classes (classes 1–3) of spigot and socket pipes are specified. Flanged pipe wall thicknesses (classes 3 and 4) are somewhat greater. Ring and/or bar test pieces are taken from 1% of a consignment for tensile tests, and may be selected and tests witnessed by the inspector. With BS 4622 a minimum tensile strength of 160 N/mm$^2$ is required from sand cast material, but rises to 400 N/mm$^2$ for pipes up to 300 mm diameter centrifugally cast in metal moulds. Maximum hydraulic working pressures are 10–12·5–16 bar for class 1, 2 and 3 centrifugally cast spigot and socket pipes respectively, whilst for flanged sand cast pipes (to classes 3 and 4) they are 10–12·5 bar. If iron pipes are required for use at greater pressures then a ductile iron must be used.

The development of nodular or spheroidal graphite iron (e.g. to BS 2789) has provided a material for the production of pipes and castings having greater strength and ductility which is suitable for use under more onerous conditions than normal grey cast iron. The molten iron is usually treated with a magnesium type alloy to obtain these results.

The British Standard for ductile cast iron pipes of this type, is BS 4772. The wall thickness required is some 70% of that specified for the corresponding diameter of grey iron pipe to BS 4622. The tensile strength required is not less than 420 N/mm$^2$ (27 ton/in$^2$), and the elongation not less than 8%. Each pipe should be consecutively numbered so that in the event of any deficiency the affected batch can readily be identified and rejected.

Such pipe may be used for the transmission of liquids and gases at pressures higher than permissible with grey cast iron, and particularly in locations subject to ground instability or traffic effects, or where the risk of transit damage is unduly high. With suitable flexible joints often of a proprietary design they can deflect and still maintain a positive seal.

A works proof test is required by all specifications on each pipe and fitting and may be witnessed by the inspector. It is carried out hydrostatically and before any coating that may be specified.

The hydrostatic works test pressure for BS 4622 is 35 bar (3·5 N/mm$^2$) for centrifugally cast spigot and socket pipe (20 bar for flanged), and 16 or 20 bar for sand cast pipe.

The works hydrostatic proof test pressures required by BS 4772 are:

(i) from a maximum of 50 bar (for diameters from 80–300 mm) down to 25 bar (for diameters from 1400–1600 mm) for pipes with flexible mechanical joints;

(ii) from 32 down to 16 bar (according to flange type and increasing diameter) for pipes with screwed or welded on flanges.

Gas pipes with mechanical joints may, where specified, be tested in addition with air at 3·5 bar. Total immersion in water, or some other method, may be used to detect leaks or porosity. Coating or dipping with some suitable material after testing is usually required and the inspector should see that pipes etc. are clean, dry and free from rust before coating. Using ductile iron maximum sustained hydraulic operating pressures of up to 40 bar for pipelines without flanged joints and up to 25 bar with flanges is possible. With pipelines properly anchored field tests of up to 45 bar can be employed.

Methods of interconnection between metric and inch size pipes and fittings are detailed in BS 4622 and BS 4772 some of which entail the use of change pieces made from ductile iron in accordance with BS 4772. Inspectors should note that pipes having screwed on flanges must be sealed at the threaded joint by a sealing compound suitable for use with raw and potable water up to 100°C, gas and domestic sewage. The sealing compound for pipes used for other duties should be specified.

Pipes and fittings having cracks and tears are specifically excluded from repair, but minor surface imperfections may be removed by simple dressing. Other defects, where applicable, may be rectified by an approved and type tested welding procedure. Cast iron pipes must not be used for steam or blowdown duties; grey iron pipes must not be used when the design temperature exceeds 220°C; ductile iron pipes must not be used when the design temperature exceeds 350°C.

## 4.8  Plastic pipe manufacture and inspection

In the manufacture of plastic pipe considerable attention must be paid to quality control and testing procedures if the best results are to be obtained.

The compound must be correctly formulated, the extrusion process must be properly carried out, and cleanliness must be watched.

The materials most commonly used are polyethylene (both low- and high-density types) and polyvinyl chloride (unplasticized and high-impact modified rigid PVC). ABS co-polymer piping made from acrylonitrile-butadiene-styrene rubber resin blends may also be used, and these are serviceable over a somewhat higher-temperature range than high-impact PVC but have a lower tensile strength. Polypropylene piping has also been tried in various chemical plants, but this material should not be used where there is the slightest risk of fire.

A number of British Standards for plastic pipe are in use whilst American Standards are also available (see Table 4.5); but these may not cover all the materials and tests available. British Standards for polythene pipe call for the addition of suitable antioxidants and for tests, for example, involving photomicrographic examination to determine the effective dispersion of carbon black required to protect the material against the effects of ultra-violet radiation and to provide the opacity to avoid algae growth in water conveyed in exposed pipe, so ensuring its long-term performance. To ensure effective dispersion very thorough hot mixing of the compound is necessary in a Bridge Banbury type mixer.

**TABLE 4.5**

*Rubber and plastics hose and pipe specifications*

| BS No. | Similar ISO No. | Description |
| --- | --- | --- |
| **Hose** | | |
| 1435 | 1823 | Rubber hose assemblies for oil suction and discharge services |
| 3212 | | Flexible rubber tubing and hose for use with LPG vapour phase and LPG/air installations |
| 3832 | 1436 | Wire reinforced rubber hoses and hose assemblies for hydraulic installations |
| 4089 | | Rubber hose and hose assemblies for LPG lines |
| 4983 | 3949 | Textile reinforced thermoplastics hydraulic hose & hose assemblies |
| 5118 | 2398 | Rubber hoses for compressed air |
| 5119 | 1403 | General purpose rubber waterhoses |
| 5120 | | Rubber hose for gas welding and allied processes |
| 5122 | | Rubber hose for saturated steam |
| 5173 | 1402, 1436 | Methods of test for hoses |
| 5244 | | Recommendations for application, storage and life expiry of hydraulic rubber hoses and assemblies |

**TABLE 4.5** *concluded*

| BS No. | Similar ISO No. | Description |
|---|---|---|
| 5780 | | Polymer-reinforced hoses for suction and discharge |
| 5842 | | Thermoplastic hose assemblies for dock, road and rail tanker use |
| 6066 | | Thermoplastic hoses for compressed air |
| **Plastic** | | |
| **Pipe** | | |
| 1972 | R1164 and 6, 2506 | Polythene pipe (type 32)* for above ground use (for cold water services) |
| 1973 | | Polythene pipe (type 32)* for general purpose |
| 3505 | 2505, 3114, 3472–3 and 3606 | Unplasticized PVC pressure pipes for cold potable water |
| 3506 | | Unplasticized PVC pipe for industrial purposes |
| 4346 | 2035, 2043–5, 2048 | Joints and fittings for use with unplasticized PVC pressure pipes. (Part 3 deals with solvent cement) |
| 4660 | | Joints and fittings for use with unplasticized PVC underground drainpipes and fittings |
| 4728 | 1167 | Determination of the resistance to constant internal pressure of thermo-plastics pipe (acceptance and quality tests) |
| 4991 | 3212–3 | Propylene copolymer pressure pipe |
| 5391 | | Acrylonitrile-butadiene-styrene (ABS) Pressure pipe |
| 5392 | | Fittings for use with ABS pressure pipe |
| 5480 | | Glass reinforced plastics (GRP) pipes and fittings for use for water supply or sewerage |
| 5556 | 161/1 | General requirements for dimensions and pressure ratings for pipe of thermoplastics materials |
| 5955 | (replacing CP312) | Code of practice for plastics pipework (thermoplastics material) |
| 6209 | | Solvent cement for non-pressure thermoplastic pipe systems |
| 6437 | | Polyethylene pipes (type 50)* in metric diameters for general purposes |
| 6572 | | Blue polyethylene pipes up to nominal size 63 for below ground use for potable water |
| 6730 | (superseding BS 1972) | Black polyethylene pipes up to nominal size 63 for above ground use for cold potable water |

\* Type numbers indicate safe working stress (in bars) with water at 20°C.

Specifications may call for accelerated ageing tests on, for instance, PVC and polythene pipe to ensure the attainment of a 50-year satisfactory service life.

Experiments show that tube (unplásticized PVC or polythene, etc.) held at a certain constant internal pressure and temperature will fail by bursting after, say, one hour, owing to creep of the material. Another sample stressed 10% lower will fail in about 10 hours, and a further sample stressed 10% lower still in about 100 hours. A graph of bursting pressure against time to burst, plotted on a log-log scale, gives a straight line, and extrapolation enables the constant pressure required to cause bursting in 50 years to be determined.

It should be borne in mind that plastic materials have a greater coefficient of expansion than metals and that some are much affected by moisture absorption. Consequently the temperature at which dimensional measurements are taken should be specified, and in some cases also the humidity.

British Standards for thermoplastics, pipe and fittings have been largely revised in line with metric dimensions, etc. as standardized in most European countries, generally in accordance with BS 5556 (replacing BS 3867). Standard outside diameters (in mm) and pressure ratings (in bar) have been accepted internationally (by ISO) as nominal outside diameters (DN) and pressures (PN). These are listed in BS 5556 together with the design circumferential working stresses in the material (expressed in bar and also in megapascals).*

The minimum wall thicknesses (mm) for a particular diameter of pipe can be obtained from a table (in BS 5556) by reference to tabulated figures of the ratio:

$$\frac{\text{selected stress rating } (\sigma \text{ bar})}{\text{selected pressure rating } (P \text{ bar})}$$

Some materials and standards are described below (see also Table 4.5). For polyethylene of density not greater than 0·93 g/mL a maximum working *stress* in the material of 32 bar at 20°C is recommended when in pipe form and used for water.

---

*1 bar $= 10^5$ N/m$^2$ $= 0\cdot1$ N/mm$^2$ $= 100$KPa $= 0\cdot1$ MPa $= 10$ m head of water
(approx)
$= 1$ kgf/cm$^2$
1 bar $= 0\cdot1$ hectobar $= 33\cdot3$ ft head of water $= 14\cdot5$ lbf/in$^2$
$= 1$ atmosphere (approx)
All the above expressions (and more) are used for stress and pressure in current specifications, etc. The present ISO ruling/preference is to use MPa for stress and bar for pressure.

For polyethylene greater than 0·93 g/mL a maximum working *stress* in the material of 50 bar at 20°C is recommended when in pipe form and used for water.

These *stresses* are used as a basis for calculating minimum wall thicknesses of pipes (knowing the maximum working *pressure* of the fluid in the pipe) and designate a pipe type 32 or type 50 respectively.

Low-density polyethylene pipes (type 32) are covered by BS 1972 and 1973.

High-density polyethylene pipes (type 50) are covered by BS 3284 and 6437 (superseding BS 3796).

Pipes are classified into five classes according to the nominal pressure rating in the fluid in bar at 20°C. These are designated in BS 6437 as class 2.5, 3.2, 4.0, 6.0 and 10.0 respectively (note 10 bar = 100 m head of water). BS 6437 also divides pipes into two categories PE50A and PE50B, characterized by basic properties determined by a hydrostatic rupture test carried out in accordance with BS 4728 at each of two temperatures (20°C and 80°C). Requirements for compound composition, physical and mechanical properties and a long-term hydrostatic strength test at 20°C are specified; under certain conditions the mean failure time predicted should be greater than 50 years.

BS 6572 *Blue polyethylene pipes of nominal size 20 to 63 for below ground use for cold potable water* in effect replaces part of BS 3284 and 1972. Blue identification pigment is added to indicate a buried potable water service; necessary requirements and tests are included to ensure that water after contact with pipe materials complies with the recommendations of the World Health Organization's publication *Guidelines for drinking water quality* and any other legislation, etc. A slight change from previous specifications is that minimum wall thicknesses have been calculated using a maximum working stress in the material of 6·3 MPa (63 instead of 40 bar) to sustain a working pressure of at least 12 bar at 20°C. Somewhat similar requirements and tests as with BS 6437 are specified, including the long-term hydrostatic strength test at 20°C (at 8·3 MPa) which should enable prediction of failure times greater than 50 years. An innovation is the inclusion of an appendix on quality control testing. This outlines a plan of day-to-day sampling frequency patterns to ensure continuing satisfactory quality production complying, for instance, with the requirements of BS 5750.

For above-ground service the equivalent PE pipes to BS 6730 *Black polyethylene pipes up to nominal size 63 for above ground use for cold potable water* are characterized by a carbon black pigmented colour, used for its optimum resistance to ultraviolet light.

Unplasticized polyvinylchloride (PVC-U) pipes are classified (in BS 3505/6) by their maximum sustained working pressure (in the fluid—calculated with water at 20°C) as follows:

| Class | 0 | B | C | D | E | 6 | 7 |
|---|---|---|---|---|---|---|---|
| MSWP (bar) | Nil | 6 | 9 | 12 | 15 | 36–18 | 52–22 |
| Nominal size (in) | $1\frac{1}{2}$ $-24$ | $3$ $-24$ | $2$ $-24$ | $1\frac{1}{4}$ $-18$ | $\frac{1}{4}$ $-16$ | $\frac{1}{4}$–$1\frac{1}{2}$ | $\frac{1}{4}$–$2$ |

BS 3505 covers classes C to E; classes 6 and 7 are provided to give extra thick pipes for hazardous duties and screw threading, equivalent to American Schedules 40 and 80 respectively. Note that the use of screw threading on PVC pipes is not generally encouraged.

A maximum working stress in the material of 9·8 MPa (98 bar) has been used for calculating wall thicknesses of pipe up to $\frac{3}{4}$ in nominal size; of 11 MPa from 1–7 in; and of 12·3 MPa for 8 in and above. Pipe to BS 3506 is not meant for conveying potable water, but pipe to BS 3505 has to be tested for suitability for this purpose. Although pipe dimensions are expressed in metric units, these standards continue to designate the nominal size of pipe with a number equivalent to its dimensions in inches.

Tubes taken at random are subjected to impact tests and short- and long-term hydrostatic tests. To assess long-term behaviour a bursting test similar to that outlined above and in 4.4.9 can determine the 50-year circumferential stress level.

For pipes of nominal size 3 or over a selected ring test piece is treated and notched on its internal face; when subjected to a sustained flexural stress (for not less than 15 minutes) this must withstand failure or cracking at the notch, a test force corresponding to a true fracture toughness ($K_{\mathrm{Ic}}$) of not less than 3·25 MN.m$^{-3/2}$ (for details see BS 3505; 1986 Appendices C and D).

*For acrylonitrile-butadiene-styrene* (ABS) pressure pipe (to BS 5391) maximum sustained working pressures of the fluid in the pipe are based on a recommended maximum working stress in the material of 7·5 MPa (75 bar) at 20°C when in the pipe form and are specified in bar (and are classified in the same way as PVC). For classes B–E the pipe shall withstand for at least 1 hour without failure a short-term hydrostatic test of 3·2 × sustained maximum working pressure. A special class T (of 12 bar working pressure) is made for threading to BS21.

*For propylene copolymer pressure pipe* (BS 4991) the stress used for calculation of minimum wall thickness is 49 bar at 20°C. Series 1 is used for potable water, foodstuffs and pharmaceuticals whilst series 2 is used for chemicals (including water) at temperatures up to 100°C. Working pressure ratings cover classes B to E with the addition of class A (3 bar). Short- and long-term hydrostatic tests are specified. All pipe should be capable to withstand its maximum working pressure (with water) for 50 years at 20°C.

Series 2 pipe however should withstand around 1 year at 40°C, 10 years at 60°C at half maximum working pressure, or one year at 100°C at 0·28 maximum working pressure.

*General.* All pipe shall be indelibly marked at intervals to indicate the British Standard, size and class (indicating the maximum working pressure) which is imprinted in colour in accordance with BS 5556).

**4.9 Concrete pipes**

Concrete pipes, precast, plain and reinforced, to specifications such as BS 5911, are used for drainage and sewerage. Concrete has little strength in tension, although strong in compression, hence the use of the steel reinforcing wires. BS 5911 gives three classes of strength and specifies ultimate and proof load tests. With reinforced concrete, cracks in the pipe wall not greater than 0·25 mm (0·010in) may be permitted. The concrete cover over all steel reinforcement must exceed 12 mm.

Prestressed concrete pipes to BS 4625 are essentially designed for large diameter water mains, although they have been used for other services, including gas mains. The design is such as to ensure that the concrete of the pipe is in such a state of compression that when operating at its maximum pressure and carrying the loads due to the trench backfill and traffic, etc. no tension is induced in the pipe wall.

Various methods of manufacture are used. With *cylinder pipe*, steel cylinders are formed from 16-gauge mild steel sheet (to BS 1449) welded by the submerged arc process. Steel end rings are separately fabricated to form the spigot and socket connections and, after zinc coating, are welded to the cylinder. Each cylinder must then pass a hydraulic test without leakage, which induces a fibre stress of some $140 \, N/mm^2$ ($20,000 \, lb/in^2$) in the material. Concrete of controlled composition is then applied centrifugally inside the cylinder by a spinning machine, followed by steam curing and then maturing for some seven days in the open air. High-tensile steel wire (of $1544 \, N/mm^2$ ($100 \, ton/in^2$) tensile strength to BS 5896) is then spirally wound under tension on the outside of the steel cylinder. The tension is adjusted to suit the required prestressing conditions, but must not exceed 70% of the ultimate strength. The internal bore is then honed to secure a smooth finish. A hydraulic test is then applied (at an internal pressure of 200–600 ft head or $1\frac{1}{2}$ times the working pressure according to conditions), this test also checking the spigot and socket connections, which are rubber-sealed.

A coating of concrete is then applied over the wire and cylinder to the requisite thickness (20 mm minimum), and steam-cured. For some high-pressure pipes a double-wound cylinder pipe is used, the second winding of wire being separated from the first by a layer of concrete and then protected by a final layer. Bitumastic paint may be applied internally or externally if required.

With *non-cylinder pipe*, in which no steel cylinder is used, the core is made centrifugally in a mould containing pretensioned longitudinal reinforcing wires. After maturing, the core is wound circumferentially with wire and finished and tested as for a cylinder pipe. Pipes are jointed by some method such as the Viking Johnson coupling.

Plastic linings can be applied to concrete pipes to give protection against certain kinds of corrosive attack. Amongst the plastics which are so used are PVC, phenolic and epoxy resins, polyesters and synthetic elastomers. They are applied by such processes as spraying, painting, cladding with sheeting and lining by spinning. Testing to detect pinholes or discontinuities is normally done with high-frequency high-voltage spark ('holiday') detectors (see 4.29.2).

### 4.10  Valves, flanges and fittings

All designs of valves, manufactured in a variety of materials, will be found in chemical and industrial plants and pipelines. Some of the various types which may be encountered include:

(i) Screw-down stop (globe, oblique, angle and needle), check and gate (wedge, sluice, double disc and parallel slide) valves, safety and relief, plug and cock, butterfly and float valves.
(ii) Valves for the control of pressure, temperature, liquid level, flow etc. (often with automatic features) are much used.

The graphic symbols used for pipes and valves are covered in BS 1553: Part 1.

Many specifications are in use covering the different types of valve and their testing and inspection. A selection of these is given in Table 4.6 (British) and Table 4.7 (American). In addition many proprietary and special purpose valves are available.

The specification for the material of the valve (and its parts) will depend on service conditions and is often quoted separately, together with the pipe size and any necessary class, pressure-temperature rating, standard, etc.

Detailed standards covering dimensions, tolerances, tests, pressure-temperature ratings, material requirements, etc. for pipe flanges, valves and fittings are issued by such bodies as BSI, ANSI and DIN. For instance BS 10, BS 1560, BS 3293, BS 4504 and ANSI B 16.5 deal with flanges.

European usage of flanges is mainly in accord with ISA (International Federation of National Standardizing Associations) Bulletin 5a, plus American type flanges for the petroleum industry.

**TABLE 4.6**

*Valves (British Standards)*

| BS No. | Description |
| --- | --- |
| 750 | Underground fire hydrants and dimensions of surface box frames and covers |
| 759 | Valves, gauges and other safety fittings for application to boilers and to piping installations for and in connection with boilers |
| 1123 | Safety valves, gauges and other safety fittings for air receivers and compressed air installations |
| 1212 | Float operated valves |
| 1552 | Control plug cocks for low-pressure gases |
| 1963 | Pressure operated relay valves for gas burning appliances |
| 3961 | Cast iron screwdown, stop and check valves |
| 4090 | Cast iron check valves |
| 5150 to 5160 | A series of metric general purpose standards covering cast iron wedge, gate, globe, globe stop and check, butterfly, diaphragm, parallel slide, plug and ball valves |
| 5163 | Double flanged cast iron wedge gate valves for waterworks purposes |
| 5417 | Testing of general purpose industrial valves |
| 5418 | Marking of general purpose industrial valves |
| 5793 | Industrial process control valves (Parts 1–5) Part 4, Inspection and routine testing |
| 5840 | Valve mating details for actuator operation |
| 5963 | Electrically operated automatic gas shut-off valves |
| 5995 | Method of test for electrohydraulic servovalves |
| 5998 | Quality requirements of steel valve castings |

**Valves for the petroleum, petrochemical and allied industries**

| | |
| --- | --- |
| 1414 | Flanged and butt-welding end steel outside-screw-and-yoke wedge gate valves (Classes 150–2500) |
| 1560 | Steel pipe flanges and flanged fittings (nominal sizes $\frac{1}{2}$ in to 24 in) (Agrees with ANSI B 16.5 and covers Classes 150–2500) |
| 1655 | Flanged automatic control valves (face-to-face dimensions) |
| 1868 | Flanged steel check valves (Classes 150–2500) |
| 1873 | Flanged steel globe valves, etc. (Classes 150–2500) |
| 2080 | Face-to-face etc. dimensions of flanged and butt welding end steel valves |
| 4882 | Bolting for the petroleum industry (4 grades of steel and alloy for various pressures and temperature ($-250°C$ to $1750°C$): specifies dimensions, check analysis, methods of test, etc.) |

**TABLE 4.6** *concluded*

| BS No. | Description |
|---|---|
| 5146 | Inspection and test of steel valves |
| 5351 | Steel ball valves |
| 5352 | Steel wedge gate, globe and check valves<br>(for use with pipes to API 5L and also BS 1600 for socket welding valves) |
| 5353 | Plug valves (Agrees with ANSI B 16.5 and covers Classes 150–2500) |
| 6755 | Testing of Valves. Part 1 Production pressure testing requirements. Part 2 Fire type testing requirements |

**TABLE 4.7**
*Some American specifications for valves and fittings*

| Specification No. | Description |
|---|---|
| API Std 6A | Well-head valves, fittings and flanges<br>(Now incorporates 6A, B, BX, C, CM and E) |
| API Std 6C | Flanged steel gate and plug valves for drilling and production service |
| API Std 6D | Steel gate, plug, ball and check valves for pipeline service |
| API Std 526 | Flanged steel safety relief valves |
| API Std 527 | Commercial seat tightness of safety relief valves |
| API Std 597 | Steel venturi gate valves, flanged or butt welding ends |
| API Std 598 | Valve inspection and test |
| API Std 599 | Plug valves |
| API Std 602 | Compact carbon steel gate valves |
| API Std RP14B | Recommended practice: Design, installation and operation of sub-surface safety valve systems for petroleum industry use |
| API Std 600 | Flanged and butt welding and steel gate and plug valves for refinery use |
| API Std 604 | Flanged nodular iron and steel gate and plug valves for refinery use |
| ASTM A181 | Forged and rolled carbon steel pipes, fittings and valves for general purposes |
| B 462 ASTM | 9% nickel iron columbium stabilized alloy (UNNO 8020) pipe flanges, fitting and valves for corrosion and high temperature service |
| ASTM A 522 | 9% nickel alloy steel flanges, fittings and valves for low temperature service |

**TABLE 4.7** *concluded*

| Specification No. | Description |
|---|---|
| ANSI B 16.5 | Steel pipe flanges and flanged fittings<br>(For standard pressure-temperature ratings such as 150, 300, 400, 600, 900, 1500 and 2500 lb) |
| ANSI B 16.10 | Face-to-face dimension for ferrous flanged and welding end valves |
| ANSI B 16.37 | Hydrostatic testing of control valves |
| MSS SP 37 | Bronze gate valve, 125 lb |
| MSS SP 38 | Bronze gate valve, 100 lb |
| MSS SP 42 | Corrosion resistant valves, cast flanged, 150 lb |
| MSS SP 44 | Pipeline flanges<br>(Also API Std 6B) |
| MSS SP 52 | Cast iron pipeline valves |
| AWWA C 500 | Gate valves for waterworks service |
| ASHRAE 17R | Method of rating and testing refrigerant expansion valves<br>(Also ANSI B 60.1) |
| ISA RP 4.1 | Dimensions of control valves |

In the petroleum and petrochemical industry, where American type pipe and equipment may be intermixed with British, the use of appropriate standard flanges will be necessary to ensure dimensional interchangeability.

Some standards may give a nominal pressure rating or class, but it should be noted that this refers to a pressure-temperature rating. Thus a valve or fitting with carbon steel flanges to BS 10, Table K, may be used up to 900 lb/in$^2$ at a temperature of up to 450°F, but the permissible pressure drops to 450 lb/in$^2$ at a temperature of 800°F. Similarly a Class 600 valve in carbon-molybdenum alloy steel may be used at 950°F at 600 lb/in$^2$, but at 960 lb/in$^2$ at 700°F, according to the ANSI ratings; thus a Class 300 valve might be suitable for use at 600 lb/in$^2$ and a temperature of some 500°F.

## 4.11 Inspection of valves

Inspection will generally be required to:
    (i)   Check that the specified materials have been used.
    (ii)  Check valve type, class, size, dimensions, etc.
    (iii) Examine for flaws, defects, etc. (if necessary by NDT methods).
    (iv) Carry out a pressure test (usually hydraulic) at the specified over-pressure and check for leakage.
    (v)  Check for satisfactory operation.
    (vi) Inspect for finish to specified requirements.

Before commencing inspection it is desirable to know the nature of the fluid to be controlled, and whether the valve is required for isolating or regulating, as this information can greatly influence the decisions made. If the valve is for isolating, then the speed of action and the degree of leak-tightness required should be specified.

In general, valves should not be painted, either internally or externally, until all necessary inspection has been carried out.

The inspector should pay particular attention to the valve discs and seats and the materials of which they are made, as these have to operate against frictional contact, often under adverse environmental conditions, and are required to remain tight for long periods without servicing. For some applications the seal may be spring-assisted or made with the aid of a rubber-like material or polymer. Where high resistance to erosion or corrosion is required some form of hard facing of the discs and seats is common practice. The materials used for hard facing include chromium-cobalt and nickel-chromium-boron alloys (such as Stellite) and they may be deposited from rod or powder by such processes as sprinkling and fusing, flame spraying or welding. The inspector should note that it is normal practice to maintain a controlled difference in hardness between valve disc and seat to prevent seizing (galling) in operation. Even after careful grinding-in at the operating temperature metal-to-metal sealings usually result in some slight leakage when the valve is closed (perhaps as little as 0·01% of the maximum open flow rate), but rubber-like materials can give a very tight seal. A leak-rate test may be specified.

Attention should also be paid to the gland and stuffing box, which should maintain a tight seal with the minimum of friction on the valve stem. The material in the stuffing box may be a ring of braided impregnated asbestos yarn, proprietary composition, PTFE, etc. and arrangements to protect this packing from the effects of high or low temperatures may have to be checked.

A good surface finish (perhaps some 8 $\mu$in CLA) on the valve stem will help operation. Leakage round the valve stem and stuffing box should be noted. Where such leakage cannot be tolerated a bellows type seal (generally of stainless steel) may have to be fitted to the valve plug stem, and a leak-rate test on this may be specified (see Chapter 11).

The above remarks apply as relevant to 'in-service' inspections, where valves may be dismantled for periodic examination of the internal parts. Worn, corroded or eroded seats, discs, springs, glands, etc. may need replacing or repair.

Most valves must withstand a hydraulic pressure test, usually at some $1\frac{1}{2}$ times the maximum allowable operating pressure, and this should be carried out periodically and after any repair.

Many valves will be hand-operated, but on some plants the time and effort needed for frequent hand operation may warrant the use of motor-operated valves. Such valves may be:

(i)   Solenoid-operated (usually small valves).
(ii)  Pneumatic motor-operated.
(iii) Electric motor-operated.
(iv)  Hydraulically (oil)-operated.

Inspection will have to check the details of these drives. For instance, limit switches are usually fitted, electric motors may be specified as flameproof, on/off indicator lights may be required. Operation may be carried out from controls adjacent to each valve, or from a central control panel (often fitted with an illuminated schematic diagram).

Many plants will require the use of *automatic process control valves* which respond to a control signal generated by a control instrument after comparison of the actual with the desired flow, or other parameter.

Safety considerations often dictate the use of pneumatically actuated valves, and these are widely used in the petroleum and process industries. Hydraulic actuators are often used on large valves in gas mains, etc. but the actual positioning of the valve may be controlled by a pilot valve actuated by a feedback device which compares it with the position required by the controller. This pilot valve can be positioned mechanically, electrically or pneumatically.

Electric actuators may be used in the more remote situations, and flameproof equipment may be specified. Alternatively, electronic controls may be used to operate pneumatic actuators at a distance by means of an electro-pneumatic transducer fitted on the actuator.

Most automatic control valves are of the globe type, although diaphragm valves are often used in chemical plant to handle corrosive or abrasive fluids.

BS 5146 deals with the inspection and test of valves and its requirements only apply when specifically called for in a particular valve specification.

Part 1 covers steel valves for the petroleum, petrochemical and allied industries and is comparable to API Standard 598   Valve Inspection and Test. Normally inspection by the purchaser is limited to visual examination of finished components and valves, dimensional checks and witnessing of shell and seat pressure tests. Other inspection requirements, non-destructive and other testing must be specifically called for in the purchase order.

Hydrostatic test pressures (gauge) in bar are specified for the class (nominal pressure rating in $lb/in^2$) of valve from class 150 to class 2500. For class 150 the shell test pressure (from one table) is 30 bar. For class 1500 the shell test pressure ranges from 266 to 373 bar.

The seat test pressure specified is somewhat lower and, in general, the valve must be in the closed position when tested. There must be no visible leakage during the tests, which are applied for a minimum specified time (from $\frac{1}{4}$ to 5 minutes). It should be noted that the nominal pressure (PN) is here a numerical designation which is a convenient round number for reference purposes. Thus a class 300 valve (US and old British Standard), which might be suitable for use at 600 lb/in, could be designated PN 40 (40 bar = 600 lb/in$^2$ (approx)).

The maximum allowable working pressure depends on materials, design and working temperatures, and should be selected from the tables of pressure/temperature ratings given in the appropriate standards. Should a lining of rubber, glass, PTFE, etc. be specified a hydrostatic test on the shell before and then after lining may be specified. An air test at a minimum pressure of 6·9 bar is generally required to see that there is no visible leakage past the seat. Other tests for vacuum service, leakage rate, etc. may be specified. Two design features, particularly applicable to valves for petrochemical service, may have to be incorporated and are subject to prototype testing:

(i) *Fire safe feature* (soft seated valves). The valve, in the open position, is exposed to fire in a test rig with the body and bore filled with kerosene or diesel fuel under a minimum pressure of 2 bar. A minimum temperature of 600°C should be maintained for sufficient time to ensure complete decomposition or disintegration of the soft seats and seals (which may be of PTFE). During firing there must be no visual signs of leakage to atmosphere, which might support a flame or flames (of total length over 100 mm). Within five minutes of extinguishing the fire the valve must be operable. Then, with water flowing through the valve, it is closed and the leakage rate to atmosphere (at a pressure of 1 bar) from the stem, body and/or cover joint is measured.

Finally the normal hydrostatic seat test pressure is applied and the leakage rate measured. The maximum allowable leakage rates are given in a table for each nominal size (designation DN) of valve (Note: DN followed by a convenient round number for reference purposes is only loosely related to manufacturing dimensions.) Allowable leakage rates range from 10 to 90 ml/min for total stem, body and/or cover joint, and twice this across the seat.

(ii) *An anti-static device* may be required to ensure electrical continuity between the gate plug or ball, etc. the stem and the valve body. When supplied from a power source not exceeding 12 volts, its resistance (electrical) must not be greater than 10 ohms.

Part 2 (of BS 5146 and BS 6755 Part 1) deals particularly with pressure testing for general purpose valves (see Table 4.6). The hydrostatic shell test pressure is 1·5 times and the seat test pressure 1·1 times the maximum permissible working pressure; the back seat device (to control leakage from the stuffing box) is tested at 1·1 times the maximum permissible working pressure (all tests being at 20°C).

Pneumatic tests are carried out after the shell of the valve has been tested hydrostatically at not less than 2·25 times the maximum working pressure, and the seat at not less than 1·1 times the maximum working pressure, both at 20°C. A pneumatic test pressure of 6 bar is applied for a specified time. The basis of acceptability for the hydrostatic shell test is that there should be no visible leakage, and for the pneumatic shell test that no air bubbles should break the surface when the valve is immersed under water. In other cases a leakage test has to be carried out and the leakage rate must not exceed that laid down in the appropriate valve specification. (Four leakage rates are specified in BS 5146, ranging from 10–90 mL/min full bore and twice this for reduced bore.) Note that BS 6755 Part 1 revises somewhat BS 5146.

*Note* BS 5146 Parts 1 and 2 will eventually be withdrawn and superseded by BS 6755 *Testing of Valves* Part 1: *Production pressure testing requirements* in conjunction with the appropriate valve standard. The *fire safe test* described in BS 5146 Part 1 is primarily applied to soft seat ball valves. A fire test using a different method, permitting a wider range of valves to be so tested, is now provided in BS 6755 Part 2: *Fire type-testing requirements*; this embodies the technical content of API 6D *Fire test for valves*, including valves to API 6D and API 607.

BS 6755: Part 1 specifies a hydraulic shell test pressure of 1·5 times the maximum permissible working pressure at 20°C, and a pneumatic pressure of 6 to 7 bar.

### 4.12  Some types of valve used particularly in chemical plants

(i) *Stainless steel valves.* The corrosion-resisting properties of stainless steel are an obvious advantage for its use as a valve material in many plants. However, since valves were first manufactured in stainless steel they have suffered from the poor bearing properties of stainless steel surfaces. Tests and experience have shown that there is a ready tendency for the material to gall when two surfaces of this metal are in contact, as would happen when both valve body and plug are of the same material.

The use of dissimilar materials for body and plug etc. or of similar materials heat-treated to have differing hardness values, can prevent galling.

Another method is to use stainless steel valves which are fitted with a PTFE ring, disc, etc. which can be screwed down easily to make the seal, PTFE having an extremely small co-efficient of friction. A temperature limitation of some 300°C is however imposed. Careful inspection of this PTFE component is necessary to ensure the maintenance of dimensions and the absence of inclusions of foreign matter which might be leached out by the process fluid and leave leaking voids (see 2.14.4). Also, as PTFE is soft, the presence of foreign matter in the fluid might damage the valve face.

For higher temperature use of nitrided seats and discs (up to some 500°C), a welded-on overlay of Stellite, or specially developed alloys of stainless steel (with selenium and sulphur additions) may suffice.

(ii) *Lubricated plug valves*, although widely used, may cause undesirable contamination of high-purity products. *Non-lubricated valves* (and ball plug valves) may present frictional, operational or corrosion difficulties.

*Stainless steel plug valves*, however, are now available in which the plug surface is impregnated with PTFE, which can be used dry and the properties of which eliminate galling. Consequently the stainless steel bearing surfaces can be loaded to a much higher degree than hitherto. As the valve body and plug are both of stainless steel there is no possibility of electrolytic corrosion. Such valves can be used at temperatures up to 200°C and have been operated dry up to 20,000 times without trouble.

BS 5351 *Steel ball valves for the petroleum, petrochemicals and allied industries* covers requirements for ball plug valves in which the plug is a spherical ball of carbon, chromium or stainless steel to BS 1501–6 (the surface of carbon steel balls must be rust proofed), or of nickel–copper alloy.

This standard is based on soft seat rings processed from PTFE oil-free granular resins without fillers (i.e. virgin material completely free of any reclaimed process material (see 2.14.4)). Test certificates for this material, if required, should state that it is to grade UA1/1. These seat rings are normally renewable.

Valves can be supplied with flanged, butt weld, screwed or socket weld ends in various nominal sizes from 8 mm to 400 mm ($\frac{1}{4}$ in to 16 in) and classes 150, 300, 600 and 800 (nominally the pressure rating in lb/in$^2$) for assembly with a variety of pipe connections to such standards and dimensions as laid down in BS 1560: Part 2, BS 1600, BS 1640, BS 3600, API Std. 5B and API Std 5L.

Unlike other valves covered by British Standards for the petroleum industry the nominal pressure ratings for these ball valves do not necessarily establish the pressure/temperature ratings for which they may be used. This depends upon the material (PTFE) of the body seat rings and seals. Minimum ratings are given in a table in the specification, which shows service temperatures ranging from $-30$°C to 230°C. At 200°C the pressure rating is around 10 bar (reducing as the size of valve increases); at 230°C it is nil. Higher ratings may be used if experience leads to agreement. The valve design must be such that a prototype can pass the fire-safe design test and the anti-static device test described in BS 5146 and 6755 (see 4.11).

(iii) *Diaphragm valves.* The various types of diaphragm valve have many applications in process plants, etc. The diaphragm may be of rubber, neoprene or other synthetic material, and this imposes a limit on the operating temperature. PTFE diaphragms have particular applications under corrosive conditions, and can operate up to some 200°C.

A typical diaphragm valve might be specified as ANSI rating 300 lb standard, with dimensions to BS 1655.

(iv) *Lined valves.* Valve interiors and bodies are often lined to resist particular conditions. The lining material may include rubber, neoprene and various plastics, glass, PTFE impregnated coatings, etc. Inspection must check for the correctness and completeness of the lining (see Chapter 5).

(v) *Pinch valves.* The interior of a pinch valve consists of a flexible rubber or synthetic tube which can be closed by compression between two pinch bars. Such valves are particularly suitable for slurries and corrosives, powdered cement, etc., and are frequently selected in lieu of a rubber-lined valve, the interior being easily replaceable.

(vi) *Jacketed valves.* Valves of many types are provided with a jacket through which can be circulated a fluid for heating, cooling or insulating purposes (e.g. steam-, water- or vacuum-jacketed valves). The jacket may be cast integrally with the body or welded on separately. Inspection should see that the jacket space is tested for pressure, internal and external leakage, etc.

(vii) *High-vacuum valves* (see Chapter 8 for details of high-vacuum technology). Specially designed valves should be used in high-vacuum plants. Standard commercial valves, especially those fitted with packing glands, would lead to trouble if used. Various design aspects which are of no great importance in high-pressure work assume great importance in high-vacuum work. Resistance to flow must be kept to a minimum by providing ports of large diameter, particularly in the medium- to high-vacuum range. Any restriction of the input diameter of a diffusion pump by a valve must be avoided. Generally speaking most high-vacuum valves are of the diaphragm type and when open the diameter of the port is equal to that of the connecting pipe. Alternatively a metal plate with an inset rubber type seal can be used. Vacuum tightness is secured by the use of oil-proof diaphragms or seals of synthetic rubber (such as neoprene) which will give good service at temperatures of up to 80°C. Above this, and where corrosive vapours are present, silicone and special rubbers and plastics can be used.

Where a valve spindle, subject to vacuum conditions, has to pass through the valve body it is sealed by some arrangement of lip washers immersed in oil.

Metal-to-metal gaskets are not usually fitted. Valves are usually made of steel (which may be stainless where required) or of light aluminium type alloy. The latter should not be used in circuits where mercury diffusion pumps operate.

High-vacuum valves should be tested for leak-tightness to a standard generally better than $10^{-5}$ torr litre/second (1 clusec) (see Chapter 11).

## 4.13 Valve connection and installation

Methods used for connecting valves to their associated pipework include the following:

(i) *Screwed socket end*, in which the threaded end of the pipe is coned, and the valve socket screwed parallel or coned. Leak-tightness is secured by progressive tightening of the engaging threads, perhaps aided by a smear of red lead or jointing compound. Such joints can be used up to some

250–350 lb/in$^2$ and 500°F, or at higher pressures for hydraulic applications if a suitable compression ring, grommet, etc. is used.

(ii) *Plain flanged and bolted joint*, the flanges being usually cast integrally with the valve body. A gasket suitable for the operating temperature and the fluid being handled is bolted between flanges. British Standard flange pressure-temperature ratings and dimensions are given in BS 10, Tables A, D, E and F, and the joint is used up to some 150–250 lb/in$^2$ and 400°F according to fluid and material.

(iii) *Flanged and bolted joint with raised face.* The raised face is intended to be machined dead smooth and so dispense with the need for any jointing between flanges. The flanges are cast integrally with the body or forged, and pressures up to some 2800 lb/in$^2$ at 450°F or 645 lb/in$^2$ at 900°F may be used, as covered by BS 10, Tables H, J, K, R, S and T.

(iv) *Welding neck flanges.* Forged steel valve bodies are conveniently forged without flanges, and flanges with a raised face, as in (iii), and having a neck forged on, are then butt-welded on to the body. Details to BS 10, Tables D to T, are applicable.

(v) *Butt-welded end valves.* It is common practice in refinery and petroleum applications to do without flanges and to butt-weld valves directly into the pipeline.

When installing valves they should be inspected to ensure that any dirt which may have collected in them during storage, etc. is removed before connecting up. When installing them in a pipeline, each length of pipe and valve should be bolted or fixed in position before the next component is attached. Pipelines should not, in general, be laid and spaces left for the insertion of the valves later, because the stresses set up by dragging the pipes into alignment may be detrimental to the valves and their effective operation.

Gate valves should be closed before installation.

When in service valves should be regularly inspected and maintained, perhaps at six-monthly intervals, when any necessary lubrication, grinding of seats, adjustment of packing, testing, etc. can be carried out.

## 4.14 Identification of pipework and valves, etc.

In any complex plant containing a multitude of pipes and valves it is of the utmost importance from the operational and safety aspects to ensure ready identification. This can perhaps be best carried out by a combination of colour coding and marking, and it should be ascertained by inspection that an effective system is employed.

A marked diagram of pipework and valves for reference is useful, but it does not give the ready information often required on site.

It is somewhat impracticable to provide for the definite identification by colour alone of all pipelines and services likely to be used in every industry. In the chemical industry, because of the almost infinite range of chemicals and the complexity of their names and formulae, the provision of a unique colour code for even the commonly used chemicals is virtually impossible if such a code is to be easily applied and interpreted. Consequently, if only because of the limited range of readily distinguishable colours available, some compromise is necessary.

Each industry or large organization should devise an identification code based broadly in principle on accepted standards (such as British Standards), but with details arranged to suit its own particular needs, and should stick to this code without any significant basic change. Ambiguity between different codes, or due to alternatives permitted by these or earlier editions, and any likelihood of confusion between colours (owing perhaps to considerations of lighting and ageing) *must* be avoided.*

It is important that suitable key diagrams to the colour code scheme actually in use should be displayed at strategic points throughout the plant.

Only those fluids commonly used and generally regarded as services are identified in most codes by a distinctive basic identification or ground colour, which is applied to pipework, services and sometimes to vessels, and associated items. For instance, BS 1710 *Identification of pipelines and services,* recognizes basic identification colours for general services as shown in Table 4.8.

BS 1710 is aligned with ISO/R508 *Identification colours for pipes conveying fluids in liquid and gaseous conditions in land installations and on board ship* but provides additionally a basic colour (black) for other liquids (including drainage), and another (orange) for electrical services and ventilation ducts. The previously included marking to denote a hazard (yellow with black diagonal stripes) is now in BS 5378.

The basic identification or ground colour may be applied to the pipe (i) throughout its length, (ii) as a patch or band at intervals, (iii) by means of coloured adhesive tape or a label.

To distinguish further between one kind or condition of general service and another of the same basic service, resort may be had to superimposing a band of a selected colour upon the ground colour, e.g. a water pipe (coloured green) used for fire-fighting could have a red band superimposed upon it; a vacuum pipe could have a band of white superimposed on the basic light blue ground colour designating air (see Table 4.8).

For chemicals, industrial gases and other services up to 3 different colour bands super-imposed upon the basic ground colour may be allocated by the

---

* There are some differences between the colours recognized by the current issue of BS 1710 and earlier issues. Accidents (sometimes fatal) have occurred due to this or similar causes.

user to designate the contents. BS 349 *Identification of contents of industrial gas containers* (aligned with ISO/R448) lists colours which may be applied for instance as bands to industrial gas pipelines, whilst BS 1319 lists those for medical gases. Standards dealing with identification are listed in Table 4.9. Owing to the large number of chemicals in use some duplication of colours may exist.

This may be permissible where two gases having the same code are not both used in the same plant, but nevertheless some confusion is possible. This is obviously undesirable and further means of identification may be required to supplement the colour code. This can be done by using lettering and/or additional colour bands, and is best decided in detail by each industry or organization. Care should be taken to ensure that colour bands and/or lettering are applied near to valves, junctions, walls, etc. The lettering may indicate the contents of the pipe either by name, by chemical formula or by abbreviation; the refrigerant number (to BS 4580) may be used. In addition arrows, indicating the direction of flow, and any other relevant information may be applied in black or white on the ground colour. Some examples of pipe colour coding, identification and marking are given in BS 1710.

In some plants where a limited number of industrial gas pipelines are commonly used, it may be the practice to use only one colour for each; thus argon might be blue, natural gas, yellow, oxygen black and hydrogen red, with perhaps further qualification. But fire installations are coded signal red to BS 4800 Colour No. 04E53, which is exactly the same colour band shade often designated for hydrogen, butane, etc. Also it has been common practice to colour red not only all carbon dioxide cylinders, pipework and installations used for fire extinguishing, but also hydrogen gas cylinders. Consequently the chemical plant inspector and operator must be on the alert to ensure that no confusion arises on a particular plant.

Where the contents are considered to constitute a hazard, or where one exists around associated plant, this may be indicated by painting a panel of band having diagonal stripes of black on the ground colour of the pipework, etc. If the hazard is a radioactive one this may be indicated by the appropriate radioactive sign (BS 3510).

When installing or replacing pipework of specific material it is essential that its identity is visibly maintained in order to ensure that the wrong material is not used. BS 5383 lays down a simple marking code. First, printed characters, including the specific British Standard Product Number, are applied continuously along the tube, and then (optionally) a coloured strip is applied along the tube. Some nine colours are used to identify various steel and alloy material groups. To avoid any confusion with the colour code of BS 1710 used to identify the contents or service the material colour coding should be removed after installation.

It cannot be over-emphasized that the neat and efficient colour coding

## TABLE 4.8

*Optional colour code indications for general building services, pipelines, etc.*
*(Colour names are given for guidance. When specifying colours the colour references given in*
*BS 4800 should be stated.)*

| Pipe contents | Basic identification colour (approximately 150 mm) | Colour code indication | | | Basic identification colour (approximately 150 mm) |
|---|---|---|---|---|---|
| **Water** | | | | | |
| Drinking | Green | | Auxiliary blue | | Green |
| Cooling (primary) | Green | | White | | Green |
| Boiler feed | Green | Crimson | White | Crimson | Green |
| Condensate | Green | Crimson | Em.Green | Crimson | Green |
| Chilled | Green | White | Em.Green | White | Green |
| Central heating < 100°C | Green | Blue | Crimson | Blue | Green |
| Central heating > 100°C | Green | Crimson | Blue | Crimson | Green |
| Cold, down service | Green | White | Blue | White | Green |
| Hot water supply | Green | White | Crimson | White | Green |
| Hydraulic power | Green | | Salmon pink | | Green |
| Sea, river, untreated | Green | | Green | | |
| Fire extinguishing | Green | | Red | | Green |
| **Oils** | | | | | |
| Diesel fuel | Brown | | White | | Brown |
| Furnace fuel | | | Brown | | |
| Lubricating | Brown | | Emerald green | | Brown |
| Hydraulic power | Brown | | Salmon pink | | Brown |
| Transformer | Brown | | Crimson | | Brown |

204

**TABLE 4.8** *concluded*

| Pipe contents | Basic identification colour (approximately 150 mm) | Colour code indication | Basic identification colour (approximately 150 mm) |
|---|---|---|---|
| **Other suggestions** | | | |
| Natural gas | Yellow ochre | Yellow | Yellow ochre |
| Compressed air | Light blue | Light blue | Light blue |
| Vacuum | | White | |
| Steam | | Silver grey | |
| Drainage | | Black | |
| Electrical conduits and ventilation ducts | | Orange | |
| Acid and alkalis | | Violet | |

*(Reproduced from BS 1710 by permission of the British Standards Institution)*

## TABLE 4.9

*Some standards dealing with identification, colour coding, etc.*

| Specification No. | Description |
| --- | --- |
| **British Standards** | |
| 349 | Identification of contents of industrial gas containers |
| 349C | Chart illustrating identification colours |
| 381C | Colours for identification, coding and special purposes |
| 1319 | Medical gas cylinders, valves and yoke connections |
| 1319C | Chart of colours for identification of medical gas cylinders |
| 1553 | Graphical symbols for general engineering |
| | Part 1: Piping systems and plant |
| 1710 | Identification of pipelines and services |
| 3510 | Basic symbols to denote the actual or potential presence of ionizing radiation |
| 4159 | Colour marking of plastic pipes to indicate pressure ratings (standard withdrawn and information now included in BS 5556—see Table 4.6) |
| 5378 | Safety signs and colours |
| 5383 | Material marking and colour coding of metal pipes and piping system components in steel, nickel alloys and titanium alloys (a simple code to identify materials and reduce the danger of use of wrong material) |
| 5499 | Fire safety signs, notices and graphic symbols |
| M23 | Identification scheme for pipelines (aircraft) |
| **American Standards** | |
| ANSI A 13.1 | Identification of piping systems |
| Y 32.11 | Graphical symbols for process flow diagrams |
| Z 32.2.3 | Graphical symbols for pipe fittings, valves and piping |
| MSS SP9 | Graphical symbols for spot facing |
| MSS SP 25 | Marking system for valves, fittings, flanges and unions |
| **International Standard** | |
| ISO/R 508 | Identification colours for pipes conveying fluids in liquid or gaseous condition in land installations and on board ship |

and identification of pipework, valves and services, allied to the general painting and cleanliness of the plant, is one of the facets of 'good housekeeping' which undoubtedly pays dividends.

### 4.15 Pipework models

On chemical plants of any size, involving a large amount of pipework, the identification and inspection of the layout from a set of drawings becomes a somewhat difficult and time-consuming task, as does the design and preparation of these drawings. Consequently it is becoming common practice to prepare scale models of the installation, as it is found that these result in appreciable savings in time and money by all concerned, not only in design and construction but in subsequent maintenance, operation and management (it has been estimated that some 10% of piping design costs may be thus saved).

Two main types of model are used, (i) the layout or preliminary model, which may replace the general arrangement drawings in the early stages of the project, and (ii) the pipework or final model, which is made to greater accuracy and may take the place of the final arrangement drawings and of all piping arrangement drawings.

As such models may give the only complete record of the position of all pipework, valves, fittings, items of plant, etc. the inspector will find them invaluable.

### 4.16 Pipework installations

It has been estimated that the cost of pipework and its installation constitutes some 30% of the total cost of a chemical engineering project. Consequently careful attention paid to design, fabrication, and inspection and quality control should bring ample financial rewards.

The pipework used may be ferrous, non-ferrous or plastic, according to the operational requirements. For some specific requirements there is often a choice between alternative types of pipe.

Spun iron pipes, introduced around 1930, have now almost superseded pit cast iron pipes; ductile iron pipes are now also available.

Asbestos cement pressure pipes may be used, subject to precautions (see 6.16(iv)) and prestressed concrete pipes are today often used for conveying water and for other purposes for which iron was used in the past. The use of steel pipe for plant in place of the traditional iron increased considerably in the 19th and early 20th centuries, but valves and fittings were, and are still, more generally made of cast iron.

Pipe-jointing methods used include spigot and socket, bolted and flanged, and screw-threaded connections. Either flanges are integrally forged to the pipe, or the pipe can be threaded and a threaded flange screwed on. Screwed couplings may also be used. Cast iron pipes, and other inflexible types, are liable to sudden fracture if not properly supported, and are usually fitted with flexible joints. A variety of packing materials and gaskets have been and are used for jointing, ranging from tallow and tow, asbestos yarn, etc. to PTFE.

Various, sometimes patented, jointing methods for temporary and permanent coupling are available, possibly using a rubber-like ring or gasket which is clamped between end rings. Difficulties frequently arise from leakage and the use of packing at high temperatures and pressures, and careful inspection may be necessary to obtain the best results. It was not until the introduction and perfection of welded connections that a reliable and really leak-proof system of pipework became available. Oxy-acetylene welding was first employed, but metallurgical difficulties can arise, and this process is now used mainly for cutting, having been supplanted by electric-arc welding .

The best welding method and technique to be employed for specific materials has been the subject of considerable research, and developments are continually taking place. Consequently the inspector should ensure that a proper technique is specified and is actually worked to. Some details are laid down in the various codes, specifications and standards (see 9.7 and Table 9.4). The most widely used British Standard for this work is BS 2633 *Class I arc welding of ferritic steel pipe work for carrying fluids.*

The relevant application standard should state whether class I or class II welding of pipework is required; the class depends on the operating conditions, the degree of inspection and the acceptance requirements, class I being the most onerous. Details are given in BS 2633, which also gives the BS grades of steel necessary, with the nearest similar ASTM and DIN standards. The relevant standards give details of welding processes and procedures, diagrams of typical joint preparation, etc.

The most versatile material for chemical plant pipework is mild steel, which is usually employed if at all possible, fabrication being preferably by welding. When it cannot be used as it stands, owing to corrosion problems, it is often given a protective coating (see Chapter 5). Various types of resin (e.g. stoved phenolic resin) may be used as well as the more established metallic coatings, but these coatings may wear or become damaged in service. Consequently it may be economic to use a more expensive corrosion-resistant metal which has a longer life; these materials however must be fabricated in accordance with specialized techniques and the inspector must pay great attention to ensure that these are adhered to, and that proper inspection and testing procedures are followed.

In the welding of high-nickel alloys, for instance, cleanliness of weld preparation is essential and no oil or grease must be present in the weld area (see 9.20).

### 4.17   Inspection of metallic pipework

Pipelines for chemical plant of the first importance, where defects could give rise to dangers and hazards, must be fabricated with the utmost care and skill. For welded work of such a standard the inspector should watch the following points, but they are generally applicable, as may be necessary, to all pipework inspection.

(1) Only approved materials should be used.

(2) Only approved welders and processes should be employed.

(3) The identity of the material must be maintained throughout (any identity markings being preserved or transferred).

(4) Pipe bending should be carried out by a process which does not damage the material, and in general the radius should not be less than three times the nominal bore. If filling is required during bending, then clean, dry sand should be used, and must be carefully removed afterwards. Bending is carried out either hot or cold according to an established technique for the size and material involved. Most pipe bends should have straight portions of not less than $4\frac{1}{2}$ in (112 mm) on each side.

(5) Before preparation for welding all pipes must be clean and free from scale and dirt. The use of wire brushes, steel wool, etc. which could introduce particles of metal dissimilar in composition to that of the parent metal, should be avoided.

(6) Before any weld is made the pipe ends and their preparation, and the gap, should be checked (generally a gap of $\frac{1}{16}$ to $\frac{1}{8}$ in (1·5–3mm) is the maximum permitted).

(7) Before the filling weld is made the weld should be inspected externally. If the pipe is of 1 in (25 mm) bore or over, the internal penetration should be inspected by an introscope, or if this is not possible it should be radiographed. The underbead (where a backing ring is not used) must be smooth and either convex or flush with the interior of the pipe. It should not in general exceed $\frac{1}{16}$ in (1.5 mm) but may in places be $\frac{1}{8}$ in (3 mm). It must not be concave and must be free from pinholes and oxidation. There must be complete fusion.

(8) Defects can be corrected at the discretion of the inspector. (See BS PD 6493 *Guidance on some methods for the derivation of acceptance levels for defects in fusion welded joints.*)

(9) There should be a minimum distance of 18 in (450 mm) between each weld.

(10) In general pipes should lie square with vessels, and horizontal and vertical pipes should be parallel with corresponding pipes or adjacent building walls, etc. The fall of pipes should be checked to requirements.

(11) Pipelines should be checked for continuity and freedom from blockages, foreign bodies, etc. Special pressure and/or leakage tests may be required.

(12) Radiography or NDT of some or all pipe joints may be mandatory, and the technique to be employed may be specified. BS 2633 requires that all butt-welded pipe joints must satisfy specified non-destructive tests; it gives a table of defect types to be looked for, with permissible limits for such defects.

(13) Any bellows expansion joints must have been previously inspected at works and again after installation. BS 6129: Part 1 recommends three

classes of joint, class I being for use in the most exacting conditions and class III for non-hazardous applications. For class I bellows joints full inspection and test similar to that for a pressure vessel is required, and this will include 100% non-destructive examination of all welded seams.

### 4.18  Joining of pipes when using gas-shielded welding

Inert-gas-shielded welding of the argon-arc type is used for joining high-quality pipework of stainless steel, aluminium and various alloys. More recently $CO_2$-shielded welding has been much used for steel pipe welding, particularly in the field.

Helium (as used in the USA where it is comparatively cheap) is permitted by BS 4677  *Arc welding of austenitic stainless steel pipework for carrying fluids* which also specifies the use, where appropriate, of argon either alone or mixed with oxygen (up to 5%), carbon dioxide (up to 20%, with or without 5% oxygen) or hydrogen (up to 5%). Other gases or gas mixtures may be used if found satisfactory after procedure approval tests. Suitably designed backing rings may be permitted for making the initial root run in butt joints except when using TIG welding (or as an alternative with MIG welding). With TIG (or MIG) welding this run can be made unbacked, but with the shielding gas flowing behind the weld inside the tube and purging the area. If TIG or MIG welding is used in this manner for joining two lengths of a pipeline, some difficulty will be experienced in providing the shielding gas blanket inside the tube in the vicinity of the weld. One method of overcoming this difficulty is to insert sorbo rubber plungers in the bore of the pipe on either side of the joint to be welded (Fig. 4.9). A flow of inert gas is then fed into and out of the space between the plungers during welding operations by means of inlet and outlet tubes passing through one plunger. After the operation the plungers, which are connected by a chain, are pulled out from a free end of the pipeline.

(BS 4677 requires the shielding gas for this 'purging' operation at the back of a weld to be the argon, argon/hydrogen mixture or helium already specified, or nitrogen or a nitrogen/hydrogen (up to 5%) mixture. The purging should be sufficient to remove all traces of air.)

A further difficulty arises in making the last or closing weld of a pipe run, as obviously the plungers cannot be left trapped in the pipeline. This difficulty can be overcome by drilling a $\frac{5}{16}$ in hole approximately 9 in on either side of the proposed joint, inserting a rubber balloon through each hole) with its orifice left projecting), passing the argon inlet and outlet tubes through these holes, and then inflating the balloons (Fig. 4.10). When the weld has been completed (with inert gas blanketing both the inside and outside of the joint but stopped off from entering the pipeline by the balloons), the balloons are deflated and removed (care being taken that they

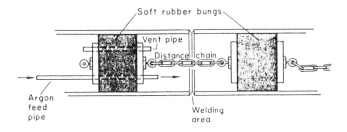

**Fig. 4.9  Argon-arc pipe welding—normal weld in pipeline.**

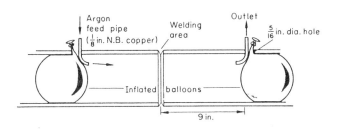

**Fig. 4.10  Argon-arc pipe welding—arrangements for making closing weld.**

do not disappear into the pipeline), and the two small holes are chamfered and welded up. This weld is then radiographed by a gamma source.

BS 4677 requires at least 10% of each welder's production of butt joints to be radiographed (and more if specified by the purchaser, etc.). Ultrasonic weld examination may be approved if satisfactory. Welding defects of the types similar to those given for instance in 3.16 may be accepted up to the limits tabulated in BS 4677.

## 4.19  Non-ferrous pipework and jointing

Non-ferrous pipework may be joined by the various methods of mechanical connection previously mentioned or by some form of welding or brazing. Brazing is applicable generally to copper and its alloys; welding in its various forms is applicable to most non-ferrous metals; for work of the highest quality metal inert-gas (MIG) or tungsten inert-gas (TIG) welding is employed (see 9.13).

*Aluminium pipework* is being used to an increasing extent in chemical, cryogenic and nuclear engineering because of its high resistance to chemical attack and good low-temperature and nuclear characteristics.

For the more exacting projects seamless tubes are used as far as possible, welded tubes being used over some 12 in (300 mm) diameter; pipe joints are generally butt-welded if possible, with flanged connections to pumps, valves, etc. For such projects a high radiographic acceptance standard for welding is set, which—although achievable in the fabrication shops— is difficult to achieve on site, and necessitates suitable weld preparations and techniques and considerable welder training and skill. If argon-arc welding is employed for site work the TIG process may be used, possibly employing U-weld preparations. In the shops simple V-weld preparations (70° or 90°) using temporary backing strips can be used, employing the MIG process, and possibly both manual and automatic welding.

Inspection must pay considerable attention to achieving an accurate fit before welding, a satisfactory root run, and a high standard of cleanliness of the parts and filler rods, etc. Generally all welds must be examined visually, possibly by dye penetrant techniques, and radiographically approved before the next operation is carried out. Any cutting out or rewelding necessitated by such examination must be carefully watched, as occasionally the repair may cause distortion or faults worse than the original, and scrapping may even be warranted.

For such cryogenic applications as the conveyance of liquid methane, an aluminium alloy containing 5-6% magnesium (such as BS 1471-NT5) has been used, which is readily weldable and non-heat-treatable, but work-hardens. The standard of welding and limits of porosity as revealed by radiographs are dealt with, for example, in API Standard 12G.

Such pipework insulated with expanded ebonite and covered by bituminous felt and wire mesh, aluminium painted, might be sufficient for transmission up to say 2 miles; beyond this distance more elaborate methods of insulation (such as perlite and/or vacuum insulation) would be needed (see 7.9).

### 4.19.1 Aluminium piping systems

Aluminium pipes and components for chemical, cryogenic and pressure systems are dealt with by BS 5222. Part 1 covers dimensions, materials and components. Dimensions and wall thicknesses generally are based on BS 1600 *Dimensions of steel pipe for the petroleum industry, Part 2 Metric units.*

Flange dimensions are based on the metric dimensions of BS 4504 and BS 1560. Welding neck flanges designed to ASME Boiler and Pressure Vessel Code Section VIII Division 1 may be used (see 3.9.).

The wrought aluminium and aluminium alloys specified in BS 5222 Part 1 Table 1 are to be used, as such materials (types from BS 1470–1474 and 4300) do not normally become embrittled at sub-zero temperatures or need impact testing.

Pipes can either be seamless or welded from plate, etc. by using an inert gas-shielded process (MIG or TIG–see 9.13). Welding procedures and the approval of welders/operators has to be carried out in a similar manner to that described for pressure vessels in BS 5500 (see Chapter 3). TIG is preferred for pipework installations.

*BS 5222 Part 2 Design*
The relative low melting point of aluminium (660°C) and its alloys limits their use particularly where conditions of fire risk can exist. The strength of the material also imposes limitations. However its behaviour at low and cryogenic temperatures is good. Aluminium pipe of high purity is of particularly low strength but has important applications because of its ability to resist some forms of corrosion. The valves in aluminium pipework carrying corrosive or hazardous fluids should not be fitted with inside screw stems, as these would be liable to accumulate deposits.

In general pipe design thickness ($t$ in/mm) is related to the internal design pressure ($p$ in bar) by the formula

$$t = \frac{pD}{20S + p}$$

where $D$ is outside diameter of pipe (mm), $S$ is the design stress (N/mm$^2$) taken from Table 1 of BS 5222 Part 2 for the material and design temperature selected.

In general pipes are designed for pressures ranging from 6 bar to 66·6 bar. Hydraulic tests are not required on seamless pipe and fittings but for welded pipe and fabricated fittings it may be specified. The test pressure can be determined by the formula

$$p_1 = 1 \cdot 5\, p_o \times \frac{S_c}{S_h}$$

where $p_o$ is the design (max. operating) pressure, $S_c$ is the permissible design stress at ambient temperature, $S_h$ is the permissible design stress at operating temperature.

Fabricated pipes and fittings should be examined visually (using any visual aids and penetrant testing) along the length of all welds. Radiography may be used to the extent called for by the order (perhaps spot radiography on 5% of the length of each seam). If full radiography is required welds may be tested and defects assessed in accordance with BS 3451 and perhaps BS 5500. Similar tests may be applied to a complete assembly of pipework, but ultrasonic methods of testing may be used in lieu of radiography if approved (as in 3.18).

A final hydraulic test of the complete system has to be made, first making sure that pipework is clean internally and that pockets of air etc. are not trapped. The test pressure should be 1·3 to 1·5 times the design pressure and should be held for at least 2 hours, the pressure drop being noted. For special installations it may be necessary to carry out a leak test, or perhaps a vacuum test (see Chapter 11); pneumatic testing at 1·1 times the design pressure, in lieu of the use of water may be necessary (as in 3.20 and 4.24).

## 4.20 Plastic pipework for chemical plant

The use of plastics for pipe fabrication has obvious advantages over metallic pipework in many chemical installations where there are corrosion problems. By choosing the right plastic material and technique for a particular job considerable saving of time, money and maintenance costs can be made. Threaded joints, as used with steel pipework, are not usually desirable, other jointing methods being more suitable.

Plastic pipe can be joined by the use of a suitable cement dissolved in a solvent (solvent welding), or by using a welding process employing some heating medium. Thus pipe ends can be suitably heated to the required temperature and pressed together, or a hot steam of air or gas may be directed at the parts being joined, and at any necessary filler rod of plastic material, in a similar fashion to normal metallic fusion welding. Fusion-welded joints depend much upon the skill of the operator.

As details of plastics welding may differ for different materials, and are constantly under development, the inspector should carefully study the technique to be employed and see that it is carried out.

Heat treatment after welding may be important for some materials and uses, and should be checked.

Sometimes it may be desirable to use specially moulded bends, tees, elbows and fittings rather than make these up from welded and bent lengths of pipe.

However, many plastic pipe installations are still jointed with metal compression fittings, and the inspector should ensure that such fittings have been properly designed for use with plastic tube and have been proved to perform satisfactorily. Fittings designed, for instance, for use with copper tube will not in general be suitable for use with polythene tube, owing to the larger tolerances necessary on polythene tube and to the hard brass compression ring usually supplied. Such fittings should preferably not be used, or they should be selectively assembled and the hard compression ring replaced by a softer one; in addition a metal supporting liner should be inserted into the tube end to prevent the plastic creeping away from the compression ring.

The use of a metal liner however is a disadvantage for chemical plant use, as the fluid will be in contact with it at the joint. The use of jointing pastes, such as those used with metal pipe joints, should be avoided, as they can for instance cause accelerated cracking of polythene.

Welding by melting the pipe ends together, a method often used with polyolefines, is not effective with PVC because its softening temperature range (80-140°C), as distinct from a softening point in the case of poly-olefines, causes a large length of pipe to become soft and makes it impracticable to press the ends together satisfactorily.

PVC pipework is often joined permanently by threading the ends and screwing them into a moulded fitting, after first having applied a solvent weld cement to the thread of both pipe and fitting. If plain spigot-and-socket solvent welded joints are required, without the use of threads, then an interference fit is necessary and two applications of cement are advised. Cleanliness is of importance. With large-diameter pipes, where an interference fit may be difficult to achieve, a gap-filling cement can be used for sealing and jointing. Alternatively, jointing may be accomplished by fitting rubber rings, compressed into a groove in the socket ends by the act of introducing the pipe; sometimes this socket is shrunk on by heating.

Cast iron specials and valves are often used with plastic pipe and are joined to it by similar methods to those mentioned above. However PVC valves and fittings are tending to replace them, especially in the smaller diameters.

Inspection of the fabrication and installation of plastic pipework will generally require:

(i) Checking that the specified materials have been used.

(ii) Examination of components such as bends, tees and valves.

(iii) Inspection of the joining or welding of pipes, etc. This will usually require the approval of the technique used, and also of the individual welders by getting them to make up suitable test specimens.

(iv) Dimensional checks. It should be borne in mind that most plastic pipe has a very high rate of expansion as compared with steel. If the installation is subject to considerable temperature variations it should be checked that the resulting expansion can be taken up by suitable expansion loops, 'O' ring-sealed piston type joints, bellow joints, etc.

(v) Testing of complete installations (by hydraulic or gas pressure); leak testing, etc.

Hydrostatic proof testing of a complete installation should in general be carried out at ambient temperature and at a test pressure not exceeding 1·5 times the maximum rated working pressure of the lowest rated component. It should be applied for at least one hour and not more than 24 hours.

Polyethylene pipe is used very extensively today, but rigid PVC is finding increasing favour in many chemical plants. Besides its original and principal use of conveying water and effluent, plastic pipework is finding increasing use for conveying gases, salt and acid solutions, etc. as reliable information on the properties of particular plastics becomes available.

When used above ground for carrying water, etc., plastic pipe should be opaque so as to prevent ultra-violet radiation reaching the fluid and encouraging the growth of algae. Polyethylene pipe is not suitable for carrying crude oil; PVC may be used if the aromatic content of the oil is low, but cellulose acetate-butyrate (CAB) is preferable.

Tests have shown that PVC pipe is not entirely satisfactory for distributing gas containing small amounts of benzol, toluene and unsaturated hydrocarbons, yet it is sometimes used. Thus, with the proviso that these susbstances are not present, PVC may be used for underground distribution. It is not recommended for use inside buildings. High density polyethylene (HDPE) is used for the distribution of natural gas and general chemical effluents (including acids). Polypropylene can also be used for many effluents etc.

Acetal resin (e.g. Du Pont's Delrin), a somewhat tougher plastic than PVC, shows promise and may prove suitable for the replacement of galvanized steel or double-wrapped mild steel pipe where soil corrosion conditions are rather severe. Although more expensive than these materials it is cheaper than the copper pipe sometimes employed. Nylon piping has been used for small-bore oil lubricating systems.

Glass reinforced PVC piping may be used for systems carrying liquid ammonia, sulphuric acid and various effluents.

ABS (acrylonitrile-butadiene-styrene) plastics can sustain a 15–20°C higher working temperature than PVC without damage, and may be used for comparatively high-strength pipe.

Thermosetting polyester and epoxy resin/glass reinforced pipe has a good strength/weight ratio and can advantageously replace metallic pipe in many instances. It may be lined internally with PVC in order to improve its chemical resistance.

Reinforced epoxy pipe can be used to supply salt water and appears to resist erosion satisfactorily. Phenolic asbestos tape can be wrapped round it for fire-resisting applications.

BS 6464 deals with *Reinforced plastics pipes, fittings and joints for process plants* and establishes a general standard for their design, manufacture, inspection and testing. A method of design calculation is given applicable to laminate construction involving a number of different thermosetting resin systems, reinforced with glass fibre. Thermoplastic linings may be included. It is a requirement of this specification that the manufacturers should be competent and suitably equipped and that the operators and welders should be required to demonstrate their competence. The glass fibre reinforcement used in the laminate should comply with BS 3396, 3496, 3691 or 3749 as appropriate. Design strength calculations are based not on stresses (i.e. force per unit area) as with metals, but in terms of unit load (i.e. force per unit width per unit mass of glass).

Polyester and epoxy resin systems should comply with BS 3532 and 3534 respectively. The amount of hardener, catalyst and/or accelerator etc. added to the resin to effect polymerization of the final product is critical but is left to the manufacturer's skill and experience.

Thermoplastics liners, if required to resist a particular fluid, may be selected from unplasticized PVC (perhaps pipe to BS 3505/6 or sheet to BS 3757), polypropylene, FEP or PTFE, etc. according to the nature of the fluid. The lining must be adequately welded/bonded to the glass reinforcement (a minimum bond strength in shear of $7N/mm^2$ and $7N/mm$ width in peel is required). After completion all production welds should be high-frequency spark tested at 20 kV.

Production samples of the completed laminate should be tested for mechanical properties (e.g. ultimate tensile unit strength, lap shear strength etc.)
Methods of test are given in Appendix B of the specification and include:

(i) Ultimate tensile unit strength (u) (the strength of a constituent layer of a laminate, expressed as a force per unit width, per unit mass of reinforcement. It is expressed in $N/mm$ per $kg/m^2$ of glass).

(ii) Unit modulus (X) (the ratio of the load per unit width per unit mass of glass to the corresponding direct strain, in a loaded tensile test piece. It is expressed in $N/mm$ per $kg/m^2$ of glass).

(iii) Shear strength of bonds and laminates $(N/mm^2)$

Acceptance limits of visual defects are tabulated in Appendix E of the specification. Cracks, crazing, discoloured areas, exposed glass or cut edges, foreign matter and surface porosity are not permitted.

Acceptable limits for pits, scores, sharp discontinuities and wrinkles are laid down; also for blisters, chips, dry spots, entrapped air (surface) where a liner is not used (but liners must be free from such defects).

BS 5480 covers *Glass reinforced plastics (GRP) pipes and fittings for use for water supply or sewerage* with or without a thermoplastic liner.

Information on stress/strain analysis of laminates is given in:

Calcote L.R., *The analysis of laminate composite structures*, Van Nostrand (1969).
Jones, R.M., *Mechanics of composite materials*, McGraw-Hill (1975).

It is up to the inspector to check, as far as possible, by making use of available data, specifications, etc. that a particular plastic is suitable for the use intended, and that the pipework has been fabricated and installed in accordance with the recommended practice.

Guidance on the application of thermoplastics pipework is given in Code of Practice CP 312 and BS 5955.

The generally low melting point and poor fire-resisting properties of thermoplastics (they can burn and give off noxious gases) restricts their use. In some areas they may only be used to convey non-flammable fluids. Glass reinforced epoxy (GRE) and glass reinforced polyester (GRP) piping have a somewhat superior resistance (and may contain flame-retardant additives). Small bore plastics tubing (used perhaps for instrument work) may in certain areas be usefully protected by sheathing or armouring.

## 4.21 Pitch fibre pipes

These pipes, which have certain resistive properties against chemical attack, have applications for water, drainage and effluents. BS 2760 *Pitch-impregnated fibre drain and sewer pipes* covers minimum inspection and test requirements for such items as:

(i) Dimensions of pipes, joints, etc.

(ii) Chemical resistance to attack by sulphuric acid, sodium sulphate and sodium carbonate.

(iii) Water absorption.

(iv) Resistance to boiling water, heat (82°C), and flattening under load at elevated temperature (65°C).

(v) Resistance to kerosene.

(vi) Wet and dry crushing strengths (1100 lb/ft for 4 in (100 mm) diameter).

(vii) Beam strength (2200 lb (1000kg) breaking load for 4 in (100 mm) diameter with 2 ft (600 mm) span).

(viii) Joint tightness (under 10 ft head of water).

During installation, as with all pipelines, especially those having little or no flexibility, attention must be paid to securing even support of the pipe invert throughout its length. No bricks or hard lumps should be used for packing. The area over which any pipe is supported below the invert has a big influence on the load it can carry without fracture. In good soil pitch-fibre pipes can be laid directly on the trench bottom, provided properly consolidated side packing is used. Hard-baked clay must not be employed, and concrete bedding is not recommended. The pipes should not be laid in waterlogged trenches in which the bottom is liable to sink. The trench width should be kept as narrow as possible, and selected fine material should be used both for bedding and for packing the side of the pipe to the sides of the trench.

BS dry-taper driven joints, with a recessed 'O' ring, are normally used and have a certain amount of flexibility. Should severe ground movement, such as mining subsidence, be anticipated then telescopic joints may be used.

## 4.22 Flexible rubber and plastics tube and hose

Flexible rubber pipe connections and hose have important uses in industrial and chemical plant for conveying air, water, steam, oil, acids, alkalis and abrasive slurries, etc. Most are still made from natural rubber, but synthetic rubbers, particularly neoprene, are used for specific applications, such as for oil suction and discharge hose. Synthetic rubbers of butadiene/acrylonitrile type are strongly oil-resisting. Butyl rubber can be used for high-pressure applications (along with suitable reinforcement), and for hydraulic systems.

British Standard Specifications exist covering test requirements, etc. for the commonly used types, and special specifications are produced for other applications (including PTFE-lined flexible hose)—see Table 4.5.

These specifications may give details of the reinforcement required and of the composition of the material, including fillers, softeners, plasticizers, anti-oxidants, etc. and generally require sheet samples for test, rubber being vulcanized in the same manner as the bulk supply. These samples or the finished hose may have to be tested for hardness, tension strength, resistance to high and low temperatures, steam, ozone, etc. and for bursting strength generally to the requirements of BS 903. A proof test, possibly on the complete delivery, at 50% of the minimum burst pressure is usual. The maximum working pressure generally should not exceed 25% of the minimum burst pressure specified.

BS 5173 *Methods of test for hoses* was originally published in six parts, Part 1 covering measurement of dimensions, and the other parts hydraulic pressure, physical, electrical, chemical resistance & environmental tests.

With the adoption of international standards (ISO) these parts (now parts 101–6) are being revised and issued subdivided into separate sections each describing individual test methods. Part 100 is a general introduction.

It has been estimated that hose used in industry gives only about one-half of the service of which it is capable. By correct installation, periodic inspection, and repair where applicable, it should be possible to increase service life by some 25%.

BS 5244 *Recommendations for application, storage and life expiry of hydraulic rubber hoses and assemblies* recommends *inter alia* that hoses should not be bent below a specified minimum radius, and illustrates configurations which are recommended and those not recommended. Also, a longitudinal line should be marked along the hose, and on no account should this line be twisted and left during the final tightening of the end connections.

Most service failures are due to the use of incorrect fittings or their improper application. Sharp edges on fittings, or any method of fixing which punctures the tube, may cause the fluid conveyed to reach the reinforcing yarn or fabric, and to travel many feet through the wall until it eventually breaks through the cover. Corrosive fluids (including steam) should be shut off at the point of entry to the hose and not at the nozzle end, and the hose should be drained of moisture when not in use in order to prevent swelling. Hose should be suitably supported, and severe kinking, straining and repeated flexing avoided. Wire armouring, whilst sometimes useful, can bring its own problems, and should not be used for steam hose; wire reinforced suction hose if crushed cannot be reshaped. Avoid laying the hose in pools of oil; even if the interior is suitable for resisting the oil, the outer cover may not be.

Rubbers deteriorate progressively at a rate dependent upon many environmental and other variables. After 3 years hoses should be subject to inspection and periodic pressure testing (at 1·5 times working pressure). After 8 years (use or storage) it is recommended that they be scrapped.

As with rigid pipelines, but perhaps more so, flexible hose is prone to defects due to leakage at fittings and unions and to chafing between lines, especially if subject to vibration. Very often only half a turn with a spanner corrects the fault, but it may take considerable time to locate (see also Health and Safety Executive publication F 18).

BS 6596 *Ratios of proof and burst pressure to design working pressure for rubber and plastics hoses and hose assemblies* gives in tabular form six categories of service (light, general, heavy, gaseous, etc. to steam service). The ratios burst pressure/design working pressure vary from 2·5 for light service to 10 for steam, whilst the ratios proof pressure/design working pressure are half these values.

BS 5118–5122 and 5342 deal with rubber hoses for compressed air, water (up to 10 or 20 bar at 100°C), gas welding etc., sand blasting, low and medium saturated steam, and high pressure saturated steam (10 and 16 bar maximum respectively). Tests for resistance to ozone, and oil-resistant covers may be specified for use with steam.

BS 6597 gives internal diameters and dimensional tolerances for rubber and plastics hoses with standard sizes ranging from 31·5 to 315 mm internal diameter for textile reinforced, general purpose and industrial applications, and to 51 mm internal diameter for hydraulic applications.


## 4.23 Transfer hoses

Flexible hoses are used for transferring products such as petroleum from one vessel to another. Owing to the collection of static electricity, or to the making and breaking of connections which may carry earth or fault currents (perhaps due to cathodic protection, see 4.29.3), an incendive spark may arise and cause a fire or explosion hazard, in spite of all the parts having been bonded to earth (see 6.11).

If a *non-conductive* hose is used, i.e. one of high electrical resistance (say rubber) having insufficient conductivity to disperse static electricity, then the hose material itself may become charged, and if two or more hoses are joined by metallic flanges a spark may jump to some object at earth potential if brought near enough.

If a *conductive* hose is used, i.e. one which, although perhaps of non-conductive material, has a continuous low-resistance wire or metallic path throughout its length and bonded to metal end fittings, then it presents a path for stray currents which may spark when a connection is made or broken.

The use of a *semi-conductive* hose would eliminate these two sources of hazard. In this type of hose the reinforcing wire is not connected to the metallic end fittings, and the hose material used is such that its conductivity is high enough to disperse static electricity, but low enough to restrict any stray currents to a level such that any sparks produced would not be incendive. (The conductance must be between $10^{-4}$ and $10^{-8}$ mho.)

BS 6501 *Flexible metallic hose assemblies. Part 1. Corrugated hose assemblies* may be used for instance to connect a fixed to a movable installation. Being made of stainless steel or copper or nickel based alloys they are electrically conductive and suitable for high pressure and hazardous operations.

Type tests include static and rolling (fatigue) bend tests, and a flame test for stainless steel hose assemblies with welded end fittings.

During installation the inspector should see that the hose is not bent beyond its minimum recommended radius, that any movement will be in one plane, and that no torsional twist has been imparted to the assembly.

## 4.24 Testing and inspection of pipework installations

A hydraulic pressure test is generally applied to each section of pipework on completion or installation on site. Equipment, such as heat exchangers, pumps, etc. is isolated as far as is practicable, but if this cannot be done it can be included provided the test pressure is within the allowable cold pressure limit of the equipment.

Generally the test pressure is not less than 100 lb/in² gauge (0·7 N/mm²) and not greater than $1\frac{1}{2}$ times the maximum working pressure, and it may be twice the lowest primary service pressure rating of fittings, flanges, etc. in the line. The test pressure is maintained for sufficient time to permit inspection for leaks and defects.

In certain chemical processes the presence of water in the system during operation is not permissible. As complete removal is difficult after a hydraulic test, some other acceptable fluid must be used. Again, on some low-pressure pipework installations, especially those of large diameter, hydraulic testing may be considered expensive or inconvenient. In such cases a test might be carried out with low-pressure air into which a tracer gas has been introduced to facilitate leak location.

It is usual to exclude from the hydraulic test all air lines for such items as air-operated valves, and instruments, and possibly all gas lines. These are then tested with compressed air, generally at the maximum working pressure. Soap solution may be used on their exterior to help in locating leaks. Any more exacting leak test requirements should be dealt with as in Chapter 11.

Pipework in carbon and low-alloy steels may be radiographed by X-ray or gamma-ray techniques. In addition ultrasonic examination may be specified for detecting certain defects, such as very fine cracks, not readily found by radiography. However some austenitic pipework, such as 18/12/1, may not give a reliable response to this technique; consequently dye penetrant inspection can be used for examining the root runs, after which the completed weld is examined radiographically. A gamma-ray source may be mounted on a 'crawler' introduced into the tube and placed in the correct positions.

Inspection should ensure that before installation all dirt, scale and foreign matter is carefully removed or blown out by air or steam from all valves, fittings, pipework, etc. During installation valves should remain tightly closed to prevent the entrance of dirt. All pipelines should be properly supported to prevent their sagging and so causing strain on valves and fittings.

After installation all pipelines should be thoroughly flushed with water, steam, air, or some suitable fluid, and any flanges should be carefully and systematically tightened if necessary.

Valves and fittings should be periodically inspected and maintained, and lubricated as necessary to ensure satisfactory operation. Any leakage should be noted and the offending valve or fitting should be reground, repacked or replaced as necessary. In some plants the amount of corrosion is checked at these inspections, and replacements made when a predetermined amount has been reached (see 12.6).

### 4.25 Pipelines and their inspection

(i) *Ferrous pipelines.* A pipeline is considered to be a line of pipes intended to convey material over a considerable distance; it may have branch lines. It does not include piping installations such as are met with in refineries, process and boiler plants, etc.

A considerable number of lengthy pipelines have been laid for the transmission of crude oil from the oilfields or the port of receipt to the refinery, and for the transmission of natural gas, refined products, feedstock, etc., to areas of utilization. Such pipelines are invariably of welded construction, the actual welding being carried out, inspected and tested in the field. Inspection and test usually includes approval and inspection of welding operations, radiographic examination and possibly other forms of non-destructive testing of the welds, pressure and leak testing of completed sections of pipeline, inspection and spark testing of protective coatings, etc.

The safety of a properly designed pipeline depends more on the standards and quality of inspection than any other single feature. Inspection should start at the factory and continue through all stages of construction. Attention should be given to possible damage to pipe and its protection before installation, and on its correct jointing and bedding down.

Oil pipelines (invariably of steel) may be laid in the open or buried, and should be suitably protected against corrosion, according to local conditions. They may vary in diameter from several inches to some 4 ft and are invariably operated by pumping stations arranged to pump in series and located at suitable points. The working pressure may be some 1000 lb/in². It is common practice for some pipelines to convey several products, the change-over being carried out, if necessary, with the aid of suitable instrumentation whilst running.

The design, fabrication, inspection and testing of pipelines follow similar practices and procedures to those dealt with earlier, e.g. as for pressure vessels, but are covered specifically by the ANSI series B 31 *Code for pressure piping* and API Standard 1104 *Field welding of pipelines*. For years no British Standards were fully comparable with the American ones. In British insurance practice the Associated Offices Technical Committee's *Rules for inspection and test of welds in pressure pipelines* ensured adequate welding standards. However BS 4515 *Field welding of carbon steel pipelines* when issued (in the early 1970s) was based on the API Standard.

BS 4515 has recently been extensively revised as *Process of welding steel pipelines on land and offshore*, and covers general requirements for welding, testing and acceptance criteria for pipelines of carbon, carbon manganese and low alloy steel. Manual, semi-automatic (in which some of the welding variables are automatically controlled but manual guidance is necessary), mechanized (in which welding parameters are controlled mechanically or electronically and may be manually varied), arc welding by manual metal arc, submerged arc, MIG/MAG, TIG, CO2 and non-shielded processes are dealt with.

British Standard Code of Practice CP2010   Pipelines is divided into 5 parts. Part 1 deals with the installation of pipelines generally, covering such matters as acquisition of land, planning, trenching, backfilling, inspection and maintenance. Parts 2 and 3 deal respectively with the design and construction of steel and iron pipelines, which may be butt-welded or may use spigot and socket and bolted flanges or other forms of connection.

Welding in the field is now often by automatic machines and by $CO_2$-shielded arc welding; the welds are inspected as made, and tested by gamma radiography. Leak testing is carried out, using similar methods to those described in Chapter 11; the halide and the infra-red leak detectors can be of considerable use.

For most oil and gas pipelines American practice tends to be followed internationally and pipe is usually specified to be to API Standards 5L or

5LX. These specifications require a high standard, particularly 5LX for high test line pipe. Mill quality has to be maintained by various process and quality control procedures, involving non-destructive testing of each section of pipe (including the use of radiography, magnetic particle inspection and ultrasonic scanning), and destructive testing of selected samples.

Modern pipeline construction equipment in the field (known as a *spread*) may be highly automated and might consist of large bulldozers, power ditching machines, tractors for the transport and lowering of pipe, automatic welding machines using the MIG process, and cleaning, coating and wrapping machines to provide a coating for the buried pipe. Such a spread may cost some £1M and can lay large diameter pipes at the rate of some $1\frac{1}{2}$ miles per day.

Because of the high capital cost of this equipment and the cost of installation, economic reasons dictate the use of the longest lengths of the highest-quality tested pipe, of the largest diameter to take the greatest possible product flow, with the minimum of wall thickness (and weight). Pipe length is usually limited by road and rail transport conditions to some 40 ft, but it is common practice to join, say, two such lengths on site prior to handling by the spread.

Doubling the pipe diameter, for instance, may require some three times as much steel but may increase the capacity ninefold. The use of thin-walled pipe will necessitate stronger material, and API Standard 5LX for high-test line pipe specifies various grades; thus X42 has a yield strength of 42,000 $lb/in^2$ and X60, a niobium (columbium) or vanadium steel alloy, has a yield strength of 60,000 $lb/in^2$ as against API Standard 5L which includes Grades A and B of 30,000 and 35,000 $lb/in^2$ yield strength respectively. All this means of course that inspection and testing of the pipe and its welding and finishing must be very thorough and not skimped in any way, so as to ensure a reliable and economic job with the minimum of material and the absence of harmful defects.

The designed wall thickness depends on the material and formula adopted and the method of obtaining the value of the design stress. In American practice the design stress may be taken as 0·4 to 0·85 of the yield point stress at room temperature, depending on the fluid being conveyed and the type of territory traversed. British practice might tend to use the tensile strength at room temperature divided by a factor such as 4, although some opinion considers that both yield point and tensile strength should be taken into account, perhaps with the lower value derived from these calculations being used as the design stress.

Cold bending of steel pipe in the field is often required, particularly in undulating country, to ensure that the pipe coincides with the ditch contour, and this is carried out by pulling the pipe until the material is stressed beyond its yield point. Each bend should be examined carefully for evidence of defects. The presence of undulations in the bend can materially decrease the strength of the material.

The checking of weld quality in the field may be carried out by radiography at each joint, or possibly by ultrasonic testing of each joint followed by radiography of 'suspect' joints. A gamma-ray isotope source suitably mounted may be pulled along inside the pipe and stopped at each weld, its position being checked by a Geiger counter; a number of photographic films are then fixed round the outside circumference of the pipe, entirely covering each weld, and become exposed owing to the radiation. Development and assessment of the radiographs can be done in a mobile laboratory, faulty welds then being repaired or cut out.

Attention must be paid to the grading of the ditch bottom and the provision of a pad of soft earth under, round and over the pipe. Backfilling and tamping of the residue can then take place, but in cultivated land care should be taken that the sub-soil and top-soil are returned to their respective positions.

The depth of the pipeline may have to be maintained at some value between, say, 18 in and 3 ft, or perhaps below the frost line. A minimum depth of 3 ft is usual in agricultural land; greater depths may be required to cater for the effects of gradients.

Steel pipes laid in trenches are flexible enough to withstand safely some yielding and distortion under load conditions; but this is not so with pipes of more rigid materials, which may fracture, nor is it necessarily so with pipe joints. Welded joints can accommodate a reasonable amount of distortion, but mechanical joints (such as compression joints using a rubber gasket, and free sealing joints relying on the internal pressure on a rubber seal) must be arranged and inspected to see that the amount of distortion is limited, otherwise leakage will occur.

The flow capacity of a given pipeline will depend on the smoothness of its internal surface, and this finish should be checked by the inspector. Pipe linings are available which not only provide and maintain a smooth surface but also give protection against corrosion.

Such linings may be applied at works and should be 'holiday'-tested there to check for continuity (see 4.29.2). Bitumen can be checked by a flattening test or by trying to peel it off (it should adhere to the metal).

Pipelines can be coated internally in situ with epoxy resin or similar coatings. Inspection must see that all surface contaminants are removed and that the coating is applied only to a clean, dry surface. Although some form of grit blasting or rotating wire brushing may be possible in certain cases, in situ surface preparation is usually carried out by trapping solvent emulsions, detergents, water, acids, etc., between two rubber plugs and propelling them through the pipeline by compressed air. Various scrapers and brushes may also be used, and the interior of the pipeline is inspected, if possible, at any available inspection points. A batch of the coating material is then trapped between two specially designed rubber plugs, and they are propelled through the pipeline by compressed are. Care must be taken to ensure that the air is exhausted from the space between the plugs. The coating thickness applied may be of the order of 0·006 in per coat.

Cement mortar or concrete lining can be applied to steel pipes internally in situ by drawing a mandrel through the pipe and so squeezing the mortar onto the wall, or by using a centrifugal lining machine which throws the mortar on to the pipe wall as it travels along inside the pipe. Spun linings are essentially applied in the factory.

On completing the construction of a section of pipeline a *gauging pig*, having a gauge plate measuring 95% of the internal diameter of the pipe, may be passed through to prove the bore of the pipe. *Swabbing pigs* are propelled through by water to sweep the air out of the pipeline prior to hydraulic testing.

Generally a hydrostatic test of $1\frac{1}{2}$ times working pressure is applied. This may be followed by a leak test, the water filled pipeline being left under pressure for a period to stabilize conditions. The test pressure should be maintained by pumping and the rate of loss of water from the pressure relief valve should be determined at intervals. A diminishing rate of loss should be an indication of satisfactory performance. The standard of acceptance should be stated. For non-absorbent pipelines such as steel and iron a generally accepted standard is a loss not exceeding some 1 gallon per inch of pipe diameter per mile of pipeline per day for each 100 ft head of pressure applied (0·1 litre per mm of pipe diameter per km of pipeline per day for each 30 m head of pressure applied).

After successful completion of this testing the swabbing pigs are repeatedly propelled through by compressed air to clear the pipeline of water. This moisture may sometimes prove troublesome. Other pigs may be used from time to time for cleaning, scraping, etc. The use of rubber diaphragms on these pigs greatly reduced the possibility of their sticking at bends in the pipeline. Suitable arrangements for launching, and trapping and removing these pigs must be made.

Purging with an inert gas such as nitrogen may be necessary or desirable before putting a pipeline into service. A slug of inert gas may be introduced between two different commodities to prevent their mixing during operational use. Suitable venting arrangements should be made at the ends of gas pipelines for the safe collection or disposal (e.g. by flare) of any surplus gas.

Other ferrous pipelines of steel, wrought and cast iron pipe using spigot and socket, or flanged connections, etc. between pipes may be employed for the conveyance of water and gas, etc. at lower pressures than welded pipelines. Pipes such as those to BS 534 may be protected against corrosion by wrapped sheathed or plastics coverings, and should be 'holiday' tested (see 4.29.2).

(ii) *Asbestos-cement pipelines* are used for the conveyance of water slurries and sludges, sewage, trade waste and brine. The pipes may be joined by a variety of fittings including asbestos-cement sleeves, cast iron or steel sleeves and flanges, etc. 'O' rings of rubber, or similar elastomeric material, may be fitted into grooves in the sleeve to form a flexible joint (see for instance BS 2494). The pipe itself may be made to BS 486. All pipes are tested to the specified hydraulic test at works. A burst test may be carried out on a selected short length of pipe; the bursting pressure must not be less than the specified works test pressure multiplied by a factor varying from 1·25 (for large diameters) to 2 (for diameters up to 100 mm). The maximum sustained operating pressure must not exceed half of the specified works test pressure. Before laying, the pipes should be inspected for damage and for signs of hair cracks in the region of the inside of their turned ends. Testing and commissioning etc. follow along similar lines to those previously indicated for pipelines generally.

(iii) *CP2010 Part 4* (to become part of BS 8010) deals with the design and construction of asbestos-cement pipelines. Asbestos cement is essentially a mixture of Portland Cement (usually to BS 12) reinforced with asbestos fibre to which other fibres, fillers and pigments may be added.

BS 486 *Asbestos-cement pressure pipes* (corresponding to ISO 160) are most generally used for pipelines conveying water, slurries and sludges, sewage, trade waste and brine. They are joined generally by:

(a) an asbestos-cement sleeve with two grooves fitted with rubber (or elastomeric) 'O' rings to form a seal between pipe and sleeve, or

(b) a metallic sleeve with two rubber 'O' rings compressed between the sleeve and the pipe by loose flanges and bolts.

Such joints given a certain degree of flexibility as specified in BS 486. Cast iron fittings are generally in accordance with BS 78, 4622 or 4772, steel fittings to BS 534 and flanges to BS 10, 4504 or 1560. Joint rings and gaskets may comply with BS 2494, or other suitable materials by agreement.

All asbestos-cement pipes to BS 486 are tested at works to the specified hydraulic pressure for the particular class of pipe. Pipes of nominal diameters of up to 1000 mm are given class numbers from 5 (by fives) to 35, and from 6 (by sixes) to 36, the class number representing the works hydraulic test pressure in bar. Pipes over 1000 mm diameter are designed to specific requirements. The maximum allowable sustained pressure for each class of pipe should be half of the specified works test pressure.

The design pressure of a pipeline should be the maximum operating pressure (or static pressure) plus an allowance for surge pressure (i.e. that due to a change of velocity caused by, for example, the closing of a valve). A bursting test is carried out on a short length cut from randomly selected pipe and placed in the hydraulic testing apparatus (in principle somewhat similar to Fig. 4.3) and internal hydrostatic pressure is applied until fracture occurs.

The bursting pressure should not be less than the specified works test pressure multiplied by a factor of:

2 for pipe of up to 4 in (100 mm) nominal bore,
1·75 for pipe of 5 to 9 in (125–225 mm) nominal bore, or
1·5 for pipe of 10 in and over (250 mm and over) nominal bore.

From the bursting pressure the ultimate tensile strength (bursting strength) of the material of the pipe may be calculated and should not be less than that specified in BS 486 (where it is in general 22 N/mm$^2$ ) or other appropriate standard.

The bursting strength ($\sigma$) may be calculated from the following equation:

$$\frac{\sigma}{(\text{N/mm}^2)} = \frac{p(d + t)}{2t}$$

where $p$ = internal pressure at fracture (N/mm$^2$)
$d$ = internal diameter of pipe (mm)
$t$ = average thickness of pipe (mm measured along the line of fracture)

A transverse crushing test is required on a number of pipe samples cut to a length of 200/300 mm, after immersion in water for 24 hours. The load is applied via press blocks and the breaking load ($p_e$) in newtons is recorded. From this the transverse crushing strength ($R_e$) may be calculated and should not be less than 44 N/mm$^2$. The following formula may be used:

$$R_e = 0·3 \frac{p_e}{1} \frac{(3d + 5e)}{e^2}$$

(where $d$, $e$ and $l$ are the internal diameter, thickness at fracture and length of the test piece (mm)). Other optional tests, such as longitudinal bending, water absorption and chemical resistance may be required by the relevant specification. When cutting or sawing asbestos-cement pipes care should be taken to avoid inhalation of dust. Damping will reduce dust emission. Respirators, etc. may be worn, and of course during all operations, particularly during manufacture, all the relevant safety regulations with respect to asbestos must be observed (see 6.16).

BS 5927 gives guidance on the laying of asbestos-cement pipelines. If it is decided that pipe joints are to be individually inspected during field pressure testing the trench should be backfilled only over the barrel of each pipe and the backfill compacted to prevent movement of the pipe during testing. Any permanent anchor blocks should be in place. Field pressure testing of some 1·5 times the operating pressure and leak testing, backfilling, etc. are carried out in a similar way to that already mentioned for steel pipelines. The pipe joints are examined for leaks and corrective action taken if any should be found. If backfilling has been fully completed before testing then acceptance after testing must be based solely on the measured amount of make-up water required to maintain the test pressure for a period of usually at least 24 hours. Asbestos-cement will absorb water initially, but after a period of service this absorption should become negligible. Repeat pressure tests may be necessary to ensure that any specified leak rate has not been exceeded. It should be possible to reach a standard of acceptance not exceeding that previously quoted for steel.

For pipes of 900 mm diameter and above, where backfilling may be necessary immediately after laying, a method (type 2) is detailed in BS 5886 for hydrostatically testing each pipe joint or coupling as laying proceeds.

(iv) *CP2010 Part 5* (to become part of BS 8010) deals with the design and construction of prestressed concrete pipelines. Some information on concrete pipes used in the construction of pipelines is given in 4.9. Laying, jointing and testing of a pipeline is carried out in a similar fashion to that previously described. But concrete is absorbent. For a pressurized concrete pressure pipe 900 mm diameter under a test pressure of 100 m head a loss of some 48,000 litres/km in 24 hours may occur, even with artificially dried concrete.

With concrete (as with asbestos-cement pipe) it may be difficult to reduce the loss to even approaching this amount, and to find any leaks. But after a concrete pipeline has been kept under a maintained test pressure, say for at least 24 hours, then if the amount of water (measured at regular intervals) needed to maintain the pressure successively diminishes, the indications are that the pipeline is satisfactory. However, should leaks by suspected sections of the pipeline may be tested separately by:

(i) visual inspection of joints, listening for leaks with a probe or a more elaborate device;

(ii) injection of a dye (if permissible) or a gas and using an infra-red or other leak detector (see 11.5.2).

After any leaks have been dealt with and when absorption of water is largely complete it should be possible eventually to reach the standard of acceptance specified. Concrete and asbestos-cement pipelines are usually restricted to the conveyance of waters, slurries and sewage, etc.

## 4.26 French pipeline practice

In French territory gas pipelines must comply with the provisions of the *Safety of gas transmission by pipelines code** (decree of 9 September 1957)

---

* Pipelines in former French North Africa were also covered by this code.

which is somewhat similar to the American Code *Gas transmission and distribution piping system* (ANSI B 31.8). This contains, *inter alia*, rules for the factory fabrication and inspection of line pipes; rules for pipeline construction; testing of pipelines before commissioning; and rules to be applied when in operation. Areas crossed by pipelines, for each of which minimum safety requirements are specified, are classified as:

Category 1 Urban and inhabited areas (includes towns, public property, road crossings and locations where houses are less than 30 metres and public establishments less than 75 metres from the pipeline).

Category 2 Other locations.

Category 3 Desert areas.

All pipes must be hydraulically tested at the works at a pressure ($P_u$) which must not exceed that which produces in the metal stresses reaching up to 90% of its yield strength.

The maximum operating pressure must not exceed:

0·67 of the factory test pressure ($P_u$) for category 1 locations,

0·83 of the factory test pressure ($P_u$) for category 2 locations,

and must in no case exceed the maximum safe pressure ($P_c$) (in hpz or bar) where:

$$p_c = 2teD$$

in which $D$ = outside nominal diameter (mm),

= minimum wall thickness (mm),

$t$ = maximum allowable hoop stress (hpz or bar) for the particular metal and category of location.

(Cat. 1 not exceeding 0·6 yield strength or 0·36 breaking strength,

Cat. 2 not exceeding 0·73 yield strength or 0·55 breaking strength if buried, or 0·44 breaking strength if exposed.)

(1 hectopieze (hpz) = $100 \times 10$ millibars = 1 bar = 14·504 lb/in².)

It should be noted that yield strength in API specifications is to the particular ASTM definition of 0·5% total elongation. This may not be the case elsewhere. In France, for instance, yield strength is defined according to AFNOR standards, and is the stress resulting in an 0·2% offset (and is some 4% to 5% lower for the same steel quality).

Coating and cathodic protection of the pipeline are also specified.

Pre-commissioning tests are required as follows:

(a) Mechanical resistance test of 24 hours during which the pipeline must hold a pressure not exceeding the factory test pressure and not less than 10% above the operating pressure, using water in category 1 locations, although gas may be used in category 2. The maximum length of pipeline tested at any one time should not exceed 30 km.

(b) Leak tests, after (a). These are made with air or gas at 70 lb/in$^2$ gauge (6 hpz) and should be held in the pipeline for 8 days minimum.

The maximum operating pressure of the line is determined after these tests as $0.9 \times$ value of hydrostatic pressure withstood during (a), taking into account any altitude changes.

All pipe should comply with API Standards 5L or 5LX. In category 1 locations 100% weld inspection is often required.

## 4.27 British pipeline practice

In the UK *The Pipelines Act* 1962 was passed to secure the orderly development of industrial pipelines. One most important object is to ensure that all pipelines laid under the Act are designed, constructed, operated and maintained in accordance with proper standards. The Act is administered by the Minister for the Department of the Environment (DoE) acting on the advice of his Pipelines Inspector. *The Gas Acts* 1948, 1965 and 1986 empowered the Gas Council and gas boards and now British Gas plc to build and operate pipelines.

As an example of a British pipeline, some details are given of the methane gas grid constructed to convey gas to the various gas boards in England.

### *4.27.1 The British methane pipeline*

Natural gas (methane) is carried by pipeline from its source to a liquefaction plant on the coast of North Africa where it is reduced in volume by 600 to one and shipped aboard special tankers at $-161°C$ and transported to a terminal at Canvey Island in the UK. Here it is discharged into insulated tanks prior to evaporation, as required, into the UK distribution pipeline.

This pipeline has a maximum working pressure of 1000 lb/in$^2$, and is to 'Class 600' standard, its diameter being 18 in, 14 in, 12 in or 8 in according to location.

The main 18 in line pipes were ordered to API Standard 5LX, grade X46, with a wall thickness in open country of 0.406 in derived from the ISO formula relating internal pressure with wall stresses. The pipe wall stress (after considering ANSI B 31.8 Chapter IV) was fixed at 55% of the yield strength of the steel, but 45% in positions of proximity to buildings (e.g. less than 75 ft from houses, etc.) Some further details of the specification are given in Table 4.10.

## TABLE 4.10

*Some specification details, etc., for coated and wrapped steel line pipe*
(Based on those laid down for the UK methane pipeline scheme with acknowledgment to the North Thames Gas Board)

| *Specification for pipe manufacture* | API Std 5LX *(latest issue)* |
|---|---|
| Material | Grade X46 |
| Tensile strength | 63,000 lb/in$^2$ |
| Yield strength | 46,000 lb/in$^2$ |
| Minimum elongation on 2 in gauge length | 23% (on calculated wall thickness of 0·312 in and over) |
| Carbon content | 0·26% maximum |
| Manganese content | 1·1% maximum |
| Steel manufacturing process | Open-hearth or electric-furnace |
| Pipe manufacturing process | Hot-finished seamless or electric-fusion welded |
| Pipe maximum working pressure | 1000 lb/in$^2$ gauge |
| Pipe outside diameter (main line) | 18 in ⎫ other sizes specified |
| Pipe wall thickness (in open country) | 0·406 in min ⎬ as required |
| Pipe length | 40 ± 5 ft ⎭ |
| Pipe sizing | Pipes sized throughout their lengths shall form not less than 0·5% of total |
| Pipe ends | Sized to bore and bevelled 30° + 5° −0°. Root face $\frac{1}{16} \pm \frac{1}{32}$ in |
| Pipe marking | Paint stencilling on inside of each length. Die stamping not permitted |
| Jointers (i.e. 2 pieces welded to make a standard pipe length) | Not acceptable |

*Specification for coating and wrapping*
Descale, pickle, phosphate treat to BS 3189 Class B, wash and dry.
Paint interior with red lead paint to BS 2523 Grade A without delay.
Paint exterior with coal tar primer tested to AWWA/C203-57.
Paint exterior with coal tar enamel tested to AWWA/C203-57 (or to ASTM procedures to yield a separately specified enamel).
Inspect interior paint and primer for uniformity of coating, missed spots and cleanliness.
Inner wrap: 0·02 in thick Fibreglass 'L', high porosity.
Outer wrap: Tissue of approved size impregnated with coal tar enamel (Thermoglass (Andersons)).
Factory wrap to be applied by a coating and wrapping machine which gives 2 coats of hot coal tar enamel simultaneously with the wrapping to produce an overlap of $\frac{1}{2}$ in minimum. Pipe to be above 450°F before applying enamel.
Minimum thickness of enamel: $\frac{5}{32}$ in (for pipe over 16 in diameter).
Minimum overall coating thickness: $\frac{3}{16}$ in (for pipe over 16 in diameter).

**TABLE 4.10** *concluded*

---

*Specification for coating and wrapping*

---

A minimum of $\frac{1}{32}$ in of enamel is required between pipe surface and inner wrap and between inner and outer wraps.
Inspect coating for bonding, smoothness, etc.
Test each pipe for 'holidays', laminations and other defects. Holiday detector voltage set for $\frac{3}{8}$ in spark.
Exterior finish: Kraft paper or whitewash as required.
The coating and wrapping to be trimmed off for 6 in from each pipe end.

*Specification for field welding*
Generally to API Std 1104.

*Cathodic protection*
Separately specified.

---

Spherical valves were ordered for full-bore in-line positions, and inverted plug valves elsewhere, plus a few gate valves in special circumstances. The major valves were fitted with safety actuators which operate when the rate of decay of pressure increases beyond 10 lb/in$^2$ per minute. Some valves were arranged for remote operation.

Inspection of all pipe, valves and fittings was carried out at works by an independent inspection organization, and this included inspection of the internal and external coatings. It was decided to 'factory-wrap' rather than line-wrap in the field, as the latter operation might be held up by bad weather and so cause delay to laying operations. Non-destructive testing was carried out and, as far as field welding was concerned, a specification based on API 1104 was used. All welded joints were ultrasonically tested, and one radiographer was allocated to each 'spread' to interpret the nature of any apparent defects and to monitor the work.

Bends were made at works from pipe generally one wall thickness greater than that required by the API schedule for the adjacent pipe to allow for thinning resulting from 'fire bending'. Cold bending (except for field bending) was generally limited to small sizes ($6\frac{5}{8}$ in diameter and below). Hydraulic testing of the first fews bends from each source was carried out. If this was found to be satisfactory, then 20% or less of the remaining bends were so tested.

Welding was carried out generally downhand to specification, some of it by the $CO_2$ process.

Pressure testing was carried out hydraulically on pipes in the mill at 1650 lb/in$^2$ gauge, whilst in the field, after passing a 95% gauging pig and two swabbing pigs preceding the water influx to exclude air, a hydraulic test at 1550 lb/in$^2$ gauge (with a suitable allowance for differences in altitude) was applied to the sections of the pipeline. The procedure was as follows:

(a) Sectional air tests at 100 lb/in$^2$ gauge sustained for 24 hours minimum.

Permissible pressure loss:

| | |
|---|---|
| 12 in diameter pipe | 0·4 lb/in$^2$ gauge |
| 18 in diameter pipe | 0·27 lb/in$^2$ gauge |
| 24 in diameter pipe | 0·13 lb/in$^2$ gauge |

(measured with a combined manometer and deadweight gauge as described in and in accordance with the Institution of Gas Engineers recommendation D 6).

(b) Hydraulic test (at 1550 lb/in$^2$ gauge) maintained for 24 hours. The quantity of water required to maintain the pressure is a criterion of the acceptability of the pipeline. This quantity may not always be specified and the decision as to acceptance may be left to the inspector or engineer. However the quantity will be small and will depend upon such factors as the presence of undissolved air, temperature variations, etc., but it should not exceed, say, a pint or so on 10 miles of 18 in pipe.

(c) The final air test at 100 lb/in$^2$ gauge for 72 hours minimum, with the same criteria as at (a).

Before commissioning a pipeline it is desirable to purge it, perhaps with dry nitrogen, to remove air and dampness and prevent the possibility of any explosion on the introduction of fuel. If there is a waiting period before fuel is available, then purging and drying to prevent the possibility of corrosion is desirable. This was done with the methane pipeline, using dry nitrogen which was readily available.

### 4.27.2 Institute of Petroleum Model Code of Safe Practice

Attention should be drawn to the UK Institute of Petroleum (IP) Code. The following parts are of particular relevance to piping and pipelines:

| | |
|---|---|
| Part 2. | Marketing Safety Code (includes material on design, inspection and maintenance of pipework and installations). |
| Part 6. | Petroleum Pipelines (deals with cross-country and submarine pipelines). |
| Part 8. | Drilling, Production and Pipeline operations in Marine Areas. |
| Part 13. | Pressure Piping Systems Inspection Safety Code. (deals mainly with in-service inspection and testing of petrochemical plant and piping). |

### 4.28 Pipeline leakage and periodic inspection

On the crude oil pipeline from Rotterdam to the Ruhr (a buried line) of 180 miles and 24 in diameter the Civil Authorities demanded that the leakage rate should not exceed 4 litres/hour, subsequently relaxed to 10 litres/hour. Periodic testing operations were said to take 3 days and to have the effect of reducing throughput by some 10%.

In America it has been stated that a certain 2000 mile pipeline is rarely, if ever, shut down and has had no major stoppages, for leakage detection, tightness proving or otherwise. Pipeline inspection is carried out frequently from the air by helicopter and there is always an instrumentation check for loss of pressure, etc.

The readings of accurately calibrated flow meters placed at the input and output of a section of pipeline may be balanced against each other as a means of leak detection; corrections for pressure and temperature variation may be necessary.

Some of the methods of leak testing dealt with in Chapter 11 can be adapted for checking pipeline leakage.

The halogen leak detector may be used prior to commissioning (or during service in certain cases) by injecting a trace of halogen-containing material (such as some 500 p.p.m. of carbon tetrachloride) into the test fluid (or product). Bar holes are then driven into the ground at intervals along the pipeline and the detector head is inserted in each to 'sniff' for leaks. The infra-red leak detector, using an injection of nitrous oxide, can be similarly used. Radioactive tracers have also been tried. It is also reported that dogs have been trained to bark when they smell gas when walking along the pipeline!

Periodic pipeline inspections are necessary. A survey to check the adequacy of reinstatement of soil, etc., should be made one year after the pipeline has been laid. Regular routine inspections should be carried out during its working life, along its entire length, to ensure soundness and safety, and to detect any encroachment. The route, which may pass across private land, will have to be inspected periodically, often by special arrangement, either physically on the ground, or perhaps by means of aircraft (often restricted to a minimum height of 500 ft).

## 4.29 Protection of pipelines

Metallic pipelines, if buried in the ground or immersed in some aqueous medium, will generally corrode quickly unless steps are taken to restrict the action. The inspector may be required to see that some specified form of protective treatment is properly applied either at the works and/or during pipe-laying operations.

A protective coating is usually applied, either alone or in conjunction with other methods. This coating must stand up to the soil conditions and should not be attacked by alkalis or damaged by abrasion with the earth. In general, non-metallic coatings are resistant to electricity to an extent depending on their nature, water content, etc.

Protective coatings are described in general in Chapter 5. Some protective coatings for steel pipelines are dealt wtih in the next paragraph. Aluminium pipelines can be protected by anodizing.

### 4.29.1 Forms of underground or underwater protective coating for steel pipe

(a) *Hot-dip bitumen coating.* This is a simple coating of bituminous composition, and can be applied to tubes from $\frac{1}{2}$ in to 72 in nominal bore. It is not normally used as a protection against soil corrosion, but finds application for mildly corrosive conditions, such as alkaline sewage, and certain mildly corrosive industrial and potable waters.

(b) *Spun lining.* This is applied centrifugally to pipes from 2 in nominal bore upwards after they have been completely descaled and coated. The minimum thickness of protection varies, depending on pipe size, from $\frac{1}{16}$ to $\frac{1}{8}$ in. The protection is usually a bituminous lining used for corrosive effluents and potable waters.

Inspection should ensure continuity of lining at the joints. This is obtained in the case of inserted joints by the use of bituminous jointing paste applied to the exposed spigot end, and on the sloping face of the lining at the socket end. The lining is completed when the pipe is pushed home.

For pipes which are large enough in diameter to permit entry, it is usual to fill up the gap in the lining between the pipe ends by strips of lining composition.

A method for obtaining continuity of lining with Johnson type coupled joints consists of bridging the gap between the pipe ends within the coupling sleeve with a removable rubber back-up ring, and filling the gap and the space between the outsides of the pipe and the inside of the coupling sleeve with bitumen run in through a tapping in the coupling sleeve. When the bituminous material has solidified the backing ring is removed for use on the next joint.

A spun fine concrete lining is sometimes used.

(c) *Sheathing.* This form of protection is applied to pipes 4 in and larger in diameter. The pipes, after being coated, are sheathed with a tough bitumen asbestos compound, of thicknesses varying from $\frac{1}{8}$ to $\frac{1}{4}$ in minimum, depending on the size of pipe. The advantage of this bitumen asbestos sheathing is that it is not only a good protection against corrosive soil conditions, but is also resistant to damage in transport and handling. Should such damage be incurred, repairs can be readily effected. The protection is lime-washed, in order to reduce the effects of solar radiation, where pipes are stored in the open.

Completion of the external protection of the joints is satisfactorily achieved by a casting process, using detachable moulds, fitted round the joint, and filled with special molten bituminous composition. Inspection should check all these points.

(d) *Security wrapping.* There are three stages in the application of this protection. The pipes are first coated, then are covered with hot bitumen about $\frac{3}{64}$ in thick. Finally, a layer of dried and chemically treated hessian cloth, impregnated with bitumen, is wrapped round the pipes. This is a standard form of wrapping and complies with BS 534 for single wrapping. It is adequate under most corrosive conditions. It is generally limited to sizes less than 4 in bore.

A further development of security wrapping is to replace the hessian cloth by glass-fibre staple tissue. The glass tissue is completely inert chemically, and free from the bacterial attack sometimes experienced with hessian.

Completion of the external protection at the joints may be effected by a similar method to that described under (c) *Sheathing.* As many joints and other connections with security wrapping cannot readily be protected by a cast bituminous preparation, an alternative development consists of a chemically inhibitive plastic composition, which is applied cold to the bitumen-painted pipe, followed by a wrapping of woven glass bandage. A further coating of the inhibitive plastic dressing is applied over the bandage. It is also possible to apply the whole protection at one time, the woven glass bandage being previously impregnated with the dressing.

(e) *Galvanizing.* Galvanized pipe is usually available in sizes up to 4 in nominal bore but larger sizes can be galvanized by special arrangement. Galvanizing is a suitable protection for a wide range of potable waters. It is not usual to lay galvanized pipe underground, unless an additional bituminous wrapping is applied.

(f ) *Coal tar based enamels.* These are generally superior to asphalt and bitumen, have a lower water absorption rate, and can be reinforced with glass fibre. They provide a high electrical resistance which remains sensibly constant, but have a narrow working temperature range, readily softening above and embrittling below this.

(g) *Plastic coatings.* Various plastics are used for pipe lining (see Chapter 5). In particular epoxy powders are so used, and can be applied, for example by the fluidized bed method or by the electrostatic spraying. In the latter case powder particles are charged as they leave the spray gun and settle on the article, which can then be cured by a separate heating process; or it can be sprayed while hot and allowed to self-cure.

Epoxy resin based coatings can also be used for the coating of concrete pipes used for such purposes as sewage and effluent disposal, and they stand up well to erosion and corrosion from sulphuric and most other acids, alkalis and many industrial chemicals. Such coatings can readily be applied on site.

Plastic tapes (such as PVC, polythene and PTFE) are also used, and have low water absorption and good electrical insulating properties, but care should be taken to see that they remain adherent to the metal pipe and do not peel off.

### 4.29.2 'Holiday' testing

A bituminous or similar type coating is an electrical insulator and the inspector must see that this coating is tested for 'holidays' (i.e. gaps and voids in the coating) by some suitable method, usually a high-voltage high-frequency spark which will jump into a void if the pipe is itself connected to earth. This test can be applied to pipes at works and/or in the field where transit and handling damage may have occurred.

High-voltage holiday detectors use a.c. or d.c. sparks and are mains- or battery-operated. Those for use in the field are of light-weight construction for attachment to the operator by a belt, and are battery-operated. A battery-driven vibrator and step-up transformer are used, giving an adjustable output voltage of up to some 15 to 20 kV on open circuit. When testing large-diameter pipes, especially those covered with a wet hygroscopic fibre, considerable capacitance is present; this may reduce the effective driving voltage and cause operational difficulties which can be overcome by rectifying the high-voltage high-frequency current.

Various types of electrodes or brushes are available for sweeping the surface of a pipe and they can be made to fit the surface or a section of a particular pipe. Phosphor bronze is usually employed, although conducting rubber brushes which limit the fault current are sometimes used. In some instruments 'holidays' are indicated by a device (such as a buzzer) operated by the fault current; in others visual observation is relied upon. In any case the inspector should carefully mark the faulty area, which should be cut out, re-filled and then re-tested. Cutting out is usually necessary because the spark may cause burning and 'coking' of the adjacent area.

An electrolytic holiday detector may occasionally be employed. This works at a lower voltage and uses a spongy pad soaked in electrolyte and attached to a metal plate electrode which is swept over the area under test. Faults are indicated by the passage of a fault current, but no destructive spark occurs. Exact location of the fault may necessitate the use of a smaller pad. The mean resistance of a coating, and hence an estimate of its thickness, can be determined by measuring the small currents normally passing through the electrolytic detector. Coating thicknesses themselves are measured by a magnetic thickness meter (10.7.3), or by ultrasonic means (10.6.3).

### 4.29.3 Cathodic protection

When a pipeline (or similar metallic structure) is buried in the ground (or otherwise immersed) corrosion can take place at uncoated or badly coated surfaces. Even when a protective coating (such as bitumen) is applied and is in perfect condition when laid, faults and discontinuities can develop and rapid corrosion can occur at such spots. This corrosion is due to a leakage of

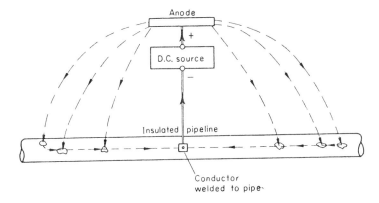

**Fig. 4.11   Outline of cathodic protection system showing current from the d.c. source flowing through the soil and entering the insulated pipeline at places where the coating is faulty.**

electric current *from* the metal *into* the ground (and it may be augmented by the presence of electric fields due to stray currents from electric railways, cables,etc.). To reduce or eliminate this corrosion the potential between the pipe and soil can be changed by connecting the negative pole of a source of direct current to the pipeline. Current then flows from the positive pole (anode) of this source into and through the earth and *enters* the pipe in places where its insulation (if any) is damaged (see Fig. 4.11). It then flows along the pipe to the junction with the conductor from the negative pole of the source and along this and back to the source. This current causes electrolytic dissolution (corrosion) of the anode metal and *not* the pipe. The potential of the pipe, due to the current flowing through it, becomes more negative, the pipe is cathodically polarized and corrosion is inhibited (i.e. corrosion currents are partially or fully prevented from leaving the pipe and entering the soil).

It is now common practice to give such cathodic protection to pipelines and certain structures, particularly in oil and chemical installations. It is not economic to protect bare pipes, so consequently it should be applied to pipelines already protected by some bituminous or other coating, which is electrically insulating, when it will give additional protection, particularly of any exposed metal or discontinuities, etc.

Such principles of protection were first applied by the British Admiralty after investigations by Sir Humphry Davy in 1824, who showed that when two dissimilar metals were connected together and placed in an aqueous medium, forming a galvanic cell, the corrosion of one metal was accelerated whilst the other received a measure of protection. Iron or zinc blocks were attached to the copper sheathing of wooden-hulled warships to protect the copper from corrosion. Later, zinc blocks were used for the protection of iron and steel hulls.

Current flows through the medium between the anode (zinc in this latter case) and the cathode (iron). The anode (zinc) goes into solution (i.e. is corroded) but the cathode (iron) remains unaffected. The metal at the base (or anodic) end of the galvanic series is 'sacrificed' and a net positive current enters the protected metal, so preventing any tendency for metal ions from this protected metal to enter into solution (i.e. to corrode)—see 12.7.

Cathodic protection can be applied to iron and steel, copper, lead, brass and aluminium, to give protection against corrosion in all soils and most aqueous media. It cannot give protection above the waterline or to the interior of tubes which are electrically screened from the current (in the latter case protection can be given by placing anodes inside the tubes).

In practice cathodic protection is applied in one of two ways:

(a) By a *sacrificial anode* system in which a galvanic cell is set up to give the required direction of current and provide the source of electrical energy. The sacrificial anode is generally of magnesium or magnesium alloy, and sometimes zinc or aluminium. Cast cylinders of this material are connected at suitable intervals to the pipeline or structure to be protected, Fig. 4.12(a), and are buried or immersed in the same medium.

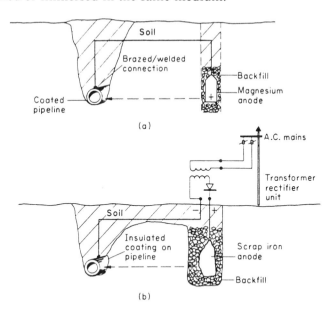

**Fig. 4.12  Cathodic protection.**
(a) Sacrificial anode system.
(b) Power impressed system.
(Arrows show the direction of currents entering faulty spots on the pipeline coating and so inhibiting corrosion at these spots.)

(b)  By a *power impressed* system in which direct current is obtained from a power supply (often from a.c. mains via a transformer-rectifier unit), the negative terminal being connected to the pipeline or structure to be protected and the positive terminal to the buried or immersed auxiliary electrode (anode), which is usually of scrap iron or graphite surrounded by a 'backfill' of coke mixture to reduce local resistance, or of aluminium, etc., in aqueous media, Fig. 4.12(b).

### 4.29.4  Testing of cathodic protection

Before commissioning a cathodic protection installation it is necessary to measure the potential between the protected structure and the electrolyte, to ensure that the structure is polarized to the open-circuit anode potential of the local action cells present so as to prevent metal ions leaving it. This potential for ferrous metals is equal to $-0.85$ volts as measure relative to a copper saturated/copper sulphate half-cell or reference electrode, or $-0.53$ volts on the standard hydrogen scale. The method of measurement is indicated in Fig. 4.13.

(Measurements of this kind are made relative to a reference electrode which has a fixed value of potential irrespective of the environment in which it used. Consequently any change will be the result of a change in the potential of the electrode under examination (i.e. the structure) and not of the reference electrode. The hydrogen scale uses a hydrogen reference electrode of zero potential. Fig. 12.1, based on the galvanic series, makes use of potentials measured with a calomel (mercurous chloride) reference

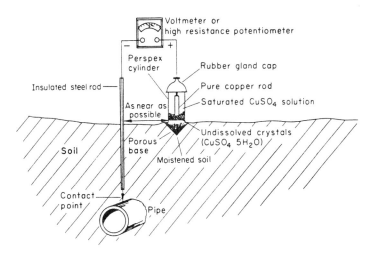

**Fig 4.13  Cathodic protection—measurement of pipe/soil potential by use of Cu/CuSO$_4$ reference electrode.**

electrode. In pipeline practice the copper sulphate reference electrode is generally employed.)

The protective potential of $-0.85$ volts given as necessary to prevent corrosion is a general figure for ferrous metals. It may have to be increased towards $-1.0$ volts in tropical waters or in bad conditions. A similar potential has been recommended for aluminium. For lead the value is somewhat less, being some $-0.675$ volts.

To ensure a minimum of $-0.85$ volts along the length of a steel pipeline, etc., sources of electrical energy must be connected to it at intervals throughout its length, and the voltage at these 'drainage points' may have to be increased to some $-1.2$ volts to allow for voltage drop. However if the steel pipe potential is allowed to be much in excess of this value an intensive evolution of hydrogen can occur which may possibly peel off the bituminous coating.

The 'drainage' current required to lower the pipe potential of each section of pipeline to these negative values increases with the length of the protected section, and depends on the resistivity of the soil and the nature and condition of the pipe coating. This current will have to be set initially and increased periodically as the condition of the coating deteriorates.

Galvanized pipes, tanks, etc., are of course protected sacrificially (see 5.9), but they (or rather the underlying steel) can also be cathodically protected if necessary by the application of the requisite negative potential. The potential necessary for new galvanizing will be some $-1$ volts, but as the galvanizing ages and wears and exposes the underlying steel $-0.85$ volts is sufficient.

Cathodic protection of lead and aluminium may lead to alkali attack of these metals due to the resulting build-up of alkali at their surfaces, especially if the protective potential becomes more negative than say $-1.3$ volts. The drainage current necessary to protect an aluminium pipeline can be very considerably reduced by anodizing.

The inspector should also check that cathodically protected pipelines are electrically continuous, otherwise current may leave one section and enter another via the electrolyte, causing destructive corrosion at the point where it leaves. Any bolted flanges, rubber gaskets, etc., should be bridged over with a low-resistance bond.

It should be realized that corrosion currents flowing naturally in unprotected pipelines may be quite considerable (perhaps some 3 amperes), and that the impressed current on a protected system can be even larger. Currents of some 10–100 amperes may be encountered. The breaking of such currents in *dangerous areas* constitutes a hazard which is referred to in 6.11.

Even when great care has been taken in coating and sheathing the pipe, in its handling during laying to prevent damage, and with its testing, it is surprising what large current drains do arise in what was thought to be a system coated with a continuous insulating film. Careful scrutiny for defects, and holiday testing, will reduce, but not eliminate, this current drain. When a cathodic protection system is first commissioned a heavy drain of current occurs for some 48 hours whilst the buried metal becomes polarized.

A danger with cathodic protection systems, is the possibility of interference with other structures and services, including gas mains, oil pipelines, electricity cables, etc. Leakage currents may transfer the corrosion to these foreign structures at points where they are crossed or are in close proximity. Interference tests should be carried out, using a copper sulphate half-cell and a voltmeter reading at least 1·2 volts and having a resistance of not less than 50,000 ohms per volt. Connections are made to the adjoining foreign structures. The natural potentials between these and the half-cell are first measured whilst the cathodic protection current is switched off, and then whilst it is on. If a structure then becomes anodic (positive) by more than 20 millivolts a bond between the pipeline and that structure is required. This bond may possibly be made resistive to limit the amount of protection received by the foreign structure.

If it is not desirable to have a direct metallic link between the protected system and adjoining structures or services, a sheet of metal similar to that of the foreign structure can be connected to this foreign structure. In such a case any corrosion will occur on this sheet and the foreign structure may not suffer.

Structures connected to the electric traction rails of a railway system, etc., must be kept insulated from a cathodic protection system. Even accidental contact may cause burning of the pipe at the point of contact.

A periodic potential survey of a cathodically protected pipeline should be carried out at intervals of some 6 to 12 months. If the voltage is found to be too low in places it may possibly be stepped up by increasing the drainage current, or the pipeline may have to be excavated at these places and the coating repaired.

When carrying out a potential test or survey the reference electrode is placed on the ground close to and above the pipe, so that its porous base is well inserted into moistened soil.

Connection of the potentiometer to the pipe is made by means of a sharp pointed steel rod which is well insulated other than at this point.

It is often desirable when designing an installation to arrange for the provision of permanent test (or control) points consisting of surface terminal boxes connected to the pipeline and anode and located at intervals along the length of the pipeline. Periodic 'in-use' surveys can then readily be made of potential, drainage current, etc., in order to assess and maintain the protection.

*4.29.5 Inspection of cathodic protection installations*

Care should be taken to ensure that the method of making, and the workmanship of, the joints between the conductors and pipes and anodes are satisfactory and are such that failures of the joints, particularly at the consumable anodes, are eliminated as far as possible.

Joints to the pipeline are usually made by welding onto a previously cleaned surface an L-shaped steel bar to which the copper conductor is already soldered. The welding is carried out by the Thermit or the electric-arc process. Each weld is cleaned and inspected and then the complete area is carefully insulated with bitumen.

The method of construction and connection of anodes is important. For a cast sacrificial anode a coil of iron wire or an iron rod may be placed in the mould before pouring the metal to ensure adequate electrical contact throughout its length. The anode material should be checked to ensure that it is of the required chemical composition (e.g. an alloy of magnesium with 6% aluminium, 3% zinc and 0·5% manganese is found to give excellent results); it should be free from cracks, slag, hollows and cavities, and it should not be porous. Before burying in the ground, the surface oxide film must be removed (perhaps by turning in a lathe) and the cleaned surface protected from contamination by a suitable oil or grease. The iron wire and the copper conductor are connected by soldering, without the use of an acid flux, and the completed joint is then well insulated with bitumen. Before finally connecting to the pipeline the potential between each sacrificial anode and a copper sulphate reference electrode should be measured and should be of the order of 1·1 volts for a zinc anode and 1·5 to 1·6 volts for a magnesium alloy anode. The number of sacrificial anodes required depends on the protective current necessary to secure the desired negative potential along the length of the pipeline. Not as much latitude for adjustment during installation and use is possible as when using a current-impressed system, and should a survey show that a steel pipeline potential become more *positive* than −0·85 volts then additional anodes, or recoating of the pipe, may be necessary at the affected places. Test and control points should be brought to surface junction boxes from some 10% of the anodes to assist future surveys.

As the resistivity of soil is increased by freezing, which decreases the protective current, all anodes should be buried below the freezing depth.

Besides the measuring of electrical potential, the effectiveness of a scheme of cathodic protection can be checked after a period of exposure by inspecting, weighing or otherwise testing samples or 'coupons' attached to or forming part of the structure. This method enables corrosion rates, etc., to be determined and is of use when the actual working conditions are variable or intermittent. Examination of the structure itself for pitting, etc., can of course be made, but this may involve extensive excavation.

A further method involves the measurement of the pH value of the electrolyte in contact with the protected surface. Generally speaking, an alkaline pH value of 8 or 9 will indicate adequate protection, and can be determined by the use of indicating papers, etc. (The pH value of a solution is a measure of its hydrogen ion concentration. Values below 7 are acid, and from above 7 to 14 alkaline; 7 indicates a neutral solution.)

Cathodic protection can be used to prevent the corrosion of many items of chemical plant besides pipelines, but the chemist and inspector must ensure that the installation is compatible with the chemicals being processed. Sacrificial anodes can give off objectionable corrosion products, whilst permanent anodes may generate undesirable gases.

### References and further reading

Note: American publications, although containing much pertinent information, concentrate mainly on US codes and practice.

Braithwaite, J.C., *Operational pipeline inspection*, I. Chem. E. Symposium, 1985.

BS CP 1021 *Cathodic protection*

British Valve Manufacturers' Association, *Technical Reference on Valves for Control of Fluids.*

Fearnehough, G.D., The control of risk in gas transmission pipelines, I. Chem. E. Symposium, 1985.

Helguero, M.V., *Piping Stress Handbook*, Gulf Publishing Co., Houston, Texas, 1986.

Holmes, E. (ed), *Handbook of Industrial Pipework Engineering*, McGraw-Hill, 1979.

Institution Mech. E. Conference, *Pipework Design & Operation*, 1985.

I. Mech. E. *Pipe Joints – a state of the art review*, Pt.1 Gaskets Pt. 2 Non-metallic Pt. 3 Metallic, 1985/6.

I. Mech. E. *Valve Users Manual*, 1980.

Kellogg, M.W. (Co.), *Design of Piping Systems*, Wiley, 1964.

King, R.C. (ed.), *Piping Handbook*, McGraw-Hill, NY, 1973.

Lamit, L.C., *Piping Systems, Drafting & Design*, Prentice-Hall, 1981.

Parker M.E. and Peattie E.G. *Pipeline Corrosion & Cathodic Protection: a practical manual*, Gulf Publishing Co., Houston and London, 1984.

Pearson, G.H., *Valve design*, I. Mech. Eng. Mech. Eng. Pub. 1978.

Weaver, R., *Process Piping Design*, 2 vols, Gulf Publishing Co., Houston, Texas, 1973.

Welding Institute (Cambridge) International Conference on Pipewelding, 2 vols, 1980–81.

# 5 Lined vessels and protective coatings

## 5.1 Lining of vessels and components

It has become common industrial practice, particularly in the chemical plant industry, to line vessels and components with a material which will give protection from corrosion or against specific chemical attack.

Natural rubbers (and ebonite) were amongst the first materials used for protection, and are still the most frequently employed. However these have their limitations, as they do not withstand oils or severe chemical attack, and consequently other materials have come into use, such as synthetic rubbers, PVC, polythene and other plastics (including thermosetting resins), bitumen, glass, corrosion-resistant metal, and various forms of cement.

The lining material may be applied in sheet form, with joints between sheets welded and suitably bonded to the vessel, or it may be built up as a coating by brushing or various spraying or dipping processes. Whatever the process or material it will have its design limitations, but the theoretical protection and useful life possible will not even be approached unless the process is carried out carefully to the correct instructions, and surface preparation and treatment are adequately performed. It is the duty of the inspector to watch these points and ensure that they receive proper attention. Much depends on the skill of the operator, but he must be seen and encouraged to use this skill. An inspector would be failing in his duty if he confined his examination to a final test on a lining or coating. This test might show faults and result in a rejection, but it could well be that faults due to inadequate preparation and process control would not show up until later, thus causing trouble in service.

The vessel or component to be lined may be fabricated from ferrous or non-ferrous plate or sheet, or it may be cast, forged, etc. Fabrication by butt-welding rather than riveting is preferred, so that a smooth surface for the lining can be prepared by grinding, shot blasting, etc.

Vessels constructed of concrete and plastics may also be lined. Attention is drawn to the *Factories Act* 1961, Section 30 (see 4.3.23) and the possible requirement for inspection and/or access openings (see BS 470).

## 5.2 Rubber and ebonite lining

Rubber and ebonite linings are usually applied to mild steel vessels and components, but in particular instances cast iron, brass, aluminium or even concrete and wood vessels may be so lined. Riveting of metal vessels is not desirable, owing to the projection of the rivets, and welding is preferred. If rivets are present they should be countersunk and finished flush if possible. Sharp corners and angles in the vessel should be avoided as far as possible, angles being smoothed over to a radius of say $\frac{1}{2}$ in. (12 mm). Corners might be filled in by fillet welds.

The vessels must be thoroughly cleaned, perhaps by pickling or by circulating with steam and/or by degreasing, followed by shot blasting. Surface irregularities, crevices and defects, weld spatter, etc., should be removed. Castings should be free from blowholes and porosity. Any traces of a previous finish, such as paint or galvanizing, should be removed. Only non-metallic grit should be used for blast cleaning aluminium and its alloys. The standard of surface finish required may be specified (see 10.9, BS 1134 and Swedish Standard SIS 05 5900). A somewhat rougher (but uniform) finish may be necessary with some materials to facilitate bonding. After blasting all debris, dust, etc. should be carefully removed by vacuum cleaning and/or brush.

Suitable bonding agents (usually isocyanates or rubber solutions), often of proprietary type and undisclosed composition, are then applied by brush or spray before the cleaned surface has had time to deteriorate. For first-class work the inspector may find it helpful, with some solutions, to ensure that they are thoroughly stirred and to see that moisture and air bubbles have been eliminated.

Unvulcanized rubber sheets, usually some 3–6 mm thick perhaps tested to specific requirements of BS 903, should have been prepared previously for the lining. They should have been checked for consistency of thickness and freedom from blisters, etc. and then tailored to fit. Pre-shrinking may be necessary to secure a satisfactory and lasting fit, particularly with some carbon-black loaded compounds; this can be done by placing the sheets on a hot-plate at some 60°C for about a quarter of an hour. Pre-vulcanized sheets may be used, usually supplied as a laminate with a soft rubber backing.

The edges of the sheets have to bevelled where joints are required. The simple scarf joint at 45° is very satisfactory if measurements are exact. The overlapping scarf joint may be objectionable in some cases if it tends to re-strict smooth flow, and it may project and tend to separate from its neighbour.

The tailored sheets are then laid one at a time onto their exact position on the prepared surface, after the solution has become 'tacky', and rapidly and carefully rolled down into position by hand over the whole area, usually by an 'edge' wheel or hand rubbing tools, taking great care to work out and expel any air trapped under the sheet. Heated iron tools may be used to expel the air. Special attention must be paid to corners and to seams between sheets. Should any air be inadvertently left under the sheet it could cause a blister during subsequent processing or in use (particularly if used under vacuum) and would greatly weaken the bond.

Trapped air can be avoided or minimized by removing surface irregularities and seeing that there are no crevices, pits, etc. Unavoidably trapped volumes can be vented by means of small holes drilled through the shell, where this is thought essential, to permit the escape of air during lining; these holes must be sealed up in an approved manner prior to final acceptance.

Some local grinding or patching may be necessary after fitting. A cover strap over a simple scarf joint may be desirable (even if this type of joint was not originally intended), and may be essential with pre-vulcanized sheet.

All the above preparatory processes should be carried out at a temperature of at least 3°C above the dew point (measured at the surfaces to be lined).

It is as well to apply a spark test before vulcanization to ensure that the metal has been completely covered. A high-voltage high-frequency Tesla coil (giving about 20 kV at 20 kc/s (hertz) according to lining thickness) is connected between a probe and the metal surface of the vessel. The probe is then carefully moved over the whole surface of the lining at a distance of about $\frac{1}{2}$ to 1 in (12–25 mm) from it. Blue streamers will streak from it into the air, but if a gap (possibly hidden) or pinhole is present in the lining at any point then a sharp bright spark will stab out to the metal through this discontinuity. For lining thicknesses of around $\frac{1}{16}$ in (1·6 mm) a spark of some 1 in (25 mm) length is recommended ($\frac{1}{2}$ in (12 mm) for PVC), while thicknesses over $\frac{3}{32}$ in (2·4 mm) in general require a spark of not less than $1\frac{1}{4}$ in (32 mm) length. Care must be taken not to puncture any thin linings unnecessarily with an excessive spark or long 'dwell' time.

After correcting any faults found during the spark test, vulcanization can commence. Most plant lining contractors possess large steam-heated autoclaves into which vessels and components are placed for vulcanization. Alternatively, vulcanization can be carried out, perhaps on site, by introducing steam into the vessel itself. Hot air or hot water can also be used. The temperature for vulcanization is usually between about 110°C and 150°C at a pressure of 40 to 60 lb/in² gauge and the time taken may be several hours, according to the type of rubber, etc. In some cases specially prepared sheet containing accelerating material, which vulcanizes under normal working or even atmospheric conditions, is used.

After vulcanization has been completed and the vessel has cooled down the lining should again be carefully inspected visually and by spark testing. If it is necessary to enter the vessel suitable footwear should be used (hobnail boots are taboo!). Blisters, cracks, blowholes and damaged or doubtful areas may be discovered. Local repairs may be authorized by the inspector. This can be done by lifting or abrading the faulty area and inserting adhesive and a prepared patch of unvulcanized rubber with not more than a 25 mm overlap beyond the defect. Such patches have then to be vulcanized and on completion re-inspected and spark tested.

It can be shown by test that, provided adequate degreasing and scale removal has been carried out, a properly bonded rubber or ebonite lining will adhere very strongly to the metal, and will normally tear before the bond breaks away from the metal. Sample adhesion tests may be required. The hardness of the vulcanized lining can be tested with a portable rubber hardness tester (to BS 2719).

If a vessel has to be pressure-tested, and particularly if it has to pass a vacuum test, it is as well if this can be carried out before lining, otherwise small leaks may be masked. The specification may however require a final test after lining.

Periodic inspection of all lined vessels, and some components, is necessary at least annually to ensure satisfactory operation, especially if corrosive liquors are used. This inspection should consist of a careful visual examination, a hardness test, and all suspected areas, or perhaps the whole vessel, should be spark-tested.

## 5.3 Synthetic rubber and plastics linings

In general the procedures and remarks regarding natural rubbers will apply with equal force to synthetic rubber and many thermoplastics sheet linings. The various grades of synthetic rubber are much used where natural rubber would be subject to chemical attack. Nitrile rubber, for instance, can be used at higher temperatures and will withstand oils and aromatic hydrocarbons; butyl rubber is used in fertilizer manufacture and the food industry; whilst neoprene withstands oil and the action of heat and many solvents. Plasticized PVC can be used up to some 60°C and 60 lb/in$^2$.

Amongst other thermoplastics used in sheet lining are:

Polyethylene (PE)—suitable for use up to some 30–55°C (according to grade—low to high density)
Polypropylene (PP)—suitable for use up to some 60°C
Fluorocarbons (PTFE, PVDF, FEP)—suitable for use up to some 250°C.

The sheets will be prepared, hot formed (where necessary), welded and if required bonded to the vessel. Type tests on welds to BS 2782 Methods

320A–F may be required. The welds should have at least 85% of the strength of the parent material. The above thermoplastics (and also nylon) can be applied to the coating of vessels (not concrete) by various dipping or spraying processes, using powder or a dispersion coating (with fluorocarbons). The coatings are normally thin and several coats may sometimes be applied (see also 5.15–5.17).

Fluorinated rubbers (e.g. Viton) and fluorinated plastics (e.g. Teflon types FEP, FPA and PVDF) are available for lining vessels for use up to some 200°C, Teflon type linings may be fitted loose, or laminated to a glass fabric which is then cemented to the vessel wall.

Thermosetting epoxide and phenolic resins may be applied to vessels as a thin coating, the first coat preferably by brush. Further coats, at least four, may be applied by spraying until the required thickness is achieved. Drying between coats is necessary and for phenolic resins stoving between coats may be carried out followed by a final stoving at a higher temperature (some 150°C to 180°C). These materials may be used at temperatures up to some 70–120°C under wet conditions and some 120–150°C under dry conditions. They are resistant to most acids, to neutral salts, and to a wide range of solvents. Epoxides are resistant to alkaline solutions, but phenols only to mild alkaline solutions (see also 5.15 and 5.17).

Tables showing the chemical resistance of various rubber and plastics linings to a wide range of industrial products are available from the Plant Lining Group of the Federation of British Rubber and Allied Manufacturers and the Rubber and Plastics Research Association, Shawbury (see also BS CP 3003 and BS 6374).

## 5.4 Lining of pipework and other components

Pipework and fittings can of course be lined with various rubbers and plastics in the same general manner. For smaller pipe sizes it is often convenient to draw a fairly close-fitting tube of uncured rubber through the metal tube, attach end flanges and then vulcanize under steam pressure. The pressure forces the rubber against the metal and, with the aid of a bonding agent, secures an effective bond. Larger tubes can be lined by hand-rolling. It is preferable to use seamless tubes. Although obvious, the inspector should bear in mind that lining will reduce the internal bore of a pipe, which may necessitate the use of a larger-size bore. Screwed fittings are not recommended.

Normally all branches and connections to lined parts must be flanged. The lining must be taken over the flange face to prevent the ingress of process fluid between the lining and the substrate (pipe or vessel).

Rubber-lined tanks are used extensively for the transport of various chemicals and products by road, rail and sea. A comparatively recent development is the use of flexible containers. These generally consist of an impervious lining material suitable for the liquid, etc., to be transported, bonded to a strong but flexible synthetic fibre, such as nylon. The exterior is usually coated with neoprene to give protection from weathering, sunlight and ozone, etc. With one type the flexible material is supported on an aluminium framework (semi-rigid), but the non-rigid sausage-like flexible container can be constructed to a great size and used, for instance, as a towed oil or chemical tanker.

## 5.5 Glass lining and vitreous enamelling

Glass, particularly of the alumino-silicate and other 'borosilicate' varieties, is used for the lining of steel and other process vessels and components, storage and transport tanks, etc.

The inspection of the lining process is of some importance. The steel tank, of welded construction, has to have all scale and blemishes removed, usually by shot or grit blasting and is left with a roughened surface to act as a key for the coating. This coating is then applied, either by dusting dry glass powder into the heated tank or by spraying a wet slip into the cold tank, letting it dry, and then heating to fusion. Several coats are usually needed and the first often contains a proportion of cobalt oxide to help bonding between the steel and glass. The coefficient of expansion of this glass is kept below that of the steel so that on cooling the glass is put into a state of compression rather than tension. Glass is very weak in tension but comparatively strong in compression. A well produced lining should be able to withstand considerable thermal shock and stresses up to the elastic limit of the steel. As the operating temperature is increased the compressive stress in the glass due to the difference in expansion between it the steel decreases and it is less able to stand thermal shock. A shock sufficient to put the lining in tension would tend to cause fracture. Without thermal shock (say a sudden drop of some 50–100°C) borosilicate glasses can be used up to approaching 300°C.

Regular 'in-use' inspection of such linings is recommended, both visually and by low voltage electrical testing (see 5.17).

Somewhat akin to glass lining is the process of vitreous enamelling, sometimes applied to the interior of cast iron reaction vessels, etc., to resist corrosion, and generally, applied to steel components. Again, inspection of the preparatory treatment is important; methods of testing vitreous enamel finishes are dealt with in BS 1344.

## 5.6 Earthing of tanks and vessels

It is normal requirement that all tanks, vessels, components (including covers and stirrers), etc., are effectively bonded to earth to prevent dangerous electric charges arising (see 6.11). A special case arises if a vessel, etc., is lined with a layer of non-conducting material (of insulation resistance exceeding 1 megohm) and is used to contain a liquid liable to become charged. This charge cannot then leak away to earth and it may be necessary to insert an earthed plate in the bottom of the vessel in contact with the liquid.

## 5.7  Metal-clad and lined vessels

Vessels (including pressure vessels) may be constructed of integrally clad plate (such as stainless steel or nickel-clad steel plate) in which the corrosion-resistant surface is backed by mild steel. Alternatively, the vessel may be lined with corrosion-resistant sheet attached by welding. Methods of fabrication, inspection and testing are dealt with in the ASME Boiler and Pressure Vessel Code, Section VIII, Part UCL (see also 3.11 (iii) and Fig. 5.1). In particular, besides the usual checking of the main welds of the vessel, the jointing of the cladding or lining must be checked for cracks, etc., by radiography or other methods such as liquid penetrants. A test for tightness of any applied lining is recommended. Periodic inspections in service are also desirable to check the nature and rate of corrosion, and the extent of any deterioration (see 12.6).

*Nickel and its alloys*, such as Monel and Inconel, are frequently used for lining steel chemical plant. With loose lining the inspector should ensure that the pieces of lining material are a good fit in the vessel, and that both they and the interior of the vessel are scrupulously clean before welding is commenced (see also 9.20).

Integrally bonded clad plate, particularly of *stainless steel*, is much used for resisting corrosion. Depending on the severity of service expected, supervision, inspection and testing during and after manufacture of the plate may be desirable. The methods of manufacture employed usually rely on thorough cleaning of the surfaces to be bonded, with the introduction of a thin sheet of very-low-carbon steel or a layer of nickel to act as a bonding agent, and some form of sealing to prevent contamination by air or furnace gases. The compound plate is then heated to forging temperature and roll-bonded down to size. (Fig. 5.2 shows the 'sandwich' method of producing roll-clad plate.) Samples containing the bond can be taken for micrographic examination and testing for shear strength, etc.; ultrasonic testing to check the quality of the bonding may be desirable on each plate, particularly near regions where openings, etc., will be cut.

Components and vessels which have to withstand corrosive attack, particularly thick ones, are now sometimes clad with a stainless steel lining deposited by a submerged arc welding process which lays down a strip at a time from stainless steel wire. Inspection of the process has of course to ensure that a good continuously adherent layer is produced.

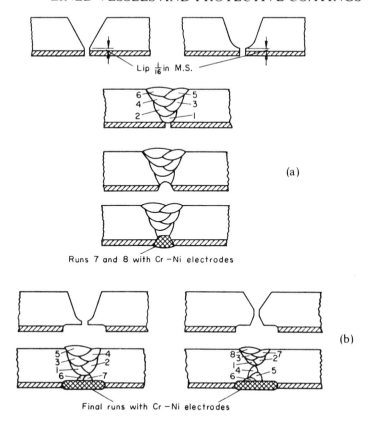

**Fig. 5.1   Welding of metal-clad plate. (The Welding Institute.)**
(a) 'V' and 'U' edge preparation and procedure.
(b) Cut back edge preparation and procedure.

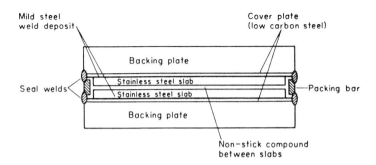

**Fig. 5.2   'Sandwich' method of producing roll-clad plate.** After roll-bonding the
two plates are separated by cutting the packing bars.
(*National and Vulcan Engineering Insurance Group.*)

Thick-walled pressure vessels are difficult and costly to construct. A double or multi-layer construction can often be adopted with advantage. The inner layer can be of stainless or special alloy steel to resist corrosion, etc. from the process fluid. An outer layer or layers of ordinary steel can be built up of courses rolled into a ring and hoop welded. These courses can then be heat treated and shrunk on to the inner shell. A thin steel strip wound on to the outer surface of the inner shell, in conjunction with the gaps between courses of the outer shell, will provide an escape route for any hydrogen diffusing through the inner shell and so prevent it from becoming trapped and causing hydrogen embrittlement in the material of the outer shell (see 6.14).

*Chemical lead,* its alloys and homogeneous lead (i.e. lead bonded to sheet steel, or sometimes copper, for strength) are much used for lining vessels of steel, concrete, wood, brick, etc. The lining may be loose or bonded to the surface; if the latter, careful surface preparation is necessary. A loose lead lining must be adequately supported, and the method of welding should be approved. Before lining concrete vessels they should be allowed to dry out naturally for some 28 days, and should then be given a suitable bitumen coating to prevent corrosion of the lead by contact with free alkali from the concrete; materials such as coal tar pitch (which contains phenol) should be avoided.

Similarly, wooden vessels may need a resistant coating or a layer of plastic, asphalted felt or water-proof building paper between wood and lead to prevent corrosion due to acids emanating from the wood. The wood can be preserved by treatment with creosote.

Where it is impracticable to provide adequate support for a loose lead lining, homogeneous lead must be used; such a lining is necessary for lead-lined ferrous metal vessels required to operate at pressures below atmospheric. A test for adhesion can be made on such a vacuum vessel by subjecting it to steam pressure (10 lb/in$^2$) and then to vacuum (some 25–28 inHg), and checking that any part of the lining does not 'lift'. A further examination of the lining for signs of rust after 7 days should check for porosity. Dye penetrant tests can also be used.

Non-pressure vessels lined with loose sheet can have leak-indicating holes drilled through the shell; these will help to indicate faults in the lining which would not otherwise be apparent until penetration of the shell occurred in service.

Some comment on the welding of titanium linings should be made. Clad plate is stripped back (generally as described in 3.11 (iii) and Fig. 5.1 (b)) but it is important that molten mild steel and titanium should not intermingle in the weld, otherwise a hard brittle alloy, subject to cracking, is formed. Separation can be ensured by a layer of pure silver, soldered or brazed between the titanium and the mild steel before making and filling the mild steel weld. This weld is then covered by a titanium backing strip. Titanium sheet, rather than clad plate, is more often used for the lining of vessels, but the same principle applies—the molten titanium must not touch the steel backing. The argon-arc process must be used (see 9.13); dry box techniques may be employed (see 6.2).

## 5.8 Protective coatings

Many materials and processes can be applied to metals to give them some measure of protection against corrosion. The materials include metals, plastics and paint. The metals are applied by such processes as electroplating, hot-dipping and spraying; and the plastics by spraying.

Although important items of plant may be constructed in expensive materials giving considerable protection against corrosion and chemical attack, it should be remembered that the ancillary parts, including structural steelwork, may be exposed to the weather or difficult environmental conditions and will need periodical maintenance and treatment to avoid the necessity of complete replacement. Owing to the increasing cost of labour today it is becoming economic to use more sophisticated protective treatments than conventional painting (in which labour costs for surface preparation and the application of several coats far exceed the cost of the paint) in order to maintain these ancillary items.

In engineering applications it is the *surface* of any material or component which has to withstand the external environment, be it weather (or process) conditions, corrosion, or attack from process fluids, materials and/or conditions such as friction, wear and fatigue, etc. Many engineering failures arise from deficiencies of the surface of a material in withstanding such attacks.

In general it is more economic to choose a strong but cheap bulk material and to use a special surface material, finish or coating to withstand the environment. The desired surface properties can be obtained by the application of specialized coatings, by the attachment (perhaps by welding) of a layer of the resisting material, or by some process which modifies the surface of the bulk material.

Whatever method of protection is used it is essential that the bonding of the surface layer of resisting or treated material to the bulk of the parent material should be proved by test to be satisfactory, and preferably is of a strength equal to that of the parent material.

Of prime importance is the preparation of the surface of the material to ensure cleanliness. Oils etc. must be removed first, usually by a vapour or solvent degreasing agent, followed if necessary by rinsing and drying, acid etching or pickling. Clean surface roughness may improve adhesion.

An electrical form of protection, cathodic protection, suitable for certain structures is described in 4.29.3–5.

## 5.9 Zinc coating

Zinc is widely used in industry as a protective coating for iron and steelwork.

The zinc coating acts primarily as a slowly corroding barrier between the atmosphere and the steel, its corrosion products being dense and adherent and tending to slow down further corrosion. Secondarily, under certain, conditions (such as in aqueous media), it can protect scratches and small imperfections sacrificially (zinc being near the anodic (+ve) end of the galvanic series—see 12.7 and Fig. 12.1). When two dissimilar metals such as zinc and iron are connected together and placed in a conducting medium (such as impure water), a galvanic cell is formed and current flows through the medium between the anode (zinc) and cathode (iron). The zinc goes into solution, i.e. it is corroded, but the iron remains unaffected. This is the essential principle of all cathodic (or galvanic) protection. (See 4.29.3).

However the inspector should note that should for instance copper equipment be present in any aqueous circuit involving galvanized tanks or pipework, etc. (or even traces of copper dropped in perhaps inadvertently) then galvanic corrosion of the zinc will take place, perhaps rapidly.

The principal methods of zinc coating are:
(i)    Hot-dip galvanizing.
(ii)   Plating (electro-deposition).
(iii)  Zinc spraying.
(iv)   Cementation (sherardizing).
(v)    Painting with zinc-rich paint.

These methods are complementary to one another rather than optional, and each has its particular applications.

*Hot-dip galvanizing* is the most widely used process and consists basically of thoroughly cleaning the articles and then dipping them into a bath of molten zinc. Layers of zinc-iron alloy are formed, and upon removal a layer of pure zinc is retained on the surface. The cleaning process is important and should be watched; it is generally achieved by pickling in dilute acid, or by shot blasting. The minimum weight of zinc coating specified in BS 729 *Hot-dip galvanized coatings on iron and steel articles* is 305 $g/m^2$ (equivalent to 1 oz/ft$^2$) and this is applicable to threaded work and other articles which are not centrifuged. Heavier coatings up to 610 $g/m^2$ for steel articles 5 mm thick and over are laid down, and this coating weight is specified for grey and malleable iron castings. Higher and lower coating weights may be agreed, and it may be necessary to grit-blast before galvanizing in order to obtain a required heavy coating. Details of tests on this coating and of visual examinations are given in BS 729 and in BS 443: *Testing zinc coatings on steel wire and for quality requirements.*

The mass of coating may be determined by either a gravimetric or volumetric method, the latter method being preferred for routine testing and the former as a referee method. The volumetric method depends on the fact that a metal dissolved in acid (25% HCl is used) always releases a quantity of hydrogen proportional to the amount of metal dissolved (1 gram of zinc releases 343 mL of hydrogen at 0°C and 1014 mbar). Uniformity of coating is tested by a copper sulphate solution (Preece dip method).

Details of these tests and of the visual examination required are given in the standards. Adhesion of the coating to wire is checked by wrapping the wire at least six times round a specified cylindrical mandrel after which the zinc must not crack or flake away after rubbing with the fingers. The minimum mass of coating ($g/m^2$) for various diameters of wire is specified.

A coating of 1 $g/m^2$ gives an average radial thickness of 0·1407 μm. A coating of 1 $oz/ft^2$ gives an average radial thickness of 42,926 μm.

*Zinc plating* is applicable to the protection of smaller and more delicate articles of complex shape rather than to structural steel work. Zinc anodes are suspended in the plating solution (either an acid sulphate solution or an alkaline cyanide solution) and the zinc is electro-deposited uniformly on the articles by the action of a direct current. The weight of zinc deposited is small compared with hot dipping, 0·1 $oz/ft^2$ often being sufficient. Details of the process, methods of checking weight, thickness, adhesion, quality, etc., are given in BS 1706.

*Zinc spraying* is a method of projecting particles of molten zinc at high velocity in a stream of compressed reducing gas or air onto a surface which has previously been prepared by shot or grit blasting. A specially designed pistol is held in the hand and the area to be covered is worked over systematically. Three basic types of pistol are available commercially, using either metal powder, wire or molten metal. An annular flame from the pistol, produced by the combustion of oxygen with propane, acetylene or other suitable gases, provides the heat source. Sprayed zinc is slightly porous which is an advantage because it permits the formation of the protective corrosion products throughout the coating, and provides a good key for painting. The coating will withstand hammering and bending. If desired, porosity can be avoided if the coating is fused after spraying.

Flame spraying can be carried out on site, provided that the shot or grit blasting can be performed there, and it is much used for the protection of iron and steel against atmospheric corrosion. Spraying should take place as soon as possible after the blasting operation. Thick coatings can be built up where necessary to a weight of some 5 or 6 $oz/ft^2$. Much depends on the skill of the operator, and even so the inside of deep cavities cannot be reached.

BS 2569 *Sprayed metal coatings:* Part 1 *Protection of iron and steel against atmospheric corrosion* deals with details and methods of test and gives a minimum zinc thickness of 0·004 in (0·1 mm) (with a minimum local thickness of not less than 75% of the nominal) which should be measured by means of a magnetic or electromagnetic thickness meter of agreed type and of ±10% accuracy (see also 5.14.1). An adhesion test is also specified. Part 2 deals with protection against corrosion and oxidation at elevated temperatures.

*Sherardizing* is a method of fusing zinc onto small steel articles by rotating them in a drum containing zinc dust heated to a temperature slightly below the melting point of zinc. The zinc diffuses slightly into the steel surfaces, forming an even, thin coating of zinc-iron alloy. If nuts and bolts are so treated inspection must see that tolerances have been allowed on the screw threads for the thickness of the coating.

BS 4921 *Sherardized coatings on iron and steel articles* specifies two classes of coating thickness and the reference method of determining this thickness.

*Peen plating* is a somewhat similar process except that neither heating nor electro-deposition are used. Small articles are put into a tumbling barrel with impacting material, promoter solution, the coating metal in the form of dust, and water. Particles of metal are welded onto the articles by the hammering action of the impacting material, the process taking about 45 minutes. Other metals besides zinc may be used, and the process is useful for articles such as spring washers and powder metallurgy parts which might suffer deterioration after conventional plating.

*Zinc-rich paints* which can deposit some 90% of metallic zinc have been developed and will protect steel work sacrificially. They are generally air drying and may use binders of plasticized polystyrene and chlorinated rubber. They do not in general give as good results as other forms of zinc coating, but are better than conventional paints.

For the best all-round service zinc, applied by hot-dipping, electro-deposition or spraying, is followed by painting. In the first two cases, before applying the paint, the surface should be treated by phosphating or weathering in the open air for not less than six months. When a zinc coating is not painted, or when a paint film breaks down, the protective life of the metal is proportional to its thickness. The life of a paint film on zinc spray is estimated to be at least 10 times as long as when applied to clean bare steel. Corrosion of steel can take place under a normal paint film, and once it has started it extends very rapidly, but no rusting of the steel can take place if zinc is present. Thus a zinc-sprayed component, further protected by a paint film properly maintained, could have an almost indefinite life under most atmospheric conditions. It is important to select the right grade of paint primer; in general zinc chromate primers are recommended and lead-based primers should not be used.

### 5.9.1 Zinc embrittlement of steel, etc.

Certain steels may occasionally become embrittled after galvanizing. The hot dip process involves immersion in a bath of molten zinc for up to 5 minutes at around 450°C, and this can accelerate the onset of strain-age embrittlement in susceptible steels which have been severely cold worked.

To avoid risk of such embrittlement:

(a) use a steel made by the open hearth, electric or oxygen processes and not the Bessemer process;

(b) avoid severe cold working, e.g. punching of holes or severe bending. Cold punched holes are generally satisfactory in other than Bessemer steels, up to a thickness of 18 mm; otherwise fabricate by hot working or stress adhere at over 600°C before galvanizing.

Embrittlement may also occur when malleable and spheroidal or modular graphite cast irons are galvanized. A low phosphorus content or alternatively heating to some 650°C and quenching in water should avoid this trouble.

It is particularly necessary to give a warning regarding *zinc embrittlement of austenitic chromium nickel stainless steel*. At high temperatures zinc will melt (at 419°C) and penetrate stainless steel (above 450°C). Under high stresses and temperatures above about 750°C this penetration will cause severe and rapid embrittlement of the steel and can rapidly cause catastrophic failure. Only a small amount of zinc needs to be present but the high stresses and temperatures needed to cause failure are not to be expected under normal operating conditions. However abnormal occurrences such as a fierce fire on a plant containing stainless steel pipework in the vicinity of zinc-coated fittings or galvanized wire mesh perhaps holding insulation in place, could cause a catastrophe (such conditions existed during the Flixborough disaster (see 13.6.3)).

## 5.10 Tin coating

Tin is used as a protective coating on iron and steel (tinplate), and also on copper. Tinplate has been made by mass production methods since the early 19th century, the sheet steel being first cleaned thoroughly, then passed through a suitable flux and into a bath of molten tin. In one process the sheet emerges from this bath between rollers and passes under cover of a bath of hot palm oil to prevent oxidation, from which it emerges to pass under fleece-covered rollers surrounded by bran to scour and clean it. The thickness of the tin layer is about 0·0001 in or more, and the deposit may be uneven or porous. Most tinplate, however, is now coated electrolytically, generally a more reliable and economical process. The solution may be alkaline (stannate) or acid (stannous sulphate). Careful control is required to secure a firmly adherent coating; with an alkaline solution this necessitates maintaining a yellow or green film on the anodes. Inspection should watch the methods of checking the weight and completeness of coating (see BS 2920 *Cold reduced tin plate and black plate*). Pinholes must be avoided. Tinplate used in the canning industry for food packaging, etc., absorbs about half of the world's tin production. Tin is also deposited electro-lytically on fabricated articles of iron, steel, copper, etc. (see BS 1872 *Electroplated coatings of tin*).

A less expensive material than tinplate, sometimes used for tanks, heat-exchange equipment, etc., where toxicity is unimportant, is known as terneplate. The coating material applied to the steel plate is an alloy of some 80% lead and 20% tin. It gives a somewhat dull finish (terne (French) meaning dull).

### 5.11 Other sprayed metallic coatings

Aluminium is used as an alternative to zinc as a protective coating and in some cases gives better protection against chemical attack. When applied by flame spraying the coating weight should be a minimum of $0.5$ oz/ft$^2$ ($0.0002$ in thick), and no special surface treatment prior to painting (should this be desired) is necessary. Where final painting is not desired, or if periodic maintenance painting is not carried out, the minimum recom-mended thickness of the applied coating should be doubled. This also applies to zinc spraying.

Besides its use for protection against atmospheric corrosion aluminium spraying is used to give protection to iron and steel at elevated tempera-tures. For use at temperatures above 550°C and up to 900°C, after thorough shot or grit blasting and aluminium spraying (to a nominal thickness of $0.007$ in), the components are additionally coated with coal tar pitch solution and then heat-treated at 800–900°C.

This additional coating can be omitted if an aluminium alloy (containing $0.5–0.75\%$ cadmium) is used, but the heat treatment (in a mildly oxidizing atmosphere) is still necessary.

The inspector should watch for any signs of distortion which might occur at these high temperatures, and should carry out thickness and adhesion tests. For further details see BS 2569: Part 2. This specification also deals with nickel-chromium alloy spraying for service temperatures of 1000°C; such a coating should be followed by aluminium spraying if sulphurous gases are present. The actual class of coating required must be specified.

Other metals which may be flame-sprayed on to steel to give cathodic protection include tin (for food and pharmaceuticals, etc.) and lead (for protection against acids, X-rays, etc.). An alloy of zinc and aluminium is sometimes used.

Copper, Monel, etc., may also be flame-sprayed but do *not* give cathodic protection.

Stainless steel can also be flame-sprayed on to, say, mild steel.

A hard-wearing metal or alloy (such as Stellite and other proprietary materials) can be flame-sprayed onto specific portions of components to give resistance to wear and abrasion at these points. This technique can be used for building up or repairing worn components.

Flame spraying of metals on to plastic board, etc., and even paper can be carried out without scorching the material. Electrostatic spraying of metal powder can also be carried out (see 5.15).

### 5.11.1 High-temperature spraying of metallic alloys

Various proprietary and semi-proprietary processes are widely used for the spraying of metallic alloy coatings on to substrates to resist wear and corrosion.

*Plasma spray technology* uses a d.c. electric arc (developing some 15,000°C) to strip off outer electrons from the gas flow and to dissociate di-atomic gases and then allow them to recombine. This results in an extremely high energy density and local temperature rise at the torch anode and nozzle. Metallic powder is introduced into the plasma stream and reaches a high speed and temperature when it impacts upon the substrate. An inert gas shroud is usually introduced in front of the nozzle to prevent the hot powder from reacting with atmospheric oxygen.

In *Detonation Gun (D-Gun) technology)* (as used by Union Carbide) oxygen and acetylene gas are introduced into the torch and by a series of controlled detonations initiated by a sparking plug impart energy to the stream of metallic powder particles. These particles, now semi-molten, impact upon the substrate where they produce a very strong mechanical/metallurgical bond.

The coating materials applied by the above processes include tungsten carbide/cobalt, chromium carbide/nickel-chromium and aluminium oxide. The deposited surface roughness is generally of the order of 200–300 micro inch CLA (see 10.9.).

Bond strength measurements can be made to ASTM 633.

### 5.12 Phosphate treatment and chromating

For general outdoor use where a metallic coating has not been used some additional protection can be given by the use of phosphate treatment prior to painting and by the use of a steel containing 0·2% to 0·3% of copper. The former is dealt with by BS 3189 *Phosphate treatment of iron and steel for protection against corrosion*, which also covers the inspection and testing procedure.

*Chromating* (chromate coating) can be used for the protection of magnesium and zinc alloys by treating, for instance, in hot potassium dichromate type solutions. This is a foundation treatment and should be followed by painting.

### 5.13  Electro-deposition and anodizing

Electro-deposition of many metals besides zinc and tin is of course regularly undertaken for purposes of protection against particular environments, or to provide a thin surface of a specific rare metal for technical reasons. British Standard and other specifications exist covering many such plating processes, and the inspector should refer to these where necessary (see Table 5.1).

BS 3382: Part 7 deals with thicker platings which provide a greater degree of protection against severe corrosive conditions than is possible without interference on the standard threads covered in Parts 1–6.

Most plastics can be electroplated to give a metal surface for mechanical, electrical or decorative purposes, with great saving in weight compared with conventional metal parts; in addition corrosion resistance is enhanced. The surface of the plastic is first treated with a chemical conditioner, or by vapour blasting, to provide a key for a metal conducting layer deposited by spraying, after which conventional electroplating is carried out.

## TABLE 5.1

*Some electroplating specifications*

| BS No. | Description |
|---|---|
| 1224 | Electroplated coatings of nickel and chromium |
| 1615 | Anodic oxidation coatings on aluminium (includes BNF sulphur dioxide corrosion test) |
| 1706 | Electroplated coatings of cadmium and zinc on iron and steel |
| 1872 | Electroplated coatings of tin |
| 2816 | Electroplated coatings of silver for engineering purposes |
| 3382 | Electroplated coatings on threaded components |
| |     Parts 1 and 2: Cadmium and zinc on steel components |
| |     Parts 3 and 4: Nickel or nickel plus chromium on steel, copper or copper alloy components |
| |     Parts 5 and 6: Tin and silver on copper and copper alloy components |
| |     Part 7: Thicker platings for threaded components |
| 3597 | Electroplated coatings of 65/35 tin-nickel alloy |
| 4641 | Electroplated coatings of chromium for engineering purposes |
| 4758 | Electroplated coatings of nickel for engineering purposes |
| 5599 | Hard anodic coatings on aluminium for engineering purposes |
| 6161 | Methods of test for anodic oxidation coatings on aluminium and its alloys |
| MOD DEF 151 | Anodizing of aluminium and aluminium alloys (supersedes DTD 910 and 930) |

Tests to check adhesion (a peel test), climatic tests, and tests of mechanical and electrical properties may be required.

*Anodizing* (anodic oxidation) is a process used for intensifying with nascent oxygen the protective oxide film that is normally present on the surface of aluminium and its alloys. The component to be treated (protected) is made the anode in an electrolytic cell using an electrolyte of sulphuric acid, chromic acid (the Bengough and Stuart process) or oxalic acid. The cathode may be of carbon, lead or stainless steel. Voltages up to 60 V are gradually applied (d.c. only in the case of the Bengough and Stuart process).

Decorative effects made by impregnating with dyes are used commercially.

Magnesium alloys may also be anodized using more complex electrolytes.

BS 1615 *Anodic oxidation coatings on aluminium* classifies coatings by thickness only, without reference to the type of electrolyte; it is necessary for the purchaser to state the clauses which are relevant, the grade (thickness) number and/or the agreed standard of performance. Tests which may be used for control and acceptance purposes are outlined. Other tests and requirements may be specified, and vary according to the use.

The latest revision of BS 1615 has been metricated and covers thickness grades from AA25 down to AA1, the number designating the average coating thickness in micrometres (1 $\mu$m = 0·001 mm = 0·00004 in).

BS 5599 deals with hard anodic coatings (Type 3 of DEF–151) of minimum thickness 25 $\mu$m and Vickers hardness number not less than 350.

BS 6161 deals with methods of test for anodic oxidation coatings on aluminium, etc. and is issued in some dozen separate parts, each describing tests for thickness, sealing qualities, corrosion resistance (CASS test), etc. which will replace the appendices in BS 1615 and eventually that standard.

More specifically, Ministry of Defence Specification DEF–151 *Anodizing of aluminium and aluminium alloys* gives three processes of anodic coating:

Type 1 Sulphuric acid process.

Type 2 Chromic acid process.

Type 3 Hard anodizing process.

The Type 1 process normally provides a thickness of some 0·0003 to 0·0005 in. Inspection should note that the coating should be sealed in a chromate solution and that it is not suitable for parts containing riveted, lap or folded joints owing to possible seepage of the acid electrolyte. This process should be used for the protection of parts in contact with concentrated hydrogen peroxide (HTP), but in this case the sealing should not be carried out.

The Type 2 process gives a relatively thin coating of some 0·0001 in and is preferred for most castings, and some components, because of the innocuous nature of any electrolyte which may be retained in pores or crevices. Seepage of the yellow electrolyte from any flaws, etc., will aid in their detection. This process should be used on thin components (less than 0·01 in thick) and on any which may be in contact with or in proximity to explosives (although in this case yellow staining due to seepage is not permissible); it minimizes any loss of fatigue strength due to anodizing.

The Type 3 process, which may use a sulphuric acid electrolyte, is used to produce harder and thicker coatings (of some 0·001 to 0·003 in thick), and to provide greater resistance to abrasion, corrosion and electrical breakdown. It is necessary to maintain the electrolyte at a low temperature (0° ± 5°C) during the process. The treatment may reduce the fatigue strength by about one-half, but this can be largely restored by sealing the coating in an aqueous dichromate solution, with some loss of abrasion resistance.

The sulphuric and oxalic acid processes yield a transparent or translucent film; the chromic acid process yields an opaque or semi-opaque film. The sulphuric acid process may give a clear or 'off-silver' finish, whilst the oxalic acid process may give a yellow, brown or brassy finish.

All coatings on inspection should appear dense and continuous. A powdery outer layer should be rejected as it generally indicates an electrically discontinuous coating. (Slight surface bloom which can be removed with a dry cloth may be satisfactory.)

Sealed coatings are generally subjected to a low-voltage electrical test for continuity. A 10 volt d.c. supply connected to a copper brush type electrode is passed lightly and slowly over the anodized surface, the other pole of the supply being connected via an indicator lamp or buzzer, so that it makes metallic contact with the component. No discontinuities (as shown by the passage of current) should be evident, although discontinuities on the edges of components can generally be disregarded.

The electrical resistance of the coating depends on the process used. The breakdown voltage on test for Types 1 and 3 should not be less than 200 volts, and for Type 2 not less than 50 volts.

A dye test for quality is usually applied to coatings of Types 1 and 2. Before any sealing process a methyl violet dye is applied by using a rubber stamp or pad (or a copying ink pencil) on the moistened anodized surface. Vigorous scrubbing with a damp cloth should not appreciably remove the dye marking. This test should not be applied to parts for use with concentrated hydrogen peroxide (HTP).

### 5.14 Testing of protective coatings

In general, to ensure a satisfactory coating the process must be adequately supervised, and tests on the component, or a sample, are required to check the coating's thickness, porosity and continuity, adhesion, purity, hardness and resistance to corrosion.

*Thickness* can be measured by various non-destructive testing methods (see 10.6.3, 10.7.3 and Fig. 10.3), which will show up local variations in thickness. If desired samples are sectioned and examined and measured under a microscope. The sample coating can be chemically stripped and its average thickness calculated from the loss in weight per unit area; alternatively, it may be electrolytically stripped, when the thickness will be directly proportional to the quantity of electricity required (coulombs) divided by the area tested (the coulometric method). A further method is to apply a jet test, in which the time required for a specified jet of solvent, under controlled conditions, to penetrate the coating is taken as a measure of its thickness; standard samples with coatings of known thickness are used for calibration purposes. The BNF jet test uses a mixture of ferric chloride, acetic acid and copper sulphate; a temperature correction is made and time converted to thickness by means of a calibrating graph.

*Porosity tests* can be made on samples exposed to a corrosive or other environment, and results expressed in terms of the number of pores exposed in a given area.

*Continuity tests* can be made by spark testing, or other electrical methods in suitable cases. Samples may also be immersed in a liquid which will attack the base metal, but leaves the coating unaffected. Continuity often breaks down at sharp corners or edges.

*Adhesion tests* may involve flexing or rubbing of the sample under controlled conditions, or heating and quenching in water, or filing an edge, followed by examination to determine whether the coating has 'lifted'.

*Ductility tests* may involve bending a sample around a specified mandrel and examining for cracks.

*Chemical tests* to determine the *purity* of the coating can be made, and various spectrographic methods (see 2.11) are useful when dealing with minute samples stripped from the base metal.

*Micro-hardness tests* are often required on thin precious metal coatings. For instance, with gold, the best wear resistance results from a hardness of 100–120 DPH on a coating of some 0·0002 in (0·005 mm) thick. Good 'solderability' of gold-plated components usually requires a thickness of the order of 0·00004 in. (0·001 mm).

BS 6286 *Methods of Measurement of total or effective thickness of thin surface hardened layers in steel* is not applicable to thin surface layers not continuous with (part of) the basis metal. It applies to thicknesses equal to or less than 0·3 mm obtained for example by shot blasting or peening, flame or induction hardening, or by carbonitriding, carburizing and hardening etc. Measurement is carried out by a micrographic or a microhardness method. For methods of determining the effective depth of carburized and case-hardened steels see also BS 6479 and BS 6481.

*Corrosion tests* are often required, especially on thicker coatings for severe conditions. Such tests are intended to give accelerated corrosion under simulated conditions, but do not correspond generally with service use; they should be used to compare the quality of coatings obtained by a specific procedure, and not to make comparison of one type of coating with another. Amongst the tests used on plated coatings are the sodium chloride/acetic acid spray test (specified by ASTM B 287), the copper-accelerated acetic acid/salt spray (CASS) test (ASTM B 368), the Corrod-kote test of nickel-chromium coatings using a corrosive paste (ASTM B 380), all of which are now included in BS 1224, and the sulphur dioxide test.

When specifying a protective finish, etc., it is usually necessary to state the service conditions expected. For instance, BS 1224 *Electroplated coatings of nickel and chromium* gives four grades of service conditions (corresponding to various thicknesses), designated from 1 (the most severe) to 4, followed by an initial letter denoting the basis metal; within these grades the type of plating and thickness can be further specified. Samples must withstand the appropriate corrosion test for a specified number of hours, according to grade. Employing BS 3745 *Method for the evaluation of results of accelerated corrosion tests on metallic coatings*, a rating is assigned to each sample tested representing its relative freedom from spots at which the coating is penetrated (assessed from the number of spots exposed in the area of the sample). For acceptance this rating must be at least 8. Surface deterioration will generally occur during the test, but is not as serious as penetration, and should be assessed on its merits.

### 5.14.1 Magnetic or electromagnetic methods of measuring coating thickness

These methods may be used for measuring the thickness of conductive or dielectric coatings on a metal base; the coating or base, or both, may be magnetic or non-magnetic.

With *magnetic methods* variations in coating thickness are determined by an instrument which measures the corresponding variation in magnetic attraction or magnetic flux between a detector and a magnetic base material.

With *electromagnetic methods*, by using a coil to induce eddy currents in the coating, thickness is determined by measuring the force required to lift off the detector, or the effect on the coil's conductivity or permeability.

In both methods the instrument is set up by using appropriate reference standards, and the coating thickness is determined by noting the instrument's response and using a calibration curve.

Sometimes, as for instance where the coating has a conductivity or permeability near that of the base material, these methods will give a poor response and other techniques (e.g. ultrasonics—see 10.6.3) must be used.

### 5.15  Plastic coatings (see also 5.3)

A range of plastic coatings is used in industry for coating vessels, ducting, fans, pipes and other items of plant. They resist corrosion, erosion, abrasion and electricity, and chemical attack from acids, solvents, salts, oils, etc. Amongst the thermo plastics which can be applied are polythene, nylon, PVC, polypropylene, cellulose acetate butyrate; also various thermo-setting epoxy resins, polyurethane and penton (chlorinated polyether); also used, often in fluid form, are chlorinated natural rubber, synthetic rubbers, and shellac (a natural material) mixed with powdered mica. The methods of application include dipping, brushing, attachment of sheets, or spraying (including flame and electrostatic spraying).

Thermoplastic materials (such as polythene, PVC and nylon) in powder form have been used for coating purposes for many years. Thermosetting materials (such as epoxy powders) have certain advantages in the fields of chemical resistance, physical properties, etc., but need an additional curing stage. Recent developments include lower-temperature curing (100°C instead of some 150°C). Epoxy powders are higher in cost but coatings can be thinner (e.g. 0·002 in instead of 0·010–0·020 in) (50 μm instead of 250–500 μm).

The epoxide resin based materials have good chemical resistance, hardness, adhesion and flexibility, and provide a relatively thick build-up per coat. Unlike some conventional paints, in which the binding material is attacked by solvents, they resist such attack. They may be air-dried, heat-cured, or chemically cured at ordinary temperature to produce the necessary protective 'paint' film. As with other protective finishes inspection must ensure careful surface preparation and an adequate film thickness (some 0·005–0·007 in).

As an alternative to wet dipping the fluidized bed process can be used. This consists of preheating the metal component to a sufficiently high temperature and dipping it into a bed of plastic particles so that these melt and fuse together on the surface of the component. The thermal capacity of the component may be sufficient for adequate fusion, otherwise a sintering stage is necessary.

A dispersion of the plastic in a solvent, or an aqueous base, can be made and sprayed onto the component, followed by a sintering process.

Dry or flock spraying consists of spraying plastic powder on to a preheated component, followed by sintering.

Electrostatic spraying is carried out by applying an electrostatic charge (of some 90–150 kV) between the sprayed powder and the component, followed by sintering; preheating may not be required.

Amine-cured epoxy coatings can be used for lining road or rail tankers for transporting crude oils, refined products, aircraft fuel and water/methanol mixtures. Careful attention must be paid to the inspection and pretreatment of metal surfaces to ensure cleanliness and surface finish, and to the method of application, which may be by brush (3 coats) or spray (4 coats) to provide a dried film thickness of some 0·0075 in (200 μm).

PTFE may be applied to components by a spray coating process known as 'dispersion', a suspension of the finely divided polymer in water or an organic medium. This gives good chemical resistance and an 'anti-stick' surface; however it is difficult to obtain an entirely porous-free coating. A good clean machined surface forms the best base for treatment, and sintering or curing is carried out at 400°C. Several coats may be required.

### 5.16  Plastic flame spraying

(a) The process of depositing plastic materials by flame spraying involves three stages:

(i) Preheating of the surface to be coated so that the plastic particles remain molten on impact and fuse together in intimate contact with the surface being coated.

(ii) Deposition of the required coating thickness.

(iii) Fusion of the applied coating to seal off pin holes and establish a homogeneous film.

Inspection should check the preparation of metal surfaces before spraying. This preparation is best carried out by grit blasting with No. 18 or 15 angular steel grit (BS 2451 *Chilled iron shot and grit*). A well-roughened surface is essential if a satisfactory bond is to be obtained. Improved adhesion results from first applying by metal spraying a thin coating of stainless steel, preferably of the 13% chromium type.

Preheating can be carried out with the pistol flame, whilst the powder feed is shut off. A surface temperature of 20–40°C above the melting point of the plastic should be attained before any attempt is made to apply the coating. An indication that the surface is hot enough is given if a thin adherent film is left on the surface after stroking it with a thin stick of the plastic material.

Overheating is indicated by a darkening in colour of the stick where it has made contact with the hot-plate. Cooling can be accelerated by blowing a little cold air onto the surface of the plate. Overheating of the metal should be avoided, particularly if grit blasting is the only preparation, since sufficient oxidation can occur on ferrous metals even at these low temperatures to affect the adhesion of the coating.

Inadequate preheating is also undesirable and may result in poor adhesion, cracking or blistering of the coating. An oxygen-gas torch may be employed for both preheating and final fusing if preferred, using a slightly reducing flame and allowing only the extreme tip of the flame to approach the coating whilst fusing. Radiant heat from infra-red lamps or open resistance elements is also used, and small articles are satisfactorily dealt with in hot ovens.

Plastic materials, when cooled, contract much more than metals, and as might be expected adherent coatings on metals become strained when cooled from melting point to room temperature. Providing the bond strength is adequate and the surface area is small this is not a serious matter, but on a surface area of more than two or three square feet the strains produced by differential contraction may become greater than the bond will withstand and the coating can become detached from the underlying metal. This can be overcome to some extent by attention to the method of application.

The surface to be coated should be mentally divided off into squares about 6 in × 6 in (150mm × 150mm) and each square should be coated in turn, following a definite pattern. Preferably the pattern should resemble a chess board, all the black squares being completely coated and fused before commencing the white squares. In this way the contraction stresses are broken up or sub-divided, and, if the preparatory treatment has been done satisfactorily, heavier coatings can be applied without impairing the adhesion.

(b) *Spraying conditions.* The application of the coating depends on three variable factors:

(i) The quantity of heat available from the flame.

(ii) The volume of propellant air.

(iii) The feed rate of the plastic powder.

The amount of heat available is governed by the rate of flow of the combustion gases, and the optimum requirement is the amount which when mixed with the propellant air and powder/gas mixture provides an average temperature slightly higher than the melting point of the plastic being deposited. The gas flow is under the control of the operator and depends on the pistol supply pressures.

The correct pressures for a particular plastic can easily be found by the following test. The flame is ignited and the propellant air and powder feed supplies are turned on. The resulting spray is directed on to a non-metallic surface at a nozzle distance of 6–7 in (150–175mm) and the behaviour condition of the deposited particles noted.

If the deposit flows together immediately, too much heat is available and the gas and oxygen pressures should be gradually lowered (oxygen before gas). If the particles do not flow together, even after prolonged spraying on the same spot, insufficient heat is available and the pressures must be increased (gas before oxygen). The aim should be to get coalescence of the deposit within one or two seconds of deposition—a condition which, together with preheating, provides a fluid coating.

Typical processing figures are as follows:

| | | |
|---|---|---|
| Propane | 6 lb/in$^2$: | 8 ft$^3$/h |
| Oxygen | 10 lb/in$^2$: | 25 ft$^3$/h |
| Propellant air | 5 lb/in$^2$ | $\Big\}$ 6 ft$^3$/min |
| Feed air | 3 lb/in$^2$ | |
| Feed rate: Nylon | 17 oz/h: 13 ft$^2$ @ 0·010 in thick | |
| | Polythene 20 oz/h: 15 ft$^2$ @ 0·010 in thick | |

Although the fusion temperature of polythene is much lower than nylon almost the same preheat temperature is required (some 200–260°C as against 220–260°C for Nylon 6). This is necessary because the melt is extremely viscous and does not flow quickly enough to form impervious coatings at lower temperatures.

It may be found more difficult to apply a satisfactory flame-sprayed plastic coating than a metal-sprayed one, especially with some thermoplastic materials. The high temperature required for satisfactory melting and adhesion may be very close to the degradation temperature of the plastic, and much depends on adequate control and the skill of the operator.

### 5.17 Testing plastic coatings

Most plastic coatings are inert to a wide range of chemicals but they all suffer to some extent from prolonged exposure to ultra-violet radiation. Unlike zinc or aluminium coatings, they offer no protection at discontinuities and it is therefore essential that they completely envelope the article if it is to be exposed to a severely corrosive environment. The coating must be impervious to gases and moisture, and consequently the entire surface must be carefully tested.

One satisfactory non-destructive test for discontinuities involves the use of high-voltage high-frequency current. An e.m.f. adjustable between 2000 and 5000 volts is suitable. The output lead is connected to a heavily insulated handle carrying a metal probe which when brought near to a plastics-coated metal object emits streamers of faint blue sparks. When the probe is within about half an inch of a discontinuity in the coating the streamers converge on the fault and increase in intensity. The instrument is simple to operate, gives positive and consistent results, and when used systematically enables large areas to be rapidly tested (see also 5.2).

The high voltage frequency spark tests should not be used for testing epoxide and phenolic linings. Instead a high voltage direct current probe should be moved systematically over and lightly touching the surface to be tested. The voltage should be adjusted to 75% of the previously determined breakdown voltage of a good coating. Any pinhole or crack will then permit a current to flow, which can be indicated by the lighting of a neon lamp.

Another method of test (the wet sponge test) applicable to most forms of coating is to connect one terminal of a 12 volt d.c. supply to the outer (conducting) shell of the lined vessel and the other, via a milliammeter, to a cotton wool swab or sponge (moistened for instance with a dilute (2%) aqueous solution of ammonium hydroxide, or perhaps common salt). If the swab is then moved systematically over the whole surface of the lining any faults will be indicated by a reading on the milliammeter. If the moisture from the sponge is given sufficient 'dwell' time it can penetrate minute pinholes (say from 15 down to 1 μm diameter) and these will be indicated provided that the instrument has the right sensitivity (around 1 megohm resistance through the instrument and electrolyte).

The coating thickness is under the control of the operator and thickness tests generally cannot be made until the article has cooled and the deposit hardened. Magnetic thickness meters can be used if the basis metal is magnetic, and coatings that are too thin can be built up to the required thickness after carefully reheating the faulty area.

## 5.18 Painting and its inspection

A paint may be considered as a material which can be spread as a thin coating and which will dry to produce a continuous solid film over a surface in order to protect and/or to decorate that surface.

Much depends on the correct selection, preparation, application and maintenance of the materials involved. The provision of 'good' paint may be negatived by inadequate and slipshod preparation of the surface to be coated. The labour costs of proper preparation and application far exceed the cost of the paint. Consequently, the most suitable paints having been specified for a job, inspection should ensure that adequate surface preparation is carried out before applying any paint.

In general, loose and foreign material must be removed and a clean surface obtained. Grit blasting may be desirable on iron and steel, but is not used on non-ferrous metals, where the use of a stiff bristle brush, and possibly wiping with white spirit, is usually sufficient. The various paints are then properly applied in the correct order.

Galvanized structural steelwork, if used in sulphurous atmospheres, may be further protected by painting. Good paint adhesion to the galvanized surface may be secured by treating it with a phosphoric acid solution.

Paint consists essentially of three components:

(i)   A film-forming material or binder.

(ii)   A solvent for carrying the material so that it can readily be applied to and spread on a surface. This solvent then evaporates and takes no further part in the process.

(iii) A pigment or pigments to give colour, finish and/or anti-corrosive properties.

For industrial use a minimum of four coats (including primer) giving a total thickness of some 150 μm is usually necessary.

A wide variety of materials have been and are being used in paint manufacture, which is a somewhat complex subject. Some idea of these materials can be obtained from Fig. 5.3.

British Standard Specifications cover a number of the more commonly used paints, driers, extenders (for reinforcing), oils, etc., for use in paint making; methods of test are dealt with (see Table 5.2).

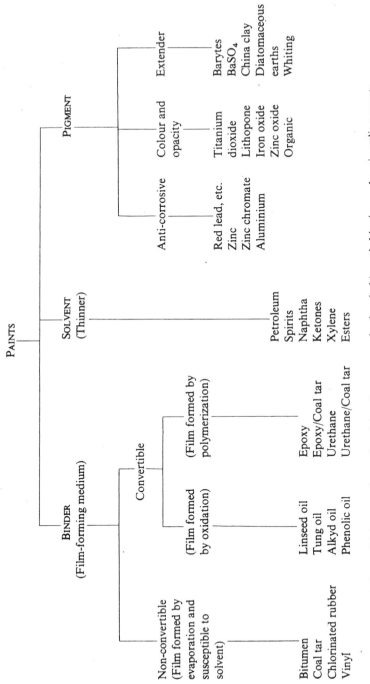

Various additives may be used as driers (manganese, lead, cobalt), anti-skinning and anti-settling agents.

**Fig. 5.3  Materials used in paint manufacture**

272

**TABLE 5.2**

*Some standards dealing with linings and protective treatments*

| Specification No. | Description |
|---|---|
| **Linings** | |
| BS 6374 (formerly BS CP 3003) | Lining of equipment with polymeric materials for the process industries |
| | Part 1: Lining with sheet thermoplastics |
| | Part 2: Lining with non-sheet applied thermoplastics |
| | Part 3: Lining with stoved thermosetting resins |
| | Part 4: Lining with cold curing thermosetting resins |
| | Part 5: Lining with rubbers |
| **Coatings, treatments, etc** | |
| BS 729 | Hot-dip galvanized coatings on iron and steel articles |
| BS 3189 | Phosphate treatment of iron and steel |
| BS 4164 | Coal tar based hot applied coating materials for protecting iron and steel, including suitable primers where required |
| BS 4495 | Recommendations for the flame spraying of ceramic and cermet coatings |
| BS 4761 | Sprayed unfused metal coatings for engineering purposes |
| BS 2569 | Sprayed metal coatings |
| | Part 1: Protection of iron and steel by aluminium and zinc against atmospheric corrosion |
| | Part 2: Protection of iron and steel against corrosion and oxidation at elevated temperatures |
| BS 6781 | Continuously organic coated steel flat products |
| BS 5493 (formerly CP 2008) | Protective coating of iron and steel structures against corrosion |
| BS CP 3012 | Cleaning and preparation of metal surfaces |
| **Testing, etc** | |
| BS 1344 | Methods of testing vitreous enamel finishes |
| BS 2649 | Methods for the analysis of glass (Part 2 deals with 'borosilicate' glasses) |
| BS 3745 | Evaluation of results of accelerated corrosion tests on metallic coatings |
| BS 5411 | Methods of test for metallic and related coatings (some 14 parts dealing with thickness and other tests) |
| BS 5466 | Methods for corrosion testing of metallic coatings (some 7 parts dealing with neutral salt spray (NSS), acetic acid salt spray (ASS), copper-accelerated acetic acid salt spray |

**TABLE 5.2** *continued*

| Specification No. | Description |
|---|---|
| | (CASS), thioacetamide (TAA), corrodkote (CORR) tests, etc |
| BS 6041 | Method of sampling of electro-deposited metallic coatings and related finishes: procedures for inspection by attributes |
| BS 6286 | Methods for measurement of total or effective thickness of thin surface hardened layers in steel |
| BS 6479 | Method for determination and verification of the effective depth of carburized and hardened cases of steel |
| BS 6481 | Method for determination of effective depth of hardening of steel after flame or induction hardening |
| BS 6917 | Corrosion testing in artificial atmospheres: general principles (accelerated tests (24–2016h) using heat, corrosive agents, etc) |
| ASTM A 90 | Methods of test for weight of coating on zinc-coated (galvanized) iron or steel articles |
| ASTM A 279 | Method of total immersion corrosion test of stainless steel |
| ASTM B 117 | Method of salt spray (fog) testing |
| ASTM B 244 | Measuring thickness of anodic coatings on aluminium with eddy current instruments |
| ASTM B 287 | Acetic acid/salt spray (fog) testing |
| ASTM B 368 | Copper-accelerated acetic acid/salt spray (fog) testing (CASS test) |
| ASTM B 380 | Corrosion testing of decorative chromium plating by the Corrodkote procedure |
| ASTM E 216 | Measuring coating thickness by magnetic or electro-magnetic methods |
| ASTM G14 | Impact resistance of pipeline coatings (falling weight test) |

The BNF Jet Test for local thickness measurement of nickel and other coatings (see S.G. Clarke, *J. Electrodepositors' Tech. Soc.*, **12**, 1–18, 1937)

**Painting**

| | |
|---|---|
| BS CP 231 (now BS 6150) | Code of practice for painting of buildings |
| BS 388 | Aluminium pigments (deals with four types of powder or paste forming leafing or non-leafing 'flake') |
| BS 2015 | Glossary of paint terms |
| BS 2523 | Lead based priming paints |
| BS 3698 | Calcium plumbate priming paints |

**TABLE 5.2** *concluded*

| Specification No. | Description |
|---|---|
| BS 3699 | Calcium plumbate for paints |
| BS 3900 | Methods of testing for paints (based originally on MOD Spec. DEF-1053); multi-part test series. Includes Group H: Evaluation of paint and varnish defects |
| BS 4232 | Surface finish of blast-cleaned steel for painting (gives 3 quality levels (with diagrams), and methods of control and inspection) |
| BS 4310 | Permissible limit of lead in low-lead paints |
| BS 4726 | Methods for sampling raw materials for paints and varnishes |
| BS 4756 | Ready mixed aluminium priming paints for woodwork |
| BS 5358 | Low-lead solvent-thinned priming paints for woodwork |
| BS 6742 | Electrostatic painting and finishing equipment |
| ASTM D 1186 | Measurement of dry film thickness of non-magnetic coatings of paint, etc, applied on a magnetic base |
| ASTM D 1400 | Measurement of dry film thickness of non-metallic coatings of paint, etc, applied on a non-magnetic metal base |
| Swedish SIS 05 5900 | Pictorial surface preparation standards for painting steel surfaces |

## 5.19 Aluminium paints

Considerable use is made today of a paste of aluminium powder as a pigment for protective industrial paints. The aluminium pigment forms into 'flakes' which, in a suitable liquid, will float to the surface and form a continuous metal film. This process is known as 'leafing', and paints of this type possess properties similar to that of the aluminium coatings previously described. The high reflecting powers of this film can also be advantageous when painting storage vessels containing volatile liquids, where it is necessary to restrict evaporation and/or to keep internal temperatures as low as possible, or to prevent undue heat losses from heated vessels. They are used extensively on pipelines exposed to high temperatures.

'Non-leafing' aluminium paints are also produced in which the aluminium film sinks to the bottom of the paint allowing any colouring matter to become visible. Such paints have applications as primers for wood and structural steel, and there are indications that they have a longer life than the more traditional types. (See BS 388 *Aluminium pigments* (Table 5.2) which also describes test methods.)

### 5.20  Electro-polishing

To maintain a good corrosion-free surface, or for technical reasons, it is usual to provide a polished surface on items of plant, vessels, etc., made in stainless steel and certain other materials.

The traditional way to do this is by mechanical polishing, using a rotating mop and polishing compound. It is difficult to get into awkward corners and hand polishing is sometimes necessary, so increasing the cost of a somewhat expensive operation.

An alternative process (the reverse of electroplating), known as electro-polishing, can be used, however. This does not normally produce a mirror finish, as can be done by mechanical polishing, but removes about 0·001 in (0·025mm) from the surface and smooths out any fine scratches. It is claimed that the surface produced is cleaner and free from polishing grit and metallic and other impurities (which tend to be dissolved during the process), and consequently tends to resist corrosion better than mechanical polishing. It is also stated that the surface resists the adhesion of chemicals and is easier to keep clean.

### 5.21  Quality assurance

Some of the methods of coating or otherwise protecting materials (especially metals) have been practised for many years. Even the technology of electroplating is now time-honoured. Some more recent developments involve high technology and specialized equipment, and knowledge embracing the further fringes of chemistry, physics, metallurgy, electronics and vacuum technology.

To obtain good results at competitive prices requires much industrial 'know-how', not necessarily detailed in specifications, and a good system of quality assurance.

Consequently many firms in the industry, in order to demonstrate and maintain their expertise, have sought approval to the requirements of BS 5750 (see 9.4 *et seq.*).

### 5.22  Specialized surface modification processes and developments

Amongst such processes (not as yet covered by standard specifications) are:

(i) *Chemical vapour deposition (CVD)*. This is a process involving a suitably arranged chemical reaction, and is sometimes called gas plating. Basically the material it is required to deposit is transferred from the gaseous phase to form a solid surface layer on the substrate (basis) material by an often complex chemical reaction. Extreme cleanliness of this substrate material is desirable, coatings which may be applied range from metals and their alloys (including tungsten and rare metals) to carbides, borides and PTFE. They may be deposited on substrates ranging from metals to ceramics. Coating thicknesses can vary from say 0.1 μm to 100 μm, as required. One application is the deposition of hard ceramic coatings on cemented carbide cutting tools; an extension of tool life of well over 300% is possible.

(ii) *Physical vapour deposition (PVD)* techniques include evaporation, sputtering and *ion beam processes* (sometimes known as ion plating). However ion beam processes are carried out in a vacuum environment and ion plating in a plasma environment. Briefly, with ion plating, by making use of vacuum techniques (see Chapter 8) a chamber is evacuated to some $10^{-5}$ torr or better, and argon gas is admitted. The article to be 'plated' (i.e. the substrate) forms the cathode and is subjected to ion bombardment, first to clean the surface, and then by ions of the required metallic vapour. At present the main practical application of the technique is the coating of steel cutting tools with titanium nitride.

Excellent adhesion can be achieved, coating thicknesses being some 1–5 μm; surfaces normally incompatible can often be joined. Ion implantation is a somewhat similar technique for modifying the surface properties of metals, etc. and is much used in the manufacture (doping) of semiconductors, and can be used for the nitrogen implanting of press tools and punches, etc. to improve wear resistance and life.

(iii) *Lasers* can be used for a variety of surface treatments including cladding and surface alloying. The optical energy from a laser can be directed precisely where required and can heat up the top few atomic layers of a metal. The process (as used by Rolls Royce) is to blow the powdered cladding material into the laser-generated melt pool on the substrate. As an example, uniform layers of stainless steel of excellent assessed quality can be produced on mild steel substrate.

For further information see:

Bunshah, R.F. *et al.*, *Deposition technologies for films and coatings: developments and applications*, Noyes Data, Park Ridge, NJ, 1982.

Bunshah, R.F. et al., *Plasma and detonation gun deposition techniques and coating properties*, Noyes Data, Park Ridge, NJ, 1982.

*Recent developments in surface coating and modification processes* (I. Mech. E. seminar) Mech. Eng. Pub., 1985.


## References and further reading

Carter, V.E., *Metallic coatings for corrosion control*, Newnes-Butterworth, 1977.

Holland, L., *Vacuum deposition of thin films*, Chapman & Hall, 1968.

Papers read at International Metal Spraying Conferences (periodically), The Welding Institute.

Society of Automotive Engineers. Manual on shot-peening (SAE J808a), SAE, Warrendale, Pa., 1984.

*Surface Coating for Savings in Engineering*, The Welding Institute, 1973

*Surface Journal* (quarterly) – deals with surface coating by spraying, welding, plasma arc process, etc., The Welding Institute.

# 6    Hazardous environments

## 6.1 Introduction

In dealing with the safety and satisfactory operation of any hazardous plant the first line of defence is to have in being an effective (preferably total) quality assurance scheme (see 9.4 and Chapter 13). This should help to ensure high quality in both design and manufacture of all components and equipment, and reliability (see 13.2) in operation. The scheme will infer the employment of highly trained staff (including inspectors and operators) and the use of well thought out procedures during manufacture, operation and maintenance. (See Chapter 9 (particularly 9.4) and Chapters 12 and 13 generally.)

The second line of defence is to assess the faults that are likely to occur, with possibly an estimate of their failure rate (see Chapter 13, particularly 13.7) and to provide means, such as NDT (see Chapter 10), instrumentation and controls, to indicate approaching failure or preferably to take automatic action in the event of the most common failures. This line of defence may be extended (for highly hazardous plants) to cover faults *unlikely* to occur under normal conditions, so that perhaps some prior indication may be given, or if a specific unlikely, but extremely hazardous, situation did occur plans would be in existence to mitigate its effects. Reliability and failure rate calculations may be made, but it should be realized that no amount of mathematics can build increased reliability into an existing component, however well or poorly made. The provision of duplicate components (redundancy) for important items or even different types of equipment to perform the same task (diversity) may be desirable.

### 6.1.1 Controlled and gaseous environments

Many processes and operations are today carried out in a controlled atmosphere or in a gaseous environment. Large enclosures, laboratories, etc., may be needed which are kept supplied with filtered air, and with the temperature and relative humidity controlled within stated limits. ISO recommendations, suitable say for laboratory test conditions at near ambient temperatures, are:

(i) *Normal control*

| Temperature (°C) | Relative humidity (%) |
|---|---|
| 20±2 | 65±5 |
| 23±2 | 50±5 |
| 27±2 | 65±2 |

(ii) *Close control*

| | |
|---|---|
| 20±1 | 65±2 |
| 23±1 | 50±2 |
| 27±1 | 65±2 |

*Note:* Whilst conditioned air is flowing the air will become warmer or cooler owing to heat gains or losses. If there is no addition or removal of moisture, then as the air becomes warmer its relative humidity will decrease and as it becomes colder its relative humidity will increase.

Windows and doors should, as far as is practicable, be kept shut during operations, and sources of heat and of moisture should be kept under close control to prevent undue variations in the controlled conditions. For further information see BS4194: *Design requirements and testing of controlled atmosphere laboratories.* Delicate operations may be performed in a glove box supplied with dry, filtered air, the operator using rubber gloves hermetically sealed into the glove box wall. In some cases a special gaseous environment may have to be provided. This gas may be inert and take no part in the process, or it may react with certain materials as part of the process. Again, operations may have to be conducted in the possible presence of a hazardous atmosphere or environment.

Any gas required can be supplied from compressed gas cylinders, or possibly in liquid form, perhaps feeding into a suitable gasholder; alternatively, if large quantities are needed, a specially designed gas supply plant may be installed. Instrumentation is usually required not only to measure such things as pressure and flow rate of the gas, but also its quality, e.g. degreee of purity, moisture content, freedom from undesirable constituents, etc.

If a high standard of gas purity is required, then the gas supply and purification system and the various items of plant must be clean and leak-tight to a high standard, and these standards must be maintained during operation by an adequate system of periodic inspection and maintenance. Properly controlled welding or brazing of pipework, etc., is essential, whilst removable joints must be of approved design. Leak testing of the system by some such method as pressurizing with Arcton (Freon) gas and probing with a halogen leak detector (see 11.5.2), will pay dividends, and quite often is essential.

The drying and purification of the gas is important, and various types of equipment, such as silica gel, activated alumina or calcium driers, gas scrubbers, 'de-oxo' units, may be used. The driers usually incorporate a regenerative arrangement whereby the gas in use is routed through one drying unit, whilst another drying unit which has become contaminated and damp during previous operation is being regenerated (dried) by electrical heating. The change-over valves on such a drier should be checked periodically for tightness. A small leak here, when the system had to be regenerated whilst under vacuum, has been known to result in a subsequent process gas explosion.

Before putting into operation, and periodically when required, it is usual to 'purge' a gas system of air or other vapours and gases by allowing the purge gas to pass through it until the required degree of purity is obtained. This 'purge' gas is usually, but not necessarily, the same as the gas used in operation.

## 6.2 Dry and glove box technique

When obnoxious, poisonous, radioactive or other dangerous materials have to be manipulated and cannot safely be handled with bare hands, some form of protection is necessary, and a dry or glove box technique may be employed. The box, usually with Perspex sides, is filled with an inert gas, such as argon, to a pressure of a few inches water gauge, and is provided with glove ports, or suitable tongs or manipulators operated if necessary by remote control.

Flammable materials or those having a pyrophoric dust hazard can also be safely handled and machined in an inert atmosphere by this method.

Alpha particle emitting radioactive materials and low-energy beta sources, including uranium, can in general be handled with rubber gloves when contained in an argon-filled Perspex box. Gamma-active materials require the use of thick walls (possibly incorporating lead or lead glass) and manipulators to protect the operator, i.e. a *shielded box.*

The term *glove box* is usually taken to include *dry box* (where moisture is excluded) and *hot box* (for handling radioactive materials). Gloves can normally be replaced under working conditions without breaking the glove port seal. The gloves, themselves manufactured under quality assessed conditions, must be frequently inspected whilst in service (at least daily) to ensure their freedom from defects, leaks, etc. Besides handling material the operator will of course use the gloves for handling tools and manipulating controls, etc., inside the box.

Plant for the control and purification of the inert gas is provided, the gas usually being supplied commercially in cylinders. Standards of purity for the gas are laid down and instruments are supplied to indicate the degree of purity. A rough indication of purity can be obtained by observing the colour of the electrical discharge between electrodes in a glass tube connected to the gas system and comparing this with a chart. Accurate determination of purity is a laboratory job and may be carried out by mass spectrometer methods.

## 6.3 Inspection of glove boxes

The actual glove boxes themselves, in which operations are carried out in the inert-gas atmosphere, can vary very widely in size and complexity. A small box, fitted with six glove ports for carrying out, say, simple assembly work, is shown diagrammatically in Fig. 6.1. Larger boxes are designed to house complete machine tools or process plant, and the material may be handled remotely by specially designed manipulators. Flame-proof or dust-tight electrical equipment and lighting fittings may be built into the box.

The inspection of this type of dry box is extremely rigorous. A typical specification called for the framework to be fabricated by fusion welding from mild steel plates and angle iron, to BS 15 for structural steel, and BS 538 or 693 for welding. Glazed sides, windows, etc., would be of polymethyl methacrylate (Perspex) to MOD Specification DTD 5545, formed, cemented and machined and heat-treated where necessary to DTD 925. Copper pipework and fittings (to BS 659 and 864) should be hard-soldered to BS 1845 using Type 3 easy flow flux. They should be cleaned and leak-tested before assembly.[†]

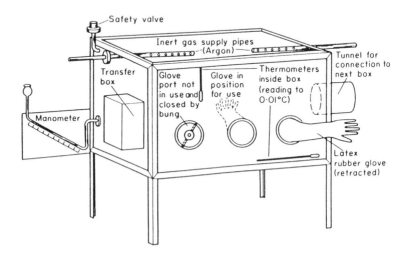

**Fig. 6.1   Glove box under test.**

All joint faces should be clean, flat and free from irregularities of defects so as to prevent the possibility of leakage. Rubber joint rings should be placed between the metal framework and the Perspex windows.

Repairs to defective welding should only be carried out with the approval of, and in the presence of, the inspector. Defects should be cut out by chipping, grinding or machining and not by using the welding torch.

A smooth internal finish is essential, and crevices where material may lodge must be avoided. In the first instance all rust and scale should be removed by either shot blasting or wire scratch brushing. If wire brushing is used, this should be followed by cleaning with trichloroethylene,* and then painting to the specified requirements. It should be noted that neither trichloroethylene cleaning nor painting should be carried out *until* the box, or any component thereof, has satisfactorily passed its pressure and leak tests.

Doors and flanges, if of aluminium, should have a polished finish, and if of steel should be cadmium-plated to DTD 904.

Glove boxes are often made in stainless steel rather than mild steel where conditions of cleanliness are required to be of a very high order, and where extreme purity of the gas used in the box must be maintained. Semi-conductors, for instance, may be assembled in such boxes. The stainless steel surface can be polished, or etched if a matt surface is required. Electro-polishing is often specified in lieu of mechanical polishing, as the latter would be difficult and costly to carry out on some components. Moreover, it is claimed that electro-polishing gives a cleaner surface. Inspection should see that screw threads and sealing flanges are properly protected during this operation, as it removes some 0.001 in (0.025mm) of the surface.

### 6.4 Pressure and leak testing of glove boxes

A pressure test must be carried out on the assembled box, complete with its fittings, filters, purge pipes, tunnels, etc. Clean dry air at a pressure of $15 \pm 1$ in water gauge should be used for this purpose. (Any manometer or pressure gauge normally fitted to the box, and of lesser pressure range, should be removed for this test.)

A leak test using halogen leak detection equipment should then be carried out. With the cabinet sealed at atmospheric pressure Arcton gas No. 6 (Freon 12) from a cylinder is introduced and the cabinet pressurized to 4 in water gauge. A portable electric fan should be installed inside the box and left running during the test in order to ensure complete mixing of the gas with the atmospheric air (Arcton is heavier than air).

---

†Many of the quoted specifications have now been replaced.
*Because of possible toxic hazards a less toxic proprietary solvent (such as Triklone, Genklene, etc.) would be desirable.

The entire outside surface of the box should then be slowly and carefully gone over with the probe of the leak detector. Any leaks found must be marked and rectified to the satisfaction of the inspector. (For further details of such leak testing see 11.5.2(b)).

### 6.5 Leak rate test (see also Chapter 11)

After satisfactorily passing the leak test a *leak-rate test* should be carried out with the cabinet pressurized to 4 in water gauge. The leak rate must not exceed 0.05% of the cabinet volume per hour.

As this leak rate test is carried out before painting and final assembly of certain fittings, it should be followed by a final leak rate test after painting and assembly and after installation. Periodic leak rate tests should also be carried out in use, and after any modification to the equipment.

Leak rate tests at a slight negative pressure are sometimes specified; the reduction of pressure within the box can be obtained by using a rotary vacuum pump or an ejector.

### 6.6 Method of leak rate testing of glove boxes

The method that was generally adopted for the leak rate testing of glove boxes was to pressurize them with air at 4 in water gauge (twice the normal working pressure), and then to isolate them over a period of usually 8 hours, observing the fall in pressure, and hence calculating the leak rate. The main difficulty in carrying out such a test lies in the considerable effect of the continual variations in atmospheric pressure and temperature during the long period of the test.

Assuming that the atmospheric pressure and temperature *did* remain constant during the test, then a leak rate of 0·05% of the box volume per hour (the specified maximum leak rate) would cause the box pressure to fall in this time by:

$$\frac{0 \cdot 05}{100} \times 13 \cdot 6 \times 30 = 0 \cdot 204 \text{ in water gauge}$$

(where $13 \cdot 6$ = specific gravity of mercury).

Consider now the effect of a barometric pressure variation of 1 mm of mercury (noting that a *rise* in barometric pressure will cause a *fall* in box pressure):

$$1 \text{ mmHg} = \frac{13 \cdot 6}{25 \cdot 4} = 0 \cdot 536 \text{ in water gauge}$$

(i.e. it will give the effect of over 2½ times the maximum allowable leak-rate).

Similarly the effect of a rise of temperature during the test of 1°C (assuming the initial temperature to have been 22°C and the barometric pressure throughout was 760 mmHg) can be calculated as follows:

$$p_2 = \frac{p_1 T_2}{T_1} = \frac{760 \times (273 + 22 + 1)}{(273 + 22)} = \frac{760 \times 296}{295} = 762 \cdot 5 \text{ mmHg}$$

therefore a 1°C rise causes a rise in box pressure of:

$$762 \cdot 5 - 760 = 2 \cdot 5 \text{ mmHg} = \frac{2 \cdot 5 \times 13 \cdot 6}{25 \cdot 4} = 1 \cdot 34 \text{ in water gauge}$$

(i.e. it will give the effect of over $6\frac{1}{2}$ times the maximum allowable leak-rate).

Consequently in order to assess with any degree of accuracy the leak-rate over a given period the changes in barometric pressure and in temperature must be very accurately measured, and allowed for in the calculations. It will be seen that the same effect as a leak of the maximum allowable amount (0·204 in water gauge) would be produced in a leak-tight cabinet by a temperature variation of:

$$\frac{0 \cdot 204}{1 \cdot 34} = 0 \cdot 15°C$$

or by a pressure variation of:

$$\frac{0 \cdot 204}{0 \cdot 536} = 0 \cdot 38 \text{ mmHg}$$

By taking readings at intervals over a period of some hours, calculating the leak rate at these intervals, and averaging out the results, inaccuracies due to the difficulty of reading small changes can be ironed out.

The instruments necessary for accurate measurements are enumerated below:

(i)   A Fortin standard barometer reading to 0·1 mmHg.

(ii)  An inclined water manometer for measurement of box pressure, reading to 0·01 in w.g. (a pressure difference of 1 in w.g. is arranged to be read off over a length of 10 in).

(iii) Glass thermometers of the Beckmann or other suitable type with a long scale, graduated to read to 0.01°C.

Two accurate reading thermometers are placed in the box, one usually at high and one at low level. The average of their readings is taken, in order to allow for variations of temperature within the box. With a large box it might be desirable to have a fan running inside it to lessen errors from this source (see Fig. 6.1).

Glove ports, doors, etc., are carefully adjusted to ensure tightness, and the box is then pressurized with air to 4 in water gauge (the water manometer now being connected to the circuit). The box must then be allowed to stand for a minimum period of 1 hour for conditions to settle down and the temperature to become steady.

It helps considerably if the tests are conducted in a location free from draughts and of an even temperature. (Quite often actual installations may be in air-conditioned buildings.)

Readings of box temperature and pressure, and of barometric pressure, should then be taken at half-hourly intervals over a period of usually 8 hours. However, to reduce the number of readings and the amount of calculation, a fair result could be obtained by taking the first and last readings.

As an example, consider a box under test for 8 hours. The difference between first and last box pressure readings showed an *increase* of 0·04 in water gauge. (At first sight this seems the reverse of a leak, but of course it is due to combined effects of temperature, barometric pressure *and* leakage.)

The difference between first and last temperature readings showed an increase of 1·04°C in box temperature. This, assuming no leakage, would cause the box pressure to *rise* $(1·04 \times 1·34) = 1·394$ in water gauge.

The difference between first and last barometric readings showed an increase of 0·7 mmHg. This, assuming no leakage, would cause the box pressure to *fall* by $(0·7 \times 0·536) = 0·375$ in water gauge.

Combining these figures, *assuming no leakage*, the box pressure would rise by 1·394 in w.g. due to temperature rise, and fall by 0·375 in w.g. due to barometric pressure increase, a net rise of $(1·394 - 0·375) = 1·019$ in water gauge.

The actual readings however show that owing to leakage the box pressure has risen only 0·40 in w.g. The difference between these two figures $(1·019 - 0·40) = 0·619$ in w.g. represents the fall in box pressure due to leakage. As this has occurred over a period of 8 hours, then leakage rate per hour:

$$= \frac{0·619}{8} = 0·0774 \text{ in w.g.}$$

Now a leakage rate of 0·204 in w.g. per hour is equivalent to a leakage rate of 0·05% of the box volume per hour (the specified maximum—see 6.5). Therefore the leakage rate of the box under test will be:

$$\frac{0\cdot0774}{0\cdot204} \times 0\cdot05\% = 0\cdot01897\% \text{ of box volume per hour}$$

Possibilities of considerable errors in calculated leak rates obtained from first and last readings arise owing to errors of observation and, particularly, owing to conditions not having settled down when the first readings are taken. Therefore it is always recommended that a series of readings and calculated leak-rates be obtained at regular intervals and averaged out. The minimum length of test should be 4 hours and the maximum interval between readings should be 1 hour.

Note 1: Using today's SI units the specified maximum leak rate of 0·05% of the cabinet volume per hour would be:

$$\frac{pV}{t} = \frac{0\cdot05 \times 0\cdot01 \; V}{60 \times 60} = \frac{0\cdot0005 \; V}{3600} = 13\cdot88 \times 10^{-6} \; Pa \; m^3 \; s^{-1}$$

Note 2: Today, no doubt, a more sophisticated and quicker leak rate test could be arranged, rather than the above described method which makes use of first principles.

## 6.7 Gas cylinders and transportable gas containers

Industrial gases are stored in steel cylinders at high pressure (up to some 2000 lb/in² (140 bar) or more). At such pressures the so-called 'permanent' gases (e.g. air, oxygen, hydrogen, nitrogen, etc.) remain in gaseous form, but the 'liquefiable' gases (e.g. carbon dioxide, nitrous oxide, ethylene, etc.) condense to liquid form.

The manufacture, testing and inspection of such cylinders is dealt with by the British Standards listed in Table 6.1; hydraulic tests, flattening tests and mechanical tests of the material are included.

Inspection should ascertain that filled cylinders are handled carefully, and not used, for instance, for supporting components which are to be welded, cut, hammered or otherwise manipulated. They should be adequately protected from the weather and the direct rays of the sun, and stored and used away from sources of heat and away from any possible contamination with oil. In particular, with oxygen cylinders, it is essential that no oil, grease or lubricant be used on valves or any connections, in order to prevent any possibility of combustion or explosion. Such cylinders should not be handled with greasy hands or gloves. They should be used in an upright position, and secured so that they cannot be accidentally overturned.

Valve connections must be clean, and the thread, etc., undamaged before

**TABLE 6.1**

*Standards for gas cylinders and containers*

| Specification No. | Description |
|---|---|
| BS 341 | Valve fittings for compressed gas cylinders |
| BS 349 | Identification of contents for gas containers |
| BS 349 C | Chart: Identification of contents of industrial gas containers |
| BS 1319 | Medical gas cylinders and anaesthetic apparatus |
| BS 1319 C | Chart for medical gas cylinders and anaesthetic apparatus |
| BS 2718 | Gas cylinder trolleys |
| Home Office | Gas Cylinders and Containers Committee Recommendations: Periodic examination and test of seamless cylinders and welded containers used for the conveyance of compressed gases |
| Home Office | Code of Practice for keeping LPG in cylinders and similar containers |
| BS 5045 | Transportable gas containers |
| | Part 1: Seamless steel containers (includes cylinders for 'permanent' liquefiable and atmospheric gases, etc. and supersedes BS 399, 400, 401, 1045, 1287 and 1288) |
| | Part 2: Steel containers up to 130 litres capacity with welded seams |
| | Part 3: Seamless aluminium alloy containers above 0·5 litre water capacity and up to 300 bar charged pressure at 15°C |
| | Part 6: Seamless containers up to 0·5 litre water capacity (steel or aluminium) |
| BS 5188 | Non-refillable metallic containers for liquified or compressed non-flammable gases |
| BS 5329 | Non-refillable metallic containers of up to 1·4 litres capacity for LPG |
| BS 5355 | Spec. for filling ratios and developed pressures for liquefiable and permanent gases |
| BS 5430 | Periodic inspection, testing and maintenance of transportable gas containers |
| | Part 1: Seamless steel containers |
| | Part 2: Welded steel containers of water capacity 1 litre up to 130 litres |
| | Part 3: Seamless aluminium alloy containers (applies also to containers made to Home Office specifications HOAL 1, 2 and 3) |
| BS 6071 | Periodic inspection and maintenance of transportable gas containers for dissolved acetylene |
| Liquefied Petroleum Gas Industry Technical Association (UK) | |
| LPG Codes 5 | Filling of LPG containers fitted with visual contents indication |
| 7 | Storage of full and empty LPG cylinders and cartridges |
| 12 | Filling of LPG cylinders at depots |

pressure regulators, etc., are attached. The cylinder valve must be kept shut when the cylinder is empty or not in use. It should be opened slowly when a regulator is attached.

Left-hand and right-hand thread connections are specified for different types of gas (left-handed for flammable* gases).

Gas cylinders should be properly identified by colour coding according to contents (see BS 349 and also 4.14).

The inspection of gas cylinders was traditionally controlled by the Home Office, the main instrument of control being the Gas Cylinders (Conveyance) Regulations 1931/1947/1959. These Regulations require that cylinders be constructed and tested in accordance with the specifications contained therein, which are embodied in or are similar to those contained in British Standards. Various exemption orders have been made, but in some cases cylinders may only be manufactured and inspected by manufacturers and independent inspection organizations who have received Home Office approval.

On a manufacturer asking for such approval the Home Office takes advice from a number of bodies and arranges tests to destruction on sample cylinders of each relevant type. The approval of inspection organizations follows a similar pattern. The Home Office keeps a Register of Approved Manufacturers and another of Approved Inspection Organizations (see also 13.8).[†]

### 6.7.1 Transportable gas containers

As a result of the recommendations of the Home Office Gas Cylinders and Containers Committee (1969) the Pressure Vessels Standards Committee of BSI at the request of the Health and Safety Executive prepared BS 5430, 5045 and 5355. BS 5045 deals with the design, construction and testing of gas containers for conveying (and storing) gases under pressure. It includes matter dealing with cylinders for 'permanent' (critical temperature below $-10°C$) 'liquefiable' and atmospheric gases covered by earlier superseded standards. BS 5430 deals with the inspection and assessment of these containers after a period of service to establish their suitability for further use. To this end tables are provided giving, for a range of named gases, the intervals permitted between each full inspection (including hydraulic testing). Generally such inspection and tests are required at intervals of some 2 to 10 years. A full external inspection only may be carried out at shorter intervals. For gases not listed the period of, and procedure for, retest and inspection of the containers can be obtained from H.M. Inspector of Explosives.

*'Inflammable' and 'flammable' have the same meaning.
[†]The duties of the Home Office mentioned in this paragraph have now in general been taken over by the HSE.

Further tables etc. detail mechanical damage, defects, excessive corrosion, loss of mass (exceeding 3%) and other faults necessitating withdrawal of a container from service for full inspection and test, repair or destruction. Methods of marking to indicate dates of inspections are given.

It is intended that legislation will be introduced to make these requirements mandatory for all containers intended for conveyance by road; furthermore it will be a statutory requirement that all testing stations carrying out periodic inspection and testing of gas containers be approved by the Health and Safety Executive. It should be noted that BS 5430 excludes dissolved acetylene containers, which are covered by BS 6071, also certain gases are not permitted to be conveyed in aluminium alloy containers (see BS 5045: Part 3).

If a container is completely full of liquid or liquified gas and it heats up, then very high pressures will develop. It is therefore essential that some free space be left in the container. The permissible extent of filling is specified in terms of the filling ratio and the temperature reached in service (see BS 5355).

Test pressure requirements depend upon this reference temperature, whether the gas is liquefiable or permanent, and the proof stress/tensile strength ratio. For oxygen and a 200 bar charging pressure, the test pressure at the UK reference temperature of 60°C is 352 bar. In Australia (a hotter country) the corresponding test pressure is however surprisingly lower—at 318 bar. The corresponding test pressure throughout Europe (in accordance with RID/ADR regulations (International Regulations for Transport of Dangerous goods by road (1978)) and EEC requirements) is 300 bar irrespective of the gas contained. This 3:2 ratio will probably be adopted in the UK and universally.

Note that a gas cylinder or container under pressure may explode if involved in a fire. Also if the valve is fully opened, and circumstances permit, a container may be projected like a rocket. Should the gas be flammable a further hazard arises. Death or injury may result. Serious trouble can also arise if the passage of cold liquefied gas freezes the valve and prevents its closure. See also 7.1 for LPG and LNG containers etc. operating at low temperatures.

HSE Guidance Notes: CS4 The keeping of LPG in cylinders and similar containers.
CS6 The storage and use of LPG on construction sites.
CS8 Small scale storage and display of LPG at retail premises.

## 6.8 Water-sealed gasholders

The *Factories Act* requires that water-sealed gasholders of not less than

5000 ft$^3$ capacity must be of sound construction and properly maintained and must be inspected at least once every two years. The *Gasholders (Record of Examinations) Order* 1938 (S.R. and O. 1938 No. 598) requires particulars as to the condition of the crown, side sheeting (including grips and cups), guiding mechanism (roller carriages and pins, rails or ropes), tank and any other structure; whether the tank and lifts are sufficiently level for safe working; the date of examination and by whom carried out. Records must be kept of the date of construction (and of the oldest lift). Repair or demolition may only be carried out under the direct supervision of a specially qualified person.

Any small gasholders used in chemical plant should be similarly inspected.

## 6.9 Specially hazardous plants

In many industries and situations where special hazards exist, or are likely to arise, involving risks from gas, vapour, fumes or dust, which may lead to fire or explosion, special precautions are necessary both with the actual design layout and installation and with the equipment supplied for use. Consequently inspection is involved at several stages.

It may be necessary to provide separate buildings for the different operations of a process. These buildings must be sited at sufficient 'safety distances' from each other and from outside buildings to prevent damage in the event of a fire or explosion. Protective screens or blast walls may be necessary.

It may be necessary to provide ventilating or exhaust fans in some buildings to remove obnoxious or dangerous fumes, and these must be kept running at all times when the process is working and for a sufficient time afterwards. Where the risks are great an alternative source of power should be provided which would come on automatically in the event of a failure of the main supply. Maximum permissible concentrations of dusts, vapours, etc., may be laid down. Processes may have to be carried out 'wet'.

The heating of buildings should be provided generally by steam or hot water, the maximum surface temperatures being limited in accordance with the nature of the process or product. Process heating, if any, should be arranged so as to prevent flammable gas, etc., coming into contact with flame or any hot surface likely to cause ignition. Electricity may be used for space and process heating either indirectly via a medium such as air or water, or directly where this is convenient.

No internal combustion engine, electric motor or electrical equipment capable of generating sparks of sufficient incendivity to constitute a fire hazard should be installed or used in the danger zone unless it is of an explosion-proof or flame-proof or other approved type.

There are obviously severe restrictions on the use of electrical equipment, and any used must be efficiently bonded to earth. All items on which static electricity is liable to collect, such as pipelines, belt drives and vessels (particularly portable ones for flammable liquids), should also be earthed. Structures must be protected against lightning.

Certain intrinsically safe items of electrical equipment are available and can be used, e.g. approved portable electric lamps. Miners' electric safety lamps are permitted.

Other precautionary measures can be taken in the danger areas, such as the prohibition of smoking and the carrying of matches, lighters, etc., and the provision of non-sparking tools, footwear, trucks, etc. Maintenance and repair should be permitted only under strict supervision, and clearance certificates, permits to work, etc., may be required by various rules, both local and statutory.

Inspection requirements and safety codes will vary according to the type of plant or process involved. Consultation with the safety officer of a particular plant can result in useful advice. Some detailed requirements affecting certain industries and hazards will now be given.

*6.9.1 Electrical installations and equipment and their hazards*

Electricity is a good servant but if not properly controlled can itself give rise to a hazardous environment affecting safety due to:
. (i) The danger of electrocution
  (ii) The risk of fire
  (iii) Incorrect connection or operation of equipment.

(i) Death by electrocution can occur when a person contacts a live conductor, etc. in such a manner than an electric current (usually of over 15 milliamps) passes (for perhaps less than a second) through his body usually because it is in contact with the earth at the same time. Voltages of over 200V (a.c. or d.c.) are extremely dangerous. Reduced voltages of 24–50V are often used as a safety measure for some control and lighting circuits, etc.

An electric shock causes disturbance of the nerves and muscles. The muscles may react and cause the person to be thrown forcibly away, for instance off a ladder; in this case he may break a leg but may not die from electric shock. However, a moderately severe shock (say over 20 milliamps) may cause a muscular spasm which prevents the victim from releasing his grip of a live conductor, tool, etc. Unless the current can be quickly switched off his position is likely to be serious; a fuse in even low power circuits is unlikely to blow as a result of a current to earth of this order. However on some circuits it may be possible to fit an earth leakage circuit breaker which might operate in a few hundredths of a second on a current as low as perhaps

30 mA; in such a case it is hoped that the shock would not prove fatal.

The value of the shock current depends upon the resistance of the human body (which varies over wide limits depending upon area of contact, state of health, male or female and, particularly, the degree of moisture present in the contact area) to which must be added the resistance of any footwear, carpet, etc. between the victim and earth.

A person wearing hob nail boots standing on a metallic floor in the rain would be at very serious risk, whilst one in rubber boots standing on a carpet in a dry room would pass very little if any current to earth.

Perhaps strangely, the resistance of the human body seems to vary also with the applied voltage. Using round figures it may have a resistance of some 2000 ohms at 240 volts, but this may rise to over 16,000 ohms at 12 volts. Thus the maximum current which could pass through it would be in the first case $240/2000 = 0.12$ (amps) (120 mA), and in the latter case $12/16,000$ or $7.5$ mA.

With alternating current its peak voltage is (usually) $\sqrt{2}$ higher than its declared (or r.m.s.) value. Also unfortunately at a frequency of 50 hertz (c.p.s.) the value of the current at which a victim cannot let go is at its minimum (maybe some 15 mA). Direct current (to some extent) and high frequencies (particularly VHF) are relatively more easily handled (but see 6.16.2 for VHF radiation) but burning (and heating) may be a problem. A person may recover from electric shock but the after-effects of burns (particularly those sustained at extra high voltages) may be severe—and even fatal.

Most fatalities from electric shock seem to be due to ventricular fibrillation of the heart, which if continued for a short time prevents its effective pump action. Thus even a small current through or near the heart may prove fatal. Cases are on record of fatalities apparently after receiving a shock from a 25V a.c. tool, and even from a 12V d.c. car supply, but there may have been other extraneous circumstances.

Under the Electricity Regulations (Reg. 29) instructions for the treatment of electric shock must be affixed in all premises where electricity is used at over 125V a.c. or 250V d.c. Victims must be treated *immediately* and the treatment continued for at least an hour even if there appears to be no response. See also BS 2745 *Construction of electrical equipment for protection against electric shock.*

(ii) Statistics show that electrical faults have been the most frequent cause of large fires in recent years. An electric current always generates heat, and sometimes sparks, and any conductor or apparatus must be designed to contain or utilize this heat safely. All conductors and wiring must be protected by fuses or circuit breakers which will open the circuit when the permissible current (and hence heating effect) is exceeded. A loose connection on a current-carrying conductor, whether it be a loose screw in a domestic plug or a loose cable or other connector on heavy plant, will cause overheating and perhaps sparking which may gradually destroy insulation, etc. and may eventually result in a fire. (A small fault of this nature has been known to start a small fire which then spread to flammable plastic roof tiling and caused the death of a large number of people.)

(iii) Incorrect operation of equipment will usually be apparent on final test but in some cases (as with limit switches or safety devices incorrectly set or connected ) this may be of no avail. Incorrect connection of domestic plugs (e.g. the 13 amp type to BS 1363) is a major hazard. Surveys have shown that a large proportion of such plugs have been incorrectly assembled. (Reversal of polarity (i.e. connection of the live conductor to the neutral terminal) is quite common. The earth terminal may even have been confused with the neutral conductor.) Incorrect operation may be due to the development of faults in service, or to human failings.

### 6.9.2 Electricity Regulations

In the UK before any electrical installation can be connected to the Area Board's supply it must comply with the requirements of the Electricity Supply Regulations 1937 and possibly the Electricity (*Factories Act*) Special Regulations 1908 and 1944 (see Table 14.3). Most good installations usually specify compliance with the IEE Wiring Regulations (Institution of Electrical Engineers' Regulations for the Electrical Equipment of Buildings). These regulations, although not themselves statutory, are accepted as 'deeming to comply' with the Electricity Supply Regulations and are very comprehensive. The latest issue (15th edition) takes account of international rules, etc.

Certain types of electrical installation are covered by Statutory Regulations (e.g. mines and quarries, refineries, terminals and service stations). Where not called for by statute, Section 4 of the *Health and Safety Act* 1974 would imply the desirability of complying with the IEE Regulations.

Inspection and testing of an electrical installation requires at least:
(i) Verification of polarity
(ii) Tests to ensure effectiveness of earthing
(iii) Test and measurement of insulation resistance (some equipment may require a high-voltage 'flash' test)
(iv) Continuity tests of wiring
(v) Visual inspection for correctness, detection of faults, etc.

The IEE Regulations give detailed requirements and guidance on many matters including design, testing and inspection. Compliance with them may be mandatory, as for instance if they are included in contract conditions. In any case they are a guide to good and safe electrical installation practice.

### 6.9.3 The testing of electrical machines—fundamental tests

(i) *Open-circuit test* (no load-loss) for exciting the magnetic field and measuring the magnetizing current and total open circuit power loss (iron loss). These values are approximately constant at all loads. In the case of rotating machines the power spent in friction and windage will be included.

(ii) *Short-circuit test* for measuring the voltage and power required to send current (particularly full load current) through the windings of the machine, and hence to ascertain the impedence of these windings and the power lost (copper loss) in heat at various loads.

(iii) *Load test* (particularly at full load power) for measuring the temperature rise and ascertaining the satisfactory performance of the machine at various loads.

(iv) *Insulation tests* for measuring the insulation resistance of the dielectric of the machine, and a high voltage flash test between windings and earth.

With transformers it is usual to carry out the short-circuit test by connecting a suitable conductor across the low-tension winding and to gradually increase the voltage applied to the high-tension winding taking measurements until full load current (and above if necessary) is flowing in this low-tension winding.

A full load test may be carried out economically by a 'back-to-back' loading connection to a similar transformer (see BS 171 Part 2).

With alternators and most rotating electrical machines the open-circuit test may be carried out by driving it at constant normal speed with its armature winding open-circuited and then applied gradually increasing excitation current to the field and plotting curves of the quantities.

In general the efficiency of electrical machines may be calculated from the equation:

$$\text{Efficiency}\,(n) = \frac{\text{Output}}{\text{Output} + \text{losses}} \quad \text{or} \quad \frac{\text{Input} - \text{losses}}{\text{Input}}$$

Further details are given in appropriate specifications, such as those listed in Table 6.2.

BS 415 *Safety requirements for mains operated electronic and related apparatus* (now harmonized with CENELEC requirements and corresponding with IEC publication 65) is used by the British Electro-technical Approvals Board (BEAB) as the requirement, where relevant, for granting its certification mark. Equipment complying with this British Standard also meets the requirements of the Electrical Equipment (Safety) Regulations 1975 and 1976 (HMSO).

BS 415 details many requirements and tests such as permissible temperature rises (in both moderate and tropical climates), e.g. in moderate climates external metal parts should not exceed a temperature rise of 30°C, and non-metallic parts 60°C; wiring, etc. should not exceed 60°C rise for PVC, or 45°C rise for natural matter. Switches, etc. should withstand 10,000 cycles

## TABLE 6.2

*Some standards dealing with electrical machines and their testing*

| Standard | Description |
|---|---|
| BS 171 | Power transformers (issued in 5 parts) |
| | Routine tests detailed in Part 1 of the standard include: |
| | measurement of no-load loss and current (as in (i) above) |
| | measurement of impedance voltage, short-circuit impedance and load loss (as in 6.9.3 (ii)) |
| | measurement of winding resistance, voltage ratio and check of vector relationship |
| | over-voltage withstand tests (detailed in Part 9 of the standard) |
| | Type tests include: |
| | temperature-rise requirements (detailed in Part 2 of the standard and as in 6.9.3 (iii)) |
| | dielectric tests (detailed in Part 3 of the standard and in 6.9.3 (iv)) |
| | Part 4 deals with tappings and connections and Part 5 with ability to withstand short circuit (demonstrated by calculation and/or tests). BS 171 does not call for efficiency calculations as such, although they can be deduced from its requirements |
| BS 923 | Guide on high-voltage testing techniques |
| BS 5953 | Guide on power transformers |
| | (For the fire hazard arising from the use of transformers see 12.10.1) |
| BS 4296 | Methods of test for determining synchronous machine qualities (applies to 3 phase alternators, etc. of 1 kVa and above |
| BS 4999 | General requirements for rotating electrical machines (especially Part 102: Methods for determining losses and efficiency from tests—see 6.12.2) |
| BS 5000 | Rotating electrical machines of particular types or for particular applications (especially Part 2: Turbine type machines which specifies performance, design and characteristics) |
| | *Note:* Many large turbine type alternators used in power stations are now hydrogen- and/or water-cooled. This introduces a further hazard (see 6.12 and 6.13) |

of operation without damage. Personal protection against ionizing radiation is specified (see 6.17.1).

Methods for the construction of electrical equipment for protection against electric shock include:

(i) The use of a safety extra low voltage (selv) supply which does not exceed 50V a.c. r.m.s. between conductors, or between any conductor and earth

(ii) The use of a non-detachable earthing conductor connecting all metal parts of the equipment which can be touched (and which are themselves

normally separated from live parts by basic insulation) to a solid earth
connection

(iii) The use of double insulation in which the live parts are enclosed in
basic insulation which is itself enclosed in supplementary insulation (with
or without the interposition of a metal layer between them).

BS 2754 is a memorandum (not a specification) on the subject originally
issued to explain the methods of double insulation (which is an alternative
to earthing recognized under the Factories Act and can be made to comply
with the IEE Regulations). It describes design and test requirements for all
the above methods of construction.

BS 4444 Guide to electrical earth monitoring deals with methods of:

(i) direct earthing (the excess current blows a fuse)

(ii) current operated earth leakage protection (operates on a much
smaller current than needed to blow a fuse)

(iii) voltage operated earth leakage protection (operates if the equipment
casing reaches an excess voltage) to earth (see BS 842).

## 6.10 Classification of hazardous/dangerous areas

In the petroleum industry dangerous areas are classified from the safety
angle as:

Division 0   An area in which a dangerous atmosphere is *continuously
present.*

Division 1   An area in which a dangerous atmosphere is *likely to occur*
under normal operating conditions.

Division 2   An area in which a dangerous atmosphere is likely to occur
*only under abnormal operating conditions* (sometimes
known as a remotely dangerous area).

All other areas are considered safe.

The term dangerous atmosphere here refers to dangers arising from
ignition of flammable gas or vapour. Where other dangers may arise they
must be specifically mentioned, e.g. an associated toxic risk.

The classification of dangerous areas given is that of the Institute of
Petroleum, also defined in British Standard Code of Practice CP 1003. It
has also been applied in general to industries (other than mining) where
there is danger of fire or explosion from the ignition of a gas, vapour, liquid
or dust.

It should be noted that the British Standard Code of Practice relates
particularly to electrical apparatus as a possible source of ignition, and that
many other sources are possible.

A new Code of Practice, BS 5345 (see Table 6.3) in effect a revision
of CP 1003 incorporating the International Electrical Commission's
recommendations (IEC 79.10), will eventually replace CP 1003: Parts 1, 2

and 3 but this older CP is being retained temporarily as a reference guide for use with the many existing plants installed in accordance with it. The new code should be used for all new installations and major changes, but minor changes may be made using the earlier code. It should be noted that dangerous areas are now called hazardous areas and that divisions are now called zones, and that their definitions although similar are somewhat different:

Zone 0   In which an explosive gas–air mixture is *continuously present*, or present for long periods.

Zone 1   In which an explosive gas–air mixture is *likely to occur* in normal operation.

Zone 2   In which an explosive gas–air mixture is *not likely to occur in normal operation*, and if it occurs it will exist only for a short time.

An area not classified as above is deemed to be a non-hazardous or safe area with respect to this code, and normal electrical techniques will apply therein. It should be noted that this new code also applies only to dangers from explosive gas–air mixtures; American (ANSI) practice includes combustible dusts, liquids, fibres, etc. British Standards deal with dusts separately (see BS 6467).

The gases and vapours normally encountered in the petroleum industry are heavier than air and will tend to spread outwards and downwards. Consequently (using an interpretation of one code) a dangerous area was not normally considered to extend above a height of 25 ft from the source of hazard, and beyond a distance of 50 ft measured horizontally from it. Beyond 25 ft from the source in the horizontal plane the vertical extent may be reduced to 25 ft above ground level. Where the normal movement of the gas is restricted these reductions are not permitted. Pits or trenches will have a more dangerous classification.

If gases other than the normal (heavier than air) are encountered each case must be considered on its merits.

Imperial Chemical Industries (ICI) have long operated their own detailed systems of area classification. Their latest edition (*Engineering Codes and Regulations* Group C Electrical, vol. 1.5 (published by ROSPA)) corresponds generally with IEC Zones and requirements with some variations; for instance, it deals also with flammable gases.

American practice is based on the National Electrical Code NFPA No. 70 (ANSI C1) Chap. 5, Articles 500–503, which caters for: Hazardous (classified) locations, Division 1 and Division 2 which correspond somewhat with IP Division 0, Division 1 and Division 2 respectively. (The additional term Class I refers to those locations that may be hazardous due to flammable gases or vapours, whilst Class II locations refer to those that may be hazardous due to combustible dusts and Class III locations refer to those that may be hazardous due to the presence of easily ignitible fibres of filings.) (see 6.12 (vii)) See also:

American Petroleum Institute, *API Guide for Inspection of Refinery Equipment*, Chap. 14, Electrical systems

API RP 540 *Recommended Practice for electrical installations in petroleum plants*

API RP 500 *A Recommended Practice for classification of areas for electrical installations and in petroleum refineries*

Institute of Petroleum Part I Electrical Safety Code.

The ICI Code gives a wealth of guidance some in the form of tables and diagrams, on area/zone classification and the extent and dimensions of a hazardous area, but states generally ... 'The extent of a hazardous area depends on the estimated or calculated distance which a flammable atmosphere is capable of travelling before it disperses to a concentration in air below its lower flammability limit (lower explosive limit (LEL)).'

It will be seen from Table 6.3 that Code of Practice BS 5345 is divided into 10 parts, only part 2 of which deals with classification of zones. The other parts in general deal with the different forms of protection, which will be commented upon in what follows.

Much argument has taken place on how to classify areas which seem a borderline between zones, but there is little argument as to what is a hazardous/dangerous region (e.g. Zone 0) and a safe one. However, the onus of classification rests with the occupier or his appointed representative (who may have to substantiate his decision to a statutory inspector, etc.). The zonal classification can be carried out initially by a multi-disciplined team, and BS 5345 Part 2 gives some guidance, including a question and answer (Yes/No) chart to help in the selection.

However, it was felt that better guidance on determining the zone boundaries, and in dealing with the limitations of existing codes for this complex subject was needed, especially by the smaller companies. Consequently a group formed by the relevant engineering institutions and other interested bodies commissioned a Hazardous Area Study from Loughborough University of Technology.*

### 6.11 Selection and inspection of electrical apparatus for use in hazardous/dangerous areas

Electrical apparatus or circuits intended for use in a dangerous area must be tested and inspected initially to ensure safe and satisfactory operation

---

*See *Annual Reports* of the Inter-Institutional Group on the Classification of Hazardous Locations (Secretariat-Inst. Chemical Engineers, Rugby (starting 1986–7)).

in service. Many designs are type-tested and a certificate of approval for use under specified conditions is issued by some appropriate body (e.g. what was known as the Buxton certificate was issued by the Safety in Mines Research Establishment (SMRE), now forming part of the British Approvals Service for Electrical Equipment in Flammable Atmosphere (BASEEFA) under the control of the Health and Safety Executive (HSE)). It is the duty of the inspector to see that any appropriate type-test certificates have been issued, and that the equipment actually supplied has been inspected to this design and found satisfactory. Periodic in-use inspection must ensure that it remains satisfactory.

*In general,* conduit wiring systems should be avoided, as they may form a path for hazardous gases, etc. Mineral-insulated metal-sheathed cables are preferable. Any stranded wire conductors should receive particular attention to ensure that strands are not broken, so causing overheating and perhaps sparking; it is usual to specify a minimum size of strand.

Mains-operated portable handlamps may be used in Division/Zone 1 and 2 areas and should be flame-proof or explosion-proof operating at a voltage not exceeding 55 volts above earth (25 volts is recommended, and can be obtained by using a 50-volt transformer winding earthed at its mid-point). The lamp should be connected to the source of supply by a flexible metallic screened cable, further protected by a tough rubber or similar covering and carrying an earth continuity conductor if the handlamp contains exposed metal work. This cable should be regularly inspected.

All electrical equipment should be effectively bonded to earth in accordance with IEE Regulations, which include earthing the neutral connection of three-phase four-wire transformers, etc., and the non-current-carrying metallic parts of electrical equipment. In addition, in order to provide for the discharge of lightning and static electricity, all structures (such as smoke stacks and towers), and process plant (such as tanks, compressors and pumps) and all pipes where they enter or leave a dangerous area, must be bonded to earth by suitable copper-rod electrodes, a minimum of two for each earthing system.

The resistance to the general mass of earth should not exceed 4 ohms for the electrical equipment, and 7 ohms for the lightning and static discharge. These two earthing systems, when existing side by side, may sometimes be combined, when the earth resistance must not exceed 4 ohms. Bare, mechanically strong, earthing connections should be used.

Lightning protection is now dealt with in BS 6651 (previously CP 326) which states that the whole of the earth termination network should have a combined resistance to earth not exceeding 10 ohms without taking account of any bonding to other services (which would reduce this resistance). Any reduction of the resistance to earth to a value below 10 ohms is recommended and has the advantage of reducing the potential gradient around the earth electrodes and hence the danger to people and animals in their vicinity when discharging heavy lightning currents. It also may reduce the risk of side-flashing to pipes, wiring or metal in or on a structure (e.g. a fire detection system within 'striking distance' of a lightning down conductor). If the instantaneous potential gradient (during a heavy current lightning discharge) between any part of the lightning protection system and any adjacent metal exceeds the electric breakdown strength of the intervening space, be this air, brick or whatever, a side flash can occur whether this metal is earthed or not. If wood or flammable material is present fire can readily commence. Furthermore if the alternative metallic path is flimsy and inadequate to carry the diverted current mechanical damage and arcing will take place and the fire risk will be great.* Down conductors, connecting the air termination with earth electrode/s, may consist of a metallic strip or rod (of some 50 mm$^2$ minimum cross-sectional area) on the external face of the building, or they may include parts of the building framework (e.g. steel reinforcement in concrete). The number of down conductors depends upon the size and configuration of the building. The earth termination/electrodes system may be arranged in various patterns, including ring formation, the electrodes being driven into the ground and preferably buried some 1 m beneath the surface. In general the greater the number of down conductors/ earth electrodes in parallel the less the earth resistance and the less the risk of side-flashing and possible fire.

Inspection must ensure that all these requirements are attained initially, and subsequently maintained in spite of repairs and adjustments; regular inspections are necessary, at least every 12 months and more often when conditions dictate. Particular watch should be kept to detect deterioration due to wear or corrosion of flexible cables, joints, or clamping of armouring; cracks in metal or glass, and failure of cement around flame-proof and explosion-proof enclosures, etc.

Care should be taken to ensure that components do not become insulated accidentally by paint, linings, gaskets or the formation of deposits.

Gas-detecting instruments to give warnings in dangerous areas should be provided and inspected periodically.

When filling tanks, fixed or mobile, static electricity hazards can arise, and the tanks should be earthed so that the resistance to earth is less than 10 ohms.

The liquid, particularly if flammable or in an area where a flammable atmosphere may exist, should not be splash-filled, but should for instance enter from a pipe reaching towards the bottom of the tank.

Despite effective earthing, sparking hazards can still arise in certain cases. Many petroleum products have low-conductivities and consequently, if they become electrostatically charged and are passed into an earthed tank,

---

*Side-flashing somewhat as described may have caused the York Minster fire of July 1984.

their charge will only slowly dissipate and may cause a spark to jump to a nearby object. One way of dealing with this is to allow the charge to dissipate naturally in a safe place; another is to introduce an additive into the liquid to increase its conductivity.

The use of conductive, semi-conductive and non-conductive hose for transporting petroleum and similar products is dealt with in 4.23.

The special case of tanks, etc., lined with insulating material is dealt with in 5.6. Tanks made entirely of insulating material should have an earthed metallic screen on the outside. See also BS 5958, *Code of practice for the control of undesirable static electricity* particularly Part 2, which gives recommendations for particular industrial situations.


### 6.12 Construction and protection of electrical apparatus in hazardous zones

When electrical apparatus is to be used in a potentially explosive atmosphere careful attention must be paid to the prevention of an explosion as a consequence of sparks from or hot surfaces on the apparatus. For an explosion to occur the gas and the source of ignition must be present simultaneously. For many well designed, open air installations the hazardous area will be predominantly of Zone 2 classification, with small areas of Zone 1 classification and very few of Zone 0. The hazardous atmosphere when present may surround the apparatus. It may also penetrate inside the apparatus where the result may be more severe than a similar release in the open, and any enclosure must prevent any resulting ignition reaching the outside. In many installations in Zone (Division) 0 the apparatus or circuit may have been certified as intrinsically safe (perhaps to BS 1259), or perhaps installed in a pressurized ventilated or segregated system. However it is recommended that, if practicable, electrical apparatus should be excluded from such an area. In Zone (Division) 1 the apparatus or circuit may have been certified as flameproof (to BS 229) or explosion-proof (to the American National Electrical Code). Similarly in Zone (Division) 2 the apparatus or circuit may have been of a non-sparking type such that under normal operating conditions it will not produce an incendive spark capable of igniting a surrounding hazardous atmosphere. The guidance given in BS 4137 may have been utilized. Perhaps hermetically sealed equipments (h), electronic valves, mercury switches, etc. may have been used or suitable industrial apparatus may have been approved. Where the use of industrial non-sparking apparatus is not possible (e.g. for Zones 0 and 1) special types of protection or enclosures to prevent an explosion must be used. Some of these techniques have been used for many years; others have been introduced only recently. British standards for the older techniques exist. A comprehensive British Standard (BS 5501) covering old and new has now been issued. Most of these types of protection, the internationally agreed symbols for them, the zones applicable, and the relevant British Standards and other codes, etc. are given in Table 6.3.

**TABLE 6.3**

*Standards and codes of construction and protection for electrical equipment in hazardous zones (for use in potentially explosive atmospheres)*

| Zone | Type of protection | Symbol | Construction Standard | BS Code of Practice |
|------|--------------------|--------|-----------------------|---------------------|
| 0 | Intrinsically safe | Ex 'ia' | BS 1259<br>BS 5501 Pts 7 and 9 | CP 1003 Pt 1<br>BS 5345 Pt 4 |
| | Special | Ex 's' | None issued (but apparatus must be specifically certified for use in Zone 0) | BS 5345 Pt 8 |
| 1 | Flameproof | Ex 'd' | BS 229<br>BS 889*<br>BS 4683 Pt 2<br>BS 5501 Pt 5 | CP 1003 Pt 1<br>BS 5345 Pt 3 |
| | Intrinsically safe | Ex 'ib' | BS 1259<br>BS 5501 Pt 7 | BS 5345 Pt 4 |
| | Pressurization | Ex 'p' | BS 5501 Pt 3 | CP 1003 Pt 2<br>BS 5345 Pt 5 |
| 1 & 2 | Increased safety | Ex 'e' | BS 5501 Pt 6<br>BS 4683 Pt 4<br>BS 5000 Pt 15 | BS 5345 Pt 6 |
| 2 | Non-sparking<br>Division 2 | Ex 'N'<br>or Ex 'n'<br>(British) | BS 4683 Pt 3<br>BS 5000 Pt 16<br>BS 4533 Sect.2.1<br>(luminaires) | CP 1003 Pt 3<br>BS 4137 — old,<br>superseded by<br>4683 Pt 3<br>BS 5345 Pt 7 |
| | Oil immersed<br>(not common in UK) | Ex 'o' | BS 5501 Pt 2 | BS 5345 Pt 9 |
| | Powder (sand) filled<br>(also not common in UK) | Ex 'q' | BS 5501 Pt 4 | BS 5345 Pt 9 |
| | Encapsulation | Ex 'm' | BS 5501 Pt 8 | |

*Notes:*

(i)   Equipment suitable for Zone 0 can be used in Zones 1 & 2 and that suitable for Zone 1 in Zone 2.

(ii) The new BS 5501 Pt 1 (General Requirements) to Pts 7 and 9 (Intrinsic Safety) corresponds to European Norm Std (EN 50014 to 20 and EN 50039) issued by CENELEC and to German (DIN), French, Dutch and other European standards of the same or similar numbers. They also correspond to the appropriate international IEC Std in the series 79.0 to 79.10. (German VDE recognize them as regulations.)

The prefix 'Ex' signifies that approval has been given by BASEEFA the UK certifying authority.

(iii) BS 5501 Pt 9 refers to *Intrinsically safe electrical systems 'i'* intended for use, as a whole or in part, in potentially explosive atmospheres. It supplements Pt 7 which deals with *apparatus*.

BS 5345 Pt 10 refers to *the use of gas detectors.*

(iv) *BS 889 *Flameproof electric lighting fittings* covers three tempera- ture range classes, and refers to BS 229 for flameproof requirements. Only fittings using well glasses are normally certified. BS 4533 Sect.2.1 covers *Luminaires with type of protection 'N'* (previously entitled *Lighting fittings for Division 2 areas*).

(v) BS 4137 (now superseded by BS 6941) and CP 1003 (being replaced by BS 5345) will be withdrawn when no longer required.

(vi) EEC Directives require that equipment complying with harmonized standards must be permitted to be freely marketed and used throughout the European community. Further EEC Directives may be issued to incorpo- rate amendments to the harmonized standards.

**TABLE 6.4**

*Relationship between apparatus group, the former gas group and apparatus class*

| BS 4683 apparatus group | Representative gas | Former definitions | |
|---|---|---|---|
| | | BS 229 gas group | BS 1259 apparatus class |
| I | Methane (firedamp) | I | 1 |
| IIA | Propane | II | 2c |
| IIB | Ethylene | III | 2d |
| IIC | Hydrogen | IV | 2e |
| Not yet allocated | Acetylene* | IV | 2f |

*Notes:* Group 1 is reserved for apparatus for mining use only. Apparatus certified for use in a higher sub-groups (e.g. IIC) can, in general, be used in a lower sub-groups (e.g. IIB—but not vice-versa).

*BS 5501: Part 5, whilst allocating acetylene to Group IIC, states that flanged joints are not permitted for apparatus at Group IIC intended for use with this gas. Spigot joints which may be used are illustrated.

**TABLE 6.5**

*Relationship between T class and maximum
surface temperature*

| Temperature class | Maximum surface temperature °C |
|---|---|
| T1 | 450 |
| T2 | 300 |
| T3 | 200 |
| T4 | 135 |
| T5 | 100 |
| T6 | 85 |

*Note:* Some flammable gases, vapours and liquids are listed in BS 5345 Part 1 together with their appropriate apparatus group and temperature class.

Where flameproof and intrinsically safe apparatus have been selected it is necessary to specify the appropriate gas group in which they are to be used (see Table 6.4). In all cases the appropriate maximum operating surface temperature should be specified (see Table 6.5).

(i) *Special protection (Symbol 's').* In some cases, perhaps of advanced technology where full details of working conditions and of the exact nature of the fluids concerned may not be known (or are confidential), the designation 'special protection' ('s') can be used and the inspector may have to collaborate with the designer. BS 5345 Part 8 offers some guidance. 'Special' apparatus does not meet the requirements of the standards for other types of protection but can be shown (by test or otherwise) to be equally safe. As a consequence of the flexible approach adopted for protection 's', which allows, *inter alia*, for the development of new design ideas, etc. no detailed national or international standards of construction have been issued regarding it. (BS 5345: Part 8 is a Code of Practice *only*.) However, BASEEFA has issued a certification standard (SFA 3009) which indicates some methods of protection that are considered as 's' for certification purposes. Apparatus with such types of protection 's' may normally be used in Zone 1, and by implication, in the less hazardous Zone 2; they may also be developed specifically for Zone 0, or even for Zone 2 only. The relevant documentation, etc., should indicate the specific zone for which the equipment is certified, also the gas grouping (II, IIA, IIB or IIC or any specific gas) and temperature class (maximum temperature reached by unprotected surface under prescribed conditions (T1 to T6)).

(ii) *Intrinsically safe* electrical apparatus and circuits (symbol 'i') for use in explosive atmospheres (see BS 1259 and BS 5501 Part 7; also (in the USA) NFPA493) are in general those in which any electrical sparking that may occur under normal working conditions is of insufficient incendivity to cause ignition of the prescribed flammable gas or vapour.

The prescribed gas group (I, II A B or C) should be stated; also the temperature class for Group II gases. Such apparatus and circuits may be used for relatively low-power applications, such as control and instrumentation. Apparatus categorized as 'ia' may be used in all zones; category 'ib' is suitable for Zone 1 and less hazardous zones.

Intrinsic safety can be obtained by limiting the spark energy by the insertion of additional components (such as resistors, inductors and capacitors). Should these components become defective there is a risk that they may be purposely shorted out or removed to get the equipment working again, so rendering it unsafe to operate in a dangerous area. Precautions must also be taken to prevent connection between the conductors of an intrinsically safe circuit and any other circuit, or to prevent currents being induced from nearby circuits. Requirements for minimum clearance and creepage distances between bare conducting parts must be met.

By restricting the apparatus in the danger areas to transducers and regulating units and keeping the signal level in these circuits to some 10 mA and 20 V they can be made intrinsically safe. All other apparatus is then located in a control room situated in a safe area. A *safety barrier* consisting of a network of Zener diodes and resistors is located at the junction of the safe and danger areas. Should the voltage rise above a certain level the diodes would conduct and so limit the power which can enter the danger area, but the normal instrument signals are not appreciably affected. A *Code of Practice on Zener Barriers*, giving details of certificates issued by HM Inspector of Factories is published by the British Industrial Measuring and Control Apparatus Manufacturers' Association.

The change from thermionic valves to transistors and then on to integrated circuits and microchips has reduced the energy level required enormously and performance has consequently improved. With integrated circuits an operating voltage of 12 and a working level of 1mA is sufficient, whilst with microchips this may fall to 5 V and 0·01mA.

See also BASEEFA certification standards:

SFA 3004 Shunt diode safety barriers

SFA 3012 Intrinsic safety.

(iii) *Flameproof* electrical apparatus (symbol 'd'—generally to BS 5501 Part 5 and BS 5345 Part 3) is capable of withstanding, without injury, any explosion of the prescribed gas or vapour within it (under normal operating and recognized overload conditions) and will prevent the release or transmission of flame such as would ignite the prescribed gas or vapour surrounding it.* Flameproof enclosures for four groups of gases or vapours (including those given off by flammable liquids) are recognized (see Table 6.4).

The effectiveness of a flameproof enclosure depends on the provision and maintenance of a flanged gap at flameproof joints. Any burning gas must be sufficiently cooled in passing through this gap so that it is incapable of igniting any of the gas outside. The enclosure itself must be strong enough to withstand any combustion pressures generated inside it. The inspector must ensure that the dimensions of these gaps do not exceed the maximum figures laid down in the relevant specification for the gas or vapour group in question, and that the minimum length of flameproof path between the inside and outside of the enclosure is as specified. In addition all bolts, cover plates, etc., should be checked for correctness and tightness (see Table 6.6). Periodic inspections should be carried out to ensure that these gaps are maintained, and the flanged joints should occasionally be separated and the faces examined for possible defects resulting from corrosion and other causes. Care should be taken to avoid obstructing the gap with paint or other coatings or matter. The flanges, after cleaning, may be coated with vaseline or silicon grease† to protect against the ingress of water. Outside obstructions near the flanges should also be avoided, particularly for Group IIC (hydrogen).

The subdivisions A, B and C given in BS 5345: Part I (see Table 6.4) are based on the maximum safe gap (MESG) for flameproof enclosures or on the minimum ignition current (MIC) for intrinsically safe electrical apparatus.

The limits are:

Subdivision A—MESG above 0·8 mm
Subdivision B—MESG between 0·5 and 0·9 mm
Subdivision C—MESG below 0·5 mm

For intrinsically safe apparatus gases and vapours are subdivided according to the ratio of their MIC to that of methane.

These limits are:

Subdivision A—MIC ratio above 0·8 mm
Subdivision B—MIC ratio between 0·45 and 0·8
Subdivision C—MIC ratio below 0·45

BS 5501 Part 1 (European Standard EN50 014) in Annex A contains a list of gases and vapours with their appropriate subdivisions.

The importance and difficulty of maintaining the required gap between terminal boxes, flanges, shaft outlets, etc., is illustrated by considering a

---

*The gases within and without an enclosure may differ in some cases.

†Silicone grease may poison the elements of some types of gas detector. Joints should not be treated with substances which harden in use.

typical test using town gas and air (Group III of BS 229) in which the gap was variable. With 20 tests at each gap setting, a 0·027 in gap resulted in external ignition 20 times, a 0·025 in gap 4 times, and a 0·024 in gap none.

For hydrogen (Group IV of BS 229) the maximum experimentally determined safe gap was 0·004 in (0·1 mm), and this implies manufacture (and maintenance in use) to smaller limits than are practicable or economic on a quantity production basis. A simple, small, enclosure for Group IV gases can be produced on a 'one off' basis, but certificates are only granted if production runs are possible. Consequently for this gap and group no maximum permissible safe gap was specified in BS 229. However BS 5501 Part 5 tabulates for various sizes of Group II enclosures maximum gaps of from 0·1 to 0·3 mm.

Flameproof apparatus unless otherwise specified is designed for use in reasonably dry situations. If it is to be used in damp or humid conditions, or under adverse conditions likely to lead to rusting or corrosion, the inspector should see that adequate steps are taken to provide some protection, e.g. painting, galvanizing, or perhaps the provision of a suitable weather shield or enclosure. Any unused cable entries should be sealed off. Some flameproof equipment can also be designed to be weatherproof.

To guard against fire hazards when using light alloy enclosures the alloy used must not contain, by weight, more than 15% in total of aluminium, titanium and magnesium and more than 6% in total magnesium and titanium for Group I apparatus; for Group II apparatus the alloy must not contain more than 6% of magnesium.

The degree of protection of ventilating openings for external fans, etc. of rotating electrical machines must be at least classification IP 20 on the air inlet side and IP 10 on the outlet. With Group I machines IP 10 is only adequate if foreign bodies above 12 mm cannot fall or be carried on to the moving parts (see BS 4999 Part 20, IEC34–5 and 6.12.2).

Flameproof equipment (symbol 'd') has perhaps been the most commonly used in the UK, as it is suitable for Divisions (Zones) 1 and 2. Perhaps to err on the side of safety it has been used unnecessarily when other, maybe cheaper, methods of protection would have been suitable. Originally flameproof equipment (to BS 229 and 889) certified by Buxton was marked with the letters FLP enclosed within the outline of a crown. Since the formation of BASEEFA in 1969 it has been marked 'Ex' enclosed with a crown with letter 'd' marked additionally (and on the label). The 'Ex' indicates the equipment has been approved by BASEEFA and covers all types of protection. The full UK designation consists of 'Ex' followed by the international symbol (e.g. 'Ex d'). If a further 'E' is prefixed (e.g. 'EExd') this indicates that the equipment also complies with a European Norm Standard. The gas grouping (see Table 6.4) may also be marked (e.g. IIC indicates hydrogen to the latest BS and European standards (but IV is correct to the older BS 229). Other gases may or may not be included. In case of doubt check with the maker. The T (temperature) classification may also be marked (e.g. T6 indicates 85°C as the maximum surface temperature—see Table 6.5). See Table 6.6 for an example of an inspection schedule for apparatus with type of protection 'd'.

*Explosion-proof** electrical apparatus (to National Electrical Code (NEC), USA) is capable of withstanding an explosion of a specified gas or vapour within it, and of preventing the ignition of any of this gas or vapour surrounding it. It is designed and tested to NEC Article 500. For other than mining applications four classes of explosive atmosphere are at present prescribed, that applying primarily to the petroleum industry being designated Class 1.

(iv) *Electrical apparatus with type of protection 'N'* was originally so termed for use in Division 2 areas and was not formally certified, but was often a selection of acceptable industrial non-sparking apparatus meeting the specification requirements of the Oil Companies' Materials Association (OCMA). Later, guidance was given by the issue of BS 4137 *Electrical equipment for use in Division 2 Areas* (1967) and by BS 4683 Part 3 Type of protection 'N'. The philosophy of Zone 2/type 'Ex N' equipment is that in normal operation it is not capable of igniting a surrounding explosive atmosphere and that this atmosphere will never envelop it long enough for a fault capable of causing ignition to occur. It can ensure adequate safety at least cost. Its use implies that in the unlikely event of a gas cloud spreading into the area the source of electric power must be switched off or corrective action must be taken to disperse the gas.

Until BASEEFA commenced certifying 'Ex N' apparatus the Factory Inspectorate would often issue a 'letter of no objection' and the equipment could be marked 'Division 2 approved'.

In the UK it is still not a legal requirement to certify such equipment but the publication of recent British Standards specifically for type N protection, and in addition the influence of the HSW Act (particularly Section 6(1)(a) and (b), has created a demand for certification.

Electric motors (non-sparking types) are now tested and certified to BS 5000 Part 16 *Motors with type of protection N*.

New IEC Standards for type 'n' apparatus will also include methods to protect against sparking (the sparking device may be protected by the established methods or by such methods as encapsulation or restricted breathing).[†] In addition type n (now obsolescent) (or N) differs from Division 2 approved apparatus (to BS 4137 and 4683) in that the latter is limited to a maximum surface temperature of 200°C whilst type n (or N) is classified according to a particularly specified maximum temperature class

---

*Explosion-proof is synonymous with flame-proof.
[†]The symbol 'n' has been reserved internationally for such new and pending IEC standards. The symbol 'N' is used at present in the UK for Division 2 apparatus.

**TABLE 6.6**

*Example of inspection schedule*
(Reproduced from BS 5345 Part 3 (1979) by permission)

| Checks that | Inspection category* | | Notes |
|---|---|---|---|
| | Initial | Periodic | |
| Apparatus is appropriate to area classification | A | B | |
| Surface temperature class is correct | A | B | |
| Apparatus subgroup is correct | A | B | |
| Apparatus carries the correct circuit identification | A | B | Apparatus should be positively identified with its circuit to ensure that correct isolation can be carried out. |
| Obstructions do not conflict with clause 13 | A | A | |
| Enclosures, glasses and glass/metal seals are satisfactory | A | A | |
| Gaps are free from corrosion, dirt and paint | A | B | |
| Dimensions of gaps are correct | A | B | |
| There are no unauthorized modifications | A | A | |
| Bolts, glands and stoppers are complete and tight | A | A | |
| There is no undue accumulation of dust or dirt | B | B | Accumulation of dust or dirt can interfere with heat dissipation and result in surface temperatures higher than those permitted in the hazardous area. |
| All conduit runs and fittings are tight and free from corrosion | A | B | |
| Earthing is satisfactory | A | A | |
| Condition of enclosure gaskets is satisfactory | A | B | |
| Electrical connections are tight | A | B | |

**TABLE 6.6** *concluded*

| Checks that | Inspection category* | | Notes |
| --- | --- | --- | --- |
| | Initial | Periodic | |
| Motor fans and couplings are not rubbing on cowls/guards | A | A | |
| Lamp rating and type are correct | A | B | An 'initial' inspection is necessary after relamping. |
| Electrical protection is satisfactory | A | A | |
| Stopper boxes and cable boxes are correctly filled | A | B | |
| There is no leakage of compound from stopper or cable boxes | B | B | |
| There is no obvious damage to cables, cable sheaths or cable glands | A | A | Particular attention should be paid to flexible cables used with portable apparatus. |
| Apparatus is adequately protected against corrosion, the weather, vibration and other adverse factors | A | A | |
| Guards, where used, are present and correctly located | A | B | |

* Category A inspections should be carried out in all cases and, where 'periodic', at intervals not exceeding two years. More frequent and/or more detailed inspection will be necessary where there is a corrosive or other adverse atmosphere, a high risk of mechanical damage or vibration, or where there are other onerous circumstances. The need for more frequent inspection may also be determined by operating experience.

The need for, the method, and the frequency of category B inspections is at the discretion of the engineer responsible. It is not intended that periodic inspections should incur undue disturbances of apparatus, unless considered necessary by the engineer responsible.

ranging from 85–450°C (see Table 6.5). The inspector should ensure that Division 2 equipment is not installed in areas where gases or vapours having ignition temperatures less than 200°C may be present; also the impact test specified for Division 2 apparatus is less severe than that required by type n (or N).

(v) *Requirements for electrical apparatus protected by pressurization 'p' and by continuous dilution, and for pressurized rooms* are covered by BS 5501: Part 3 and BS 5345: Part 5.

Pressurization is intended to exclude the external atmosphere (which may be explosive) from an enclosure by maintaining a protective gas, which may be air, or an inert gas (but should not be combustible—the use of flammable gases is not covered by this code) therein at a pressure above that of the external atmosphere.

Continuous dilution is intended to maintain an overpressure by a continuous flow of the atmosphere inside an enclosure at a concentration below the lower explosive limit of the flammable atmosphere that may be emitted into that enclosure. (For some special applications this continuous atmospheric flow may be used for motor cooling, etc.) The enclosure must have a degree of protection of at least IP 40 of BS 4999 Part 20 (IEC 34–5; see 6.12.(viii)) A minimum overpressure test of 0·5 mbar (50 Pa) must be maintained relative to the external pressure. Both pressurization and continuous dilution, either separately or together, permit installation in hazardous areas when the use of other types of protection is impracticable or undesirable, i.e. for large rotating machines; also offshore accommodation modules; small instruments can also be protected by 'pressurization p'. Unlike earlier specifications this code is not intended to apply to the use of such techniques in Zone 0, for which the flexibility of the code for protection 'S' might be applicable. The pressurizing apparatus and drive motor/s should preferably be installed in a non-hazardous area. Pressurized enclosures should be purged (usually with air or an inert gas) before commissioning, re-commissioning or switching on the electrical supply so that any explosive atmosphere present is reduced to a concentration significantly below the lower explosive limit.

America uses National Fire Protection Association Std (NFPA) 496 *Purged and Pressurized enclosures for electrical equipment* which provides for enclosures and control equipment varying in complexity according to the Division (Zone) in which the installation is to be carried out. For Division 1 it requires monitoring of enclosure pressure, a pre-purge, and automatic disconnection of the electrical supply if the pressure fails; an alarm must also be given. For Division 2 an alarm only is necessary if the pressure fails (the operator then taking appropriate action).

(vi) *Electrical apparatus with type of protection increased safety 'e'* is constructed and tested to BS 5501 Part 6, or BS 4683 Part 4 and selected, installed and maintained to BS 5345 Part 6. The technique may only be applied to apparatus that does not normally arc or spark, and does not contain hot surfaces that might be a source of ignition, or attain a temperature exceeding that associated with the relevant temperature class (see Table 6.5). The design involves:

(a) the use of insulation materials of high integrity which are temperature de-rated

(b) enhanced clearance and creepage distances between conductors, connections, etc.

(c) specially designed terminals (to avoid any possibility of arcing, etc. or of conductors or screws working loose)

(d) enclosures to provide protection at least to the requirements of classification IP 54 of BS 4999 Part 20 (see 6.12.(viii)) for Zone 1, and IP 44 for Zone 2, and to resist impact

(e) in some cases the control of temperatures, air gaps and running clearances.

The technique may be applied to lighting equipment, some motors, instruments and instrument transformers.

(vii) *Protection against explosive combustible dusts.* Electrical machines (such as motors) for use in atmospheres where there is a dust hazard can be designed with dust protection.

Suspended dust particles of many kinds in air create a risk of explosion. This is so, for instance, when machining certain metals, such as magnesium, which can give rise to pyrophoric dust. In explosives factories dust-tight enclosures are insisted on in situations where there are, or may be, loose explosives. Government department specifications are issued for totally enclosed, dust- and hose-proof machines. No dust may gain access to the interior, and the machines must also be proof against water when being hosed down. A modified flame-proof enclosure is usually employed, the flanges being machined flat and smooth to fine limits. No gaskets are used, but high-melting-point grease is applied to prevent rust and ensure dust tightness.

In the American National Electrical Code NFPA No. 70 (ANSI C1) Class II locations are those that are hazardous because of the presence of combustible dust. Class III locations are those in which easily ignitable fibres, etc. are handled. Each location is divided into Divisions 1 and 2 depending on whether the hazard is present normally or abnormally. The zones in the ICI Code deal with flammable atmospheres, which include dusts as well as gases.

BS 6467 covers *Electrical apparatus with protection by enclosure for use in the presence of combustible dusts.* Part 1 specifies requirements based on the maximum surface temperature of the enclosure and on the restriction of dust ingress to the enclosure by the use of dust tight or dust protected enclosures. Part 2 is a guide to the selection, installation and maintenance of such apparatus.

The protection specified is for use where combustible dust may be present and could lead to a fire, etc., but is not for dust from materials regarded as 'explosives' (for which see BS 5501 or 4683) or for use in mines.

The maximum surface temperature of the enclosure is determined by test under the most adverse electrical conditions likely to be encountered, taking into account the designated and expected maximum ambient air temperature (normally 40°C) and adding at least 10K above that temperature. The enclosures must be either (a) dust-tight for degree of protection IP6X as specified in BS 5490 (see 6.12 (viii)) or BS 5420 as appropriate or (b) dust-protected to IP5X as specified in (a) above, or in BS 4999 Part 20 and must be type-tested accordingly. Requirements are laid down for the mechanical strength of the enclosure and its testing, for seals etc., for spindles and shafts, for joints, and materials for cementing and sealing cable and conduit entries. Combustible dusts may of course be ignited by a variety of sources other than electrical.

Useful information is given in: *Guide to Dust Explosion Prevention and Protection* (Inst. of Chemical Engineers, Rugby). Amongst the methods discussed are venting, ignition prevention, containment, inerting, suppression and isolation. Legal requirements dealing with explosions of flammable dust or gas are given in the *Factories Act* 1961, Sect. 31 (see 14.4.24). See also 6.16 for HSE and other publications. Relevant US codes are:

NFC63 Prevention of Dust Explosions in Industrial Plants
NFC68 Prevention of Dust Explosions Venting Guide
NFC69 Prevention of Dust Explosions Prevention Systems

(viii) *General protection by enclosures.* BS 5490 *Classification of degree of protection provided by enclosures* is the main standard for all types of electrical equipment where the voltage does not exceed 72·5 kV. The designation is indicated by the letters IP (for Institute of Petroleum) followed by two characteristic numerals. The first indicates the degree of protection (from 0–6) against contact with or approach to live or moving parts. The second characteristic numeral indicates the degree of protection against the harmful ingress of water (numbered from 0–8)—see Table 6.7.

Suitable tests are laid down for each condition (e.g. a standard metallic test finger is poked against any openings; a suitable water test is specified which does not use salt sea water unless requested).

(ix) *Rotating electrical machines.* BS 4999 and 5000 are multipart blanket specifications for rotating electrical machines. BS 4999 originally in up to 72 parts deals with general requirements including marking, dimensions, rating, efficiency, characteristics and tests. BS 5000 in some 99 parts deals with requirements for particular types or applications. In due course the individual parts of BS 4999 (when all are issued) will be renumbered to bring them into line with IEC Publication 34 and will incorporate all relevant requirements of BS 2613, 3979 and 4362. BS 5000 supersedes in whole or part BS 2730, 3979, 170, 741 and 4362. As far as machines for use

**TABLE 6.7**

*Degree of protection and characteristic numerals*

| First character-istic numeral | Degree of protection | Second character-istic numeral | Degree of protection |
|---|---|---|---|
| 0 | Non-protected | 0 | Non-protected |
| 1 | Protected against entry of solid objects greater than 50 mm diam. | 1 | Against dripping water |
| | | 2 | Against dripping water when tilted up to 15° |
| 2 | ditto greater than 12 mm diam. | 3 | Against spraying water |
| | | 4 | Against splashing water |
| 3 | ditto 2·5 mm diam. | 5 | Against water jets |
| 4 | ditto 1·0 mm diam. | 6 | Against heavy seas |
| 5 | Dust protected (dust does not interfere with | 7 | Against effects of immersion |
| | satisfactory operation) | 8 | Against continuous |
| 6 | Dust-tight | | submersion |

*Examples:* IP 44, IPX4, IP4X (X indicates omitted protection)

IPW44 (W indicates additional protection against specified weather conditions)

IP44M or S (M indicates tested against ingress of water when in operation. S indicates tested against ingress of water when not in operation. The absence of M or S indicates testing was carried out both when operating and stationary.)

in hazardous environments are concerned the following parts are particularly relevant:

BS 4999 Part 20 *Classification of types of enclosure* classifies degrees of protection:
(a) afforded to persons against contact with live or moving parts within the enclosure
(b) afforded to machines against the ingress of solid foreign bodies
(c) afforded to machines against harmful ingress of liquids.

The degree of protection is designated by the letters IP followed by two characteristic numerals in a similar manner to that described in BS 5490 (see Table 6.7 and 6.12 (viii)).

A further letter may follow: S indicating that when tested against the ingress of water the machine was not running, and by M that the machine was running. The absence of any letter means that testing was carried out both running and stationary. The letter W placed between IP and the numerals means that the machine is weather-protected and will operate correctly under specified conditions of rain, snow and airborne particles. For example some frequently used degrees of protection include IP 11S, IP 23 S, IP 5, IPW 44. A series of tests are specified to establish that the enclosures provide the degree of protection required. Dust tight machines (IP 6) are not at present catered for.

BS 4999 Part 21 *Classification of methods of cooling* assigns designations to the methods used—a simplified and a standard code. In the simplified code the method of cooling is designated by the letters IC and two characteristic numerals. The first signifies the cooling circuit arrangement (numerals 0–9) and the second the method of supplying power to circulate the coolant (numerals 0–8). This code only covers air-cooled machines of commonly used types. The arrangements are tabulated with sketches in the standard.

Thus IC 31 designates an inlet and outlet duct ventilated machine with self-circulation fan cooling. For machines with self-circulation the second characteristic numeral may be omitted (IEC Publication 34–36) and the designation may be written IC3. In the complete standard code the same designation would apply, and the nature of the coolant may be added. Thus ICN37 signifies inlet and outlet ducts with cooling gas (nitrogen) supplied from a separate system.

BS 4999 Part 22 symbolizes (with sketches) types of construction and mounting arrangements designates them by IM (International Mounting) followed by a capital letter and a number (up to 31) for Code I for the simpler machines (with end shield bearings and one shaft extension). Code II is for the more complex machines.

Part 60 deals with tests, including arrangements for overspeed, commutation, short circuit, temperature rise, vibration, high-voltage and overload tests, etc. Part 101 deals with rating and performance.

BS 4999 Part 102 Methods for determining losses and efficiency from tests replaces Part 33 (to which it is identical (and also to IEC Publication 34–2)). It superseded BS 269.

It may be called up by another standard (such as BS 5000 Part 2 or Part 3) when it is required to determine losses and hence the efficiency of a machine by the summation of losses. Details are given of various methods of measuring particular losses, such as by calibrated machine test, retardation method, back to back tests and calometric tests.

BS 5000 Part 2 *Turbine-type machines.* (Note: the coolant may be hydrogen; its total outlet temperature must not exceed 110°C.)

BS 5000 Part 15 *Machines with type of protection 'e' (increased safety).*

Part 15 states that machines shall comply with BS 5501 Parts 1 and 6 or BS 4683 Part 4 and with the general requirements of BS 5000 Part 99 as appropriate.

BS 5000 Part 16 *Motors with type of protection 'N'* gives design and construction requirements and makes reference to certain requirements in BS 5000 Part 99, BS 4999 Parts 20 and 71, and BS 5501 Part 1.

Part 17 *Machines with flameproof enclosure* states that the machines shall comply with one of the following:

(a) BS 5501 Parts 1 and 5
(b) BS 4683 Part 2
(c) BS 229

and with the general requirements of BS 5000 Part 99 as appropriate.

BS 5000 Part 99 Motors for miscellaneous applications. This specifies requirements not covered by any other part of BS 5000.

Non-flameproof industrial electrical machines and apparatus may be used in specific locations in chemical plants, etc. Types of enclosures are covered by BS 6467 and 4999 Part 20, whilst dimensions and other details of electric motors are covered by the appropriate part or section of BS 2048, 4999 and 5000.

Totally enclosed machines are preferred, so that the enclosed air has no connection with the external air (but they may not necessarily be air-tight). Any cooling required may be provided by a fan blowing air over the carcase, if necessary via a closed circuit provided with an external cooler. Water cooling can also be employed.

If corrosive conditions are likely, it may be desirable to specify totally enclosed fan-cooled machines (TEFC) with dimensions to BS 4999 Part 10, but fitted with plastic fans and nameplates, and a cast iron fan cowl. The winding is specially impregnated and the exterior painted with chlorinated rubber based paint.

Standard industrial type machines and apparatus in dangerous areas may be permitted if some form of pressurization is adopted. Purging by feeding conduit, machines, junction boxes, switches, lamp fittings, etc., with dry uncontaminated air, nitrogen, or some inert gas, at an excess pressure of some 5 lb/in$^2$, can be carried out on most electrical equipment. Alternatively the equipment could be placed in a separate room or enclosure which is pressurized, possibly by a fan.

In general the electrical performance of rotating electrical machinery is covered by appropriate parts of BS 4999 and 5000.

The use of cathodic protection for the prevention of corrosion on pipelines, manifolds, tanks and jetties, etc., is widespread but has introduced hazards when used in dangerous areas in the petroleum and similar industries.

Cathodic protection may be provided by the use of sacrificial anodes or by a power impressed system (see 4.29.3). In either case the breaking of the small currents involved may cause incendive sparking with its consequent dangers. This sparking might arise when pipelines, joints, plant, etc., are disconnected (either purposely or accidentally), or when conductive hoses (see 4.23) are connected or disconnected.

Electrically insulated gloves, footwear, etc., are widely used and give some protection against electric shock. However, when dealing with flammable atmospheres, explosives, etc., it must be realized that a fully insulated person can acquire an electrostatic charge which can cause a dangerous spark.

Where the risk from electric shock has been eliminated and it is necessary to minimize voltage build-up and to dissipate static charges in the shortest possible time, electrically conducting rubber footwear in conjunction with a conducting floor should be used.

Where there is danger of shock from defective apparatus operating at up to 250 volts, anti-static rubber footwear in conjunction with anti-static flooring should be used. A value of $7 \cdot 5 \times 10^4$ ohms is suggested as the lowest limit of resistance to give adequate protection under these circumstances.

Visual inspection and electrical resistance tests should be carried out frequently, since the resistance of the rubber, etc., may change significantly during service. Conducting footwear should be labelled as such, and identified by a red back strip; anti-static footwear should be identified by a yellow back strip (see appropriate British Standards in Table 6.8).

When electrical testing is necessary in a dangerous area several alternatives arise. It may be possible to postpone the work until the area can be made safe or gas-free (as for instance during a shut-down period); it may be necessary to install a suitable gas detector in the area and to carry out the tests during periods when the detector indicates that it is safe to do so; or it may be necessary to use certified intrinsically safe test instruments for insulation and earth continuity testing, etc.

The Health and Safety Executive now administers the British Approvals Service for Electrical Equipment in Flammable Atmospheres (BASEEFA) which provides certificates of assurance for electrical equipment used in places where flammable atmospheres constitute a hazard. Their test laboratories are located in Buxton.

The certification procedure includes scrutiny of design, testing of samples to agreed specifications and surveillance during manufacture. BASEEFA can also arrange for special inspection of batches of certified equipment before they leave the manufacturer's works.

Since British Standards are not necessarily acceptable in other countries BASEEFA may also issue certificates against certain foreign national standards.

Information on overseas standards, regulations inspection and other

**TABLE 6.8**

*Some standards dealing with environmental hazards—gases, electricity, etc.*

| Standard or Code No. | Description |
|---|---|
| BS 6651 (formerly CP 326) | The protection of structures against lightning (Deals with zones of protection, inspection, testing and maintenance) |
| CP 331 | Installation of pipes and meters for town gas |
| CP 352 (Now listed under BS 5720) | Mechanical ventilation and air conditioning in buildings |
| CP 1003 (being superseded by BS 5354) | Electrical apparatus and associated equipment for use in explosive atmospheres of gas or vapour other than mining applications |
| | Part 1: Choice, installation and maintenance of flame-proof and intrinsically safe equipment |
| | Part 2: Methods of meeting explosion hazard other than by use of flame-proof or intrinsically safe electrical equipment |
| | Part 3: Division 2 areas |
| CP 1013 | Earthing |
| CP 1015 | Electrical equipment of industrial machines |
| BS 229 | Flame-proof enclosure of electrical apparatus (Gives requirements suitable for Division 1 areas and, to a limited extent, for Division 0) |
| BS 415 | Safety requirements for mains operated electronic and related apparatus |
| BS 476 | Fire tests on building materials and structures |
| BS 889 | Flame-proof electric lighting fittings |
| BS 1259 | Intrinsically safe electrical apparatus and circuits for use in explosive atmospheres |
| BS 1747 | Methods for measurement of air pollution |
| BS 1870 | Safety footwear |
| BS 2011 | Basic environmental testing procedures (Some 50 parts give guidance and procedures for climatic and mechanical robustness tests of electrotechnical products (such as heat and cold, mechanical shock, vibration, acceleration, mould growth, resistance to chemicals, fluids, solar radiation, low pressure, etc. either alone or in combination) |
| BS 2050 | Electrical resistance of conducting and antistatic products made from flexible polymeric material (deals with conducting flooring material) |

**TABLE 6.8** *continued*

| Standard or Code No. | Description |
| --- | --- |
| BS 2754 | Construction of electrical equipment for protection against electric shock. A memorandum describing the IEC system of classification and details of design and construction for protection against shock. Briefly Class 0 relies upon basic insulation; Class I requires connection to an earthing conductor (for mains voltage operation); Class II requires additional safety precautions such as 'double insulation'; Class III relies upon supply at safety extra low voltage (selv), generally not exceeding 50 V |
| BS 3187 | Electrically conducting rubber flooring |
| BS 4056 | Method of test for ignition temperature of gases and vapours |
| BS 4066 | Tests on electric cables under fire conditions |
| BS 4137 | Guide to the selection of electrical equipment for use in Division 2 areas |
| BS 4194 | Design requirements and testing of controlled atmosphere laboratories |
| BS 4343 | Industrial plugs, socket-outlets and couplers for a.c. and d.c. supplies |
| BS 4363 | Distribution units for electricity supplies for construction and building sites |
| BS 4444 | Guide to electrical earth monitoring |
| BS 4445 | Schedule of tests for gasification and reforming plant using hydrocarbon feedstocks |
| BS 4559 | The preparation of gaseous mixtures |
| API RP 500B | Classification of areas for electrical installations at production facilities |
| BS 4683 | Electrical Aparatus for explosive atmospheres |
| | Part 1 Classification of maximum surface temperatures |
| | Part 2 Construction and testing of flameproof enclosures of electrical apparatus |
| | Part 3 Type of protection N |
| | Part 4 Type of protection 'e' |
| BS 4999 | General requirements for rotating electrical machines |
| BS 5000 | Rotating electrical machines of particular types or for particular applications |
| BS 5343 | Gas detector tubes |
| BS 5345 (see also CP 1003) | Code of Practice for selection, installation and maintenance of electrical apparatus for use in potentially explosive atmospheres (10 parts: see Table 6.3) |
| BS 5420 | Degrees of protection of enclosures of switchgear and control gear for voltages up to and including 1000 V a.c. and 1200 V d.c. |

**TABLE 6.8** *concluded*

| Standard or Code No. | Description |
|---|---|
| BS 5451 | Electrical conducting and antistatic rubber footwear |
| BS 5490 | Degrees of protection provided by enclosures |
| BS 5501 | Electrical apparatus for potentially explosive atmospheres (9 parts see Table 6.3) |
| ANSI C1 (NFPA No. 70) | National Electrical Code Chapter 5 Articles 500–517, Hazardous locations |
| BS 5720 (formerly CP 352) | Code of practice for mechanical ventilation and air conditioning in building |
| BS 5958 | Code of practice for the control of undesirable static electricity |
| BS 6020 | Instruments for detection of combustible gases |
| BS 6458 | Fire hazard testing for electrotechnical products |
| BS 6467 | Electrical apparatus with protection by enclosure for use in the presence of combustible dusts |

requirements is published by BSI (Technical Help to Exporters Section) in the form of Technical Digests, each dealing with a particular country.

### 6.13 Hydrogen and precautions when dealing with hydrogen gas plant

Hydrogen gas required for process work can be supplied from high-pressure cylinders, perhaps feeding into a gasholder, or if the quantity required is large by means of a special plant.

Hydrogen is produced on a commercial scale by the electrolysis of caustic soda solution; oxygen is also generated. The hydrogen from such a cell is between 99·6 and 99·9% pure, and contains not more than 0·05% of oxygen. The hydrogen is taken from the cells by blowers and stored in a water-sealed gasholder, after which it may be taken via a high compression ratio compressor and stored as commercial hydrogen in cylinders at some 2000 lb/in$^2$ (133 bar).

Hydrogen is also produced by separation from water-gas or coke-oven gas (a mixture of hydrogen and carbon monoxide produced by passing steam over red hot coke), or by passing steam over red-hot iron, or by 'cracking' ammonia by passing it over a catalyst. High-purity hydrogen is obtained by removing the oxygen.

One method of removing traces of oxygen from hydrogen (and other gases) is by passing the gas through a cold trap (externally cooled by liquid nitrogen) containing charcoal. For larger plant the gas may be passed through a 'de-oxo' unit containing a vanadium catalyst and then an alumina drier, and compressed into previously evacuated cylinders. The oxygen content may thus be reduced to less than 10 parts per million by volume. See also BS 3906 *Electrolytic compressed hydrogen* which covers specifications and methods of test for Type 1 (for general industrial use) and Type 2 (reduced oxygen and moisture content).

Gaseous hydrogen must of course be used and handled with considerable care, because of its fire and explosion hazard. Mixtures of hydrogen and air are explosive over a very wide range, extending from 4·1% to 74·2% of hydrogen by volume (termed the lower and upper explosive limits (LEL and UEL) respectively). Mixed with oxygen the percentage of hydrogen rises to some 94%. Spontaneous ignition in air can occur at any temperature over 400°C, and occasionally on leaking from a high-pressure system (due to the reverse Joule–Thomson effect—see 7.7).

Various forms of hydrogen detector are available and should be installed in any hydrogen plant to give adequate warning of any significant leakage (e.g. when concentrations of hydrogen in air reach above about 2%).

## 6.14 Inspection of hydrogen and other hazardous gas plants

To safeguard against the fire and explosion hazard of gaseous hydrogen (including that evolved from liquid hydrogen) the design of hydrogen plants should preferably be examined and approved before construction. Inspection of the various components and of the complete plant prior to commissioning will be necessary. Periodic in-use inspections should also be made. Attention should be paid to the various factors already mentioned, as may be relevant, and in addition the following points should receive consideration:

(1) Roof spaces, etc., should be adequately vented so that any escaping hydrogen cannot be confined. Then, if it should ignite, it will burn away rapidly without danger of explosion.

(2) Buildings, and particularly roof structures, should be of light, open construction, combustible materials being avoided. The roof may be of light, friable, non-splinterable material.

(3) Where hydrogen is, or might be, released, the suggested 'safety' distance to the nearest inhabited building is 100 ft for up to 200 lb of hydrogen at risk.

(4) All metal work should be heavily bonded to earth, and lightning conductors should be fitted. All connections should be checked regularly for deterioration.

(5) No static electric charges must be allowed to collect—even operating personnel may need to be discharged electrically before touching equipment—and tools should be of a non-sparking pattern.

(6) As commercial electrical equipment of the flame- and explosion-proof type normally used in dangerous atmospheres *cannot* (at present) be certified as safe for use in an atmosphere of hydrogen, its use in such locations will be severely restricted. Where essential, nitrogen (or perhaps dry air) pressurized equipment may be used; lighting fittings of this type are available. It may be possible to arrange for electric motors to be placed outside and to drive equipment in a dangerous atmosphere via a sealed shaft passing through a wall. In locations where the hazard is not great other arrangements may be appropriate; for instance electric plugs, etc., might be fitted at low level and interlocked to prevent their removal on load, the actual switch mechanism being in a safe remote location.

(7) The components and pipework, etc., should be tested by some method to ensure the absence of significant leakage (see Chapter 11). The relevant specification may give a maximum acceptable leakage rate.

(8) Hydrogen systems should as far as possible operate under positive pressure, so that any leakage of hydrogen will be outwards and air cannot leak in.

(9) The presence of rust in the system should be avoided, as fine oxide may cause ignition.

(10) The high-compression-ratio compressor should be free from significant leakage. Owing to the danger of combustion, it may be oil-free, lubrication and cooling being effected by water, and leather piston rings being fitted. Special oil lubrication can however be used, when precautions should be taken to ensure that the oil is kept within the various stages of the compressor. An efficient oil separator must be fitted at the final stage.

It should be checked that suction from the surrounding air is impossible. Similar remarks to the above apply, as may be relevant to plants dealing with other hazardous gases; particular attention should be paid to the hazards involved in using oxygen and oxygen equipment and the necessity for cleanliness (e.g. see BS 6869 *Code of practice for ensuring cleanliness of industrial process measurement and control equipment in oxygen service*).

Compressors may be of positive displacement (piston, diaphragm or rotary) type, or of turbo type. British Standards covering tests for these are BS 1571 *Acceptance tests for positive-displacement compressors and exhausters,* and BS 2009 *Code for acceptance tests for turbo-type compressors and exhausters* (see 8.3)

Most test codes are based on performance testing with air. With compressors used for gases other than air it is usually required that they be tested to establish that they can satisfactorily perform the duty required. This may necessitate a works test using a closed circuit testing plant employing the specified gas. For hazardous gases other than hydrogen it is usually possible to make up a suitable mixture of innocuous gases (such as helium and nitrogen) having the same physical constants as the specified gas.

From what has been said above it will be seen that the main safeguard against a hydrogen fire and explosion is to use light construction and not to confine the escaping gas. This obviously is of no use if the escaping hydrogen, burning or otherwise, carries with it toxic substances or is a danger to its surroundings (including its ability to set off a major explosion of nearby material). The position then becomes similar to that of a flameproof motor operating in an hydrogen atmosphere. It must be capable of withstanding, without injury, any explosion within it and the containment must be such as to prevent the release of the exploding gases and vapours etc. to the outside environment. The analogy with an accident at a nuclear power station such as that at Chernobyl will be clear. The design of a suitable containment building to cater for any emergency presents problems.

In any gas plant instruments should be installed and/or available for the measurement of the quality of the gas being handled and for the detection and/or measurement of any concentrations of gas inadvertently in its vicinity. Some instruments for the detection of combustible gases, their testing and performance, are dealt with in BS 6020. Accurate analysis of various gases may be carried out by infra-red gas analysers (see BS 4314), spectrographic instruments or by chemical methods. A gas will burn (or explode) in air only in concentrations between its lower and upper explosive (or flammability) limits (LEL) and (UEL).

BS 6020 Part 4 covers instruments for sensing Group II combustible gas or vapour concentrations with air (i.e. Group II instruments) up to 100% LEL. Part 5 deals with Group II instruments sensing concentrations with air up to 100% gas by volume and will indicate presence of flammable gas within any range that includes the UEL. BS 6020 Part 1 deals with general requirements and test methods. Parts 2 and 3 deal with Group I instruments which may be used in mines for the detection of firedamp (methane).

All instruments may operate from supply voltages not exceeding 600 V r.m.s. or from any type of battery. Some instruments (or parts thereof) may be used in potentially explosive atmospheres and applicable precautions must be taken (see 6.12 and particularly intrinsically safe electrical apparatus made to BS 5500 Part 7).

For on the spot detection and evaluation of hazardous gases and atmospheres various proprietary *gas detector tubes* (e.g. to BS 5343) may be used. The presence of a specific gas or atmospheric hazard is indicated by the nature and/or extent of a colour change in the tube. Tubes to BS 5343 Part 1 cover those for short-term (say 10-minute) use to evaluate concentrations in the region of occupational exposure limit (OEL). Part 2 covers long-term tubes which enables a time-weighted average (say over an 8-hour shift) exposure measurement to be obtained. Such tubes are not available for the detection of oxygen deficiency.

All tubes must be suitably graduated or accompanied by a calibration chart and used in conjunction with *Occupational Exposure Limits* (Guidance Note EH 40) published annually by HSE. Hydrogen is used for cooling large power station alternators. In this case the hydrogen under pressure has to be kept at a concentration of over 95% in order to prevent a mixture with air falling to the UEL of some 75%. See also HSE Tech. Data Note 45   Industrial use of flammable gas detectors, and BS 5345 Part 10 *The use of gas detectors.*

## 6.15  Hydrogen embrittlement

Materials of construction may be adversely affected by the presence of hydrogen, particularly at high temperatures and pressures. Metals, especially steel, may be subject to embrittlement attack. The hydrogen penetrates into the metal to an extent dependent on its nature and the temperature and pressure (palladium shows an extremely high permeability). The attack may be physical or chemical. In the former the metal may take up hydrogen during processing or use, which can then become trapped in fissures, faults, grain boundaries, etc., and under certain circumstances can set up very high pressures, with consequent stress and troubles.

In the latter chemical reaction between the hydrogen and carbon in the steel may occur, producing methane. This accumulates at discontinuities, grain boundaries, etc., and high internal pressures may be set up, resulting in loss of strength and ductility.

The mechanism of embrittlement attack is not fully understood, and its detection is difficult although microscopic and macroscopic examination may help.

To aid the inspector it can be said that:

(i) The rate of attack increases with pressure, temperature and time.

(ii) High-carbon steels are more subject to attack than mild steels.

(iii) Coarse-structured steel, welds, etc., are more subject to attack than fine-grained, hardened and tempered steels.

(iv) Alloy steels containing chromium, molybdenum, vanadium, tungsten, titanium, niobium (columbium) are more resistant to attack; nickel and silicon do not appear to help.

(v) Austenitic stainless steels (particularly the 18/8 type) are highly resistant to attack.

(vi) It has been stated that a certain pressure vessel withstood 7000 atmospheres when tested with oil, but failed at 2000 atmospheres when tested with hydrogen.

(vii) The use of stainless steel lined pressure vessels may be economically justifiable. However hydrogen will diffuse through the liner and reach and attack the outer vessel; the build-up of pressure at the interface can be prevented by drilling a number of fine holes through the outer vessel.

(viii) Tests to check for changes in hardness or localized areas of differing hardness may help to detect possible sources of trouble.

(ix) The preheating of welding electrodes, the baking of components (to prevent moisture getting into crevices of vessels, etc., and the possibility of this producing hydrogen perhaps by electrolytic action) may help. In certain cases of highly stressed high-temperature vessels the use of water for proof pressure testing may be suspect. See also ASTM STP 543 Hydrogen embrittlement testing and API Pub 941 Steels for hydrogen service, etc.

### 6.16 Some rules and regulations affecting gases and hazardous dangerous areas

(i) Under the *Factories Act* The Chemical Works Regulations (S.R. and O. 1922 No. 731), Part 1, Regulations 4(d), requires the placing of a notice prohibiting smoking, naked lights, the carrying of matches, etc., at the entrance to any place where there is an explosion hazard due to inflammable gas, etc., whilst Regulation 17, 2(e) refers to the employees' duty in this respect. Regulation 5 requires that: 'Every still and every closed vessel in which gas is evolved or into which gas is passed, and in which the pressure is liable to rise to a dangerous degree, shall have attached to it, and maintained in proper condition, a proper safety valve or other equally efficient means to relieve the pressure. Nothing in this regulation shall apply to metal bottles or cylinders used for the transport of compressed gases.' (See 3.19 for details of safety valves, etc., and 14.8 for legislation regarding gas cylinders.)

The safety device, etc., must be tested at least every three months. A pressure gauge, preferably of the recording type, should also be fitted. Provision should be made to prevent any gas or vapour discharged from polluting, poisoning or rendering inflammable the surrounding atmosphere.

No operations or repairs, etc., involving the use of an open flame, high-temperature spot or other sources of ignition are permitted in a dangerous area until the conditions have been made safe by the removal of the cause of the danger, and written authority has been given.

For instance under the Cellulose Solutions Regulations (S.R. and O. 1934 No. 990) the danger point for a hot surface, etc., is given as 180°F (82°C).

(ii) Under *the Petroleum (Consolidation) Act* 1928 it is necessary to obtain from the local authority a licence to store petroleum spirit. The local authority will probably require that: 'No fire, flame, artificial light or electrical apparatus liable to ignite inflammable vapours shall be within 50 ft of any place where petroleum spirit is kept or manufactured.' It applies to products having a flash point below 73°F, and may be extended to cover other dangerous substances and to cylinders containing compressed gases. For example, The Petroleum (Inflammable Liquids and other Dangerous Substances) Order (S.R. and O. 1947 No. 1443) brings in a considerable number of materials not apparently covered by the 1928 Act.

This Act also requires that possible leakages of flammable or dangerous liquids shall be confined by sumps, bund walls, etc., and the surrounding area and drains must be protected from contamination. The Petroleum-Compressed Gases, Gas Cylinder (Conveyance) Regulations 1931, and The Gas Cylinder (Conveyance) Regulations 1959, No. 1919 deal with flammable gases (including hydrogen) and give requirements for cylinder testing and marking, valve threads and caps, lorry loading, maximum pressures, etc. Left-hand threads mating with similar ones on the regulators are specified.

(iii) The Asbestos Regulations 1969 (SI 690) require that where a process or article is capable of giving rise to asbestos dust use should be made of exhaust ventilation to prevent it from entering the air of any work place (Reg. 7) or during the cleaning of premises and plant (Reg. 10). If this is not praticable, protective clothing and approved respiratory protective equipment (or breathing apparatus) must be provided. No one can be employed unless he has been fully instructed in the proper use of the equipment. (See Guidance Note EH 41—Respiratory protective equipment for use against asbestos.) The exhaust ventilation must be inspected every seven days and thoroughly examined and tested by a competent person every 14 months. The premises and plant must be kept clean preferably by vacuum cleaning.

The degree of concentration of asbestos dust in the atmosphere permissible without the use of the stated precautions is very small (currently reduced from 2 fibres/cm$^3$ to 0·5 fibres/ml, whilst for blue asbestos it remains at 0·2 fibre/ml, both measured over a 4-hour reference period. See HSE Tech. Data Note 13 and HSE Code of Practice and Guidance Notes (Feb. 1985) for further details, methods of sampling, instruments available etc. Also Guidance Notes EH10, and EH35–37. EH47 (1986) deals with the necessary hygiene facilities, changing rooms (comprising a clean area, shower area and dirty area) etc.

Mask, filters and air purifying respirators are suitable for use in low concentration of asbestos dust (from 2, 40 or 200 fibres/cm$^3$ upward according to type). For high concentrations, beyond some 800 fibres/cm$^3$ (40 mg/m$^3$) it is necessary to use proper breathing apparatus with a self-contained or separate air supply. With blue asbestos dust (crocidolite—the most dangerous form) approved respiratory apparatus must be worn if the concentration is above some 0·2 fibres/cm$^3$, and proper air breathing apparatus is necessary above some 80 fibres/cm$^3$. By fibre is meant a particle of length greater than 5 microns (5 μm) and having a length to breadth ratio of at least 3:1 (see HSE TDN 24).

The Asbestos (Licensing) Regulations 1983 (SI No. 1649) which came into effect in August 1984, require the licensing of companies involved with the removal of asbestos insulation material, so that the Factories' Inspectorate can control and monitor delagging operations. The magnitude of the hazard can be realized when 739 death certificates gave mesothelioma (an asbestos-related disease) and/or asbestosis as a cause of death in 1983. But there should be no over-reaction to the often ill-founded fear of asbestos in sound condition. If insulation is in good condition and properly sealed it should be left intact to do its job. But where it has to be removed a licence must be obtained and the work must be done properly and under supervision. A contractor removed asbestos from a boiler in a church without first obtaining a licence. He incurred fines and costs exceeding £8000. An elderly manager of a small company himself helped to remove asbestos, and scoffed when told of the risk of death to workers which could occur some 20–30 years later, saying he would be dead anyway by then— he also was fined!

There is no universal substitute to replace asbestos. In some applications, such as resistance to fire, asbestos has saved many people from death or injury. It is the fibrous nature of asbestos which constitutes its major health hazard. Many substitutes are available, or are being developed, for particular applications. These include glass and ceramic fibres; glass however softens and melts at around 500°C but can be specially coated to improve its performance, whilst some substitutes may conceivably have health hazards themselves, and may be dearer and of inferior performance. Some guidance on the latest position regarding substitutes is available in an HSE publication — *Alternatives to Asbestos Products: A Review* (HMSO 1986).

(iv) *The Explosives Act* 1875 and *The Explosive Substances Act* 1923 deal with the manufacture, storage and sale of certain materials. The Regulations of HM Explosives Storage and Transport Committee also deal with these subjects.

In Mining Regulations: Mines and Quarries. Form No. 11 (revised January 1955): General Regulations as to the Installation and use of Electricity (issued by the Ministry of Power), Reg. 132, is one of the few statutory guides as to the treatment of explosion hazards arising from the use of electricity.

(v) Besides statutory rules and orders, which must be observed, certain regulations and codes are issued by various organizations and large firms which lay down what are recognized as standards of good practice. Typical examples, designed to secure the safe use of electricity, include: Institute of Petroleum—Electrical Safety Code, Institution of Electrical Engineers— Regulations for the Electrical Equipment of Buildings and Imperial Chemical Industries Ltd.—Engineering Codes and Regulations: Group C—Electrical. Such codes are often included in contracts and local works regulations.

*6.16.1 Some official and other publications and reports, dealing with industrial hazards, etc.*

## Issued by the Health and Safety Executive*

*New Guidance Notes*

| | | |
|---|---|---|
| General Series | GS/4 | Safety in pressure testing |
| | GS/6 | Avoidance of danger from overhead electric lines |
| | GS/14 | Electricity on construction sites |
| Chemical Safety Series | CS/1 | Industrial use of flammable gas detectors |
| | CS/2 | Storage of highly flammable liquids |
| Environmental Hygiene Series | EH/2 | Chromium — health and safety precautions |
| | EH/3 | Prevention of industrial lead poisoning |
| | EH/5 | Trichloroethylene |
| | EH/10 | Asbestos—hygiene standards and measurements of airborne dust concentrations |
| | EH/15 | Threshold limit values |
| | EH/17 | Mercury—health and safety precautions |
| | EH/18 | Toxic substances—a precautionary policy |
| | EH/40 | Occupational exposure limits |
| | EH/42 | Monitoring strategies for toxic substances |
| Plant and Machinery Series | PM/1 | Guarding of portable pipe threading machines |
| | PM/32 | The safe use of portable electrical apparatus |
| Medical Series | MS18 | Health surveillance by routine procedures |
| Hazardous Substances Series | MDHS/14 | General methods for gravimetric determination of respirable and total dust |

*These and many similar publications are issued by HMSO and/or HSE and may be purchased when in print, and in some cases are available free from HSE.

|  | MDHS/16 | Mercury vapour in air |
|---|---|---|
|  | MDHS/39 | Asbestos fibres in air (European reference version) |
| Flixborough | Parker, The Flixborough disaster. Report of Committee of Enquiry (HMSO 1975) | |
|  | HSE/1 | After Flixborough |
|  | HSE/2 | Flixborough, the lessons to be learned |
|  | 53/1 | Zinc embrittlement of austenitic stainless steel |
|  | 53/2 | Nitrate stress corrosion of mild steel |
|  | 53/3 | Creep of metals at elevated temperatures |
| Other publications | IAL/1 | Fires and explosions due to misuse of oxygen |
|  | HSC/1 | HSW Act 1974—Some legal aspects and how they will affect you |
|  | HSC/7 | Regulations Approved Codes of Practice and Guidance Literature |
|  | Harvey, Reports of the Advisory Committee on Major Hazards (HMSO 1976 and 1979) | |

1  Lifting and carrying
6  Safety in construction work
8  Dust and fumes in factory atmospheres (gives threshold limit values of air-borne concentrations)
13 Ionizing radiations: precautions for industrial users
22 Dust explosions in factories
28 Plant and machinery maintenance
30 Storage of LPG at factories
32 Repair of drums and tanks: explosion and fire risk
34 Guide to the use of flame arrestors and explosion reliefs
35 Basic rules for safety and health at work

*Technical Data Notes*
1  Dust control — the low volume, high velocity system

14 Health — dust in industry
35 Control of asbestos dust

**Some earlier publications** (issued by the Factory Inspectorate and others)

*Form 814.* Memorandum on explosion and gassing risks in the cleaning, examination and repair of stills, tanks, etc.

*Form SHW830.* Dust explosions in factories. (Gives a classified list of dusts.)

*Series of DSIR booklets*, 'Methods for the detection of toxic substances in air'.

*Form 2150.* Welding operations on gasholders by the electric welding process.

*Forms 664 and 672.* Cutting and welding operations on gas mains.

Recent reports from these and other inspectors of the HSE have appeared as popular glossy coloured publications with titles such as:

*Annual Reports* of HM Chief Inspector of Factories.

*Annual Reports* of HM Senior Electrical Inspector of Factories.

*Form 931.* List of Certificates issued by HM Chief Inspector of Factories of intrinsically safe and approved electrical apparatus for use in certain specified atmospheres.

*Annual Reports* of HM Chief Inspector of Explosives.

*Annual Reports* of HSE Statistics.

*Testing Memorandum* No. 4. Test and certification of the flame-proof enclosures of electrical apparatus.

*Testing Memorandum* No. 10. Test and certification of intrinsically safe apparatus and circuits.

*HSC/HSE Publications* (issued annually or periodically from HMSO–titles may vary).

Health and Safety at Work Report by HM Chief Inspector of Factories (1985–new format).

Manufacturing and Service Industries Report (HMSO) (to 1984).

Health and Safety Commission Report.

Industrial Air Pollution.

Health and Safety Research and Technological Services.

Statistics Health and Safety.

Advisory Committee on Major Hazards (several reports).

**Issued by the Post Office Engineering Department:**

Z3013. Flame-proof telephone apparatus, telephone stations.

Z3902. Engineering instructions, petroleum premises, lines general.

**Issued by the Illuminating Engineering Society:**

Lighting in corrosive, flammable and explosive situations, *Report No. 1.*

**Issued by the Fire Protection Association:**

The explosion hazard from flammable dusts, *Technical Information Sheet* No. 3012.

**Issued by the Fire Research Station** (obtainable from HMSO)

*Technical Papers.*

2: Fire hazards of electricity (Fry and Lustig).

21: Explosibility tests for industrial dusts (Raftery).

920: Fires in oil refineries and outdoor chemical plant (Chandler).

**Issued by the National Coal Board:**

*Handbooks.*

The maintenance of flame-proof apparatus.

The maintenance of intrinsically safe apparatus.

**Issued by the Institution of Chemical Engineers:**

Chemical Process Hazards with special reference to Plant Design (1960 onwards).

Commissioning of Chemical and Allied Plant, 1974.

Technical Lessons of Flixborough. Symposium, 1975.

Symposium on Process Hazards, 1976.

Major Loss Prevention in the Process Industries, 1971.

**Issued by the Fire Offices Committee Joint Fire Research Organization (Dept. of the Environment Fire Research Station):**

Explosibility Tests for Industrial dusts FR Tech. Paper 21/1968.

Fire protection in process industry building plant and structures FR Tech. Note 725/1968.

Fire protection of liquid fuel storage tanks FR Tech. Note 609/1965.

Form 376 Explosions in oil drums and tanks. Report by DSIR and Fire Offices Committee Joint Fire Research Organization.

**Issued by the Chemical Industries Association:**

Precautions against fire and explosion: vinyl chloride 1978.

Major hazards—Memo of guidance on extensions to existing chemical plant 1972.

Guide for the storage and use of highly flammable liquids.

Guide to hazards and operability studies. 1977.

Code of Practice for the large scale storage of fully refrigerated anhydrous ammonia 1975.

**Issued by ICI Engineering Codes and Regulations Group C (Electrical):**

Vol. 1.1   Statutory and other rules, regulations and codes

Vol. 1.3   Plant installations: safety precautions

Vol. 1.4   Portable and transportable equipment: safety precautions

Vol. 1.5   Electrical installations in flammable atmospheres

Vol. 1.6   Group D (Miscellaneous): Liquefied flammable gases: storage and handling

**Issued by the Electrical Research Association:**
*Technical Reports:*

| | |
|---|---|
| D/T104 (Whitney) | Combustible industrial gases—Possibilities of ignition by particles of light alloys heated by arcing or by frictional impact. |
| D/T110 (Riddlestone) | The spontaneous ignition temperature of inflammable gases and vapours—A critical résumé, 1958. |
| D/T131 (Jones and Taylor) | Flame-proof enclosures. Environmental effects on the maximum safe gap for 1 in flanges with mixtures with air of (1)85:15 hydrogen/methane, (2) ethylene, (3) pentane. Supplementary note: Effect of an external obstacle at a short gap. |
| Report 70/32 | The use of light metals and their alloys in hazardous areas 3051/16 |
| Report 5092 | Flameproof enclosures: safe gaps for enclosures of small volume |
| Report 5130 | The basis of design of intrinsically-safe apparatus and circuits. |

**Issued by the Institute of Petroleum:**
Model Safe Code of Practice in the Petroleum industry (in 13 parts)

*6.16.2 Hazards due to radio-frequency radiation*

The electro-magnetic wave spectrum extends from radio and microwaves (wavelengths of longer than $15 \times 10^3$m down to less than 1mm), through infra-red, heat, visible and ultra-violet, to gamma, X and cosmic rays (less than some $10^{-9}$mm). Each type of radiation overlaps its neighbours throughout the spectrum. Wavelengths longer than 100 nm are conventionally termed non-ionizing. The corresponding frequencies can be found as the product of frequency and wavelength equals the speed of light. i.e. Frequency (hertz) $\times$ wavelength (metres) $= 300 \times 10^6$ (metres/sec).

Electro-magnetic waves produced by any radio-frequency transmitter or source (e.g. radio, radar and television transmitters) will induce voltages and currents in any conducting structure or device on which they impinge. This structure or device acts as a form of aerial.

The magnitude of the induced current depends on the configuration of the structure, its distance from the transmitter and its frequency, and the strength of the electro-magnetic field.

A hazard can exist if the following conditions occur simultaneously:
  (i) the electromagnetic radiation is of sufficient strength;
  (ii) the receiving structure responds sufficiently (like a tuned aerial);

(iii) a flammable atmosphere is present;

(iv) the induced current is broken by some action such as the separation of parts of the structure normally in contact by a small amount sufficient to permit and cause a spark to bridge the gap. (This action could, for instance, occur during maintenance, or at any time due to vibration, flexing, etc.)

(v) the energy in the spark exceeds a certain threshold value sufficient to cause ignition of the flammable atmosphere concerned.

For most industrial plants the likelihood of all these conditions occurring simultaneously is remote. However, for some chemical, explosive and petroleum plants, and off-shore platforms, tankers, etc. where for instance a powerful radio transmission may occur when hazardous atmospheres are present, the risk may be serious.

Personnel concerned, especially inspectors, should be aware of such risks and be able to assess, initially, if the hazard is not serious. If, however, a serious hazard is possible then a detailed assessment must be made, calling in expert opinion as necessary. Plant safety measures could be introduced to reduce the risk, such as bonding and insulation of parts, 'de-tuning' the 'aerial' structure, and restricting radio transmissions when gas is present.

It might be advisable to bond across pipework, valves, flanges and fittings or parts of structures, before removing them for maintenance, so that removal does not leave a momentary gap in the circuit across which a spark could jump.

It should be remembered that the nature of the gas/air mixture has a great bearing on the possibility of ignition. The energy threshold value of ignition for a Group IIC gas such as hydrogen is only 200 $\mu$ joules as compared with some 7000 $\mu$ J for group I and IIA gases and vapours like methane or petroleum. (These figures are for the most easily ignitable gas/air mixture which for hydrogen is a 21% mixture by volume with air.)

Another hazard with radio-frequency radiation may occur if the conducting structure is the firing circuit of an electro-explosive device. The induced current may then be sufficient to trigger off the device. This may cause inadvertent initiation of explosives used in mines and quarries, or the explosion of defence missiles (either planned or inadvertent).

For further information see:

BS 4803    *Radiation safety of laser products and systems*
BS 5175    *Safety of commercial electrical appliances using microwave energy*
BS 6656    *Guide to Prevention of inadvertent ignition of flammable atmospheres by radio-frequency radiation*
BS 6657    *Guide to Prevention of inadvertent initiation of electro-explosive devices by radio-frequency radiation*
ANSI/Z136 *Safe use of lasers*

Robertson, S.S.J. and Loveland, R.J., *Radio frequency ignition hazards; a review.* (Proceedings IEE Vol. 128 Pt.A No. 9 1981 607–614.)

A further hazard is the biological effect of radio-frequency non-ionizing radiation on man. No one should be closely exposed for any length of time to the radiation from a high power radio or similar transmitter. Its effects can be somewhat similar to but less severe than those from nuclear radiation. Personal protection against ionizing radiation from a high voltage cathode ray tube (such as used in video display units, television and radar) or related electronic apparatus is included in the safety requirements specified in BS 415—*Safety requirements for mains-operated electronic and related apparatus.*

The exposure rate, measured at a distance of 5 cm from the outer surface of the apparatus (e.g. a television or video) must not exceed 36pA/kg (0·5 milliröntgens/hour) (this is laid down in ICRP Publication 15 (1969) Clause 289). An exposure rate of 0·5 mR/hour for an 8-hour day, 7 days a week would give rise to some 1456 mR per year of 52 weeks i.e. 1·5 R per year (approx.). This is some 15 times the yearly amount of natural radiation to which the people of this country are exposed. Assuming that R = rem (6.17.2), then a television addict (or a video worker) closely watching a powerful set for a year could possibly receive from this source alone:

(i) more than the radiation doses promulgated in the British Government White Paper (Command 884–1959) (see 6.19).

(ii) somewhat less than the dosage on the lenses of the eye permitted for a radiation worker, but more than the tenth of this dosage permitted for the general public (see Table 6.10) under the 1969 Regulations.

(iii) about the same as that permitted for a worker in Radiation Zone Class R1 (1·5 rem/year).

See *Visual Display Units* (HSE/HMSO, 1983) which gives guidance on installation, use and safety aspects.

*Note*: the latest ICRP recommendations on which the 1985 Ionizing Regulations are based lay down a limit of 1μSv per hour (0·1 m rem per hour) at an increased distance of 100 mm.

Radio-frequency dielectric heating equipment is widely used in industry, particularly for the processing and welding of plastics, and may operate in the frequency range 10–100 MHz, but usually at a designated frequency (perhaps 28·12 MHz) to minimize interference with communications.

The article or material to be processed acts as the dielectric (insulating material) between generally two electrodes so forming a capacitor which is part of a tuned oscillator circuit fed usually by a large triode valve. Outputs may range up to 50 kW.

The radio-frequency (RF) energy causes the dielectric material to warm up, but some of this energy may reach nearby personnel and perhaps cause harmful biological effects. Suitably designed earthed metallic screening can minimize this emission of stray energy but to satisfy the requirements of the HSW Act Sect. 2(1) employers should ensure that people are not exposed to harmful levels of RF energy (which may cause deep-seated burns, warming of tissue and as yet unknown biological effects). What constitutes a harmful level is the subject of much investigation. Generally speaking over the frequency range here considered exposures averaged over 6 minutes are permitted if it can be demonstrated that the mean specific absorption rate is less than $0.4$ $Wkg^{-1}$ and the peak rate in any part of the body does not exceed 8 $Wkg^{-1}$ as averaged over any 1 gram of tissue. See also:

ANSI/IEEE C.95.1 (1982) *Safety levels with respect to human exposure to R/F E.M. fields* (300 kHz–100GHz)
National Radiological Protection Board, Proposals for the health protection of workers and members of the public against the dangers of extra low frequency and microwave radiations: a consultative document (1982)

These standards tabulate limits of power density $(Wm^{-2})$, electric field strength $(Vm^{-1})$, and magnetic field strength $(Am^{-1})$ for various frequency ranges and conditions of exposure, subject to maximum exposures generally as given above. HSE recommends that at 27 MHz, for whole or partial body exposures, these levels should not exceed 123 $Wm^{-2}$, 211 $Vm^{-1}$ and $0.59Am^{-1}$ respectively. Some guidance on these matters and on the instruments necessary to monitor and quantify the stray fields, etc. and the methods of making measurements are given in Guidance Note PM51— *Safety in the use of radio-frequency dielectric heating equipment*, published by HSE (HMSO, 1986).

### 6.16.3 Hazards due to laser radiation

A laser is a device that produces an intense monochromatic beam of non-ionizing radiation, either in the form of a continuous wave (CW) or as a pulse or series of pulses.

This beam can create a hazard, causing possible eye (retina and cornea) and skin damage. This hazard will vary with such factors as wavelength, power and pulse length. The beam obeys the laws of optics: the wavelength is generally determined by the chemical composition of the lasing medium that is being stimulated.

BS 4803 *Radiation safety of laser products and systems* in Part 2 classifies products according to the maximum permissible exposure (MPE) of eyes and skin to laser radiation (generally in accordance with the requirements of IEC and of ANSI Z–136) and is intended to protect persons from such radiation in the wavelength range 200 nanometres (nm) to 1mm. Laser products require certain built-in safety features.

Class 1 laser products are those that are inherently safe either because of their low power or because their built-in design is such that the relevant MPE cannot be exceeded. The most limiting MPE values (for direct ocular, diffuse viewing and skin exposure) are tabulated in Part 3 of the standard and are used to calculate the accessible emission level (AEL) for Class 1 products (tabulated in Part 2).

Class 2 laser products are low-power devices emitting visible radiation (i.e. in the wavelength range 400–700 nm) and no more than the AEL of Class 1 for other spectral regions. (For CW lasers the output power must not exceed 1mW averaged over 0·25 sec.) This class is not inherently safe but eye protection may normally be afforded by such responses as the 'blink reflex'.

Class 3A laser products are those emitting visible radiation with an output power up to 5mW for CW lasers and no more than the AEL of Class 1 for other spectral regions. At any accessible point of a surface the radiant power incident thereon must not exceed $25Wm^{-2}$. Note that unaided eye viewing may be protected by the 'blink reflex', but direct intra-beam viewing with optical aids may be hazardous.

Class 3B laser products are those that may emit visible and/or invisible radiation not exceeding AELs tabulated in Table 4 of Part 2 of the standard. The emission must not exceed 0·5W for CW lasers (for a duration longer than 0·25 sec) and $10_5$ J $m^{-2}$ for pulsed lasers. Direct viewing can be hazardous, but viewing via a diffuse reflector for not more than 10 sec at a minimum distance of 50 mm between screen and cornea may be permissible.

Class 4 laser products are high-output devices with outputs exceeding the AELs of Class 3B and are capable of producing hazardous diffuse reflections. Extreme caution in use is necessary; this class may also cause skin injuries and could constitute a fire hazard.

Tests, test equipment and procedures to show compliance with the relevant requirements are required during operation, maintenance and servicing. Guidance for users is given in Part 3 of the standard.

A laser product may consist of a single laser with or without a power supply or it may incorporate a complex optical, electrical or mechanical system. It may be used for material processing, measurement, data reading and storage, display of information, etc. The exposure values given in BS 4803 are not intended to be applicable to patients undergoing medical treatment.

## 6.17 Nuclear installations and radioactive hazards

Legislation regarding radioactive hazards, nuclear installations, etc. in the UK is based on the principle of placing sole and absolute liability on the operator for injury or damage from ionizing radiations (see 6.18). Various Government Departments and Inspectorates have the right of access and inspection to ensure safety and to see that the appropriate regulations are met.

In order to comply with such legislation and, as far as possible, to prevent injury and damage and to implement the recommendations of such authoritative bodies as the Medical Research Council and the International Commission on Radiological Protection regarding the maximum permissible personal level of doses of external and internal radiation and the maximum permissible concentrations of radioactive contamination in air and in water etc., it is necessary to:

(i) Measure and record the amount and type of radiation or other radioactivity inside and outside buildings, laboratories and plant.

(ii) Collect, measure and record the radioactive contamination in atmospheric dust, in water, fish and on the ground etc.

Should a specified level be exceeded, then access to the affected area must immediately be controlled, pending further instructions from higher authority.

For some notes on natural and man-made radiation and details of the latest ICRP recommendations and 1985 Regulations see 6.19.

### 6.17.1 Types of ionizing radiation

Basically radioactive substances are unstable because their atoms disintegrate from one form to another. In doing so they emit ionizing radiations characteristic of that substance. In general, radioactive substances are dangerous, even in extremely small quantities, if inhaled or otherwise introduced into the body. In somewhat larger quantities the danger arises owing to the external effects of the radiation. Burns or permanent injuries (often carcinogenic) may be caused as the energy of the radiation is absorbed in living tissue. The energy of an emitted radiation is measured in electron-volts (eV) (which is a very small unit, representing the energy of one electron accelerated across a potential of 1 volt, and is equal to $1.6 \times 10^{-19}$ joules). The most commonly encountered types of ionizing radiation are:

(i) *Alpha particles* (alpha rays). These are the nuclei of helium atoms emitted by radioactive atoms or otherwise. They have little penetrative power and only pass about one-twentieth of a millimetre into soft tissue.

(ii) *Beta particles* (beta rays). These are in effect high-speed electrons, and can penetrate up to about a centimetre in tissue. In free air they may travel some 20 metres, but are readily stopped by solid matter and can be stopped by a thin sheet of paper.

(iii) *Gamma rays.* These are electromagnetic radiations of high energy originating within the nucleus of the atom, and can penetrate the whole body and other matter, according to the energy available.

(iv) *X-rays.* These are similar to gamma rays and are usually produced artificially by electrical machines; their energies are usually expressed in keV. They have great penetrative power, depending upon voltage (kV) applied to the electron tube, and can travel several hundred metres but will be stopped by solid matter, particularly by lead (a few millimetres may suffice) or concrete (half a metre or so).

(v) *Neutrons.* These are similar in mass to the proton but have no electric charge. They interact with the nuclei of atoms, so producing ionization and inducing radioactivity. They are not normally emitted by radioactive materials, but may be produced by nuclear reactors and devices.

### 6.17.2 Units of radiation dosage and radioactivity (radioactive contamination)

Doses of ionizing radiations have commonly been expressed in the following units:

(i) *Röntgen (R).* The unit of exposure dose of X-rays or gamma rays. It is the quantity of radiation such that the associated corpuscular emission per 0·001293 gramme of dry air (1 cm$^3$ at NTP) produces, in air, ions carrying 1 electrostatic unit of quantity of electricity of either sign.

(ii) *Rad (röntgen absorbed dose).* The unit of absorbed dose of any ionizing radiation. It corresponds to the absorption of 100 ergs of energy per gramme of the absorbing medium (which equals $10^{-2}$ J kg$^{-1}$).

The röntgen and rad (in soft tissue) are approximately equivalent.

(iii) *Rem (röntgen equivalent man).* This biological unit expresses the quantity of any ionizing radiation such that the energy imparted to a biological system per gramme of living matter has the same biological effectiveness as 1 rad of 200–250 kV X-rays (i.e. it is the unit of dose equivalent).

Equal doses in rads of different types of radiation have different degrees of biological effectiveness. The dose in rads multiplied by the relative biological effectiveness (RBE) equals the dose in rems. The RBE for X-rays, gamma rays and beta rays is 1, for fast neutrons it is 10 and it may be 20 for alpha rays.

The dose of radiation may be given in terms of the maximum permissible in a week, a quarter (13 weeks) or a year, or it may be expressed as a dose rate in, say, millirems/hour. Radiation received in certain parts of the body is more dangerous than in others. For occupational workers certain limits have been laid down (see Table 6.10). For other than occupational workers in controlled areas, and for the general public, lesser rates (some one-tenth) are applicable.

*SI units.* Although the above units have been and are widely used internationally, SI units are now being used and will no doubt eventually supersede them. The SI unit of exposure is the coulomb per kilogram (C/kg)

$$1 \text{ röntgen (R)} = 258 \text{ } \mu \text{ C/kg}$$
$$1 \text{ C/kg} \simeq 3876 \text{ R}$$

The SI unit of absorbed dose is the gray (symbol Gy)

$$1 \text{ gray} = 1 \text{ J/kg} = 100 \text{ rads}$$
$$(1 \text{ rad} = 0{\cdot}01 \text{ J/kg} = 1c \text{ Gy})$$

Absorbed dose rate is the gray per second (Gy/s).

Dose equivalent (i.e. dose corrected to take account of the effect to the body of doses to the skin and deep tissue) in the SI system is measured in sieverts (symbol Sv). As an interim measure the British Committee for Radiological Units (BCRU) agreed to use 100 röntgen as the approximate equivalent of one sievert.

$$1 \text{ sievert} = 1 \text{ J/kg} = 100 \text{ rem}$$
$$1 \text{ rem} = 1c\text{Sv} = 10^{-2} \text{ Sv}$$

Considering the confusion which the Bureau International des Poids et Mesures (BIPM) found continued to exist following the adoption in 1979 of the name sievert for the SI unit of dose equivalent in the field of radioprotection they, in 1984, decided to publish the following explanation:

The quantity dose equivalent H is the product of the absorbed dose D of ionizing radiation and the dimensionless factors Q (Quality factor) and N (product of any other multiplying factors) stipulated by the International Commission on Radiological Protection:

$$H = Q N D$$

Thus, for a given radiation, the numerical value of H in joules per kilogram may differ from that of D in joules per kilogram depending upon the values of Q and N. In order to avoid any risk of confusion between the absorbed dose D and the dose equivalent H, the special names for the respective units should be used, that is, the name gray should be used instead of joules per kilogram for the unit of absorbed dose D and the name sievert instead of joules per kilogram for the unit of dose equivalent H.

(Thus in SI units: sievert = QN × gray. Compare with: rems = RBE × rads, as given above.)

For each radioisotope there is a maximum permissible concentration (mpc) of radioactivity laid down for air and for water, so that inhalation or ingestion could take place without danger for, say, a 40-hour week. This mpc has been expressed in microcuries/cm$^3$, and may be based on an average weekly dose of 0·3 rem or some factors times the natural radiation background level.

The curie (Ci) is the unit of radioactivity hitherto used and corresponds to the amount associated with one gramme of radium. It is equivalent to $3 \cdot 7 \times 10^{10}$ atomic disintegrations per second.

The SI unit of activity (of a radionuclide) is the becquerel (Bq). It is very small and corresponds to one atomic disintegration per second.

$$1 \text{ curie} = 3 \cdot 7 \times 10^{10} \text{ Bq}$$
$$1 \text{ Bq} \simeq 2 \cdot 7 \times 10^{-11} \text{ Ci}$$

*6.17.3 Radiation instruments*

Instruments for the indication and measurement of radiation and radio-activity may monitor for:

(i) High levels of radiation, which are measured in sieverts, or the older units such as röntgens, rads and rems, and expressed as (a) a dose rate (e.g. per/hour) or (b) the total dose received.

(ii) Radioactive contamination of, for instance, working surfaces, the hands and clothing, water, the atmosphere, etc. This may be expressed in $\mu Ci/cm^3$ for volumes (or, using SI units, as $Bq/m^2$ for surfaces).

All radiation instruments should be calibrated (and recalibrated periodically at least once every 14 months) from a suitable known source, such as X-rays or gamma rays from a radioisotope. For instance, it is known that 1 curie of the radioactive isotope cobalt 60 will give a dose rate of 1.3 R/hour at a distance of 1 metre (or 1 millicurie will give some 14 mR/hour at a distance of 1 foot).

Some instruments give an indication by means of counting the number of radioactive disintegrations or events which they detect. The counting of these electrical impulses may be done by means of an electronic scaler unit. The counting rate for a particular detector instrument and source is convertible approximately to a quantitative measure such as dose rate or contamination.

Contamination of the air can be monitored by drawing air through a filter continuously and measuring the radioactive concentration to see that it does not exceed the permissible maximum. An audible alarm or a light can be arranged to give warning should the level be exceeded. Then evacuation of the area should take place, or possibly respirators could be worn.

In all areas there is a background level of radiation due to a variety of reasons, e.g. radioactive matter in the earth or in adjacent buildings, cosmic radiation from outer space, etc. (The latter may be of some consequence to personnel who fly for long periods at high altitudes, especially near the poles.)

This background level can be continuously monitored, and may have to be allowed for when taking some measurements (in the UK it averages some 100 millirads/year, or in SI units 1m Sv/year).

In any area or laboratory where radioactive dust or vapours may arise these may settle onto measuring instruments and contaminate them, so giving a false reading if the instrument is taken elsewhere. Decontamination of instruments is therefore necessary from time to time.

### 6.17.4 Measurements of radiation dose and dose rate

*Personnel dosimetry.* A photographic film screened from light becomes blackened by ionizing radiations and can be worn as a badge or wrist strap, etc., by personnel liable to exposure. The films are collected at regular intervals, developed, and measured to record the integrated dose. As the film sensitivity depends on the type and energy of radiation it is necessary to know this before interpreting the blackening. By providing an open window to one part of the film, and a suitable absorber or absorbers, exposure to beta rays can be distinguished from exposure to gamma rays. Exposure to slow neutrons can also be recorded.

Quartz-fibre electrometers of the fountain-pen type may also be carried for personnel dosimetry, the fibres being repelled apart from one another to an extent dependent on the dose.

### 6.17.5 Nuclear counting instruments

Most nuclear instruments depend on the fact that charged particles and rays passing through a material cause ionization, i.e. atoms of the material are broken down into pairs of positively and negatively charged ions. Measurements are made by causing these charges to register a small current pulse or, in the case of continuous counting instruments, a steady current.

Consider a tube filled with air or a gas (such as argon or neon) at low pressure, and having an electric potential impressed across its electrodes (see Fig. 6.2), this potential being normally insufficient to cause a discharge. However, should an ionizing radiation pass through the tube, ions are formed in the gas and are pulled to the respective electrodes by the electric field. Measurement of this ion current gives an indication of the intensity of the ionizing source.

Referring to Fig. 6.2, as the potential across the electrodes is increased initially, the current increases (from A to B) indicating that the ion pairs produced are increasingly being separated and collected by the electrodes (if the potential is insufficient for quick collection the ions will recombine). At B all the ion pairs are effectively being collected and a plateau-like region persists until C. At C, however, some of the ions are moving so fast that in colliding with other gas atoms they cause further ionization, thus increasing the current from C to D. However this current is still proportional to the initial ionizing radiation. At D the fast-moving positive ions hitting the cathode knock negative ions out of it, which cross to the anode and knock

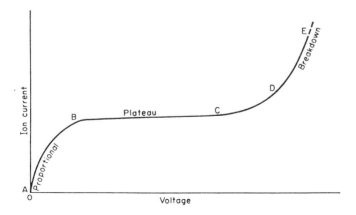

**Fig. 6.2    Gas discharge tube—nuclear counters.**

ions out of this, and so on. This process is cumulative, proportionality is lost, and finally at E breakdown occurs, the discharge becoming unstable and continuous.

If the instrument is used in the plateau region it is called an *ionization chamber*; if used in the proportional region it is called a *proportional counter*; if used in the breakdown region it is called a *Geiger counter*.

An *ionization chamber* with a valve electrometer can be used to monitor laboratories and areas liable to radiation. It should be beta-sensitive, a thin window being closed to measure the gamma radiation component. A typical instrument for environmental health physics surveying covers a range of from 0 to 15 and 0 to 150 mR/hour, (up to 1·5 mSv/hr). These are dose rates proportional to the ion current measured. Should measurement of the total dose be required then this will be proportional to the total ion charge, and this may be collected on a capacitor and measured by means of a valve voltmeter.

Pocket ionization chambers can also be carried by workers in addition to a film dosimeter to give an immediate reading of the gamma-ray dose received.

*Proportional counters* are used to measure particle energies which will be proportional to the pulse heights.

A *Geiger counter* is a pulsed instrument which is used to detect individual particles. However some arrangement is necessary to quench the discharge so that a further count can be made. Quenching may be done by an electronic circuit, or more usually by using a gas mixture in the tube, such as argon with alcohol or a halogen, which then becomes self-quenching. The counting rate is approximately proportional to the dose rate. A typical portable battery-operated survey meter will register about 100 counts per second on its scale in a gamma ray field giving a dose rate of $25\mu Svh^{-1}$. The instrument can also be used for surveying contamination levels, a typical sensitivity being down to some $10^{-4}\ \mu Ci/cm^2$ (3·7 Bq cm$^{-2}$) when using a thin mica end window.

### 6.17.6 Scintillation counters

Certain materials, especially zinc sulphide, anthracene and naphthalene, when hit by ionizing radiations, give out energy as visible and ultra-violet light. By using a photo-electron multiplier circuit this light is converted into current which will be proportional to the initial ionization. Scintillation counters can be used for the detection of alpha, beta or gamma radiations, the output pulse amplitude for each being dependent on the particular phosphor used. A very thin layer of zinc sulphide is generally used for alpha particle detection. This zinc sulphide may be deposited on another plastic phosphor which scintillates under the action of beta and gamma radiation, this radiation passing through the zinc sulphide with negligible loss. Consequently pulses of different amplitudes are produced simultaneously when mixed radiation is received, and can be analysed and recorded electronically. Such an instrument can be used for contamination measurements.

### 6.17.7 Neutron counters

A neutron does not cause appreciable ionization itself; however if it is made to produce a charged particle this can be detected. One method is to line an ionization chamber with boron. Slow (thermal) neutrons will then cause a reaction which produces lithium nuclei and alpha particles, which are detected and measured in the usual way, alternatively the chamber may be filled with boron trifluoride gas ($BF_3$) at a pressure of some half an atmosphere to operate as a proportional counter. Fast neutrons with energies in the MeV range can be slowed down by a suitable moderator and also measured. A neutron flux of 1 neutron/m$^2$/s may give a counting rate of three counts per second. An indication of the total biological dose rate over the whole energy range (up to some 100 m SvH$^{-1}$) can be given (see BS 5548 which describes characteristics and test methods for gas filled radiation detectors of this type which produce a mean current proportional to the neutron flux which is proportional to nuclear reactor power).

### 6.17.8 Contamination levels—hand and clothing monitors

Hazards due to the deposition of radioactive materials on surfaces can be limited by the imposition of maximum permissible levels for both contamination of the skin and of inanimate surfaces. Some maximum permissible levels are given in Table 6.10.

It is usual to provide a hand and clothing monitor to check all personnel entering and leaving a process area to see that these levels are not exceeded.

Such an instrument will normally monitor for alpha contamination by an air proportional counter or by a scintillation counter, and for beta contamination by a Geiger counter. Invariably two or more counters are placed on each side of the hands, and both hands are monitored simultaneously, the results being displayed on four separate meters. Independent clothing probes, one for alpha and one for beta-gamma contamination, may be provided, each connected to its own counting circuit. A background counter may be built in to monitor and to subtract automatically this level from the indicated reading. Semi-automatic whole-body monitors are available for the routine checking of workers, and also screening monitors (incorporating scintillation counters) for the rapid detection of small particles of radioactive material which may have been ingested by a worker.

### 6.17.9  Precautions against radioactive hazards and ionizing radiations

In any plant or laboratory where operations under radioactive conditions are, or may be, required, certain general precautions are usually necessary.

(i) *Control of access.* Only authorized personnel who need to go into the active area should be allowed access. A wooden barrier may guard entry to a change room where personnel can change into suitable protective clothing. This may vary from changing into shoes and overalls and a cap to the wearing of a pressurized suit. Interlocks may be provided on doors into dangerous rooms (such as an X-ray room) to prevent access whilst the unit is in operation.

(ii) *Ventilation.* Exhaust systems producing an air flow of some 100 to 200 ft/min across the openings of fume hoods, etc., may be installed. In process areas air flow should in general be directed downwards. The outlet air is usually passed through a filter or scrubber system to minimize radioactive content.

(iii) *Containment.* Process work should, as far as possible, be performed in glove boxes, etc. (6.2), in order to prevent the spread of radioactive dust. Box interiors should be maintained at a negative pressure with respect to the outside.

(iv) *Criticality.* Fissionable material of a certain critical size, mass and geometry may enter into a nuclear chain reaction if brought into contact. This possibility must be prevented (See BS 3598 which deals with procedures, technical criteria and evaluation philosophy which should be observed to prevent a possible explosion). In some cases, although the energy released may be manifested mainly as heat, the unseen radiation may be lethal. Consequently clear written operating and safety instructions should be issued and regular (and random) inspections and audits should be carried out by groups (including independent specialists) to ensure that procedures are adhered to and that safety is not endangered, perhaps by minor unsuspected changes.

(v) *Shielding.* Effective radiation shielding is required. For beta radiation 1–2 cm of Perspex is generally adequate. For gamma radiation shielding materials of high density and high atomic number, such as lead, concrete, etc., are required.

For neutron radiation water and hydrogenous materials, together with a gamma-absorbing component, are necessary.

(vi) *Viewing.* Viewing windows of lead glass blocks, or possibly liquid windows of zinc bromide solution, or, alternatively, a mirror system or closed-circuit television may be used.

(vii) *Tools and handling.* The hands should be kept at a safe distance from all radioactive materials. Rubber gloves, tweezers, paper or tongs can be used for handling in some cases; for highly active work 'slave' manipulators may be necessary.

(viii) *Monitoring.* Adequate monitoring of all the process areas, and of all personnel entering or leaving the area is required. Careful records, including details of the radiation doses received, and the time spent by all personnel in the area, are essential. Periodic medical examinations are necessary.

(ix) *Decontamination.* Personal hygiene is essential. The hands, etc., should be washed or scrubbed before leaving a process area. Equipment and materials may be decontaminated by cleansing processes such as scrubbing or immersion in acid solutions or even sand blasting.

BS 4247 deals with *Surface materials in radioactive areas.* Part 1 covers methods for measuring and evaluating the decontamination factor and Part 2 is a guide to the selection of materials which may become contaminated by radioactive substances and which will require subsequent decontamination.

Generally speaking in a radioactive laboratory or installation working surfaces, floors etc. should be made from materials which are not easily contaminated and any contamination should be easily removable. Notes on specific materials are given. Surfaces subject to serious contamination may for example be protected by chlorinated rubber which is easily decontaminated.

The decontamination factor (DF) is the ratio of the original surface contamination to the residual contamination after decontamination. It is a dimensionless number and can be calculated for a sample material by dividing the original contamination count (as for instance measured by a Geiger–Müller tube) by the residual contamination count. Alternatively surface materials having a DF of over 1000 can be described as having excellent ease of decontamination (ED), those from 100 to 1000 are good, from 10 to 100 fair and below 10 poor.

These factors provide standards of acceptance for the inspecting authority. Processes such as ageing (for instance, all plastics age on storage) and absorption of large doses of radiation can cause physical and chemical changes in materials, so affecting their ED. A guide to the radiation stability of coating materials is given in an appendix to Part 2 of the standard. The stability and radiation tolerance of rubbers and plastics is improved by the addition of more than the normal of antioxidants and plasticizers. Part 3 deals with decontamination techniques.

(x) *Waste disposal.* Special care must be exercised in the disposal of radioactive waste. Prior authorization for its disposal must, in general, be obtained from an appropriate Government Ministry. Waste may be in solid, liquid or gaseous form, and its radioactive content must be reduced to the permitted level before disposal or discharge. Solid wastes, depending on their nature and activity, might be disposed of by burial on selected sites, or by dumping at sea (although this has been frowned on), or by vitrifying in glass.

Highly active liquid wastes may have to be stored indefinitely, or until their activity subsides below the maximum permissible level, in concrete-shielded tanks. Permission to discharge low-activity liquid wastes into public sewers, the sea, rivers, etc., may be granted.

Gaseous wastes might be discharged, after treatment if required, into the atmosphere at such a height as to secure adequate dispersion. The whole subject of waste disposal arouses much controversy and is highly political.

A report from the Environment Committee of the House of Commons on Radioactive Waste (3 volumes, HMSO, 1986) gives much information on the management of radioactive waste, its disposal, the dose limitations, discharge and disposal authorizations, reprocessing and the law. A government-sponsored company, UK NIREX Ltd, charged with the safe disposal of low and intermediate level waste, can run into much opposition when selecting sites for its burial.

## 6.18 Some legislation relating to radiological health and safety

*The Radioactive Substances Acts* 1948 and 1960. These Acts include registration and legislation to prevent injury by ionizing radiations and to secure the safe disposal of radioactive waste. Persons with rights of entry and inspection may be appointed. The Acts and the Orders made thereunder are enforced by Radiochemical Inspectors of the Department of the Environment acting directly or indirectly under the authority of the Health and Safety Executive.

*The Atomic Energy Authority Act* 1954. This Act, which resulted in the setting up of the UKAEA, also provides that it is the duty of the Authority to secure that no ionizing radiations from premises occupied by them, or from any waste discharged therefrom, shall cause any hurt or damage to persons or property. The Authority's liability is without financial limit.

*The Nuclear Installations Act* 1965, incorporating *The Nuclear Installations (Licensing and Insurance) Act* 1959 and *The Nuclear Installations (Amendment) Act* 1965. This Act provides for the control, in the interests of safety, of the building and operation of nuclear reactors, etc. Legislation is provided so that no person (other than the AEA) shall install or operate any land-based nuclear reactor or ancillary installation without first obtaining a Nuclear Site Licence from the Ministry concerned. The determination of conditions for the issue of licences and the carrying out of inspections to ensure compliance with their terms are the responsibility inter alia of the Inspectorate of Nuclear Installations, (see 12.10).* A licensee has the same obligation as the AEA (under the 1954 Act) to avoid hurt or damage from ionizing radiation. In general, compensation may be claimed within 30 years, as distinct from the normal three-year period. Consequently very full and accurate radiation exposure and health records must be maintained.

The Ionizing Radiations Regulations 1985 (SI 1985 No. 1333) take over and supersede earlier regulations (including those issued in 1969 for sealed and unsealed sources). They impose duties on employers to protect employees and others from hazards arising at work with radioactive substances and other sources of ionizing radiation and impose certain duties on employees. Limits are imposed on doses of ionizing radiation which employees and others may receive in any calendar year (SI units (sieverts) are used instead of rems—see Table 6.10). Controlled and supervised areas are defined and regulations require the appointment of radiation protection advisers and supervisors. Many records have to be made and preserved. Those containing prescribed particulars, including radiation dose and medical records of all *classified persons* have to be kept for at least 50 years. An approved Code of Practice, The Protection of persons against ionizing radiations arising from any work activity, has been issued by the HSE together with Guidance Notes for the use of Safety Representatives.

Employers and others must not expose themselves (or others) to ionizing radiations to an extent greater than is reasonably necessary, and must make proper use of any personal protective equipment provided. They must ensure that:

(i) no radioactive sealed source is held in the hand (or manipulated directly by the hand) unless the instantaneous dose rate to the skin of the hand does not exceed 75 $\mu$Svh$^{-1}$; and

(ii) as far as is reasonably practical, no unsealed radioactive substance (or article containing substance) is held or directly manipulated by the hand;

(iii) no one eats, drinks (except from an uncontaminated water fountain), smokes, takes snuff or applies cosmetics in a controlled area (in general an

---

*Now part of the Health and Safety Executive

area where the instantaneous dose rate exceeds 7·5 µSv per hour—see 6.19).

An approved dosimetry service and a medical surveillance service must be set up to carry out routine monitoring and examinations, accident/incident dosimetry and any contingency plans relating to any reasonably forseeable acident.

An employer must where relevant (see 6.19) make hazard assessments and contingency plans for dealing with any forseeable incidents.

BS 5288 *Sealed radioactive sources* specifies general requirements, tests, method of classification, etc. for such sources used particularly for industrial and medical radiography. Basically the general requirements are that the source capsule shall be free from surface radioactive contamination and also leak-free. (But scientifically speaking these requirements cannot be met—everything leaks!) However, if after wiping the surface with a swab the detected radioactivity on this is less than 5 n$^{Ci}$ ($5 \times 10^{-9}$ curie), then the sealed source is considered free from surface contamination. (To ensure that the capsule is initially free from surface contamination it may be necessary first to clean it thoroughly and then, after waiting at least 7 days, carry out the above swab test.)

Similarly, using one of the leak test methods specified (in Appendix D of the standard), e.g. the vacuum bubble test, the requirement for freedom from leaks is considered satisfied if no bubbles are observed over a period of not less than one minute, this being considered as being equivalent to a leak rate of the order of less than $10^{-5}$ torr litre/sec. (see 11.2). Note that this standard (issued in 1976) does not employ pure SI units for leak rate or radioactivity.

More exact measurement of leak rate can be made using commercial instruments employing a search gas (helium is mentioned in BS 5288) and vacuum or pressurization test methods (see Chapter 11); leak rates down to the order of $10^{-7}$ to $10^{-12}$ torr litre/sec. may then be detectable. The degree of concentration of the search gas should be known. If the actual leak rate determined is not greater than $10^{-5}$ torr litre/sec. for non-leachable* (solid) content or $10^{-7}$ torr litre/sec. for leachable* (liquid or gaseous) content then the sealed source is considered to be leak-free.

The International Atomic Energy Agency advises that a leak rate of $10^{-4}$ torr litre/sec. for solid content and of $10^{-6}$ torr litre/sec. for liquid and gaseous content is generally considered to be equivalent to a radioactivity release of 50 n$^{Ci}$.

The Ionizing Radiation Regulations 1985, under Regulation 18, requires that suitable tests for leakage of radioactive substances, etc. should be carried out at intervals in no case exceeding 26 months, and that records of such tests should be kept for at least 3 years. The actual measuring

---

*Non-leachable—meaning the radioactive material is virtually insoluble in water.

instruments used for monitoring radiation, etc. must be examined and tested at least once in every 14 months.

*Classification.* A series of tests for abnormal low ($-40°C$) and high temperature (up to 800°C), external pressure (up to 170 MPa), impact, vibration and puncture are laid down. For each of these types of test up to 7 classes of increasing severity may be specified (numbered from 1 (meaning no test) to 6), and then X for special (separately specified) test. A coded classification system enables test requirements for particular uses, etc. to be specified. This consists of the standard number (BS 5288 or ISO 2919) followed by a letter C indicating radioactivity below a certain level or E indicating radioactivity above this level, and then by five digits.

The first digit designates the class number of the test dealing with temperature. The second to fifth digits designate the class numbers of the test dealing with external pressure, impact, vibration and puncture respectively.

Thus a typical designation could be BS 5288/C43515 and a special designation BS 5288/EX65XX.

After the specified tests have been carried out their success depends upon passing the required leakage tests. A signed certificate giving relevant details must be provided with each sealed source or batch.

It should be noted that the above requirements and tests have been used over a comparatively long period with considerable success in attaining and maintaining a high standard of safety. The same general principles apply to other sources of radioactivity, where exposure to dangerous ionizing radiation may occur. Although in the generally accepted sense such sources are required to be 'leak-free' it will be realized that some perhaps minute leakage does occur. It is the inspector's duty to see that any such leakage is kept within the internationally agreed limits, and for the designer/engineer/inspector to ensure that, making use of all current available information, the working environment is maintained 'so far as is reasonably practicable' safe and without risks to health. Some standards dealing with radiation are given in Table 6.9.

### 6.19 Natural and man-made radiation and the evolution of the 1985 dose limits

Man's environment has always included exposure to radioactivity. Buried in the earth are many sources of natural radiation including radium, uranium and thorium. Even such materials as granite add to the amount of radiation which men on the surface of the earth have to live with. A miner deep in the bowels of the earth may be subject to an even greater exposure level and may breathe radioactive radon gas. The oceans are said to contain about 4000 million tons of uranium and other radioactive materials. The

**TABLE 6.9**

*Some standards dealing with radiation, etc*

| Specification No. | Description |
|---|---|
| BS 3385 | Direct-reading pocket type electroscope exposure meters |
| BS 3510 | A basic symbol to denote the actual or potential presence of ionizing radiation |
| BS 3598 | Recommendations for criticality safety in handling and processing nuclear materials |
| BS 3664 | Film badges for personnel radiation monitoring |
| BS 3890 | General recommendations for the testing, calibration and processing of radiation monitoring films |
| BS 3895 | Guide to the design testing and use of packaging for the safe transport of radioactive materials |
| BS 3909 | Ingot lead for radiation shielding |
| BS 4094 | Recommendation for data on shielding from ionizing radiations |
|  | Part 1: Shielding from gamma radiation |
|  | Part 2: Shielding from X-radiation |
| BS 4247 | The assessment of surface materials for use in radioactive areas |
|  | Part 1: Methods for measuring and evaluating the decontamination factor |
|  | Part 2: Guide to the selection of materials |
|  | Part 3: Decontamination techniques |
| BS 4513 | Lead bricks for radiation shielding |
| BS 4877 | Recommendations for general principles of nuclear reactor instrumentation |
| BS 5243 | General principles for sampling airborne radioactive materials |
| BS 5288 | Sealed radioactive sources (similar to ANSI N5.10) |
| BS 5548 | Radiation detectors for the instrumentation and protection of nuclear reactors: characteristics and test methods |
| BS 5552 | Code of practice for in-core instrumentation for neutron fluence rate (flux) measurements in power reactors |
| BS 5566 | Recommendations for installed exposure rate meters, warning assemblies and monitors for X or gamma radiation of energy between 80 keV and 3 MeV |
| BS 5915 | Equipment for minehead assay and sorting radioactive ores in containers |
| BS 6078 | Guide to the application of digital computers to nuclear reactor instrumentation and control |
| ANSI C95.1 | Safety level of electromagnetic radiation with respect to personnel |

activity of all these materials decays in accordance with their respective 'half-lives' (the time taken for their radioactivity to diminish by one half—which for different materials may differ from seconds to thousands of years). But this does not mean that the world's radioactivity will in time decay away. Cosmic rays from outer space continually add radioactivity to the atmosphere (including tritium—an isotope of hydrogen, $H_3$). A person in a high flying aircraft, particularly at the poles, will get several times the 'normal' radiation dose. Whether or not the total amount of radioactivity in the world (or the universe) remains sensibly constant (like matter) is a moot point. Like poison it is the concentration (or dose in a given time) received by a person that is of importance. Some radioactive material will be ingested into the body organs in food and drink.

The magnitude of natural radiation varies from place to place; in the UK it is some 0·1 rem per year, but in Kerala in India it may rise to some 3 rem per year due to the presence of thorium in the soil. To this must be added man-made radiation received for medical purposes and from industrial test equipment (X-rays, etc.) which in the UK averages some 0·03 rem per person per year, and various smaller amounts due to fall-out from nuclear tests, air travel, nuclear wastes, luminous watches, etc.

After the discovery of X-rays and radium it was gradually realized by ex-perimenters and users from the beginning of the 20th century that they could have harmful effects (as was evident from an examination of the hands of experimenters demonstrating X-rays). Their initiation of longer-term illnesses of the cancerous kind did not become apparent until much later. For example, many women employed during World War I painting aircraft instrument dials with luminous paint containing radium (and licking their brushes to maintain a fine point) died from jaw bone cancer up to some 30 years later. In 1928, an international commission agreed on a unit of radiation—the röntgen, and with reliable methods of measurement it was possible in 1937 to agree a tolerance dose of 1 röntgen per week. The International Commission on Radiological Protection (ICRP) was formed in 1950 and reduced this dose to 0·3 R/week, assuming this to be a threshold value below which no harmful effects could occur. This was subsequently reduced to 0·1 R/week (which may now be expressed as 5 rems per year, or in SI units 50 mSv/year). In addition the tolerance for radium (and radionuclides) deposited within the body was fixed at 1 ten-millionth of a gram (0·1 μCi).

The ICRP radiation tolerance levels were interpreted by the Medical Research Council (MRC) to give maximum permissible concentrations of various radionuclides in air and drinking water, etc. and codes of practice and statutory regulations are now based on these—both external radiation and the effective dose equivalent of the intake of radionuclides.

Taking the ICRP recommended limit as 5 rems per year for the whole body for occupational workers, ICRP recommended for individual members of the general public a limiting annual dose of one-tenth of this (i.e. 0·5 rem or 5 mSv per year). For workers a long term limit was laid down at $5(N-18)$ rem where $N$ is the present (current) age of the worker.

The British Government White Paper 'The Control of Radioactive Wastes' (Command 884–1959) had promulgated the following guidelines:

1   To ensure, irrespective of cost, that no member of the public should be exposed to a radiation dose exceeding the ICRP limit.
2   To ensure, irrespective of cost, that the whole population of the country shall not receive an average dose of more than 1 rem per person in 30 years.
3   To do what is reasonably practical, having regard to cost, to reduce doses to far below these levels.

It will be seen that the people of Kerala, India, receive *naturally* more than the ICRP limit for the general public in the UK, and that a person in the UK receiving each year the average medical radiation only will clock up 0·9 rem in 30 years, just under the requirement of (2) above.

The early UK Magnox reactors were said to release some 0·01 rem per year (i.e. one-tenth of the natural radiation rate). More modern types (tested by the United Nations Scientific Committee on the Effects of Atomic Radiation) gave dose rates averaging only about one-hundredth of the ICRP limit of 0·5 rem a year for the general public and far less than the natural radiation rate. Consequently when operating properly it would seem that the general public should have little to fear from radiation emanating from nuclear power stations. It is up to inspection and the relevant nuclear authorities, etc., to ensure that *all* nuclear installations meet the ICRP requirements and that they operate and *continue to operate* properly.

However some problems are still complex. For instance the radioactive content of the materials in waste water and radioactive waste from nuclear installations may be within the maximum permissible concentrations (MPC) authorized by the ICRP but it is sometimes found that certain materials are collected preferentially by certain human organs, or by certain forms of animal and plant life which may then find their way into the human body as food. Consequently undesirable concentrations of these radioactive materials may be formed therein.

Therefore in the 1985 Regulations the dose limits (now, using SI units, expressed in milli-sieverts) are taken to be the sum of the effective dose equivalent received per year from external radiation *plus* the effective dose equivalent received from contamination and the committed dose equivalent from that year's intake of radionuclides (see Table 6.10 Parts I, II and III and also 12.10). The 1985 Regulations also give dose limits for women workers (pregnant or otherwise) and details are tabulated of those quantities of radionuclides, etc. which if present call for specific action.

It has been pointed out by NRPB that readings below the dose limits do not necessarily indicate a safe situation, rather that readings above them indicate an unacceptable situation.

There is a somewhat complex relationship between the discharge limits

## TABLE 6.10

*Limits on ionizing radiation*

SCHEDULE 1    Regulations 2(1), 7, 13(3)( f),
28(1) and 30(1)

DOSE LIMITS

| | | Equivalent dose limit (rem) |
|---|---|---|
| PART I | | |
| DOSE LIMITS FOR THE WHOLE BODY | | |
| 1. The dose limit for the whole body resulting from exposure to the whole or part of the body, being the sum of the following dose quantities resulting from exposure to ionizing radiation, namely the effective dose equivalent from external radiation and the committed effective dose equivalent from that year's intake of radionuclides, shall in any calendar year be— | | |
| *(a)* for employees aged 18 years or over, | 50 mSv | (5 rem) |
| *(b)* for trainees aged under 18 years, | 15 mSv | (1·5 rem) |
| *(c)* for any other person, | 5 mSv | (0·5 rem) |
| PART II | | |
| DOSE LIMITS FOR INDIVIDUAL ORGANS AND TISSUES | | |
| 2. Without prejudice to Part I of this Schedule, the dose limit for individual organs or tissues, being the sum of the following dose quantities resulting from exposure to ionizing radiation, namely the dose equivalent from external radiation, the dose equivalent from contamination and the committed dose equivalent from that year's intake of radionuclides averaged throughout any individual organ or tissue (other than the lens of the eye) or any body extremity or over any area of skin, shall in any calendar year be— | | |
| *(a)* for employees aged 18 years or over, | 500 mSv | (50 rem) |
| *(b)* for trainees aged under 18 years, | 150 mSv | (15 rem) |
| *(c)* for any other person, | 50 mSv | (5 rem) |
| 3. In assessing the dose quantity to skin whether from contamination or external radiation, the area of skin over which the dose quantity is averaged shall be appropriate to the circumstances but in any event shall not exceed 100 cm². | | |

**TABLE 6.10** *concluded*

|  | Equivalent dose limit (rem) |
|---|---|
| PART III | |
| DOSE LIMITS FOR THE LENS OF THE EYE | |
| 4. The dose limit for the lens of the eye resulting from exposure to ionizing radiation, being the average dose equivalent from external and internal radiation delivered between 2·5 mm and 3·5 mm behind the surface of the eye, shall in any calendar year be— | |
| *(a)* for employees aged 18 years or over, 150 mSv | (15 rem) |
| *(b)* for trainees aged under 18 years, 45 mSv | (4·5 rem) |
| *(c)* for any other person, 15 mSv | (1·5 rem) |

Note: For convenience dose limits in the older units (rem) are given in the righthand column

of radioactivity for various radionuclides worked out by MAFF/DOE and the 1985 ICRP statutory limits of radiation which now supposedly include them. Prior to the 1985 Regulations discharge limits of radioactivity seem to have been worked out separately for each site so as to give a figure very much lower than the radioactivity which could be released without itself exceeding the ICRP radiation dose limits.

The question may be asked as to what constitutes a lethal dose of radiation. It is thought (mainly from Hiroshima experience) that victims receiving more than 1000 rem (10 Sv) quickly will die within a week; up to 700 rem—within two months; and at around 300 rem about half may survive perhaps for some years. In medical treatment patients have received some 300 rem (3 Sv) over a period in an attempt to save life—some have survived.

In Schedule 2 (see Table 6.11) column 2 tabulates for specific radionuclides (column 1) that minimum quantity (measured in Bq) which must be reported forthwith to the HSE if it should become lost or stolen; conversely work on such radionuclides can be carried out without prior notification to the HSE if the quantity involved does not exceed this tabulated figure.

The figures in columns 3, 4 and 5 refer generally to the minimum quantity of radioactivity, expressed respectively as air concentration $(Bq/m^3)$, surface contamination $(Bq/cm^2)$ or total activity (Bq) for any

**TABLE 6.11**

*Limits on radionuclides*

| 1<br>Radionuclide name, symbol, isotope | 2<br>Quantity for notification— regulation 31(2) and schedule 3(b)<br>(Bq) | 3<br>For controlled areas (internal radiation)<br>Air concentration schedule 6<br>(Bqm⁻³) | 4<br>Surface contamination schedule 6<br>(Bqcm⁻²) | 5<br>Total activity schedule 6<br>(Bq) | 6<br>Assessment report— regulation 26(1)<br>(Bq) | 7<br>Notification of occurrences— regulation 31(1)<br>(Bq) |
|---|---|---|---|---|---|---|
| **Actinium** | | | | | | |
| Ac-224 | $5 \times 10^4$ | $1 \times 10^2$ | $8 \times 10^3$ | $1 \times 10^7$ | $2 \times 10^{13}$ | $2 \times 10^9$ |
| Ac-225 | $5 \times 10^3$ | $1 \times 10^0$ | $2 \times 10^2$ | $1 \times 10^5$ | $2 \times 10^{11}$ | $2 \times 10^7$ |
| Ac-226 | $5 \times 10^4$ | $2 \times 10^1$ | $6 \times 10^2$ | $1 \times 10^6$ | $2 \times 10^{12}$ | |
| Ac-227 | $5 \times 10^3$ | $2 \times 10^{-3}$ | $8 \times 10^{-1}$ | $2 \times 10^2$ | | |
| Ac-228 | $5 \times 10^4$ | $3 \times 10^1$ | $1 \times 10^4$ | | | |
| **Aluminium** | | | | | | |
| Al-26 | $5 \times 10^4$ | $3 \times 10^2$ | $1 \times 10^3$ | | | |
| **Americium** | | | | | | |
| Am-237 | $5 \times 10^6$ | $1 \times 10^6$ | | | | |
| Am-238 | $5 \times 10^5$ | | | | | |
| Am-239 | $5 \times 10^6$ | | | | | |
| Am-240 | $5 \times 10^6$ | | | | | |

Schedules extracted from SI 1985 No.1888 (with acknowledgements to HMSO).

*Notes*: 1 becquerel (Bq) = $2.7 \times 10^{11}$ curie.
1 becquerel of natural uranium corresponds to one alpha disintegration per second (dps) (0·489 dps of U-238, 0·489 dps of U-234 and 0·022 dps of U-235).

radionuclide specified in column 1, beyond which the area concerned must be designated a 'controlled' area.

A special hazard assessment and report must be made to the HSE if it is desired to commence work on site (or to transport) more than the quantity of any radionuclide substance (measured in Bq) specified in column 6 of Schedule 2, or, in the case of fissile material, a greater mass of that material than that specified in para (6) of the Regulations. In certain circumstances contingency plans for dealing with foreseeable incidents must be made.

In column 7 of Schedule 2 those quantities of any radionuclide listed in column 1 (measured in Bq) are tabulated which, if exceeded and released into the atmosphere, spilled or otherwise can give rise to significant contamination, and consequently must be notified to the HSE.

For further information on designation of controlled areas see Schedule 6 of the regulations, or consult with the relevant radiation protection adviser. By and large, a controlled area is one in which doses of ionizing radiation are likely to exceed three-tenths of any dose limit for employees. As in Schedule 1 the annual dose limit per year for employees over 18 years of age is 50 mSv, then (subject to certain exemptions in Schedule 6) the instantaneous hourly dose rate (for a 40-hour week and a 50-week year) for a designated controlled area is one which is likely to exceed:

$$\frac{3}{10} \times 50 \text{ mSv}/(40 \times 50) = 7 \cdot 5 \text{ } \mu\text{Sv per hour (or } 0 \cdot 75 \text{ millirems per hour)}$$

A 'supervised area' is, generally speaking, one in which the radiation exceeds one-third of the above.

### 6.20 The ALARP principle

The UK has accepted the advice of the NRPB that use of the 5 mSv per annum limit of the 1985 Regulations combined with 'optimization techniques' (improvements, etc. called *as low as reasonably practicable* (ALARP) or *best practicable means* (BPM) will in most cases result in an average dose rate equivalent to a critical group of people (such as the local fishing community) of less than 1 mSv a year of life-long whole-body exposure from all sources of radiation.

This ALARP principle, whilst it is normally being achieved in practice, introduces difficulties to an inspector used to working to stated limits. (It is like stating that the current must not exceed 5 amperes but should be ALARP. What does the inspector do if the current is 4·9 amps? Does he accept, or does he put pressure on the contractor to get it reduced in value— and if so by how much? The problem seems as short as a piece of string.)

At the Sizewell B Inquiry (see also 13.14) this ALARP principle was criticized by the Inspector because of the absence of a clear definition or a widely understood meaning. Different NII (Nuclear Installations Inspectorate) Inspectors might give different interpretations and the licensee often did not know what was expected—and might spend a large amount of money to achieve a negligible increase in safety—or he might do nothing!

However the Inquiry Inspector decided not to replace the principle as it provided a useful impetus in the direction of safety. For the Sizewell B workforce (for whom the legal maximum effective dose equivalent is at present 50 mSv per annum), the CEGB aims at an average of 5 mSv per annum.* The Inspector recommended that this average dose equivalent should be regarded as an operational investigational level, and if it (including any committed dose equivalent—due perhaps to medical treatment reasons) were to exceed this level then the NII should investigate to ensure that risks should be reduced to a level which is ALARP.

Some doubts were expressed regarding the accuracy of ICRP's recommended risk factors (used to estimate the risk of fatal cancer from low levels of radiation) and the precise form of the relationship between dose and the probability of an effect (and hence of the relationship between dose (in mSv) and radioactivity (in Bq)) for each radionuclide. The NRPB's justification for its endorsement of the ICRP's recommendations was also doubted. The inspector thought it prudent to assume (for the time being) that there is no threshold of radiation dose below which there is no effect.

### 6.21 Some effects of radiation

High levels of irradiation (expected only in a dire emergency) can cause death, or effects on health within a short time.

Low levels are said to increase the probability of cancer and similar hereditary diseases which however may not emerge for many years after exposure. It was thought by the Inspector at Sizewell that the CEGB's target for worker doses was ambitiously low (and might be affected by large amounts of unplanned maintenance).

He recommended that nuclear installations which potentially give doses to the same members of the public over many years should be subject to the lower ICRP recommended annual limit (at present 1 mSv to members of critical groups, including committed dose).

### 6.22 Doses to the public from nuclear installations

Although the public would be exposed to radiation, principally from liquid and gaseous discharges from both the existing Sizewell A and the projected

---

*The CEGB's target for maximum annual dose is twice that of its target for average dose. The legal workers' limit for effective dose equivalent (see Table 6.10) is at present 50 mSv (i.e. 10 times the CEGB's average).

Sizewell B. The Inquiry evidence showed that during normal operation the releases are likely to be small in relation to the dose limits currently recommended by ICRP for members of the public (see 6.19). The releases from Sizewell B are likely to be less than those from Sizewell A. The maximum additional individual dose to a member of the public from Sizewell B the Inquiry evidence showed that during normal operation the releases are likely to be small in relation to the dose limits currently additional part in a million to the collective UK dose from natural background radiation.

The annual dose from other nuclear installations, particularly Sellafield (Windscale), although higher than that from CEGB stations, has to be kept within the statutory limits (e.g. 50 mSv) and much money is being spent to this end.

Some 155,000 people in the UK die each year from cancer or cancer-related diseases, which is some 22% of the total of deaths from all causes. A large percentage of these deaths may be due to smoking.

Of those given radiation treatment for cancer many eventually die from the disease, although for some their life may be prolonged by the treatment. A comparatively small percentage are permanently cured. Perhaps an even smaller percentage having being diagnosed as having malignant cancer, apparently throw off the disease.

Thus in 30 years the total deaths from cancer in the UK may be some 4,650,000. Similar proportionate figures apply to most Western civilized countries. Various attempts at estimating the extra number of deaths which have occurred or will occur as a result of man-made radiation have been made. For instance it has been variously stated that the effects of the Chernobyl disaster will give rise to some tens of extra deaths in the UK over the next 30 years; in Russia the figure has been estimated at many thousands. Estimates of the extra deaths due to the use of nuclear power when kept under control are of course much smaller.

Perhaps more rigorous inspection of X-ray and other radiation equipment, and more restriction on any unnecessary use, could cut down casualties from these sources. Estimates of death (short-term and long-term) from a possible nuclear accident are frightening, and it is hoped that with effective inspection and QA they will remain just estimates.

Radiation undoubtedly causes damage to human genes, chromosomes, etc. and thence illness. But correctly guided radiation can destroy cancer cells. For a long time it has been stated by the experts that radiation damage would be transmitted to future generations with dire results.

However, it would seem from medical evidence in Japan that the offsprings of those affected by Hiroshima and Nagasaki apparently display no genetic damage!* On the contrary, one might add facetiously, judging by

---

*Quoted by Professor Sir Frederick Warner FRS (who has been there) at an IEE lecture given in Farnborough 12 May 1987: 'No evidence of an increase in hereditary defects caused by radiation has been found in irradiated human

the increasingly high technical achievements of the present day Japanese, especially in the field of quality assurance, their intellectual powers seem to have been increased!

### 6.22.1 Doses from natural radiation due to radon

An HSC Code of Practice giving guidance on the Ionising Radiations Regulations 1985 regarding exposure to naturally occurring radon came into effect in April 1988. It deals with work, etc involving exposure to isotopes of radon and their decay products (known as 'short lived daughters'). Such exposure may occur in mines, caverns and underground (including civil engineering) workings, and some ground level or basement work places or dwellings, particularly in Devon and Cornwall or where radon gas can permeate through rock containing uranium.

**References and further reading**

Cole, H.A., *Understanding nuclear power*, Gower Technical Press, 1988.

Fordham Cooper, W., *Electrical safety engineering*, Butterworth, 1986.

Inst. of Chemical Engineers, (Lunn), Venting gas and dust explosions— a review, 1985.

Inst. of Chemical Engineers, (Muir), A user guide to dust and fume control, 1985.

Inst. of Chemical Engineers, (Schofield), Guide to dust explosion prevention and protection, 1986.

Inst. of Electrical Engineers Symposium, Electrical safety in hazardous environments, 1971/1975.

Inst. Mech. Engineers, *Clean room design*, 1986.

Porteous, A. (editor), *Hazardous waste handbook*, Butterworth, 1985.

Withers, John, *Major industrial hazards: their appraisal and control*, Gower Technical Press, 1988.

---

populations, such as the survivors from the atomic bombs dropped on Japan.' (See HSE publication *The tolerability of risk from nuclear power stations* (para. 62) (HMSO 1988).) But, as always it seems in these matters, further evidence from new fatal cancer risk estimates on the 60,000 survivors (not offspring) of Hiroshima and Nagasaki prompted the NRPB in November 1987 to recommend to the HSE new exposure limits for radiation workers; doses now should not exceed an average of 15 mSv per year.

Until HSE take any action, the present legal limit for workers is 50 mSv/year, but CEGB (according to the Sizewell Report) are aiming at the 'ambitiously low' level of 5 mSv/year. So bearing in mind the existing natural and other radiation levels, workers in reprocessing plant, radiography, high technology medicine and mines may now become legally at risk.

# 7 Refrigeration and cryogenics

## 7.1 Introduction

Many engineering and chemical plants deal with low-temperature processes. Conventional refrigerating plant is used to attain temperatures down to the order of $-80°C$ by reducing the pressure on a suitable liquid (refrigerant) so that it boils and thus extracts latent heat from its surroundings.

To attain and utilize lower temperatures than are possible with conventional refrigerating plant involves the technology of what is now known as cryogenics. By common usage this embraces the study, production, control and application of temperatures between say 100 K ($-173°C$) and absolute zero (0 K or $-273·16°C$), although no upper limit is set. Such temperatures are obtained by the liquefaction of gases having critical temperatures below those naturally encountered. (The critical temperature of a gas is that temperature above which it is not possible to liquefy it however great the pressure.)

At low temperatures the properties of materials may be appreciably affected, whilst at cryogenic temperatures some strange effects can be observed. For instance, materials may loose their strength or become brittle, whilst the electrical resistance of pure metals (and some alloys) becomes very low and approaches zero as the absolute zero of temperature is approached, so that an induced current in such a conductor tends to become self-sustaining. This latter phenomenon is known as superconductivity. Again, the thermal conductivities of some metals and alloys change considerably and the specific heats of all solids become progressively smaller as the temperature is lowered. Consequently the inspector should know something of these facts if he has to deal with low-temperature plant.

One big industrial application of cryogenics is in the separation of gases.

Large-scale plants for the liquefaction of air and the separation of its constituent gases by fractional distillation are widely used. Such gases obtainable from the atmosphere (oxygen, nitrogen, carbon dioxide, and the rare gases neon, argon, helium, krypton and xenon), and those obtainable by the low temperature separation of industrial gases, can be conveniently stored and transported in liquid form at low temperature in special insulated cryogenic vessels.

Hydrocarbons including methane, ethane, propane and butane are processed by the petrochemical industry. All these are gases at normal temperature and pressure (NTP) but they can be liquefied and handled in the liquid phase at low temperatures and/or high pressures. Propane and butane are supplied commercially as a fuel, and liquefied petroleum gas (LPG) is available in containers under high pressure or from self-contained storage tanks and installations.

Natural gas (mainly methane) obtained from wells worldwide has replaced coal gas in the UK where it comes mainly from the North Sea. It may be shipped as liquid natural gas (LNG) in specially designed cryogenic ocean-going tankers, stored in cryogenics tank farms and piped into the public gas supply system. Natural gas liquids (NGL), mainly ethane, propane and butane, can also be delivered by pipeline.

Liquid oxygen and other cryogenic liquids, besides having many industrial uses such as liquid oxygen for high-quality steel manufacture, are used in aircraft, long-range rocket and space vehicle work. Liquid hydrogen is used as a fuel for rocket propulsion.

Liquid nitrogen forms a convenient way of providing very low-temperature refrigeration for storage of certain foodstuffs and for many industrial applications.

Liquid helium (4·2 K or −269°C) can be used to obtain the maximum sensitivity from various radar and electronic devices, infra-red detectors and masers (as at cryogenic temperatures the electrical noise produced by thermal vibrations of the atoms is much reduced), and for cryo-pumping to produce ultra-high vacuum (see 8.11).

All these gases present severe hazards, the hydrocarbons mainly from fire and explosion. Also, owing to the extremes of temperature and pressure involved in their distribution, storage and use there may be severe problems with the materials of construction (for plant, tanks and pipelines, etc.) due to corrosion, brittle fracture, creep, fatigue, etc. and disasters have occurred. Such troubles can be kept at bay by application of methods such as those in Chapter 3 (for pressure vessels) and Chapter 6, and by thorough inspection during manufacture and service.

Some details concerning cryogenic plant and its inspection and of the materials employed will be given later.

## 7.2 Conventional refrigerating plant

The refrigerant in a conventional plant must change readily from the liquid to the gaseous state, and vice versa, under conditions of temperature and pressure which are readily attainable. In order to utilize the same refrigerant over and over again, and so provide a continuous closed refrigerating cycle, the pressure on it whilst in the gaseous state is increased, so causing its temperature to rise. Whilst in this state it is passed into a *condenser*, where a suitable cooling medium (usually water or air) causes it to change to the liquid state—giving up heat to the cooling medium.

The liquid refrigerant, still under high pressure, is then passed through an *expansion valve*, or some other device, into the low-pressure region, where it rapidly boils in the *evaporator*, taking its latent heat of evaporation from the surroundings. The low-pressure vapour is then passed to a *compressor* (or region of high pressure) and the cycle is repeated.

Commercial refrigerators can be divided into two distinct types:

(1) The *vapour compression* type, in which the regions of high and low pressure are provided by means of a suitable pump or compressor.

(2) The *vapour absorption* type, in which the region of low pressure is created by the rapid absorption of a vapour by a liquid (or sometimes a solid), and the region of high pressure by heating this liquid and its absorbed vapour in another vessel, thereby driving off the vapour at a relatively high pressure.

Vapour absorption refrigerators are used principally for small installations of the domestic type. The refrigerant employed is invariably ammonia.

An outline diagram of an elementary vapour compression machine on test is given in Fig. 7.1. Cooling and liquefaction of the hot compressed vapour is effected by means of cold water circulated through the condenser; an expansion valve is fitted between the high- and the low-pressure sides; the latent heat required for the change of state in the evaporator is taken from brine (or calcium chloride or other suitable liquid having a low freezing point), which thus falls to a low temperature and is circulated around the refrigerated space.*

Sometimes the evaporator is used to remove heat directly from the space it is desired to cool. In other cases (as in Fig 7.1) an intermediate fluid (sometimes called a secondary refrigerant) is itself cooled by the evaporator and piped round the installation (such as a cold room) it is desired to cool.

This secondary refrigerant may be water (as with air conditioning plant), a form of brine (usually calcium chloride), a form of anti-freeze solution (such as ethylene glycol which freezes at temperatures down to some $-35°C$

---

*Some additional cooling occurs when the fluid passes through the expansion valve, owing to the Joule-Thomson effect—see 7.7.

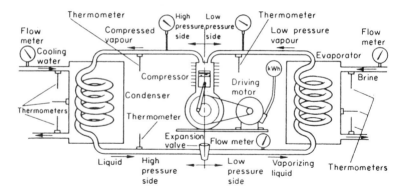

**Fig. 7.1  Vapour compression refrigerator on test.**

as its density is increased to some 1·09), or for very low-temperature work certain halo carbons (such as R12), or alcohol.

## 7.3 Choice of refrigerant

The refrigerant should liquefy at a pressure which the compressor, or other pressure-producing arrangement, can readily produce without imposing any undue strain on it or the gas-tightness of the system, and at a temperature which can readily be maintained by the cooling medium. It should possess a large latent heat of vaporization, and should boil at a pressure not far below atmospheric (and which can readily be attained by the low-pressure producting arrangement). At this low pressure its actual boiling point should be sufficiently low for it to 'freeze' (by extracting heat) to the required degree.

Large commercial refrigerating plants are invariably of the vapour compression type and generally employ ammonia ($NH_3$) or carbon dioxide ($CO_2$) as the refrigerant.

Ammonia has the largest latent heat of normal refrigerants, and is a colourless, noxious gas, with a pungent odour. Care must therefore be taken when using it to avoid leaks, and the appropriate safety regulations must be observed. As it attacks brass and copper the materials of the equipment must be carefully selected. The presence of oil with ammonia can create a hazard and the design of the compressor must ensure oil-free ammonia.

Carbon dioxide is a colourless and practically odourless gas, and whilst not in itself poisonous it is heavier than air and so can sink into a confined space, thereby displacing the air and being liable to cause suffocation. Its specific volume is small and its pressure high at normal temperatures, consequently $CO_2$ machines are smaller, but more massively constructed than ammonia machines (at 0°F its saturation pressure is 305·8 lb/in$^2$ (abs.)

and it approaches 1000 lb/in² as its critical temperature 87.8°F is approached).

Methyl chloride ($CH_3Cl$), a toxic and odourless fluid, ethyl chloride ($C_2H_5Cl$), a very inflammable substance, and sulphur dioxide ($SO_2$) may be used as refrigerants in medium-sized vapour compression plants. Owing to its extremely toxic properties sulphur dioxide should not be used where there is any possibility of a leak occurring, although it can readily be traced owing to its pungent odour. In many cases these traditional refrigerants are being replaced by the various 'Freons' (e.g. Freon 12—dichlorodifluoromethane ($CCl_2F_2$), also known as Arcton 6). In some respects the Freons may be regarded as ideal refrigerants and their use in larger plants is growing rapidly. They are neither toxic (although in large volumes they can cause suffocation) nor inflammable and are non-corrosive to most metals.* Saturation temperatures and pressures are also very convenient for refrigeration purposes, being (for Freon 12), 5°F at a pressure of 26·5 lb/in² (abs.) and 86°F at a pressure of 107·9 lb/in² (abs.).

Freon 12 and 22 are widely used and are often known as R 12 and R 22 from the refrigerant numbering system of the American Society of Heating, Refrigeration and Air Conditioning Engineers (ASHRAE). Standard numbered designations are given to all refrigerants; the total involved is quite large and includes halocarbons, hydrocarbons and organic and inorganic compounds (these designations have been agreed internationally—see ISO 817, also BS 4580).

In industries and processes where such compounds and gases are available they may be used for refrigeration. For instance the liquefaction of natural gas prior to shipment from North Africa is carried out by a triple refrigeration process using propane, methane and ethylene.

Refrigerants may be classified into three groups:

Group 1 are non-flammable

Group 2 are toxic, and R40, R611, R160 and R1130 are also flammable

Group 3 are all flammable

Where the quantity of any flammable refrigerant exceeds a specified and calculable amount relative to the size of any room in which any part of the refrigerating system is installed, then no flame producing device or surface above 400°C shall be permitted therein and all electrical equipment must comply with the requirements for hazardous areas (see 6.9–6.11).

## 7.4 Performance of refrigerators

The *thermal efficiency* of a heat engine is represented by:

---

*Objections have been made to the large-scale release into the atmosphere of some of these gases (which are also used for pressurizing hairsprays, etc). Allegedly, they may accumulate over the South pole, making a gap in the ozone layer in the upper atmosphere, with eventual dire results for life on earth.

$$\eta = \frac{\text{work done}}{\text{heat extracted}}$$

(work and heat being expressed in the same (SI) units).

In order to obtain a measure of the performance of a refrigerator the inverse of the above expression is used and is called the coefficient of performance:

$$\text{Coefficient of performance (c.o.p.)} = \frac{\text{heat extracted}}{\text{work expended}}$$

$$\text{or performance factor} = \frac{\text{refrigeration effect}}{\text{work expended}}$$

The most efficient refrigerator will therefore be that which possesses the highest value of this coefficient.

The coefficient of performance of an ideal (Carnot) refrigerator would be:

$$\frac{H_2}{H_1 - H_2} = \frac{T_2}{T_1 - T_2}$$

From this it will be seen that for a given amount of work done the heat extracted, and therefore the coefficient of performance, will be greater the smaller the range of absolute temperature $T_1 - T_2$ through which the working fluid is taken.

The actual coefficient of performance obtained with a practical refrigerator can be compared with the ideal coefficient of performance of some theoretical cycle in a similar manner to that used for comparing the thermal efficiency of heat engines.

We then obtain:

$$\text{Efficiency ratio of refrigerator} = \frac{\text{actual coefficient of performance}}{\text{ideal coefficient of performance}}$$

The coefficient of performance of vapour compression type machines is higher than that of absorption types.

It is difficult to devise a standard unit of refrigeration capacity to express the performance of a machine as this depends largely on the temperature range and conditions of working of the plant.

In the UK the rated refrigerating capacity of a machine was expressed as the number of British thermal units (Btu) it could extract in unit time under specified conditions. Alternatively heat extraction could be expressed in joules, or in calories.

One calorie per second = 342·8 Btu/day (in SI unit 4·186 J/s or watts).

One kilocalorie per second (kcal/s) = 45 kg (99 lb) ice melting per hour = 4·186 kW.

1 Btu/h = 0·29307W

On the Continent the *Frigorie* (or kilogramme calorie per hour) may be employed, and is equal to 4·186 kJ/h or 1·163 watts. (1 thermie/h = 1·163 kW.)

The *American ton of refrigeration* (TR) is widely used and is equivalent to 2000 lb ice melting per 24 hours, or 200 Btu of heat extraction per minute (12,000 Btu (3024 kcal) per hour, or 288,000 Btu/day). In SI units this represents 3·5168 kW.

The *British ton of refrigeration* (of 2240 lb) is little, if ever, used.

Commercial refrigeration units are now rated, and tested, to determine their performance for:

(a) *Refrigerating capacity* ($\phi_o$). The refrigerating effect, calculated from the product of the measured mass flow rate of the refrigerant and the difference between its specific enthalpy (heat content) at inlet and discharge from the unit (taken from recognised enthalpy tables for the particular refrigerant).

Using SI units the units of $\phi$ will be expressed in

$$\frac{kg}{s} \times \frac{J}{kg} = \frac{J}{s} = \text{watts (or kW as the case may be)}$$

Using imperial units or American practice refrigeration capacity can be expressed in Btu/hour, or tons refrigeration. (It is nominally equivalent to and sometimes known as evaporator duty.)

(b) *Power input rating.* The measured power taken by the driving unit (expressed normally in kW).

(c) *Performance factor.* This is the ratio of the refrigerating capacity to the power supplied (both expressed in the same units, normally kW).

Using imperial units or American practice it may be expressed as Btu extracted per watt-hour of input, or kW per ton of refrigeration, etc.

(d) *Condenser cooling water consumption* (measured usually at the rated refrigerating capacity), together with the corresponding temperature rise and water pressure drop.

Test conditions suitable for the climatic conditions under which the units are intended to operate (e.g. temperate or tropical) should be specified. (Fully detailed descriptions of actual test methods (using SI units) are given in specifications such as BS 3122 Part 1, which should be referred to as necessary.)

Test readings should not be taken until steady conditions have been established. The following items are amongst those which could also be stated in any test report, or for application ratings:

(a) Saturation temperature of refrigerant vapour entering compressor.

(b) Actual temperature of refrigerant vapour entering compressor.

(c) Saturation temperature of refrigerant vapour leaving compressor.

(d) Refrigerant used, and its designation (see BS 4580).

(e) Method of cooling compressor.

In addition, the following may be required:

(f) Volume displaced by compressor under specified (e.g. standard ton) conditions. This will depend on the refrigeration effect and the volume of specific refrigerant. Thus to give 1 ton of refrigeration on test might need a volume of 19·6 in³ (or 0·4215 lb) of ammonia per minute, or 162·8 in³ (or 3·528 lb) of carbon dioxide per minute. (In SI units it would be expressed in m³/kW.)

(g) Volumetric efficiency of the compressor. This is the ratio of the volume of vapour or gas actually discharged (referred to the suction temperature and pressure) to the swept volume of the compressor.

(h) Total starting current with compressor and fan motor/s locked (locked rotor amps, LRA).

(i) Total maximum running amps (MRA).

### 7.4.1 Refrigerator design details

*Pump unit.* In compressor type machines the pump unit may be either of the *reciprocating* (piston and cylinder) or the *rotary* kind. With some machines more than one stage of compression may be used.

In large installations the pump is usually driven by an engine or electric motor through a belt or geared drive. In some cases the pump piston rod may be directly connected to the piston of a steam engine (donkey pump). Medium-sized installations driven by an electric motor may have belt drive or the motor may be close-coupled, two bearings only being used. In the latter case the pump will have to be designed to run at the same speed as the motor.

In some widely used types of small refrigerator the pump and motor are directly connected inside a hermetically sealed container, through which the refrigerant circulates. The design of this type has been so perfected that failures necessitating changing of the complete sealed unit are rare, whilst being sealed it cannot, of course, be tampered with.

To ensure long service, leakage from the system must be eliminated, and in consequence stringent leak testing is required. If the system contains Freon or some other halogen compound, then inspection by means of a halogen-type leak detector is an obvious choice (see 11.5.2 (b)).

A single-stage vapour compression refrigeration system using, say, Arcton 4 (Freon 22) can reduce the temperature of a cold chamber to about −40°F (−40°C). A two-stage compound system would reduce the temperature more quickly and could give an ultimate temperature of about −60°C.

A two-stage cascade system might give temperatures of the order of $-75$ to $-80°C$, or perhaps lower.

Cold chambers and rooms should be designed in such a way that their outer surfaces will not sweat at the range of internal temperatures attained and the outside climatic conditions envisaged. All joints and seams within the cold room should be sealed to prevent the entry and accumulation of potentially contaminating substances. Seals must be provided to prevent any significant leakage of air into or out from the cold room. All internal finishes must be corrosion resistant. Nickel or chromium plating is permissible, but cadmium plating must not be used inside a cold room, particularly where food may be stored.

ANSI B31.5 specifies that screwed joints must not be used with ferrous pipe for brine piping in sizes larger than 6 in (150 mm); nor for refrigerant piping above 3 in (75 mm) when the design pressure is 250 psi or below or $1\frac{1}{4}$ in (31 mm) when the design pressure exceeds 250 psi. Any exposed threads must be coated to inhibit corrosion. Any ferrous pipe lighter than Schedule 40 must not be threaded.

## 7.5 Solid carbon dioxide

Carbon dioxide has a freezing point of $-70°F$ ($-57°C$) and in its solid form, known by such trade names as Cardice or Drikold, is used extensively for testing materials and components at low temperatures, and for certain process operations. It sublimes directly from the solid to the vapour state—a harmless and practically non-corrosive vapour. It is often used where a full refrigerant system would be uneconomic. The surface temperature of solid $CO_2$ is $-112°F$ ($-80°C$), but when used in a cold chamber the ultimate temperature obtainable would vary with the heat given up by the components or parts under test. The temperature can be controlled at some point higher than that of the $CO_2$ by introducing a thermostatically controlled heater and fan.

## 7.6 Testing and inspection of refrigeration plant

### 7.6.1 Performance

As refrigeration plants carry out such a variety of duties and as any particular duty can be effected in a number of ways, it is difficult to specify test and inspection methods in detail.

However any refrigeration plant has essentially to extract heat at one temperature and to discharge it at a higher temperature, and a test will be necessary to ensure that the specified heat or refrigeration load (expressed usually in kW, Btu/h or tons refrigeration) is attainable at the required extraction and dissipation temperatures and under any duty conditions specified, e.g. the dry and wet bulb temperatures at which the output is required (where the condenser gives up its heat to atmosphere). The duty load will not necessarily have to be met under the most severe conditions likely to be encountered, and some deduction in output under these conditions is normally acceptable. However it may be desirable to check that driving motors, condensers, etc., are satisfactory under these conditions.

The plant may be hand-operated, semi-automatic (starting and stopping automatically, but requiring attention and adjustment from time to time), or fully automatic (non-attended). These features should be tested and it should be ascertained that the specified maximum running hours per day can be achieved without trouble.

The usual commercial performance tests are given in 7.4. Other items which can be tested or checked include:

(i) Safety precautions

(ii) Leak testing and leak location

(iii) Insulation resistance (generally not less than 1 megohm at 500 V d.c.)

(iv) High voltage flash test between electric circuits and accessible metal parts/earth (generally to BS 923)

(v) Checking that electric motors comply with their appropriate specification and any other specified requirements

(vi) Checking for any radio interference (generally to be within the limits laid down in BS 800)

More detailed type tests may be required initially on selected refrigerators which have already passed their production tests.

All measuring instruments used should also be checked, particularly the thermometers, which must be capable of registering accurately quite small temperature differences.

On the day of test it may not always be possible, owing to atmospheric or other reasons, to carry out the exact terms of a detailed specification, and some adjustment or compromise may have to be agreed.

### 7.6.2 Pressure testing

Any pressure vessels in the installation should be designed, inspected and tested in accordance with the specified, or a recognized, code, such as BS 5500 *Unfired fusion welded pressure vessels* (see Chapter 3); or BS 7005, BS 5387 or BS 4741 for storage tanks for low-temperature service (see 7.11.1). Inspection should check that a gas space is left above the highest connection to any vessel.

The whole of the rest of the plant should be tested at the maker's works, initially by hydraulic means to check mechanical strength, etc., and then by air or gas pressure to prove gas-tightness, appropriate precautions being taken (see 3.20). Leak testing of certain components or pipework to stated limits may be required (see Chapter 11). The details and duration of any pressure or leak test should be as specified or at the inspector's discretion. In general the gas test pressure should not be less than the refrigerant's saturated vapour pressure at 150°F (65°C), and the hydraulic test pressure not less than $1\frac{1}{2}$ times this amount.

BS 2501 requires all parts of the refrigeration system to be production tested at pressures not less than those given in Table 7.1.

### TABLE 7.1

*Refrigeration plant—Some recommended minimum production test pressures*

| Refrigerant | High pressure side (bar (gauge)) | Low pressure side (bar (gauge)) |
| --- | --- | --- |
| R22 | 31 (435 psig) | 17·5 (230 psig) |
| R12 | 19 (235 psig) | 10·5 (140 psig) |
| R115 | 25·5 | 15·5 |
| R502 | 32·5 | 19·5 |
| For other refrigerants | Its saturation vapour pressure at 74°C | Its saturation vapour pressure at 49°C |

The pressure should be sustained for a minimum of 2 minutes without showing signs of leakage or distortion. The complete installation must be tested for leaks after charging with its refrigerant.

Note: 1 bar $= 10^5 \text{N/m}^2 = 0·1 \text{ N/mm}^2 = 1$ standard atmosphere (760 mmHg)

Gauge bar pressure means a pressure gauge reading above that of the prevailing atmosphere.

(Adapted from BS 2501 with permission)

After erection on site the complete refrigeration installation, including pipework, circulating systems, etc., should be further checked to ensure correctness of connections, cleanliness, quality and leak-tightness of joints, etc. For a large plant a final air or gas pressure test on the complete system (or parts of it in turn) may have to be maintained for upwards of 12 hours to permit a thorough check. During this period a drop in pressure after isolation will probably occur, but if all the components and joints have been properly made and tested this pressure drop will be largely accounted for by temperature change, etc., and not by leakage (see 11.6.1 and 6.6).

BS 4434 Part 1 Requirements for refrigeration safety states that every component shall be subjected to a pressure test for strength of at least 1·5 times maximum working pressure (for castings) and 1·3 times maximum working pressure (for steel construction and other rolled or drawn materials), followed by a leakage test carried out with a non-dangerous gas (e.g. nitrogen or air) to at least the maximum working pressure but not exceeding 1·1 times this. After assembly and before putting into service each complete system shall be subjected to a pressure test with a suitable gas to the same specified pressure. Some safe refrigerant may first be introduced into the system to enable leaks to be more easily detected. The use of oil/air mixtures, and of carbon dioxide for testing ammonia plants can be dangerous. The use of oxygen is prohibited.

### 7.6.3 Leak location

Should any leakage be found during testing, then the source of trouble must be tracked down to a particular component and corrected.

When dealing with plants containing ammonia, the presence of leaks can usually be smelt, or detected by the use of a chemical test paper, and can be dangerous. Even comparatively small leaks can be unpleasant. Respirators for use in case of trouble should be provided in strategic positions and personnel trained in their use.

During manufacture, and in use, comparatively large leaks in components, etc. can be found by the pressurizing and bubble-seeking methods dealt with in 11.5.1. Such simple methods can be used when flame or electrical instruments are not permitted for reasons of safety. Otherwise pressurizing pipelines, etc., with a halogen as a search gas and using a halide torch or a halide diode detector, in cases where Freon or some other halogen compound itself is the refrigerent, is particularly useful (see 11.5.2).

Another method, particularly where ammonia is used, is to fill the volume to be tested with ammonia vapour, and make use of a suitable indicator on the outside.

Three types of indicator can be used:

(i) Suspected areas are painted with a phenolic paint. Leaks are shown up by a bright red coloration.

(ii) Suspected areas are painted with hydrochloric acid. Leaks are located by the evolution of clouds of the white vapour of ammonium chloride (a lighted sulphur stick gives the same effect).

(iii) Suspected areas are probed with $CO_2$ as a search gas, using a transparent hood. Leaks are located by the evolution of clouds of ammonium carbonate.

Indicator (i) is the most sensitive (it is claimed that leaks down to 5 microtorr litres/second ($\frac{1}{2}$ clusec) may be found—see 11.2).

Indicator (ii) has about one-tenth of this sensitivity, and the use of the corrosive acid may be objected to.

Indicator (iii) is the least sensitive.

If carbon dioxide is used in the plant it can be pressurized to about 15 lb/in$^2$ and the suspected surface areas sprayed at about 70°C with an alkaline agar-agar solution of phenolphthalein. (Composition: Agar-agar 1 part, distilled water 40 parts, anhydrous soda 0.1 part, phenolphthalein 0.15 part.) After an interval of some 5–6 minutes the solution, which is normally red, will show white spots at any leaks. Best results are obtained if the plant is free from traces of acid or alkali, and the air free from contamination. A sensitivity of about 1 clusec is claimed. The solution can be removed by blowing with compressed air after the test.

### 7.6.4 Removal of moisture from system

After satisfactory completion of leak testing, and before any charging of the system with refrigerant, the complete condensing unit (i.e. compressor, condenser, liquid receiver (where required), interconnecting pipework, etc.) should be dehydrated. The pressure of water may cause trouble by ice formation, particularly at the expansion valve. Also it may form a corrosive acid with fluorocarbon refrigerants. Furthermore it may cause electrolytic action with any copper tubing present.

Copper tubing used in the installation should be to BS 2871 Part 2 *Copper tubes* for general purposes, which gives specific requirements for copper tubes for use in refrigeration plant. Such tubes should be smooth, dry and chemically clean inside, and should be supplied in air-tight polythene (or paper) bags sealed against the entry of dirt or moisture.

### 7.6.5 Inspection of safety arrangements

Various safety devices may be specified or required by statute. These could include:

(i) A high-pressure cut-out fitted on the compressor side of the delivery stop valve which would automatically cut out the driving motor, etc., in the event of a pressure higher than designed being developed.

(ii) Pressure-relief valves (e.g. a spring-loaded cylinder head safety valve), or bursting discs, provided in strategic places, possibly in addition to the high-pressure cut-out, in order to give quicker pressure relief.

(iii) Low-temperature cut-outs arranged to stop the driving motor in the event of abnormally low temperatures being reached, which might, for instance, freeze solid the liquid in an evaporator.

(iv) Low-pressure cut-outs.

All these devices should be inspected initially for general construction and operation, and should be checked periodically to ensure that they are operating satisfactorily.

As many refrigerants are toxic, noxious, or will suffocate if present in sufficient quantity, precautions should be taken against leakage. Thorough leak testing is desirable, but even so accidents or accidental release of vapour may occur. Consequently respirators should be provided in readily accessible positions and should be inspected once a month. Some refrigerants, notably ammonia, methyl chloride and methane, form explosive mixtures if present in the air in certain concentrations, and may for instance be ignited by a spark from non-flame-proof electrical equipment.

Adequate means of escape from all places into which refrigerant may leak must be provided, under the requirements of the *Factories Act*, and all doors in general must be openable from either side.

Any refrigerant stored in cylinders should be kept in a separate compartment free from excessive heat. Identification of cylinders, pipelines, valves, etc., should be in accordance with British Standards or other recognized codes (see 4.14).

Generally a person should not work alone in a cold room. Should this be necessary, his safety should be checked every hour. A responsible person should, in any case, make a duty round to ensure that no one has remained behind. Emergency lighting and/or luminous paint should be available to indicate a safe method of exit.

### 7.6.6 *Inspection of insulation and its installation*

Inspection should supervise generally the installation and thermal insulation of the plant, remembering that most insulation needs protection from water (and water vapour) and industrial liquids, otherwise it will lose its insulating properties; absorption of moisture may also cause swelling and consequential damage.

The various insulation materials used will include slag wool, cork, expanded polystyrene and polyurethane, glass fibre, constructional timber, and vulcanized expanded rubber. Samples of these should have been checked before installation for thermal conductivity ($k$) (see 7.9) (when dry or at a particular temperature), moisture absorption, spontaneous ignition temperature, etc.

Particular attention should be paid to the vapour seal and the method of sealing joints between it and parts, such as valves, which protrude through it.

After the installation has been tested at its operating temperature for a sufficient or specified period of time it should be given a thorough final inspection during which the following points, and any possible defects, should be looked for.

(i) Check that the specified thickness of the correct insulation has been evenly applied and is satisfactory under working conditions.

(ii) Check for any serious cracking in finishes, floors, etc.

(iii) Check for any evidence of condensation (or ice) on the outside (warm side) of the insulation, particularly where anything (such as steelwork) projects through it. A good and separate vapour barrier is usually necessary on the warm side.

(iv) Check for any evidence of ice formation inside the structure. This would indicate free air leakage through the insulation. Consequently small crevices in the structure, brickwork, etc., must be avoided.

(v) Check the fitting and sealing of doors, and for any evidence of swelling or shrinkage of woodwork, etc. When closed on it, the door seal must offer resistance to the withdrawal of a paper strip of, say, 0·075 mm thickness (and 50 mm wide).

(vi) Examine the vapour seal on the insulation of items of plant and equipment for any evidence of cracking, particularly where metal or other surfaces protrude through it. Any evidence of frost formation on its surface might indicate insufficient insulation.

(vii) Check for any evidence of trapped condensation which cannot run away.

(viii) Check for any evidence of leakage of refrigerant or cooling fluid, etc., through the insulation. (This should not occur if leak testing has been carried out effectively.)

### 7.6.7 Maintenance inspection

Periodic inspections of the plant during its life should be carried out along similar lines. Particular attention should be paid to evidence of corrosion. Hydraulic tests may be applied, particularly to items which are corroding.

Calcium chloride brine, used as a secondary refrigerant in some installations, can be very corrosive especially in the presence of air, which should if possible be excluded from the brine circuit. The addition of sodium chromate or dichromate to make it slightly alkaline (until a pH value of over 7 to some 8·5 is obtained) will reduce the trouble.

Should water be added to a secondary refrigerant system, or if the system is or becomes open and absorbs moisture, its freezing point will rise and performance may be affected. Checks should be made to see if and when reconcentration is necessary. Suitable precautions should be taken during reconcentration depending upon the refrigerant used and if it can give off toxic or flammable fumes.

Some standards relevant to refrigeration testing and inspection, etc, are given in Table 7.2.

### 7.7 Cryogenics—liquefaction of gases

A gaseous substance can be liquified by:

(a) Cooling it below its boiling point at or around normal atmospheric pressure (as for example in the case of steam).

**TABLE 7.2**

*Some standards dealing with refrigeration*

| Specification No. | Description |
|---|---|
| BS CP 334 | Part 3 Selection and installation of gas refrigerators for food storage |
| BS 874 | Methods for determining thermal insulating properties, with definitions of thermal insulating terms |
| BS 1041 | Code for temperature measurement |
| BS 1586 | Methods for performance testing and presentation of performance data for refrigerant condensing units |
| BS 1608 | Electrical-driven refrigerant condensing units (covers construction, testing for rating, etc.) |
| BS 2501 | Commercial refrigeration storage cabinets of the closed reach-in type (covers methods of testing and performance) |
| BS 2502 | Manufacture of sectional cold rooms (walk-in type) |
| BS 2626 | Lubricating oils for refrigerant compressors (for ammonia or halocarbon refrigerants—gives notes and tests) |
| BS 2852 | Testing for rating of room air-conditioners (cooling performance and rating test methods are described) |
| BS 3053 | Commercial refrigerated cabinets for sale and/or display of food products |
| BS 3122 | Refrigerant compressors |
| BS 3759 | Frozen food storage compartments in refrigerators (design, testing, classification) |
| BS 3879 | Refrigerated room air-conditioners |
| BS 4434 | Requirements for refrigeration safety (based on ISO/R1662) |
| BS 4580 | Number designation of organic refrigerants |
| BS 4788 | Rating and testing of refrigerated dehumidifiers |
| BS 5429 | Code of practice for safe operation of small scale storage facilities for cryogenic liquids |
| BS 5491 | Rating and testing unit air conditioners of above 7 kW cooling capacity |
| BS 5643 | Glossary of refrigeration, heating, ventilating and air-conditioning terms |
| BS 5970 | Code of practice for thermal insulation of pipework and equipment in the temperature range of $-100°C$ to $+870°C$ (supersedes CP 3005) |
| BS 6148 | Methods of test for commercial refrigerated cabinets |
| BS 7005 | Design and manufacture of carbon steel unfired pressure vessels for use in vapour compression refrigeration |
| ANSI B9.1 | Safety code for mechanical refrigeration |
| B53.1 | Refrigeration terms and definitions (based on ASHRAE Std 12) |
| B60.1 | Method of rating and testing refrigerant expansion valves |
| B79.1 | Number designation of refrigerants (based on ASHRAE Std 34) |

(b) Cooling it below its critical temperature at a sufficiently high pressure (as for example in the case of the so-called permanent gases).

The cooling of the gas can be carried out by:

(i) Bringing some cooling medium into proximity with it.

(ii) Adiabatic expansion in some form of engine.

(iii) Free expansion (the Joule-Thomson effect).

Modern methods for the liquefaction of air and other gases make use of method (iii) either alone (the Linde or Hampson process) or in conjunction with (ii) (the Claude process). The Joule-Thomson effect is the small cooling effect produced when a gas is allowed to expand freely without doing external work, provided the gas is kept below its inversion temperature (above this temperature a heating effect results). Although the cooling effect is small, the process can readily be made cumulative in order to reach cryogenic temperatures. Hydrogen has to be cooled below $-80°C$ before the Joule-Thomson cooling effect commences.

Liquefiers and refrigeration plant working at cryogenic temperatures are commercially available. A liquefier has provision for tapping off the liquefied gas formed in the low-temperature part of the equipment, whilst in a refrigerator the liquefied gas is allowed to circulate in or around the low-temperature working space where it boils off and is recycled, there being no net consumption of gas.

Inspection should ensure that the air or gas used in a cryogenic plant is of high purity. Contaminants such as oil and water vapours, carbon dioxide, etc., would solidify whilst passing through the system causing blocked passages, jammed parts, etc. Consequently gas purification plant, and perhaps oil-free compressors, as described in 6.14 and 8.1, should be employed.

A schematic arrangement of a Hampson or Linde liquefier is shown in Fig. 7.2 (left). High-pressure air (at some 1000 lb/in² and at ambient temperature) passes through the heat exchanger coil and is allowed to expand through the throttle valve (where a temperature drop of some 15°C occurs) into the low-pressure region where it passes round the outside of the inlet heat exchanger coils, thus extracting heat from the incoming air. The cooled incoming air then suffers a further drop in temperature as it passes through the expansion valve, and a cumulative cooling effect continues until eventually part of the air issuing from the valve is cooled sufficiently to liquefy and is then collected in an insulated (Dewar type) vessel.

To produce liquid hydrogen the gas must first be cooled below its inversion temperature. This may be done by using a Hampson air liquefier to precool the high-pressure gaseous hydrogen, see Fig. 7.2 (right), which is then passed through a further Hampson type liquefier, so producing liquid hydrogen.

Liquid helium is produced by adding yet a further stage, the high-pressure helium gas being first cooled through liquid air, then liquid hydrogen, before passing through a third Hampson type liquefier.

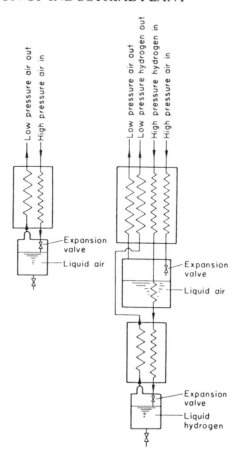

**Fig. 7.2 Hampson air liquefier (left) and Hampson hydrogen liquefier (right).** (*Cryosystems Ltd.*)

Such liquefiers are comparatively simple and reliable (at least for air) but are inefficient. Higher efficiency can be obtained by allowing the gas to expand, cool and do work in an expansion engine, usually of the reciprocating type. All gases can be sufficiently cooled in this manner without precooling, but it is not practical to allow the liquid gas to form in the cylinder of the engine. Consequently the final stage of cooling is carried out in a Hampson type liquefier using the Joule-Thomson effect, through which part of the cooled gas is by-passed (Fig. 7.3). The work done by the engine helps to drive the gas compressor. Expansion turbines are sometimes used, particularly for large plants. Fig. 7.4 shows diagrammatically a more complex arrangement, using helium, two expansion engines and a Joule-Thomson throttle valve, which can be used for very-low-temperature testing or perhaps for process work.

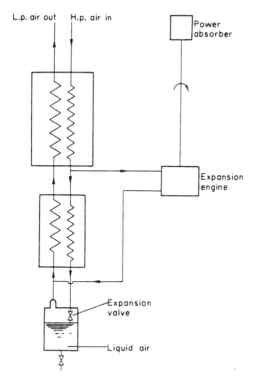

L.p. air out   H.p. air in

Power absorber

Expansion engine

Expansion valve

Liquid air

**Fig. 7.3   Expansion engine air liquefier.** (*Cryosystems Ltd.*)

## 7.8 Structural materials for low-temperature plant

When selecting and inspecting structural materials for cryogenic applications consideration must be given to their possessing certain minimum
values of tensile strength, yield strength, ductility, impact strength (and
notch insensitivity) over the required temperature range of operation.
Repeated thermal cycling should not result in the material becoming
unstable, or phase changes occurring in a metal's crystalline structure. Low
heat conductivity, low emissivity, and a small coefficient of thermal
expansion could also be important for various applications such as storage
vessels and vacuum transfer lines.

With some metals the transition from ductility to brittleness occurs
quickly as the temperature is reduced below a certain level. The difference
in value between yield strength and the ultimate tensile strength becomes
small, and consequently there is very little plastic flow between yield point
and fracture. Most low-carbon steels suffer from brittle failure in this way at

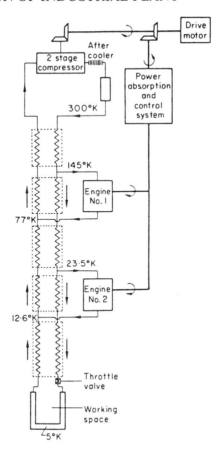

**Fig. 7.4   Diagram of helium refrigerator.** (*Cryosystems Ltd.*)

low temperatures, the actual temperature range at which failure occurs varying with the alloy content, etc. Carbon manganese steels should not be used below −50°C. Metals which have a crystal lattice structure of the so-called body-centred cube pattern are known to undergo a rapid increase in yield strength, and hence resistance to plastic flow, as the temperature decreases below a certain range. Consequently they suffer from brittleness at low temperatures. Therefore certain steel and other metals may be required to pass an impact test at a specified low temperature before they can be used on plant operating at even moderately low temperatures. Their transition temperature under specified conditions may have to be determined.

Metals having a face-centred cube lattice structure do not suffer from this marked rise in yield point at low temperatures, although their tensile strength may rise. Hence such metals in general are ductile at low temperatures and do not suffer from brittleness.

Austenitic materials, in particular austenitic stainless steels (such as the 18/8 variety), have this type of crystalline structure and in consequence are very suitable for use in cryogenic plant.

Again, body-centred cube structure metals are found to lose their ability to undergo continuous work hardening (suffering large fluctuations of load-carrying capacity in the plastic range), whilst face-centred cube structure metals retain this ability and do not suffer from unstable plastic flow.

Phase transformations in crystalline structure may occur with some materials and it does not necessarily follow that a material which is normally face-centred will remain so at cryogenic temperatures.

The structural materials mainly used for cryogenic plants at the lowest temperatures (down to $-270°C$) are thus the austenitic stainless steels (18/8 type, BS 970, Type 304 S12, BS 1510, AISI 300 series (e.g. ASTM A 240 type 304), etc.). Various aluminium (e.g. aluminium/magnesium) alloys, because of their face-centred cube structure are used, down to the lowest temperatures particularly where weight is of prime importance, and titanium to a limited extent for special applications. Monel metal, copper, bronze and brass may be used mainly for small items or special items.

In general, non-ferrous metals do not suffer a marked loss of impact strength at sub-zero temperatures, their static tensile strength increases as the temperature decreases and their ductility is not affected significantly; therefore low-temperature impact tests are not generally required. After teething troubles in development and fabrication nickel steels ($3\frac{1}{2}$ and 9% nickel) are now used for cryogenic work (down to $-100°C$ and $-200°C$ respectively). Amongst plastics, PTFE retains many of its properties at low temperatures. It can be used for sliding surfaces and bearings and has a low thermal conductivity.

*Stainless steel.* In general, of the three types of stainless steel—austenitic, martensitic and ferritic—only the austenitic stainless steels are recommended for use with cryogenic plant, owing to the poor ductility of the other types at low temperatures.

Most of the austenitic stainless steels show a fair increase in tensile strength as the temperature is lowered, but only a relatively small increase in yield strength, hence they remain ductile. Cold working also increases both tensile strength and yield point, but the ductility suffers somewhat. Their coefficients of thermal conductivity and of thermal expansion are less than those of other materials used structurally in cryogenic plant. The addition of some 0·2% nitrogen increases both tensile and proof stress. The corrosion resistance of austenitic stainless steels is generally better than that of the other stainless types, and satisfactory welding techniques are available.

In connection with the welding of these stainless steels reference must be made to the problem of intercrystalline corrosion which is dealt with in 2.13.1 and 9.21.4.

*Aluminium.* Aluminium is a useful material for cryogenic plant, particularly where its strength-to-weight ratio is of importance. It can be fabricated and welded readily, the argon-arc method of welding being particularly suitable. Its ductility and impact strength at low temperatures are satisfactory, although it has not in general the high tensile strength of the stainless steels. Pure aluminium has uses where corrosion resistance to certain forms of chemical attack is desirable, whilst the various types of aluminium alloy, besides having good resistance to oxidation, may have high strength in the annealed condition. Aluminium however has a high thermal conductivity and high coefficient of expansion, which may be disadvantageous in certain applications.

Various types of aluminium have been used for cryogenic plant and equipment, including storage vessels, at liquid oxygen and liquid nitrogen temperatures. Aluminium-magnesium alloys (such as BS 1470 NT 5 and ASTM B 209 (ANSI Alloy Designations 5052 and 5083)) have been so used.

Before specifying a particular material for cryogenic use it should be examined to determine whether its properties are suitable at the temperature range and conditions required. A programme of tests may be necessary, if not already carried out. Inspection should verify that the specified materials have been employed and that there is evidence that any tests on them have been performed with satisfactory results.

## 7.9 Thermal insulation of storage vessels for cryogenic use

When storing cryogenic liquids the storage vessel must be so constructed that the 'boil-off' rate of the liquid is kept to a minimum. The vessel must also be safe and convenient in use.

The method of thermal insulation adopted depends on many factors, such as the type of fluid , weight and economics. The effectiveness of the insulation can be measured in terms of its apparent mean thermal conductivity ($k$), which can be defined as the quantity of heat which passes per unit time through unit area of a slab of the substance of indefinite extent and of unit thickness, when unit difference of temperature is established between its faces.

It should be noted that $k$ depends to some extent on the thickness of the insulation and the temperature range $T_1$ and $T_2$. It gives a comparative value for different insulations under similar conditions.

It can be expressed in the following units:

(a) Imperial: $\dfrac{\text{Btu ft}}{\text{ft}^2 \text{ h } ^\circ\text{F}}$      (b) SI: $\dfrac{\text{W m}}{\text{m}^2 \, ^\circ\text{C}}$

Extreme care should be used when dealing with a quoted value of $k$ to ensure that the intended units are known (e.g. some authorities use thickness in feet and some in inches; time may be in hours or seconds; the metric units used may differ; note the comparative simplicity of the SI expression).

Note: Multiply the imperial expression by 1·7307 to obtain SI.

The various types of thermal insulation in use include the following:

(1) *Externally applied insulation*, such as asbestos, magnesia, cork, fibre glass, balsa wood. In particular plastic foam insulants are of importance. These foams, which include polyurethane, polystyrene and glass foam, can be manufactured with densities and physical properties which vary over wide limits. They have a cellular structure due to the bubble formation during manufacture. The foaming agent used to produce these bubbles during manufacture may be carbon dioxide, Freon (Arcton) or air. At cryogenic temperatures the vapour pressure of these gases is reduced by cryo-pumping action and the heat insulation is improved.

It should be noted that owing to slow diffusion the gas in the foam bubbles may change slowly with time. Should the original gas have been carbon dioxide or Freon and should it have been slowly displaced by air, then an increase in the thermal conductivity of the foam will result, maybe after many months of service.

Polyurethane foam has the lowest $k$ value of any insulating material in common use, and is resistant to most chemical atmospheres, solvents and oils; it is rot-, vermin- and fungus-proof. If a face of the foam is exposed to moisture penetration, inspection should check that this is coated with a vapour seal such as asphaltic mastic or an epoxy coating.

The coefficients of expansion of the foams and that of the container material will differ considerably, and, although the foam may be fixed to the container wall by a suitable adhesive, it is as well to note that the stresses set up in service may effect the structural soundness of the insulation scheme.

A method of preventing air entering the insulation is to enclose the insulation in an air-tight plastic envelope.

(2) *High-vacuum insulation.* The vessel is surrounded by an outer container and the air in this space is evacuated. The walls are made reflective, the arrangement being similar to the thermos or Dewar flask. The vacuum required is of the order of $10^{-6}$ torr (mm of mercury). Any structural members spanning the vacuum space will convey heat by conduction, but with good design this can be reduced to a minimum and the heat loss will approach that due to radiation only. 'Sealed-off' Dewars of glass or copper are much used for the storage of small quantities of liquid gas. The gradual release of gas (outgassing) from the surfaces of the evacuated space (especially in other than glass Dewars) tend to gradually spoil the vacuum. Inspection should verify that adequate manufacturing processes, such as heating during evacuation and the use of 'getters' (to adsorb gases), are adopted. Larger vessels could have a vacuum pump

system attached, which could be operated as required.*

(3) *Evacuated powder insulation.* The provision and operation of a high-vacuum pumping system, comprising a diffusion pump backed by a mechanical pump (see 8.17), is a complication on medium to large cryogenic storage vessel. This can be mitigated by filling the space between the inner and outer containers with a suitable powder and then evacuating this space to the relatively coarse (medium) vacuum obtainable from a straightforward mechanical rotary vacuum pump, connected up temporarily.

Amongst the materials used as porous powder insulants are silica aerogel, diatomaceous earth (Fuller's earth), expanded perlite and fibre glass. The addition of aluminium powder may also improve the performance of perlite and silica gel. As the pressure is reduced the thermal conductivity falls and eventually tends to level out at low values of pressure. A good mechanical pump giving an ultimate vacuum of better than 10 millitorr ($10^{-2}$ torr (mmHg)) is sufficient to provide an effective insulating medium even when a slight leak or outgassing occurs. Many liquid oxygen and nitrogen containers having evacuated powder insulation are in service, and have maintained the required degree of vacuum ($10^{-2}$ to $10^{-1}$ torr), without any repumping for periods of around five years. Provision is made for the connection of a vacuum pump when required.

Before introducing powder insulant into a system it should be examined and, if necessary, thoroughly dried by heating, as it readily absorbs moisture.

(4) *Non-evacuated gas-filled powder insulation.* Non-evacuated powder or fibre insulation is placed in a jacket around the container and this is then filled with a gas. The jacket should preferably be leak-tight. Condensation on cold surfaces should be avoided. Perlite with a gas filling of helium or nitrogen has been tried.

(5) *Liquid nitrogen shielding.* For storing and transporting liquid hydrogen or liquid helium use can be made of a liquid nitrogen shielded vacuum container. Fig. 7.5 shows the arrangement of a Dewar of this type, commercially available in sizes ranging from 2 to 100 litres (or more). The vacuum spaces are evacuated to a high degree and sealed off. An absorbent material (e.g. charcoal) is placed in these spaces to help maintain the vacuum. Liquid nitrogen, providing a thermal barrier, is introduced into the shielding space and cools the vessel down before the introduction of the liquid hydrogen or helium to be stored. The loss rate of the stored liquid is quite small, and can be as little as 0.5% evaporation per day with the largest sizes.

Inspection must ensure that the inner container is always under a slight

---

*For details of vacuum technology and of the units employed see Chapter 8 (particularly 8.2 and Table 8.1 SI units are now preferred).

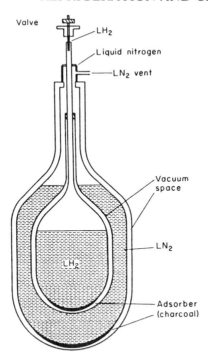

**Fig. 7.5  Liquid nitrogen shielded container for storing liquid hydrogen**

positive pressure to prevent air entering and solidifying in it. Besides the obvious disadvantages of such ice blocking outlets, etc., the presence of frozen air (and particularly oxygen) crystals in liquid hydrogen is fraught with serious hazards (see 7.14). A protective cap or valve should be fitted to the outlet to maintain this positive pressure.

Some much larger liquid nitrogen shielded vacuum tanks have been developed for special liquid hydrogen applications.

(6) *Super-insulation.* Developments (by Linde and the National Research Corp., USA) have made available evacuated insulants having thermal conductivities of about one-tenth of that of the best evacuated powders. These are often proprietary items of which the details are unknown or vague. It is stated that NRC2 consists of a number of 0·00025 in layers of polyester film, which have been metallized and crinkled, packed in a vacuum enclosure.

## 7.10  General design of cryogenic vessels

A spherical storage vessel is inherently stronger than any other shaped vessel of the same general thickness and material, both against internal or external pressure. Consider a cylindrical vessel of length equal to its diameter; then its surface area is about 14% greater than that of the corresponding sphere. Consequently its 'boil-off' rate will be 14% greater. In addition its weight, for the same capacity and working conditions, will be about twice that of the spherical vessel.

On other hand cylindrical vessels are generally easier to manufacture. No hard and fast rule is possible but, for vessels small enough to be readily transported and erected in the factory and of relatively low pressure, the cylindrical shape is probably more economical. Transport problems generally favour large cylindrical vessels, but, where erection on site is possible and high internal pressures are required, weight and economic considerations favour the spherical vessel. In practice the greater 'boil-off' rate of a cylindrical vessel is not of great importance owing to the efficiency of modern methods of insulation.

The choice of materials will depend of course on the service envisaged, with austenitic stainless steel or a suitable aluminium as preference for the inner vessel where the lowest temperatures are likely to be met. The outer vessel may be of a different material such as a high-strength ductile carbon steel (perhaps Colville's Coltuff, or ASTM A 285 Grade C) or a mild steel. The choice of insulant has already been dealt with.

The general design, thickness of materials, construction, testing and inspection will be governed by an appropriate specification, somewhat similar to BS 5500 *unfired fusion welded pressure vessels for general purposes*, or the similar ASME Boiler and Pressure Vessel Code, as far as applicable.

A space should be left between the lowest portion of the vessel and the ground to allow for ventilation and prevent freezing to the ground, etc.

Should a manhole be necessary to give access to the inner tank, for maintenance purposes, etc., it should be kept to the minimum size (18 in diameter), as it constitutes a heat leak. A bellows type of construction connecting the inner and outer shells would be suitable.

The sealing of the inner and outer shells should be arranged so that the joint is away from contact with the cryogenic liquid. Problems of welding dissimilar metals may arise here, and the correct techniques should be used and closely watched by inspection.

Differential expansion between dissimilar metals may well cause leaks to appear when the vessel is at its operating temperature, and the design should endeavour to eliminate such trouble.

## 7.11 Construction and inspection of cryogenic vessels

A cryogenic storage vessel must be able to withstand its operating conditions in safety for a long (if not indefinite) period. It must be able to do this without leakage of the cryogenic liquid. In addition, if vacuum-insulated, the vacuum spaces must be so fabricated that even under operating conditions the vacuum leakage rate is exceedingly small and does not exceed the permissible design figure. Consequently mechanical soundness and leak-tightness of the vessel are of paramount importance. Only by using good design, sound methods of fabrication, welding and heat treatment, etc., adequately controlled by an efficient inspection organization, can the desired objective be attained.

As a first step, the raw materials of construction should be obtained from an approved source, the supplier furnishing test certificates giving data regarding the tensile tests, bend tests, hardness, impact and notched bar tests, etc., and details regarding heat treatment, coupon tests, welding, etc. The materials should be identified and segregated for the job as necessary. Dimensional limits in forming, trimming and welding must be watched and in general fabrications should be inspected prior to welding.

All welding must be carried out by approved techniques and by approved welders. The quality of a weld is difficult to determine by inspection (although generally speaking a 'good' weld looks good), and depends largely on the skill of the welder. Consequently all welders have to make test welds by fabricating standard test pieces, which are then examined and tested by the appropriate authority before the particular welder is allowed to carry out any welding on the job.

In addition 'coupon' welds for various parts may be required. The procedure for approving welders and techniques is given in British Standards and in Section IX of the ASME Code (see 3.9, 3.14 and 9.21). In addition various approving authorities have their own, generally similar, requirements. The production of welds which are not only strong but leak-tight is difficult.

Only by using the proper techniques, backed by continous but helpful inspection, can welds of the required high quality be obtained.

The various construction codes may require certain welds to be X-rayed. However with cryogenic vacuum vessels the welds on both the inner and outer containers should all be X-rayed. The radiography should be done whilst fabrication is in progress. If faults are detected (which may effect strength or leak-tightness) the welds affected can be chipped out and repaired at once before further work is done. It is far cheaper in time and money to carry out a 100% X-ray examination of welds during construction than to find leaks which have developed later during testing at working temperatures.

In order to prove the tightness of the vessel a preliminary rought test may be carried out using perhaps hydrostatic pressure. However this may not always be possible. For instance with a large tank the weight of water required might severely overload it if it was meant to store a fluid of lesser density.

However, it should be remembered that a pressure overload of a vessel (particularly of steel) is less likely to cause a failure in service than is brittle fracture at low temperature. Correct choice of the material is therefore very important.

An air pressure test might then be required. The pressure of air required should be kept to a minimum and strength and safety requirements closely watched. The outside of the vessel could be coated with glycerine solution, which greatly helps in the detection of bubbles resulting from leakage.

Alternatively, if possible, the vessel might be immersed in water. Leak tests on important welds might be carried out while pressurised with nitrogen and using a teepol solution.

When any major leaks have been eliminated then more sensitive leak detection methods can be applied. Such methods are dealt with more fully in Chapter 11, but the most commonly employed are the halogen leak detector and the mass spectrometer (a more expensive instrument).

The vacuum space should be cleaned and degreased and then evacuated by a suitable pump down to the order of $5 \times 10^{-2}$ torr or better. This may be difficult to achieve in a reasonable time owing to outgassing, but provided that the space has previously passed its leak test a vacuum of up to about 0·5 torr might be permissible, as cryo-pumping action in use could take the vacuum down further.

Before powder insulation is put into a vacuum space it should be thoroughly dried. A filter should then be fitted between the vacuum pump and the space.

It is difficult to carry out leak detection after the vessel has been filled with its cryogenic fluid and cooled down. If control of manufacture and inspection have been effectively carried out, then operation of the vacuum pump on the cooled vacuum space for some time should result in the vacuum attaining a value of the required order of 50 millitorr. Outgassing from the metal and the evolution of moisture from the insulation will continue for a long while, probably for some time after the vessel has been put into use. If the pump was shut down and the vacuum space isolated a gradual rise in pressure would be detectable, but this must not be confused with leakage. Some *very slight* leakage will occur, however, as it is not practicable to make a *completely* leak-tight system. Consequently it is possible, especially with a large vessel, that there will be a need for pumping either continuously or at intervals during service. With smaller vessels, effectively constructed, the rise of pressure due to outgassing, leakage, etc., may be so small that the vessel can be operated for years at a time without the need for connecting up to a pump and re-evacuating.

### 7.11.1 Welded storage tanks for low temperature (including cryogenic) service

(i) BS 2654 *Manufacture of vertical steel welded storage tanks with butt-welded shells for the petroleum industry* contains much information on the materials, design and testing of tanks for use by the oil and other industries at temperatures down to $-10°C$. It is of interest in that it states that material selection is based on the results of notched and welded Wells Wide Plate Tests (WWP tests) on carbon and carbon-manganese steel plates carried out at the Welding Institute and that WWP test data indicate that resistance to brittle fracture depends on:

(a) Notch toughness of the material.

(b) Plate thickness.

(c) Extent of crack-like defects (if none are present brittle fracture at normal loading is not expected to be a problem).

(d) Degree of local embrittlement at tip of pre-existing defects (suitable post-weld heat treatment is effective in removing severe embrittlement arising from welding and/or flame cutting operations).

A method is specified for determining the notch toughness required for a given thickness of material for design temperatures down to $-10°C$ (and below) based on WWP and Charpy V-notch impact tests. From this the minimum water temperature for avoiding brittle fracture during hydrostatic testing may be determined. Note that the minimum Charpy V-notch requirements derived take into account an anticipated improvement in safety as a result of the hydrostatic test. The degree of security against brittle fracture may be increased by subsequent hydrostatic loading.

For comparatively thin materials (not exceeding 13 mm) with tensile strengths up to $490 N/mm^2$ impact tests are not required as brittle fracture is not anticipated. For thicker materials with tensile strengths of $430 N/mm^2$ or less impact tests should show not less than 27J Charpy V at $+20°C$ or at the test temperature determined in the last paragraph if lower. For higher tensile strengths an impact value of 41J Charpy minimum at $-5°C$ or $-15°C$ (at above $490 N/mm^2$), or at the test temperature determined (as above) if lower, is required.

(ii) Steel storage tanks of somewhat similar design for low-temperature service down to $-50°C$ are dealt with in BS 4741 which also makes use of WWP tests. The selection of materials is made by performing Charpy V-notch impact tests on all materials and the average absorbed energy must be at least equal to the values shown in a table (in effect 27 and 41 J for somewhat similar cases to those given in BS 2654) for tabulated test temperatures similar to the minimum design metal temperatures ($-10$, $-35$ or $-50°C$) for material thicknesses equal to or greater than 20 mm, and 10° or 20°C lower for thicknesses up to 30 or 40 mm respectively.

(iii) Vertical cylindrical welded steel storage tanks for service down to $-196°C$ are dealt with in BS 5387 and are of double wall construction. The inner tank is for the storage of liquefied gases (having temperatures in the range $-50°C$ to $-196°C$) and is made from one of a selected range of aluminium alloys, austenitic stainless steels and 9% nickel steels. These materials are not considered to be susceptible to brittle fracture at the thicknesses and temperatures permitted by this standard. Greater thicknesses could lead to fast fractures and might warrant checks by fracture mechanics tests. Design stress is based upon the strength of the parent plate, or of the weld metal if lower, divided by the appropriate factor of safety, as with these materials it is not possible to guarantee the strength of the weld. The outer tank contains the thermal insulation (not liquid) and is constructed in a similar manner to and from the materials selected and specified as in BS 2654. The insulating material is not specified, but it could be in the form of blocks, loose-fill material or powder (see 7.9).

It is necessary to check that the insulation is sufficient to maintain the outer tank at or above the outer tank design temperature when the inner tank is full of its specified liquefied gas, and that the boil-off rate of this liquefied gas is within acceptable limits.

(iv) General requirements. BS 2654 covers storage tanks with a maximum internal design pressure of 56 millibars. BS 4741 and BS 5387 cover internal pressures up to 140 mbar and all are designed for a vacuum of 6 mbar (1 mbar $= 100$ Pa $= 0.75$ torr). All these standards give details of fabrication, welding procedure and welder approval, radiographic testing and acceptance levels of defects found by radiographic examination, post-weld heat treatment, hydrostatic testing, etc. which follow generally the procedure outlined elsewhere for pressure vessels. The earlier issued standards (BS 4741 and 5387) give porosity charts showing acceptable radiographic porosity standards. The latest issue of BS 2654 (1984) gives a table (abridged but similar to BS 1113 and BS 5500) showing acceptance levels for defects found by radiographic examination.

## 7.12  Cryogenic installations

Any cryogenic installation will generally consist of storage vessels and the necessary pumping systems, valves, instruments and transfer lines. Storage vessels have been dealt with, and similar observations to those already made regarding materials, fabrication, inspection and testing will apply to the other components of the installation.

Pumping of the cryogenic fluid may be carried out by pressurizing the surface of the fluid by means of a suitable gas, or by using specially developed cryogenic pumps placed in the liquid line. Pressurization necessitates the use of thicker-walled storage vessels than might otherwise be required, and consequently increases their weight and cost. Mechanical pumps present problems of design, especially in connection with bearings and seals. Some pumps have been successfully designed to operate immersed in the cryogenic fluid. The basic arrangement of the two system is shown in Fig. 7.6.

Valves for cryogenic use may be standard types made of stainless steel or

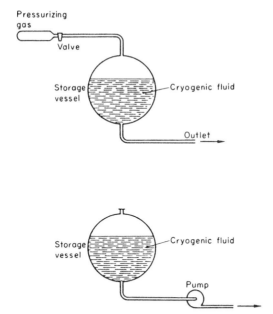

**Fig. 7.6 Methods for pumping cryogenic fluids**

other suitable material, perhaps with modifications to the packing material and an extended spindle to suit the low temperature envisaged. Valve seats may be of PTFE or similar material. Occasionally specifically developed valves may be met. Insulation can also be carried out, if required, by one of the various methods already described.

It is sometimes necessary to carry out a meticulous inspection of the interior of a valve, used perhaps in liquid oxygen service, to ensure freedom from foreign matter, including grease, hydrocarbons, dirt, etc., which may find its way into the system and cause trouble, including (with oxygen) a serious fire and explosion hazard. Such an inspection may be necessary prior to installation, and also periodically during use. If the contaminant is difficult to see, the component can be wiped with a white filter paper, or ultra-violet light may be used.

Inspection for contaminants may necessitate the setting up of a component-cleaning process, or it may follow such a process as a matter of routine. A typical cleaning process would require valves, components, etc., to be disassembled, degreased with trichlorethylene,* dried with hot air, and reassembled under clean conditions. New gaskets might be fitted and all openings suitably sealed. After assembly into the system, this could then be

---

*A less toxic solvent would be desirable.

flushed through with a suitable fluid to ensure that any remaining particles are removed. An inspection of any filters, etc., in the system should be made to detect any undue and unsuspected contamination which would necessitate re-inspection and treatment.

BS 5429 *Code of practice for safe operation of small-scale storage facilities for cryogenic liquids* deals with the hazards, etc. encountered with the widespread industrial use of oxygen, nitrogen, argon and natural gas in liquid form as a refrigerant, etc. (these have temperatures (boiling points) at atmospheric pressure of $-183°$, $-196°$, $-186°$ and $162°C$ respectively). Up to 135 tonnes of liquid oxygen (or the liquid volume equivalent of some other gases) can be stored in the UK without the special planning permission required beyond this capacity. However a licence (renewable annually) has to be obtained from the relevant local authority for the storage of *any* quantity of liquid natural gas (LNG).

The special hazards associated particularly with oxygen are emphasized. The normal oxygen content of air is 20·9% by volume. Less than 18% is potentially dangerous. Below 10% permanent brain damage can arise, and of course—death when the percentage falls lower towards zero. An oxygen-enriched atmosphere greatly increases the possibility of fire, and even human hair will ignite; dirty and oily clothes are a danger (wool clothing is best). Many materials will readily burn in oxygen and are not easily extinguished except by eliminating the source of supply of oxygen.

See also National Fire Protection Association (Boston, Mass):

NFPA 50 Bulk Oxygen Systems at Consumer Sites

NFPA 53M Fire Hazards in Oxygen-Enriched Atmospheres

NFPA 59A Production Storage and Handling of LNG

It may be necessary to carry out tests for compatibility of materials with liquid oxygen; specification ASTM D 2512 deals with a method of test, using impact sensitivity threshold technique.

Valves should of course be leak-tested to an appropriate specification, and should be type-tested to ensure satisfactory operation under working conditions.

Transfer lines are required for economically conveying the cryogenic fluid between storage vessels and other items of plant. Fig. 7.7 shows the basic arrangement. To begin with, the cryogenic fluid is forced into the transfer line and vaporizes, cooling the line in the process. Eventually a steady condition is reached, the temperature of the line reaches a sensibly constant low value, and the liquid flows to where it is required. The design of the transfer line will depend to some extent on equating the cost of the cool-down and steady-state losses of liquid with the cost of the line. In some cases a bare transfer line may be economic. High-vacuum jacketed lines are used where low heat losses are of major importance (see Fig. 7.8), but the powder-filled evacuated line has much to commend it, and if properly constructed under efficient quality control and inspection should give years

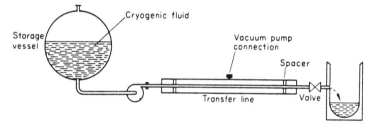

**Fig. 7.7 Use of transfer line**

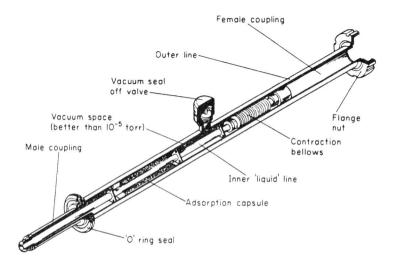

**Fig. 7.8 A section of a high-vacuum insulated liquid gas transfer line (made of stainless steel)**
Straight sections are normally up to 10 ft long and together with 'T' sections, elbows, angle sections, 'Z' bends and flexible sections are made up to suit requirements. Each section is provided with a combined 'pump out and relief' valve. Repumping should not be necessary during a normal service of 1–2 years. Sections of line are connected to each other by 'bayonet' fittings designed to have a very low heat loss. Powder-insulated transfer lines are also available. (*Spembly Technical Products Ltd.*)

of service. Spacers between the inner and outer tubes are necessary, and as these provide a heat-leakage path they should be made from a material of low conductivity, such as PTFE, nylon, Mylar, etc.

The inspection of transfer lines and components should follow similar procedures to those already given, viz.:

(i) Only approved materials and components supported by documentary evidence of mechanical tests, chemical analysis, heat treatment, etc., should be used.

(ii) Only approved welders and welding techniques (such as argon-arc) should be employed.

(iii) The requirements of any relevant code as regards fabrication, stress relieving, etc., should be followed.

(iv) Leak testing should be carried out to an approved standard.

(v) An over-pressure test (to at least $1\frac{1}{2}$ times the normal working pressure) should be performed.

(vi) All welds should be radiologically examined.

(vii) A visual examination should be carried out to check cleanliness, freedom from foreign bodies, etc., and again during installation—to ensure that cracks, scratches or damage likely to cause trouble have not materialized.

### 7.13 Liquid hydrogen

Gases such as hydrogen can be liquefied directly or indirectly by one or both of two methods:

(1) Employing the Joule-Thomson effect (internal work method).
(2) Utilizing the reversible expansion of the gas to perform external work.

The liquid hydrogen might be produced by first cooling the gas with liquid nitrogen (liquid air or oxygen could be used, but would introduce dangers) and allowing free expansion from 2000 lb/in$^2$.

Alternatively it can be liquefied by cooling with liquid helium (of temperature 4·2K, some 16K colder than liquid hydrogen) if this is available. This is a safer and more convenient process as it operates at low pressures.

A peculiarity regarding hydrogen and liquid hydrogen which should be known by the inspector dealing with cryogenics is that it exists in two forms—*ortho* and *para* hydrogen. At normal temperature hydrogen, under equilibrium conditions, contains 25% *para*, but this increases to 99.8% *para* at the boiling point ($-253°C$). Thus if normal hydrogen is liquefied the 75% of *ortho* it contained originally will undergo transition into the *para* form. As the two forms represent different energy levels (of electron spin), energy will be released by the transition and can cause considerable loss of liquid by evaporation (about 65% could be lost over a period of hours even if perfectly insulated). This loss can be reduced by passing the gas over a catalyst before liquefaction.

Because of the possibly greater rate of evaporation of liquid hydrogen compared with other gases it is especially important that a clear vent should be maintained on containers and that roof ventilation should be good.

## 7.14 Special precautions when using liquid hydrogen

Besides many of the hazards experienced with gaseous hydrogen (see 6.13) liquid hydrogen has an additional explosion hazard, since air in contact with it will condense and form 'ice' crystals. Vaporization of the hydrogen may then result in the formation of potentially dangerous mixtures of air ('ice') and hydrogen.

A much greater hazard exists if liquid hydrogen is transferred into open vessels which have been precooled to below the boiling point of oxygen ($-182°C$ or $-297°F$), since the oxygen of the air may condense and solidify and form a mixture with the liquid hydrogen which is shock-sensitive and liable to detonate readily.

Therefore when dealing with liquid hydrogen, inspection must verify that all traces of oxygen (and air) have been eliminated from the system. This can be done by 'purging' (flushing) the system previously with nitrogen or an inert gas. However it is very difficult to remove all traces of oxygen, particularly from any hydrogen gas introduced (but see 6.13), and deposits of solid oxygen may therefore build up in liquid hydrogen storage containers from which the liquid is periodically withdrawn. Consequently a programme of inspection and periodic cleaning of such containers is desirable.

In addition precautions should be taken to avoid 'burns' on the human body from the extremely cold liquid hydrogen ($-253°C$). Spilling and splashing should be avoided as far as possible, and protective clothing, gloves, eye shields, etc., should be worn as necessary.

Personnel should preferably wear wool or cotton clothing; the use of silk, nylon (and similar man-made fibres) should be avoided owing to the electrostatic charges which they can acquire. It may be necessary to provide earthing spheres to discharge personnel.

Alternatively, floors might be of conductive rubber construction (see BS 3187) and earthed, and personnel could wear conductive rubber shoes (BS 5451) (see 6.12).

Again it should be emphasized that liquid oxygen (or liquid air) should never be used near to a liquid hydrogen plant because of the explosive and detonation hazard.

## References and further reading

Barron, R.F., *Cryogenics Systems* (Monographs on cryogenics: 3), OUP, 1985.

British Cryogenics Council, *Equipment Guide*, Inst. of Chemical Engineers, 1975.

Chemical Industries Association, Code of Practice for the large scale storage of fully refrigerated anhydrous ammonia in the UK, London, 1975.

*Cryogenics Safety Manual—A guide to good practice* (compiled by the Safety Panel of the British Cryogenics Council and Published by Mechanical Engineering Publications for I.Mech.E, 1982).

Engineering Equipment and Materials Users Association (EEMUA), Recommendations for the design and construction of liquefied gas storage tanks (1987) (will form the basis of a new BS for refrigerated storage tanks)

Institute of Petroleum, Liquefied Petroleum Gas Safety Code (Part 9 of IP Safety Code

Liquefied Petroleum Gas Industry Technical Association LPG Codes of Practice include:

Installation & Maintenance of Fixed bulk LPG Storage
Safe handling and transport by road
Prevention and Control of Fire involving LPG
LPG-Air Plants

Pita, E.G. *Refrigeration principles and systems: an energy approach*, Wiley, 1984.

Inst. of Chemical Engineers, Cryogenics Safety Manual, 1970.

*Vacuum Insulated Cryogenic Pipe*, Inst. of Chemical Engineers, 1972.

Welding Institute, *Welding low temperature containment plant*, 1974.

# 8 Mechanical pressure systems and vacuum plant

## Part 1 Pressure systems and pumps

### 8.1 Design and inspection matters

In industrial and chemical plant pressure in a vessel itself, or a system, may be produced internally by the boiling of water, etc. as in a boiler, or by means of a mechanical pump or compressor. Pumps may be of the reciprocating (piston and cylinder), rotary (vane) or centrifugal type, or of special design. They may handle air or a gas, liquids or slurries; they may reduce the pressure below atmospheric; special physical types of high vacuum pump can approach pressures near absolute zero. Reciprocating pumps/ compressors may have two or more cylinders so that a high pressure may be built up in several stages. Pressures as high as 5000 atmospheres (50 hbar or 500 MN/m$^2$) can be attained. See Fig 8.1, para. 8.6 and Tables 8.3 and A3 in the Appendix for some of the units and conversion employed. Speaking generally, pumps handle liquids whilst compressors (and exhausters) handle gases (or vapours). There is no hard dividing line.

As the failure rate for pumps/compressors is greater than that of properly designed pressure vessels associated with them (see, for instance 13.7 and Table 13.2) their design, inspection and testing should receive considerable attention, particularly regarding the following:

(a) In order to prevent seizure of bearings, moving parts, etc with consequent overheating, adequate lubrication (or its equivalent) must be provided.

(b) Some pumps/compressors are required to compress air or gases without any possibility of contamination with lubricating oil. Specially designed seals, carbon rings, etc. may be fitted, and should be checked periodically for leakage. Some small machines may be fitted with 'oil-free' bearings, etc. (perhaps making use of PTFE).

397

STRESS UNIT CONVERSIONS

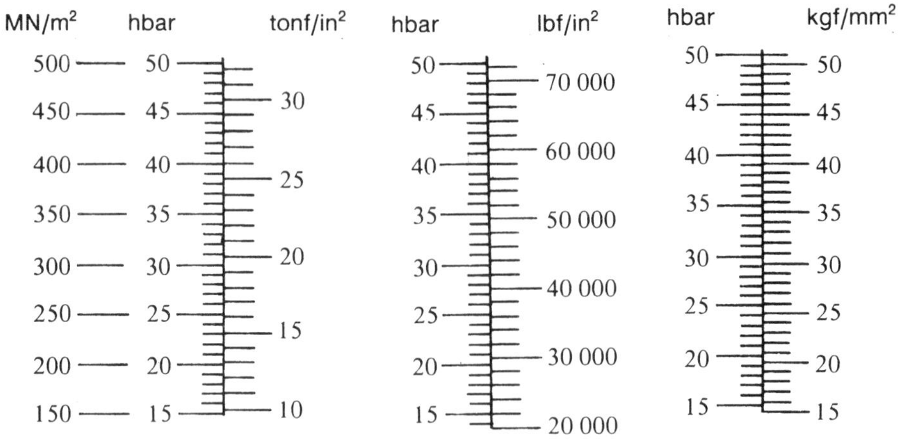

| MN/m² | hbar | tonf/in² | hbar | lbf/in² | hbar | kgf/mm² |
|-------|------|----------|------|---------|------|---------|
| 500 | 50 | | 50 | 70 000 | 50 | 50 |
| 450 | 45 | 30 | 45 | | 45 | 45 |
| 400 | 40 | 25 | 40 | 60 000 | 40 | 40 |
| 350 | 35 | | 35 | 50 000 | 35 | 35 |
| 300 | 30 | 20 | 30 | 40 000 | 30 | 30 |
| 250 | 25 | 15 | 25 | | 25 | 25 |
| 200 | 20 | | 20 | 30 000 | 20 | 20 |
| 150 | 15 | 10 | 15 | 20 000 | 15 | 15 |

PRESSURE UNIT CONVERSIONS

| MN/m² | bar | metres head | bar | lbf/in² | bar | kgf/cm² |
|-------|-----|-------------|-----|---------|-----|---------|
| 5·0 | 50 | 500 | 50 | 700 | 50 | 50 |
| 4·5 | 45 | 450 | 45 | | 45 | 45 |
| 4·0 | 40 | 400 | 40 | 600 | 40 | 40 |
| 3·5 | 35 | 350 | 35 | 500 | 35 | 35 |
| 3·0 | 30 | 300 | 30 | 400 | 30 | 30 |
| 2·5 | 25 | 250 | 25 | | 25 | 25 |
| 2·0 | 20 | 200 | 20 | 300 | 20 | 20 |
| 1·5 | 15 | | 15 | 200 | 15 | 15 |

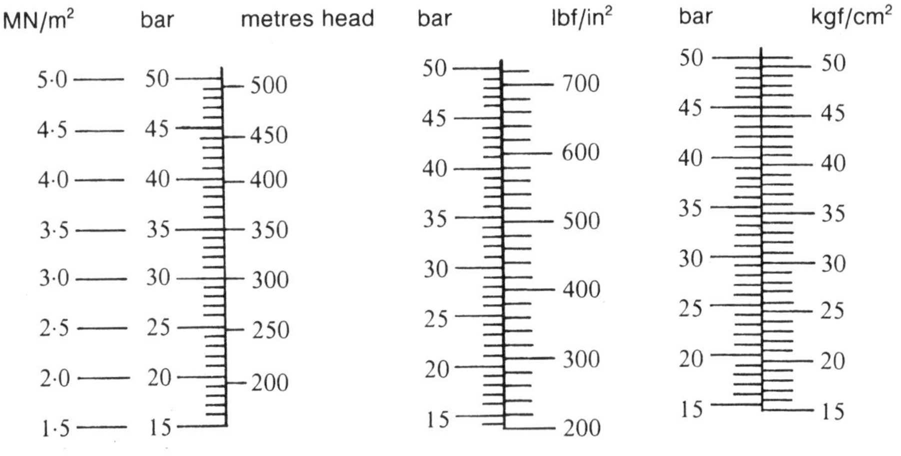

1 bar = $10^5$ N/m² = 0·1 N/mm² = 10·1972 metres head = 14·5038 lbf/in²
= 1·019 72 kgf/cm²
1 hbar = 100 bar = 10 MN/m² = 10 N/mm² = 0·647 49 tonf/in² = 1450·38 lbf/in²
= 1·019 72 kgf/mm²

**Fig. 8.1  Stress and pressure unit conversions**

For more detailed conversions see BS 350 *Conversion factors and tables*

(c) Oil-lubricated compressors with a high compression ratio may under certain circumstances discharge the air at a high enough temperature to cause ignition and explosion of the oil. If connected to an oil-mist coated pipeline this explosion could detonate down the line at supersonic speed with perhaps disastrous results. It is considered that this oil-mist coating under the action of air blast and heat forms into a readily ignitable coke. Consequently, the design should be such that the maximum temperature at a stage delivery flange does not normally exceed 110°C. An automatic shutdown device can be arranged to operate at 120°C which is below the ignition temperature of the coke.

(d) Similarly an oil mist may form in the crank case, and any serious overheating may initiate an explosion or fire. If considered necessary an explosion relief device should be fitted to the crank case.

(e) The selection of a specially developed air compressor lubricant may help.

(f) Adequate but not excessive cooling. This may be by air or liquid (usually water but oil flooded and sealed rotary compressors may be used).

(g) Pressure relief valves and/or bursting discs should be used to prevent the pressure in any part of the system from exceeding the allowable working pressure by more than 10%.

(h) Care should be taken to ensure that inlet and discharge valves are fitted in their correct positions during installation or maintenance. Accidents have happened due to incorrect assembly.

(i) Guards should be provided on all rotating and reciprocatory parts.

(j) The pump/compressor and *the whole pressure system* should be tested on completion and after any repair and during in-service inspection, to at least $1\frac{1}{2}$ times the working pressure. Many often dangerous leaks occur at the connections between pumps, etc. and the pressure system, consequently particular attention should be paid to the correct fitting of couplings, flanges, seals and 'O' rings, etc.

(k) It is highly desirable, and in some cases essential, that manufacture, inspection and testing should be under the supervision of a quality assurance organization approved to the requirements of B5 5750 or an equivalent system (as detailed in Chapter 9 (particularly 9.4)).

Some standards dealing with pumps are shown in Table 8.1. Vacuum pumps are specifically dealt with in Part 2 of this chapter. For some information on seals and sealing see 8.18 and Table 8.7.

## 8.2 Acceptance tests for centrifugal, mixed flow and axial pumps

British Standards and International Standards (ISO) recognize three classes of pump tests, A, B and C. Class A is the most accurate and class C the least.

## TABLE 8.1

*Some standards dealing with pumps, compressors, exhausters and turbines*

| No. | Description |
| --- | --- |
| | PUMPS |
| BS 4082 | External dimensions for vertical in line centrifugal pumps |
| BS 4617 | Methods for testing hydraulic pumps and motors for hydrostatic power transmission |
| BS 5257 | Horizontal end section centrifugal pumps (16 bar) |
| BS 5316 | Acceptance tests for centrifugal, mixed flow and axial pumps |
| BS 5671 | Guide for commissioning, operation and maintenance of hydraulic turbines |
| BS 5860 | Method for measuring the efficiency of hydraulic turbines, storage pumps and pump-turbines (thermodynamic method) |
| | COMPRESSORS AND EXHAUSTERS |
| BS 1571 | Testing of positive displacement compressors and exhausters |
| | Part 1 Acceptance tests (displacement, comp. and certain types of displacement vacuum pumps, capacity measurement, power consumption) |
| | Part 2 Simplified acceptance tests for air compressors and exhausters (reciprocating and rotary) |
| BS 2009 | Code for acceptance tests for turbo-compressors and exhausters (axial flow and centrifugal methods of measurement) |
| BS 6244 | Code of practice for stationary air compressors (design, construction, installation, operation, potential hazards) |
| | TURBINES |
| BS 132 | Guide for steam turbines procurement |
| BS 752 | Test code for acceptance of steam turbines (primarily for condensing turbo-generators) |
| BS 3135 | Gas turbines: acceptance tests (including thermal efficiency) |
| BS 3863 | Guide for gas turbines procurement |
| BS 5968 | Methods of acceptance testing of industrial type steam turbines (back pressure, mixed pressure, condensing and pass out). |

Class A and B tests are restricted to special cases and needs, and require more complex and accurate apparatus and methods—and hence cost more.

BS 5316 Part 1 deals with class C tests, which are the most likely to be required in normal production testing at works. Parts 2 and 3 deal with classes B and A respectively, Part 2 corresponding with ISO Standard 3555. Part 1 is identical with ISO 2548.

The purpose of the tests is to measure the various quantities involved in ascertaining the performance of a pump and so compare them with the maker's specified guarantees (and/or the purchaser's requirements). The quantities guaranteed, or specified under stated conditions and speed of rotation, include one or more of the criteria shown in Table 8.2.

**TABLE 8.2**

*Pump performance tests*

| | Quantity | Units | Detail |
|---|---|---|---|
| 1 | Volume outlet rate of flow of pump (Q) (at the agreed total head) | (m³/s) | $= \dfrac{\text{mass rate of flow (kg/s)}}{\text{density (kg/m}^3)}$  This may be measured by a weighing or volumetric tank method, or by a venturi tube or orifice plate |
| | *or* | | |
| | total head of pump (H) (at the agreed flow rate) | (metres) | This may be measured directly, by a differential pressure device, and/or calculated (see Fig. 8.4 and Note 3) |
| 2 | Power input (to the pump, measured at the pump coupling, *or* to the pump motor) | (watts) | This may be measured directly by determining the speed of rotation and torque, or indirectly by measuring the electrical power input to a motor of known efficiency. |
| 3 | Pump power output (the power transferred to the liquid in its passage through the pump) | (watts) | mass rate of flow $\times$ g $\times$ H  Expressed in units of  $\left(\dfrac{\text{kg}}{\text{s}}\right) \times \left(\dfrac{\text{m}}{\text{s}^2}\right) \times \text{(m)}$  $= \dfrac{\text{kgm}^2}{\text{s}^3} = \dfrac{\text{Nm}}{\text{s}} = \dfrac{\text{J}}{\text{s}} = \text{W}$  (NB. 1 newton (N) = 1 kgm/s²) |
| 4 | Efficiency ($\eta$) (of the pump) *or* the overall efficiency of the combined motor-pump unit | (metres) | $\dfrac{\text{pump power output}}{\text{pump power input}}$  $\dfrac{\text{pump power output}}{\text{motor power input}}$ |
| 5 | Net positive suction head (NPSH) | | This is the total inlet head, plus the head corresponding to atmospheric pressure, minus the head corresponding to vapour pressure (see Note 4). |

1. Before taking test measurements the pump must be run for sufficient time to ensure steady conditions. The duration of the test may be specified and it may be necessary to take a series of readings and to plot curves of Q versus H, and Q versus NPSH, etc. in order to verify certain guarantees. A cavitation test may be required.

2. The details apply to pumps tested with clean, cold water. Corrections may be necessary if other liquids are used. Also it may be noted that all formulae and calculations are given in coherent units, i.e. the base and derived units of the SI systems (metre, kilogram, second, joule, newton, watt, etc.) and multiples and sub-multiples of these units are not used. This aids calculation. For instance both the electrical power input to the driving motor and the mechanical output of the pump are expressed in watts. In practical measurements and calculations other units will be encountered in specifications and contracts and the correct conversion factors must be used as necessary (see Table A.3 in Appendix). A typical pump test sheet is illustrated in Fig. 8.2.

3. Head is measured from a horizontal reference plane passing in general through the centre of the pump impeller, and its value may be positive or negative depending upon whether it is measured above or below that reference. It may be measured by liquid column manometers (using either the liquid being pumped or a heavy liquid of density $\rho$), or by Bourdon gauges, etc. but must be expressed in metres.

   Total head of pump (H) is the algebraic difference between the outlet total head and the inlet total head.

$$H = \Delta H + \frac{v_2^2 - v_1^2}{2g} \quad \text{(see Fig. 8.4)}$$

Alternatively (see Fig. 8.3):

   $H$ = difference in level $\pm$ difference in gauge pressure + difference in velocity head (due to kinetic energy)

$$H = Z_2 - Z_1 + \frac{p_2 - p_1}{\rho g} + \frac{v_2^2 - v_1^2}{2g}$$

where $Z$ = distance to reference plane
   $\rho$ = density of manometric liquid
   $g$ = acceleration due to gravity

4.   $$\text{NPSH} = H_1 + \frac{\text{atmospheric pressure}}{\text{density} \times g} - \frac{\text{vapour pressure}}{\text{density} \times g}$$
   (m)     (m)              (m)                      (m)

Note that the expression $\dfrac{\text{pressure (N/m}^2)}{\text{density (kgm}^{-3}) \times g(\text{ms}^{-2})}$ reduces to metres (m)

5. For horizontal end-suction centrifugal pumps (see BS 5257) having a maximum discharge pressure of 16 bar (Flange rating 16 bar, preferably to BS 4504) the pressure casing should be tested to 24 bar (gauge pressure).

6. Pumps may be designated by three numbers, as in the following example:

| Dimensions (mm) | Inlet diam. – Outlet diam. – Nominal diam. impeller |
|---|---|
| Designation | 100    –    65    –    250 |

7. Pump dimensions and nominal duty point (e.g. Q and H for a nominal speed of an electric driving motor of 1450 or 2900 rpm) for standard pump designations are given in BS 5257.

8. The surface finish (texture) on shafts and sleeves within the seal cavities should not exceed $0.4$ $\mu$m $R_a$ (see 10.9).

9. Bearings and machine surfaces generally should be checked for any undue temperature rise (e.g. too hot to touch) and should not exceed particularly specified limits (e.g. see Table 6.5). In any case surface temperatures must not exceed the ignition temperature of fluid/s with which they may come into contact.

10. The noise level of a machine should not normally exceed a sound pressure level of 90 dB (A) for any reasonable length of time (more than 8 hours exposure is considered to be damaging). A separate compressor machine room is desirable.

## 8.3 Compressors and exhausters

Compressors and some types of exhauster used in industry may be classified into the following types:

(a) reciprocating
(b) rotary
   (i) positive displacement
   (ii) turbo-compressors

They may be used to compress or exhaust air or a gas or gas mixture and users and inspectors should be aware of any hazardous situation which might arise in any particular installation.

The materials of construction used should take account of the particular

| PUMP TEST SHEET (Class C) | | | Sheet No. | | | | | | | Nature of test | | | | | | | |
|---|---|---|---|---|---|---|---|---|---|---|---|---|---|---|---|---|---|
| Customer: | | | | | | | | | | | | | | | | | |
| Pump | Type | | | Maker's Order Number | | | | | Order No. | | Diameter of inlet:  Diameter of outlet: | | | | | | |
| Guaranteed values | Volume rate of flow ($O_G$) | | | Speed of rotation ($n_{sp}$) | | | | | Power input ($P_G$) | | | | | | | | |
| | Total head ($H_G$) | | | Efficiency ($\eta_G$) | | | | | Net positive suction head (NPSH) | | | | | | | | |
| Pumped liquid | Temperature (t) | | | | | | | | kinematic viscosity ($v$) | | | | | | | | |
| | Density ($\eta$) | | | | | | | | degree of acidity (pH) | | | | | | | | |
| Motor | Maker | | | Test certificate | | | | | Number of phases | | Voltage | | | | | | |
| | Type | | | Power | | | | | Speed of rotation | | Current | | | | | | |
| Measuring method | | Rates of flow | Inlet head | Outlet head | | (NPSH) | Torque | | Power | Speed of rotation | | Gea | | | | | |
| | Method used | | | | | | | | | | | | | | | | |
| | Constant | | | | | | | | | | | | | | | | |
| Test conditions | Room temperature  Temperature of test liquid | | | Barometric pressure | | | | | Head correction to reference plane | | Inlet  outlet | | | | | | |
| Results of measurement | | | | | | Units | 1 | 2 | 3 | 4 | 5 | 6 | 7 | 8 | 9 | 10 | 11 |
| | Speed of rotation | | | | | | | | | | | | | | | | |
| Flow rate | Time interval | | | | | | | | | | | | | | | | |
| | Reading | | | | | | | | | | | | | | | | |
| | Measured flow | | | | | | | | | | | | | | | | |
| Head | Outlet head reading | | | | | | | | | | | | | | | | |
| | Inlet head reading | | | | | | | | | | | | | | | | |
| | Outlet head | | | | | | | | | | | | | | | | |
| | Inlet head | | | | | | | | | | | | | | | | |
| | $\triangle v^2/2g$ | | | | | | | | | | | | | | | | |
| | Difference of measuring position | | | | | | | | | | | | | | | | |
| | Pump total head | | | | | | | | | | | | | | | | |
| | $r_s^2/2g$ | | | | | | | | | | | | | | | | |
| | (NPSH) | | | | | | | | | | | | | | | | |
| Power (torque) | Useful power ($P_u$) | | | | | | | | | | | | | | | | |
| | voltage | | | | | | | | | | | | | | | | |
| | current | | | | | | | | | | | | | | | | |
| | Wattmeter reading 1 | | | | | | | | | | | | | | | | |
| | Wattmeter reading 2 | | | | | | | | | | | | | | | | |
| | Total of wattmeter readings | | | | | | | | | | | | | | | | |
| | Motor power input | | | | | | | | | | | | | | | | |
| | Motor efficiency | | | | | | | | | | | | | | | | |
| | Torque reading | | | | | | | | | | | | | | | | |
| | Gear efficiency | | | | | | | | | | | | | | | | |
| | Motor power output | | | | | | | | | | | | | | | | |
| | Pump power input | | | | | | | | | | | | | | | | |
| | Overall efficiency | | | | | | | | | | | | | | | | |
| | Pump efficiency | | | | | | | | | | | | | | | | |
| Values referred to specified speed of rotation | Volume rate of flow | | | | | | | | | | | | | | | | |
| | Total head | | | | | | | | | | | | | | | | |
| | Power | | | | | | | | | | | | | | | | |
| | (NPSH) | | | | | | | | | | | | | | | | |
| Notes | | | | | | Date | | Chief of tests | | | Representative | | | | | | |
| | | | | | | | | | | | of the customer | | of the manufacture | | | | |

Fig. 8.2  **Pump test sheet** (Reproduced with permission from Appendix Z of BS 5316 Part 1 (1976)

The pump test sheet is given for guidance for presenting pump test results and to assist in their interpretation. It does not purport to include all the information required from a pump test and modifications may be necessary depending on the type of pump, its application, and the mode of calculation.

(a) *Arrangement for determining reference plane of Bourdon type gauge*

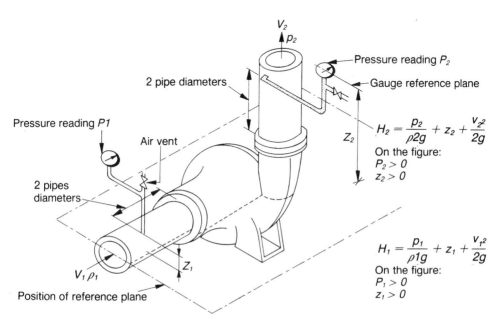

$$H_2 = \frac{p_2}{\rho 2g} + z_2 + \frac{v_2^2}{2g}$$

On the figure:
$P_2 > 0$
$z_2 > 0$

$$H_1 = \frac{p_1}{\rho 1g} + z_1 + \frac{v_1^2}{2g}$$

On the figure:
$P_1 > 0$
$z_1 > 0$

(b) *The pump inlet is under vacuum*

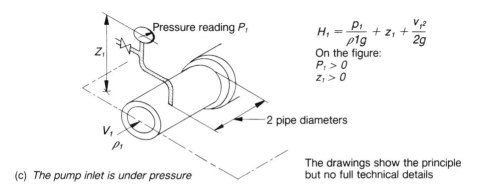

$$H_1 = \frac{p_1}{\rho 1g} + z_1 + \frac{v_1^2}{2g}$$

On the figure:
$P_1 > 0$
$z_1 > 0$

The drawings show the principle but no full technical details

(c) *The pump inlet is under pressure*

**Fig 8.3   Test of a centrifugal pump by means of Bourdon gauges** (Reproduced with permission from BS 5316 Part 1 (1976)

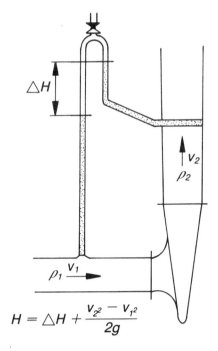

$$H = \triangle H + \frac{v_2^2 - v_1^2}{2g}$$

**Fig. 8.4 Direct measurement of pump total head** (using differential pressure device)
Reproduced with permission from BS 5316 Part 1 (1976)

gas being dealt with to prevent any failure due to possible corrosion, erosion or brittle fracture. With positive displacement compressors and exhausters relief valves should be fitted after each stage to avoid damage due to over-pressure. Cylinder discharge temperatures, etc. should not exceed 140°C in the case of oil-lubricated compressors to avoid oil decomposition and the possibility of an explosion. Temperature alarms should be fitted.

Seal and bearing materials and design should be considered to avoid possible leakage and deterioration. Any leakage of flammable and toxic vapours should be taken care of, perhaps by ventilation or piping to a safe location. Liquid separators should be fitted in suction lines, etc. if there is any possibility of free liquid entering a compressor stage and so giving rise to a hazardous condition.

Regular inspections should be carried out to check for any excessive temperature, pressure, vibration or noise. Seals and bearings should receive attention.

Some specifications dealing with compressors and exhausters, including acceptance testing, are given in Table 8.1.

## 8.3.1 Acceptance tests for compressors and exhausters

BS 1571 deals with the acceptance testing of positive displacement compressors and exhausters and is an International Standard. A positive displacement compressor is a machine where a static pressure rise is obtained by allowing successive volumes of air/gas to be aspired into and exhausted out of an enclosed space by means of the displacement of a moving member. The machine may be reciprocating or rotary.

Part 2 of the standard deals with simplified tests, only those measurements necessary to verify any guarantee or contract requirement being taken. A compressor on test will be acceptable provided the results obtained do not differ from the type test results (previously obtained in accordance with Part 1) by more than a given specified allowance (which for a 10 – 100 kW machine at 100% normal load, is ± 5% on capacity and ± 7% on specific energy consumption and at 50% normal load is ± 7% on capacity and ± 7% on specific energy consumption with an allowance on no load power of ± 20%.

Methods of measurement are laid down, and after a preliminary steadying run during which governing mechanisms and lubrication arrangements are checked, various test observations are recorded.

The principal observations and computations required include:

(a) Intake pressure and temperature (bar) (°C)
(b) Delivery pressure (bar or mm Hg)
(c) Speed (rev/sec)
(d) Power consumption (kW) (W)
(e) Capacity (FAD). This is computed from the actual volume rate of flow of air compressed and delivered, referred to conditions of total temperature, pressure and composition (e.g. humidity) prevailing at the inlet point (litre/sec.). It can be calculated from the formula:

$$q = k\frac{T_1}{p_1}\sqrt{\frac{h\,p_2}{T}}$$

where $q$ is inlet volume (litre/sec)
$h$ is pressure drop across measuring nozzle (mm $H_2O$)
$k$ is a constant for the nozzle
$T_1$ is the absolute temperature at the agreed inlet point
$T$ is the absolute temperature downstream from the nozzle
$p_1$ is the absolute pressure at the agreed inlet point (mm Hg)
$p_2$ is the absolute pressure downstream side of the nozzle (mm Hg)

Corrections may have to be made to the figures obtained. For instance:

$$\frac{\text{Corrected capacity}}{\text{(Free air displacement)}} = \frac{\text{test FAD} \times \text{guaranteed speed}}{\text{test speed}}$$

The specific energy consumption is the shaft input per unit of compressor capacity, i.e.

$$\frac{\text{energy consumption (W)}}{\text{FAD (litre/sec)}}$$

and is here expressed in joules per litre (J/L)

If other units are used the appropriate conversions must be made, e.g. specific energy consumption may be expressed in kWh/litre.

BS 2009 deals with acceptance tests for turbo-type compressors and exhausters and uses 1b/sq.in.abs., cu.ft/min., °F abs., ft1b/1b/°F, r.p.m. and horse power. It makes use of recommendations of the Compressed Air and Gas Institute of the USA.


## 8.4 Turbines

Perhaps turbines can be considered a particular form of turbo-exhauster, the gas in question being in the case of a gas turbine the high pressure and temperature products of combustion of usually a hydro-carbon oil, and in the case of a steam turbine high pressure and temperature steam. These gaseous working fluids exhaust down to a much lower pressure—in the case of a condensing steam turbine down to well below atmospheric pressure. To withstand such high temperatures and pressures the materials of construction have to be specially selected (see, for example, 2.2.)

Large steam turbine driven electrical generators form the basis of industrial power stations. Some applicable specifications are listed in Table 8.4. However detailed consideration of such matters will not be dealt with here. An excellent series of books is *Modern Power Station System Practice*, written by the CEGB for the IEE; Vol. G in particular deals with operation and maintenance and H with commissioning, etc. They should be seen by those desiring to study an up-to-date work on the subject.

Mention perhaps should be made of the theoretically very economic industrial practice of using steam to generate electricity by not exhausting it to vacuum in a condenser (as is the normal CEGB and power station practice) but using this steam for process work and the heating of hot water for industrial and/or domestic district heating. The now closed CEGB Battersea power station (built by the London Power Co. and once one of the country's largest) diverted some of its steam (via a back pressure turbine driven electrical generator) to heat a large housing estate on the other side of the River Thames. By such means power station thermal efficiencies of the order of 34% can be perhaps more than doubled. Such schemes, common on the continent, have found little favour in the UK (particularly with the CEGB), although a few UK industrial plants of this type exist (for acceptance tests on these see BS 5968). A combined heat and power (CHP) plant should preferably be located adjacent to an industrial estate and/or city centre, but city centre power stations have largely been phased out in recent years. In a similar manner the heat in the exhaust from a gas turbine (or a diesel engine) may be used to produce steam and hot water. For further details of CHP see: IEE President's inaugural address, 1986 (IEE Proceedings Part A, January 1987).

### 8.4.1 Acceptance tests on turbines

In general acceptance tests are carried out basically to demonstrate the fulfilment of contractual obligations which usually require proof of :

(i) Power output, normally the maximum continuous rating (MCR) at which the turbine may be operated continuously under specified conditions. An overload capacity test for a limited period and under certain other specified conditions may be required.

(ii) Heat (or steam) consumption at MCR and hence guaranteed heat rate. The guaranteed heat rate is for a stated output and specified conditions. Heat rate is the net flow to the turbine divided by the power output.

(iii) The correct working of the governor and overspeed systems as regards:

(a) Speed regulation. Speed must be controlled to specified conditions from no load to full load. Instantaneous removal of full load must be possible without excessive speed rise or trouble. For electrical generation the constant specified speed must be maintained at all loads with a possible adjustment or variation of $\pm 6\%$.

(b) Emergency overspeed trip. This has to operate at a speed not more than 11% over the rated speed.

Before undertaking any acceptance tests on a turbine inspection should ascertain that as far as possible all parts subject in service to a pressure above atmospheric have been tested hydraulically for leakage, etc. at a pressure at least 50% above that which could occur. After final assembly an inspection for correctness should be made and then a preliminary proving run carried out to ensure satisfactory operation. The turbine should run for at least 30 minutes before commencing measurements of consumption and the test should then last for an hour or more, readings being taken at intervals not greater than 5 minutes. The consumption (mass entering per hour ($M$/h) and the heat energy content (specific enthalpy) of the steam, etc. on entering and leaving ($H_1$ and $H_2$) expressed in $kJ$/kg) will be measured at such points, including any components such as reheaters, etc. as may be necessary.

The performance of a simple back pressure steam turbine generator can be expressed as a steam consumption rate as follows:

Let $M$ be the mass (kg) of steam entering the turbine per hour
   $H$ be the specific enthalpy of the steam at turbine stop valve (kJ/kg)
   $h$ be the specific enthalpy of the steam leaving the turbine (kJ/kg)
   $P$ be the electrical power output (kW)

then steam rate (in kg/kWh) $= M/P$ and heat rate (in kJ/kWH)
$$= M(H - h)/P.$$

Most turbines are far from simple, and comprise a number of stages, feed water heaters, reheaters, superheaters, etc. and a condenser and separately driven auxiliaries. The appropriate factor $M(H-h)$ must be determined for each item or component and summated to find the total heat energy (J) utilized by the turbine, before dividing by $P$. Heat rate is usually expressed in kJ per kWh (and not per kW-second (kWs)). Units other than SI can of course be used and may be asked for in the contract etc.

*8.4.2 Thermal efficiency*

Although the British Standards concerned with turbine acceptance (which are compatible with IEC Publication 46 *Recommendations for steam turbines*, Part 2: *Rules for acceptance tests*, as well as with UK practice) do not call specifically for a figure of thermal efficiency it may sometimes be required and can readily be calculated.

BS 752 in an appendix gives 14 tables of data and test measurements taken during acceptance testing of a typical power station turbo-generator. It concludes with a power output at the generator terminals of 522,826 kW and a heat rate of 7936·05 kJ/kWh.

BS 752 gives the following formula:

$$\text{Thermal efficiency \%} = \frac{100K}{\text{heat rate}}$$

(Alternatively if expressed as a ratio $\eta = K/\text{heat rate}$)
noting that: when heat rate is in kJ/kWs, then K $= 1·0$
          when heat rate is in kJ/kWh, then K $= 3600$

but in the test above heat rate has been measured in kJ/kWh (and as 1 hour (h) $= 3600$ seconds) so thermal efficiency then becomes 3600/heat rate. Inserting test results from above this becomes:

$$\text{Thermal efficiency } (\eta) = \frac{3600}{7936} = 0·453 \text{ or } 45·3\%$$

Alternatively: Output of electric energy in 1 hour $= 522,826 \times 3600$ kJ
          Input of heat in 1 hour          $= 7936 \times 522,826$ kJ

$$\text{then } \eta = \frac{\text{electric power output}}{\text{heat energy input}} = \frac{522{,}826 \times 3600}{7936 \times 522{,}826}$$

$$= \frac{3600}{7936} = 0\cdot453 \text{ as before.}$$

*Note 1:* This thermal efficiency is that of the turbo-generator only. To determine the overall thermal efficiency of the power station this figure must be multiplied by the thermal efficiency of the boiler plant. Assuming this to be some 75% then the power station efficiency should be 75% of 0·453 or some 34%.

*Note 2:* Using SI units it should be remembered that:

1 joule of work (J) per second is 1 watt (of power) and 1 watt-hour = 3600 joules

1 kWh = 3600 kilojoules (kJ)

Also thermal efficiency (using SI units J, W and sec.) becomes the reciprocal of heat rate.

## Further reading

Davidson, J. (ed.), *Process pump selection – a systems approach*, (I. Mech. E.), Mech. Eng. Pub., 1986.

*I. Mech. E. Conference papers*

Fluid machinery for the oil, petrochemical and related industries (papers on pumps, compressors, etc, including installation and testing), Mech. Eng. Pub. 1984/87.

Part load pumping – operation, control and behaviour, Mech. Eng. Pub. 1988.

Technical and economic impact of co-generation, Mech. Eng. Pub. 1986.

Turbomachinery – Efficiency prediction and improvements, Mech. Eng. Pub. 1987.

# 8 Mechanical pressure systems and vacuum plant

## Part 2 Vacuum plant and vacuum techniques

### 8.5 Introduction

Vacuum technology has continuously increased in importance since its first major industrial application in the electric lamp industry (from 1880 onwards), when pumps were designed to evacuate air from glass lamp bulbs to prevent rapid filament burn-out. The modern electronics industry also uses high-vacuum techniques in the manufacture of radio and television tubes, X-ray equipment, etc. Large power rectifiers can operate under high-vacuum conditions and are sometimes continuously pumped. Vacuum impregnation of transformer windings, coils, etc., is often specified to improve the insulation and performance of electrical equipment. Vacuum techniques are also exploited in the manufacture of semi-conductors, silicon chips, integrated circuits, etc.

Many chemical and industrial processes today make use of vacuum plant and techniques; examples are vacuum forming, vacuum distillation, sublimation and drying, the deposition of thin films by evaporation or sputtering (vacuum coating) and freeze drying. Vacuum metallurgy has developed from a laboratory technique to the stage where large industrial vacuum plants are used for the melting, processing, sintering and alloying of metals of all kinds, so ensuring the production of pure, gas-free and non-porous metal. Instruments using vacuum techniques are much used for the analysis and control of industrial processes. Vacuum leak testing has come into considerable use in recent years (see Chapter 11), whilst environmental testing facilities are required for simulating conditions at low pressures, such as those experienced at high altitudes and in free space. The development of atomic energy greatly increased the demand for high-vacuum plant.

This chapter includes a review of pumps for the attainment and instruments for the measurement of various degrees of vacua, together with such matters concerning vacuum plant as may be useful to an inspector. For more details of vacuum technology, and for diagrams of the equipment involved, reference should be made to works such as those listed at the end of the chapter.


## 8.6  Pressure and vacuum measurements and units

Commonly in engineering practice *pressures* were given as a conventional gauge reading; e.g. 100 lb/in$^2$ gauge (p.s.i.g.) means an absolute pressure of $100+$ atmospheric pressure (i.e. $100+$ some $14·7 = 114·7$ p.s.i.a. approximately). Again in conventional engineering a *vacuum* gauge reading of, say, 29 in of mercury assumes that a perfect vacuum is one of 30 in of mercury below that of the atmosphere, and in consequence corresponds to an absolute *pressure* of $30-29 = 1$ in of mercury, approximately. As atmospheric pressure is continually varying, such methods of expressing pressure lack precision. *In vacuum engineering all pressure (and vacuum) measurements are given as absolute pressures.*

The principal unit used has been the pressure exerted by a millimetre of mercury (mmHg), while the micrometre of mercury ($\mu$mHg), known colloquially as the micron of mercury ($\mu$Hg) or, loosely, just the 'micron' ($\mu$), has also been employed. However, by international agreement, the principal pressure unit used in vacuum technology was named the *torr* (after Torricelli, the Italian physicist). For all practical purposes the torr and the conventional barometric mmHg are identical and are equivalent to $\frac{1}{760}$th part of a standard atmosphere.

$1 \text{mmHg} = 1$ torr (to within one part in 7 million)

$1 \mu\text{mHg} = \frac{1}{1000}\text{mmHg} = 10^{-3}$ torr $= 1$ millitorr $= 1$ micron Hg

The correct SI unit of pressure (and stress) is the newton per square metre, (alternatively now termed the Pascal (Pa). This unit and its recommended multiples and sub-multiples should normally be used. However, the bar is used in certain fields, and was adopted on an interim basis for the initial expression of metric values of pressure (and stress) in certain British Standards. Some such standards specifying pressures relating to vessels, plant and equipment still use bars, hectobars and millibars. However, in high-vacuum work, the N/m$^2$ (or pascal) with its sub-multiples is recommended for future use in preference to the torr or mmHg.

Under a ruling by CGPM the torr, mmHg, mmH$_2$O, in Hg, in w.g. (water gauge) and technical atmosphere should cease to be used for legal purposes. However, the bar was allowed to continue perhaps temporarily in use with SI to express fluid pressure, whilst much of the existing literature on high vacuum makes use of the torr (the further use of which is generally deprecated by CGPM).

Perhaps because of such CGPM and EEC rulings, many high vacuum specialists and industry currently prefer to make more use of the bar rather than pure SI, whilst academic and scientific circles use SI. However, industry will supply equipment marked or calibrated in any of the above-mentioned units which may be specified.

As the bar and its multiples and sub-multiples, particularly the millibar, are widely used in certain field such as meteorology throughout Europe (and by British industry), and as they are all simply related by powers of ten to the recognized but extremely small SI unit, the pascal (and furthermore as the bar has a 'mental yardstick' relationship with atmospheric pressure — which the pascal does not), it is considered by many to be the most suitable unit for use by industry with SI for fluid pressure measurement.

Some pressure units and their respective relationships are given in Table 8.3 (a). See also Fig. 8.1 and Table A.3 (in the Appendix).

It may help in high vacuum work to remember:

1 bar = 100,000 pascals or 750 torr (mm Hg)
1 pascal = $10^{-5}$ bar = $10^{-2}$ mbar or 3/4 torr ÷ 100
1 torr = 4/3 pascal × 100 = 1.333 mbar
1 mbar = 100 Pa = 3/4 torr

Note that the millibar and the torr (and mm of mercury) are of the same order of magnitude and for *very rough* comparisons may be regarded as equivalent.

Similarly with SI units for volume and flow rate, *volume* is expressed in cubic metres ($m^3$) and *flow rate* in cubic metres per second ($m^3s^{-1}$). But European practice and British vacuum technology makes much use of the litre (now re-defined by CGPM as the cubic decimetre, but not sued to express high-precision measurements) which now has a simple relationship with SI:

1 litre = 1 $dm^3$ = $10^{-3}$ $m^3$ (one thousandth of a cubic metre exactly)
1000 litres = 1 cubic metre

Consequently volume flow rates (pumping speeds) in industry are often expressed in litres per unit of time (see Table 8.3 (b)). Similarly, mass flow rates (and leak-rates) using pure SI units may be expressed as Pa $m^3$ $s^{-1}$, or in industry as mbar L $s^{-1}$ (see 11.2).

Fluid pressure depends upon the number of molecules hitting a surface per unit of time. When pressure becomes lower the number of molecules decreases. At the top of Mount Everest the rarified atmosphere exerts a pressure of about 1/3 of that existing at sea level (and hence good tea cannot be made since water boils there at a considerably lower temperature).

At a height above the earth's surface of some 800 km pressure drops to about $10^{-9}$ torr and a particular molecule would then have to travel some 50 km before hitting another molecule (this distance is known as the *mean free path*). But even so there would be more molecules colliding with a

# TABLE 8.3

*Conversion charts for pressure etc.*

## (a) Some pressure units and their relationships

| | mbar | bar | torr | Pa (Nm⁻²) | atm | lbf in⁻² | kgf cm⁻² | in Hg | mm Hg | in H₂O | mm H₂O |
|---|---|---|---|---|---|---|---|---|---|---|---|
| 1 mbar = | 1 | $1\times10^{-3}$ | 0·75 | $10^2$ | $9\cdot869\times10^{-4}$ | $1\cdot45\times10^{-2}$ | $1\cdot02\times10^{-3}$ | $2\cdot953\times10^{-2}$ | 0·75 | 0·402 | 10·197 |
| 1 bar = | $10^3$ | 1 | $7\cdot5\times10^2$ | $1\times10^5$ | 0·987 | 14·5 | 1·02 | 29·53 | $7\cdot5\times10^2$ | $4\cdot015\times10^2$ | $1\cdot02\times10^4$ |
| 1 torr = | 1·333 | $1\cdot333\times10^{-3}$ | 1 | $1\cdot333\times10^2$ | $1\cdot316\times10^{-3}$ | $1\cdot934\times10^{-2}$ | $1\cdot36\times10^{-3}$ | $3\cdot937\times10^{-2}$ | 1 | 0·535 | 13·59 |
| 1 Pa (Nm⁻²) = | 0·01 | $1\times10^{-5}$ | $7\cdot5\times10^{-3}$ | 1 | $9\cdot87\times10^{-4}$ | $1\cdot45\times10^{-4}$ | $1\cdot02\times10^{-5}$ | $2\cdot953\times10^{-4}$ | $7\cdot5\times10^{-3}$ | $4\cdot015\times10^{-3}$ | 0·102 |
| 1 atm = | $1\cdot013\times10^3$ | 1·013 | $7\cdot6\times10^2$ | $1\cdot013\times10^5$ | 1 | 14·7 | 1·033 | 29·92 | $7\cdot6\times10^2$ | $4\cdot068\times10^2$ | $1\cdot033\times10^4$ |
| 1 lbf in⁻² = | 68·95 | $6\cdot895\times10^{-2}$ | 51·71 | $6\cdot895\times10^3$ | $6\cdot805\times10^{-2}$ | 1 | $7\cdot03\times10^{-2}$ | 2·036 | 51·71 | 27·68 | $7\cdot03\times10^2$ |
| 1 kgf cm⁻² = | $9\cdot807\times10^2$ | 0·981 | $7\cdot356\times10^2$ | $9\cdot807\times10^4$ | 0·968 | 14·22 | 1 | 28·96 | $7\cdot356\times10^2$ | $3\cdot937\times10^2$ | $10^4$ |
| 1 in Hg = | 33·86 | $3\cdot386\times10^{-2}$ | 25·4 | $3\cdot386\times10^3$ | $3\cdot342\times10^{-2}$ | 0·491 | $3\cdot453\times10^{-2}$ | 1 | 25·4 | 13·6 | $3\cdot45\times10^2$ |
| 1 mm Hg = | 1·333 | $1\cdot333\times10^{-3}$ | 1 | $1\cdot333\times10^2$ | $1\cdot316\times10^{-3}$ | $1\cdot934\times10^{-2}$ | $1\cdot36\times10^{-3}$ | $3\cdot937\times10^{-2}$ | 1 | 0·535 | 13·59 |
| 1 in H₂O = | 2·491 | $2\cdot491\times10^{-3}$ | 1·868 | $2\cdot491\times10^2$ | $2\cdot458\times10^{-3}$ | $3\cdot613\times10^{-2}$ | $2\cdot54\times10^{-3}$ | $7\cdot356\times10^{-2}$ | 1·868 | 1 | 25·4 |
| 1 mm H₂O = | $9\cdot807\times10^{-2}$ | $9\cdot807\times10^{-5}$ | $7\cdot354\times10^{-2}$ | 9·807 | $9\cdot677\times10^{-5}$ | $1\cdot42\times10^{-3}$ | $10^{-4}$ | $2\cdot896\times10^{-3}$ | $7\cdot354\times10^{-2}$ | $3\cdot394\times10^{-2}$ | 1 |

Note also: 1 dyn cm⁻² (barye) = 0·1 Pa (Nm⁻²) = 10⁻³ mbar

1 standard atmosphere (atm) = pressure exerted per square centimetre by a mercury column 760 mm high (at sea level and 0°C)

1 technical atmosphere (atu) = 1kgf/cm²

In France a bar may be termed a hectopieze (hpz)
1 tonf/in² = 1·575 kgf/m² = 15·444 MN/m²
1 kilobar (approx. 1000 atm) = 6·47 tonf/in²

*Note:* When the bar is used in standards and other publications (usually restricted to express fluid pressure) it is recommended by the British Standards Institution that a note showing its relationship with the SI unit should be given on each relevant page (e.g. 1 bar = 10⁵N/m² = 0·1N/mm² = 100 kPa; 1 hbar = 10⁷ N/m²; 1 mbar = 10² N/m² = 100 Pa)

## (b) Pumping speed units

| | Ls⁻¹ | Lmin⁻¹ | ft³ min⁻¹ | m³ h⁻¹ |
|---|---|---|---|---|
| 1 Ls⁻¹ = | 1 | 60 | 2·12 | 3·60 |
| 1 Lmin⁻¹ = | 0·0167 | 1 | 0·0353 | 0·06 |
| 1 ft³ min⁻¹ = | 0·472 | 28·32 | 1 | 1·70 |
| 1 m³ h⁻¹ = | 0·278 | 16·67 | 0·589 | 1 |

**TABLE 8.4**

*Classification of pressure ranges*

| mbar | torr (mmHg) | SI (Pa) |
| --- | --- | --- |
| $10^3$ to 1 | 760 to 1—coarse (rough) vacuum | 101,325 to 133 |
| 1 to $10^{-3}$ | 1 to $10^{-3}$—medium high vacuum | 133 to 0·133 |
| $10^{-3}$ to $10^{-8}$ | $10^{-3}$ to $10^{-6}$—high vacuum | 0·133 to 1·3 $\times$ $10^{-4}$ |
| Below $10^{-8}$ | Below $10^{-6}$—ultra-high vacuum | Below 1·3 $\times$ $10^{-4}$ |

*Note:* The absolute pressure in a vacuum type tungsten filament lamp is $10^{-3}$ to $10^{-2}$ torr; in a cathode-ray television tube it is some $10^{-6}$ torr; whilst in free space it may be from $10^{-9}$ to $10^{-14}$ torr.

surface in space than with other molecules, hence space can hardly be considered as empty.

In vacuum technology pressures below atmospheric can be classified as shown in Table 8.4.

### 8.7 Mechanical vacuum pumps

Rough vacuum can be attained by using mechanical exhaust pumps. The early forms of piston type pumps have largely been superseded by various rotary pumps. For comparatively large mass flows at absolute pressures down to the order of 10 torr, various forms of turbine type exhauster are used, the blades of which are interleaved, as in steam or gas turbine practice. Some large installations of this kind are used for the full power testing of gas turbine aero engines under high-altitude conditions. The driving power absorbed may run into some 20,000 kW.

Another type of rotary pump which can deal with large volumes of air in the rough vacuum range operates on the water-ring principle. The impeller is arranged eccentrically, or in an elliptical casing, and as it turns water is flung outwards and forms a rotating and pulsating water ring which draws gas through the intake ports and forces it out through the discharge ports. The water acts as a seal, a lubricant and a coolant; some is discharged with the gas, a water separator being fitted on the discharge side. Pressures down to some 1 in Hg (25 torr) can be attained. Such pumps may be used in process plants for extracting gases and vapours from evaporators, filters, etc., and for vacuum drying, degassing, etc; also as compressors up to some two or more atmospheres. Again, multi-unit installations absorbing several thousand horsepower can be provided if required.

Explosive gases and vapours, and those containing dust, liquid or aggressive materials can be safely handled, as there are no metallic parts to rub against one another. No oil is required, hence the gas handled cannot become contaminated by oil vapours.

## 8.8  Rotary oil pumps

For the attainment of vacua down to the order of $10^{-2}$ torr, various proprietary types of oil-sealed rotary vacuum pumps are employed. A steel rotor is eccentrically mounted in a cylindrical casing and is slotted to accommodate two vanes held apart by a spring. On rotation the vanes are held tightly against the inner wall by the action of the spring and by centrifugal force. Air is trapped in the space between the rotor and the casing, is compressed by the vane and finally forces open the exhaust valve and escapes to atmosphere. The working parts are submerged in oil, which, besides serving as a lubricant, forms a film between the rotating and stationary parts which prevents air leaking back in the high-vacuum side. The ultimate vacuum which can be achieved is limited by the dead volume in the exhaust valve outlet pipe and by air leakage past the seals.

A variation of this type of pump is the Kinney pump, which uses a rotary eccentric piston instead of a vane. Large Kinney pumps are water-cooled.

Multi-stage rotary oil pumps can be used to produce a lower ultimate pressure and greater displacement than a single-stage unit.

### 8.8.1  Pumping speed

*Displacement* or *pumping speed* is understood to mean the volume of gas removed per unit of time. It is not constant throughout the pump's working range, but is proportional to the pressure on the intake side. To compare the characteristics of different pumps it is usual to specify the pumping speeds of rotary pumps at atmospheric pressure. When working on its lowest attainable pressure the displacement of a pump will approach zero; normally rotary pumps are used at somewhat higher pressures.

Pumping speed units commonly used in vacuum work and their relationship to one another are given in Table 8.3(b).

### 8.8.2  Gas ballasting

A rotary oil pump, in removing gas from a vacuum system at very low pressure, has to compress it through a large compression ratio of the order of 760:1 or more, so that it can be ejected to the atmosphere. Inspectors should note that if the gases removed are 'permanent' gases, no great difficulties arise, but should vapours be present, as they usually are in practice, these will condense out during compression. Such condensed vapours will contaminate the pump oil (possibly causing sludging). This contaminated oil will return to the high-vacuum side of the pump and the condensed vapour will re-expand and so reduce the capacity of the pump at the next and subsequent strokes. Its vapour pressure will also reduce the ultimate pressure attainable by the pump. Large quantities of vapours often have to be evacuated in process work, whilst water vapour is normally present as it is evolved, at least, from the thin film of water which invariably clings to the walls of the vessel being evacuated. All these vapours can condense and contribute to the poor performance of a vacuum pump.

One much used method of preventing condensation in rotary oil vacuum pumps is to use 'gas ballast'. The principle involved is to admit sufficient air into the trapped space between rotor and casing during the compression stroke to reduce the compression ratio and prevent condensation. A valve is provided by which the admission of air from the atmosphere to this trapped space can be controlled from zero to about 10% of the displacement of the pump. When the gas ballast facility is being used the ultimate pressure otherwise obtainable is impaired because the gas pressure across the seals between inlet and exhaust is greatly increased with a corresponding increase in leakage. For instance, a typical Kinney pump might achieve, unballasted, an ultimate pressure of $1 \cdot 3 \times 5 \times 10^{-3}$ mbar, but will only give 7μbar when the gas ballast facility is full on.

Other methods of preventing contamination of oil by condensable vapours are used in particular applications. For instance, the whole system can be maintained at a temperature of 230°F (110°C), which will be sufficient to prevent trouble due to condensation of water vapour. The oil can be separated or centrifuged. Refrigerated traps may also be used. Drain traps should be provided at any point where there is a likelihood of vapour being condensed after passing through the pump, to prevent it from dropping back into the oil reservoir.

## 8.9 Roots pumps

When large displacements are necessary and the exhaust contains large quantities of gases and vapours at pressures in the medium high-vacuum range and below, as in many industrial and metallurgical processes, the gas ballast pump alone is inadequate. The Roots type pump, with a gas ballast rotary oil pump as a backing pump, forms a useful combination. The Roots pump, similar to the old-established Roots type air blower, is a high-speed pump having two interweaving rotary impellers, but no oil-sealing fluid between them. These impellers rotate in opposite directions and each is shaped somewhat like a figure 8. Inspection must ensure that the air gap between them, and with the housing, is kept extremely small, so restricting the amount of 'back-streaming' at low pressures. The ultimate pressure obtainable, when used with a suitable backing pump, may be better than $10^{-4}$ torr in certain cases. If used at intake pressures above some 2–5 torr over-heating and seizure may occur; for this reason a by-pass and a pressure-relief valve are usually fitted.

## 8.10 Vapour (diffusion) pumps

In the high-vacuum range, to attain pressures down to the order of $10^{-6}$ torr ($1 \cdot 3 \times 10^{-4}$ Pa), and below use is made almost exclusively of vapour pumps in which the gases to be pumped off are moved by means of a high-velocity vapour stream (or jet). These are generally known as diffusion pumps, and always exhaust to a suitable backing pump, usually of the rotary oil type. The vapour stream is obtained by boiling mercury or suitable oil. A boiler contains the pump fluid, which is heated by an electric element and caused to evaporate. The vapour streams through nozzles at supersonic velocity, finally condensing on the water-cooled walls of the chamber and returning under gravity as a liquid to the boiler. The vapour streams form, in effect, partitions between the upper and lower parts of the pump. Gas molecules in the upper part diffuse into the jet and are carried to a zone of higher pressure in the lower part, where they are removed by the backing pump. The force of the jet is sufficient to compress the pumped-off gas to a pressure of several tenths of a torr (a compression ratio of 1:100,000 approx.), and the backing pump must be suitable (even if gas-ballasted) to maintain this pressure.

There is a small chance of gas molecules in the lower parts of the pump penetrating the vapour partitions and 'back-streaming' into the upper part. To prevent this a baffle may be fitted in the pump intake.

Most vapour pumps (except small portable air-cooled models) require a constant supply of cooling water, and, should this fail, considerable damage may be caused. It is thus highly advisable to install a safety switch which will in that event switch off the heater.

Diffusion pumps using mercury vapour were first used, the mercury neither decomposing nor oxidizing greatly should there be a sudden inrush of air. Their main disadvantage is that, to obtain low ultimate pressures, they must be used with a liquid air (or similar) cold trap to freeze out the mercury vapour, which at room temperature has a vapour pressure of approximately $10^{-3}$ torr. This vapour can however sometimes be tolerated, e.g. when pumps are used in industry for evacuating such things as rectifiers and discharge tubes which will eventually contain mercury.

Oil vapour diffusion pumps use a variety of oils based on hydrocarbons, silicones and esters, which have vapour pressures ranging between $10^{-4}$ and $10^{-8}$ torr, consequently it is not generally necessary to use cold traps, although a water-cooled baffle may be fitted. Therefore the majority of industrial high-vacuum processes use oil diffusion pumps. Their principal disadvantage is that the oils tend to be unstable and to decompose should there be an inrush of air, which must therefore be avoided as far as possible.

As regards the ultimate vacuum attainable there is little to choose between selected types of oil and mercury vapour pumps. Using selected oil, certain diffusion pumps can attain better than $5 \times 10^{-6}$ torr, which is about the same as that readily attainable by a mercury pump with a liquid air cold trap. Under laboratory conditions and using the colder liquid nitrogen $(-196°C)$ a mercury pump can attain $10^{-7}$ or $10^{-8}$ torr, but so possibly can a suitable oil pump using a silicone oil. The pumping speed of oil pumps is in general higher than the equivalent sized mercury pumps.

Frequently large industrial plants require pumps capable of producing large displacements at pressures in the medium high-vacuum range but beyond the capabilities of rotary pumps, whose displacements would be small at around $10^{-1}$ to $10^{-2}$ torr. Large *booster* and *ejector* type pumps have been developed for such duties. Their design is similar to diffusion pumps, but their characteristics are determined largely by the diffusion rate of the removed gases in the jet and by the expansion of the supersonic jet. The diffusion process is slowed down compared with high-vacuum diffusion pumps. Booster diffusion pumps can give good speeds in the pressure range $10^{-2}$ to $10^{-4}$ torr, and ejector booster pumps in the range $10^{-1}$ to $10^{-2}$ torr.

Steam ejector pumps are often used to evacuate large industrial vacuum installations in the rough vacuum range down to a few torr.

## 8.11  Cryo-pumping

A cold trap or cold surface situated in a vacuum system can act as a pumping agent, since gases are deposited on the cold area in the same manner as water vapour from the atmosphere is deposited on a cold window pane. By using a particular cryogenic fluid (e.g. liquid air, oxygen, hydrogen, helium, etc.) the various vapours in the system and then air, hydrogen or helium may be deposited, the pressure in the chamber being reduced to the vapour pressure of the corresponding condensed gas. Ultimate vacua down to the order of $10^{-9}$ torr may be achieved.

Cryo-pumps backed by suitable high-vacuum pumping installations offer advantages where high pumping speeds down to very high vacua are required, and applications may include large space chambers, process plant, and equipment for depositing metallic films for industrial and electronic use.

## 8.12  Vacuum measurement

The accurate measurement of the low pressures encountered in high-vacuum work is basically a laboratory job. The instruments and gauges used in industrial plant for this purpose must therefore be adapted so that they can stand up reasonably well to the rigorous conditions likely to be found.

The effects of wide variations in ambient conditions, high temperatures, vibration, contaminated site conditions, fluctuating electrical supplies, etc., can largely be overcome by suitable design, followed by appropriate testing and inspection. Contamination of the inside of instruments and gauge elements, due for instance to some industrial process being monitored, may however present problems and may affect the accuracy of the readings obtained. A systematic maintenance schedule, involving periodic cleaning and calibration checks, is strongly recommended, especially where conditions are likely to be 'dirty'.

Different methods of measurement are adopted depending on the range required, which can vary from atmospheric pressure (about 27 million tons per square mile) to say $10^{-9}$ torr (only $1\frac{1}{4}$ ounces per square mile).

At pressures below, say, 1 torr it is necessary to supply some form of energy to the gas in order to operate the measuring device: as either the mechanical energy of compression (as in the McLeod gauge), heat energy from an electrical source (as in thermal conductivity gauges), electrical energy from thermionic emission, or even radioactive energy.

Most methods at these low pressures register the total pressure, i.e. the sum of the partial pressures of all the gases and vapours present (including vapours from oil, water, mercury and the materials of construction), and, for most, the calibration will be different for each gas and vapour. Consequently interpretation of the reading of such a gauge will be difficult when accuracy is required and conditions are subject to variation.

One method (compression gauges of the McLeod type) measures the partial pressure of the permanent gases only and, when used with suitable precautions, is a standard gauge by reference to which all other types may be calibrated.

When testing equipment it is important to realize this distinction between total and partial pressure and the limitations of the various vacuum gauges used, as their readings may differ widely when connected to the same equipment, and can be very misleading.

Table 8.5 shows the types of gauges available and their approximate range.

## 8.13 Liquid and mechanical manometers and gauges

For measuring pressures from around atmospheric down to about $0 \cdot 25$ torr the basic method is to use a liquid U-tube type manometer containing mercury. For small pressure differences a less dense liquid can be used. For greater accuracy of measurement at these small pressure differences the manometer can be inclined (as in the glove box test shown in Fig. 6.1): it may contain water or oil and will measure pressure differences readily to $0 \cdot 01$ in water gauge (some $0 \cdot 02$ torr).

$$\text{Pressure difference (mmHg)} = \frac{\text{difference in level of liquid } (h(\text{mm})) \times \text{density of liquid used}}{\text{relative density of Hg } (13.6)}$$

# TABLE 8.5
*Gauges for measuring vacuum*

| Type of gauge, etc. | Pressure range (torr) | Indication |
|---|---|---|
| Mechanical manometers | $10^3 \longrightarrow 10^0$ — — | Total pressure |
| Micro manometers | $10^0 \longrightarrow 10^{-3}$ | Total pressure |
| Liquid manometers | $10^3 \longrightarrow 10^0$ — | Total pressure |
| Liquid manometers (inclined) | $10^3$ — — $\longrightarrow 10^{-2}$ | Total pressure |
| Vacustat | $10^1 \longrightarrow 10^{-2}$ — — | Partial pressure |
| McLeod | $10^1 \longrightarrow 10^{-5}$ — — | Partial pressure |
| Thermal conductivity | $10^1 \longrightarrow 10^{-4}$ | Total pressure |
| HF spark tester (glow discharge) | $10^2 \longrightarrow 10^{-3}$ | Total pressure |
| Penning cold cathode | $10^{-2} \longrightarrow 10^{-5}$ — — | Total pressure |
| Hot cathode ionization | $10^{-3} \longrightarrow 10^{-7}$ — — | Total pressure |
| Alphatron | $10^3 \longrightarrow 10^{-4}$ | Total pressure |
| Mass spectrometer (e.g. AEI MS 10) | $10^{-4} \longrightarrow 10^{-10}$ | Can record partial pressures of constituent gases down to $10^{-11}$ |

*Type of gas.* For gauges above the dotted line, calibration independent of the gas; for those below, it is not.

*Note:* 1 torr = 133.3 pascals = 1.333 millibar

Mechanical instruments of the Bourdon tube, diaphragm, capsule or bellows type, relying on mechanical deformation of an elastic member, cover a somewhat similar range. By connecting this member to a transducer an electrical signal can be obtained and read as a change of pressure on a suitable instrument, if necessary at a distance. Various micro-manometers employing strain gauges, or inductive and capacitative effects, have been developed which extend the minimum pressure difference detectable to, say, $\frac{1}{1000}$th of that possible with a normal mechanical manometer.

The readings of all these mechanical manometers and gauges are pressure difference readings with respect to some reference pressure, often that of the atmosphere. Thus:

Gas pressure in system = barometric or reference pressure *minus* pressure due to height of liquid or gauge reading ($h$)

Instead of using the atmosphere as a reference pressure, one limb of the gauge or manometer may be connected to an auxiliary pumping system, or it may be sealed off (at perhaps nominally zero pressure) to provide the reference pressure and so give a nominally direct reading.

## 8.14 The McLeod gauge

The McLeod gauge is essentially a glass laboratory instrument. As it can be calibrated from its physical dimensions, when used with gases which obey Boyle's law, it is generally accepted as the standard for absolute measurement of pressure and is used for calibrating other gauges. However, reasonably robust McLeod gauges are much used commercially for vacuum measurement and for checking the performance of vacuum pumps, etc., whilst adaptations of it (notably the tilting McLeod gauge or 'Vacustat') can be incorporated into industrial plant.

The principle is as follows. Mercury is used to compress a known volume of the gas under test into a much smaller volume, the resulting pressure being measured. By applying Boyle's law, the original pressure of the gas can then be determined. Referring to Fig. 8.5, when the gauge is connected to the vacuum system under test mercury will rise up the main tube to a height above the reservoir approximately equal to the barometric pressure. To take a reading of the gas pressure $p$, the mercury reservoir is raised, and the mercury level rises above a Y branch in the main tube, thus isolating a definite volume $V_1$ of the residual gas in a bulb plus a closed capillary tube A. The reservoir is then gently raised further until the mercury meniscus in the parallel capillary tube B is level with the top of the inside of the closed capillary A (corresponding to zero on the scale). Volume $V_1$ has now been compressed into the much smaller volume $V_2$ (represented by the cross-

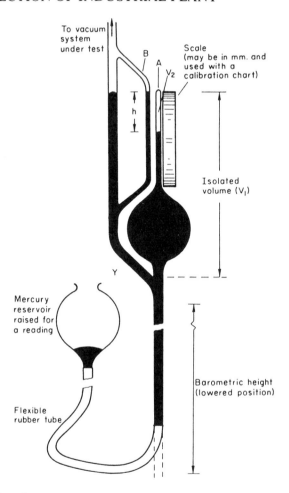

**Fig. 8.5  McLeod gauge.**
An alternative method of raising the mercury to the correct level is to keep the
reservoir under vacuum and admit air when a reading is required.

sectional area $a$ of the capillary A multiplied by $h$); its pressure is now also
measurable as the difference in mercury levels ($h$). Then by Boyle's law:

$$V_1 p = V_2 h = ah \times h = ah^2$$
$$\text{and } p \text{ (mmHg)} = ah^2/V_1$$

where $a$ and $V_1$ are constant for a particular gauge.

Calibration is carried out by accurately determining the trapped volume
($V_1$) of the bulb plus that of the closed capillary and checking the uniformity

of the bore of capillary A. It will be seen that the pressure scale obeys a square law and is spread out at low pressures. Even so, a large trapped volume and fine capillary are needed to secure a measurable value of $h$ at pressures of the order of $10^{-4}$ torr, whilst at pressures below say $10^{-6}$ torr there is a tendency for the mercury to stick at the top of the capillary A.

Generally speaking, the high degree of compression used in a McLeod gauge results in the liquefaction of any vapour, etc., in the gas sample from the vacuum system under test. Consequently the vapour pressures of water, mercury and other substances present are not measured, and the gauge in general only records the pressure of the permanent gases. This can be an advantage, particularly for calibration purposes.

It is often desirable to prevent the mercury vapour from getting into the vacuum system by using a refrigerated trap, usually containing liquid nitrogen. Continuous pressure readings are, of course, not obtainable with the gauge, as a considerable time is taken for each reading. A large McLeod gauge is used by NPL for calibration purposes; it is baked before taking a reading to remove occluded gases.

## 8.15 Thermal conductivity gauges

If an electrically heated filament is connected to a vacuum system at low pressure (below, say, 10 torr), then the transfer of heat by conduction through the gas is proportional to this pressure. At around $10^{-4}$ torr the heat transfer by conduction becomes small compared with that by radiation, and it disappears entirely with a perfect vacuum, when the heat transfer is by radiation only. Consequently, with a given voltage applied to the filament the temperature it attains (and thus its resistance) will depend on the thermal conductivity of the gas surrounding the filament, which varies with the pressure. Consequently a circuit may be set up to measure the degree of vacuum attained.

*The Pirani gauge* ia a thermal conductivity vacuum gauge in which a filament of tungsten (enclosed in a glass bulb which is connected to the vacuum system) forms one arm of a Wheatstone Bridge network.

A current passing through the filament will raise its temperature and hence its resistance—a definite resistance corresponding to a definite temperature—but the temperature of the filament will depend on the gas pressure surrounding it. By adjusting the voltage so that the bridge is balanced at some specific gas pressure, other gas pressures can be determined by measuring the out-of-balance current due to the change of resistance.

By making several modifications to the simple Pirani gauge its performance can be improved. A sealed-off reference gauge of known internal pressure can be inserted in the other bridge arm to compensate for external temperature changes which would otherwise affect the reading. The out-of-balance measuring galvanometer can be made more sensitive, but this necessitates a stabilized power supply to the bridge circuit. A more complex vacuum-balanced Pirani gauge has a four-element gauge head (consisting of two separate tubes connected to the vacuum system and two sealed-off reference tubes, one at low and one at atmospheric pressure), in which the bridge is balanced both at low pressure ($10^{-5}$ torr) and at high pressure (atmospheric).

*Thermocouple vacuum gauge.* An alternative to the Pirani type gauge is obtainable in which a thermocouple is attached to the hot filament. The e.m.f. set up by this thermocouple, which will be proportional to the filament temperature and hence to the gas pressure, can be read from a meter calibrated in terms of pressure.

Thermal conductivity gauges are normally available for measuring from 0.1 to $10^{-4}$ torr. By using a very thin wire filament in the Pirani element, and holding it at constant temperature, it is possible to extend the range to measure up to some 70 torr.

All thermal conductivity type gauges have to be calibrated and re-calibrated periodically by reference to some primary standard such as the McLeod gauge, measurements generally being made using dry air. When used with other gases or vapours a suitable calibration factor or a calibration chart must be employed.

Gauges of this type suffer from a gradual deterioration in accuracy with use and will gradually read high, because of contamination of the filament by the various gases and vapours. This can be combated to some extent by arranging periodically to 'flash' the filament by passing a heavier current than normal through it, so cleaning it. For use under dirty industrial conditions, special filaments have been developed which are relatively rough and blackened on the surface, and which will maintain reasonable accuracy.

## 8.16 Ionization gauges

(i) *Glow discharge tube.* A glass tube containing two electrodes is sometimes connected into a vacuum system to give an indication of the degree of vacuum attained. When a high voltage or high frequency is applied between these electrodes (sometimes the metal frame of the vacuum system forms one electrode) a glow discharge occurs at a pressure of around a few torr. As the pressure is reduced the colour and shape of the discharge changes and this affords a rough idea of the pressure and nature of the gas. This discharge 'blacks out' at around $10^{-2}$ torr. The actual pressures at which it is initiated and blacks out will depend on voltage, frequency and electrode shape. A somewhat conflicting factor is that the tube does not glow at high pressures, nor at very low pressures, but usually experience will prevent any confusion. The discharge point of a high-frequency Tesla coil (operating at say 4 Mc/s), if applied to a glass system, will cause a characteristic green glow in the glass work which gradually disappears as the high vacuum increases (Table 8.6).

**TABLE 8.6**

*Vacuum indication by high-voltage discharge tube (30 kV at 4 Mc/s)*

| Effect (air only in soda glass tubing) | Approx. pressure (torr) |
|---|---|
| No discharge in the tube | Atmospheric |
| Purple streamers radiating into tube | 350–300 |
| Sharp purple streamers radiating into tube | 300–60 |
| Streamers beginning to lose their sharpness | 60–40 |
| Streamers diffuse | 20–5 |
| No definite streamers but diffuse purple glow (discharge tinged with bluish glow) | Below $1 \cdot 0$ |
| Bluish diffuse glow with green fluorescence on walls of tube | $0 \cdot 5$–$0 \cdot 1$ |
| Pale blue diffuse glow with green fluorescence on walls | $0 \cdot 1$–$0 \cdot 01$ |
| Very pale whitish-blue glow with more pronounced green fluorescence | $0 \cdot 01$–$0 \cdot 001$ |
| Feeble glow in the body of the tube and green fluorescence on walls | $0 \cdot 001$–$0 \cdot 005$ |
| No discharge at all in body of tube and feeble green fluorescence | $0 \cdot 0005$–$0 \cdot 0001$ |
| No discharge and no fluorescence | Below $0 \cdot 0001$ |

*(Courtesy Genevac Ltd.)*
*Note:* 1 torr $= 133 \cdot 3$ pascals $= 1 \cdot 333$ millibar

(ii) *Cold cathode ionization (Penning) gauge.* The simple glow discharge tube can be adapted to measure lower pressures by using a different electrode arrangement and causing the discharge to take place in a strong magnetic field. Electrons are accelerated towards a ring anode, but owing to the magnetic field they follow continuous spiral paths before eventually reaching the anode. In so doing they collide with and ionize far more gas molecules than does the simple glow discharge tube. The total discharge current, being proportional to the number of molecules present and hence to the pressure, can be measured using a suitable circuit. The electrode assembly can be mounted inside a suitable glass tube connected to the vacuum system, or it may be in the form of a metal gauge-head for mounting inside large industrial type high-vacuum plant. The pressure range covered may extend from $10^{-3}$ to $10^{-6}$ torr. Owing to the spiral action of the electrons within the magnetic field, gauges of this type are sometimes known as magnetron gauges.

(iii) *Hot cathode ionization gauge.* Basically this type of gauge depends on the principle of the thermionic valve. Electrons are emitted from a carefully controlled heated filament and are accelerated towards an electrode held at a positive potential. These electrons will ionize any gas molecules with which they collide, and, as the number of molecules present depends on the gas pressure, the ionization current will be proportional to this gas pressure.

In a common arrangement of hot cathode ionization gauge, the measuring tube is designed in the form of a triode valve with its grid positively charged with respect to the cathode. An electron current, which is maintained constant, flows from the heated cathode to the grid. The positive ions formed by collision with gas molecules in this space are collected by a third electrode which is maintained at a negative potential with respect to the cathode. This ion current is amplified by a suitable amplifier and indicated on the measuring instrument, calibrated in torr (a suitable range circuit being provided).

Various designs can be made to cover the pressure range $10^{-3}$ to $5 \times 10^{-8}$ torr or thereabouts. A disadvantage of this type of gauge is the sensitive nature of the hot cathode. If exposed inadvertently to a rush of air it will quickly burn out. It can lead to the dissociation of gases and oil vapour. The performance of the gauge is also subject to deterioration, especially at very low pressures, due to the presence of water vapour and impurities which may be occluded in the metal of the tube. Provision can be made for replacing the filament by new wire from a tungsten stock in a matter of a few minutes.

To secure the great accuracy possible with this type of gauge at low pressures it is essential to out-gas thoroughly the electrodes before carrying out any tests, by fitting a special circuit to the gauge which enables the electrodes to be heated bright red by electron bombardment whilst being pumped under vacuum.

(iv) *Alphatron gauge (radioactive ionization gauge).* This gauge make use of a small radioactive source of alpha particles sealed into the discharge tube. It has a much wider operating range than other gauges, being able to measure from atmospheric pressure to $10^{-3}$ torr and beyond with fair accuracy. A radium preparation, which emits a constant stream of alpha particles, is located in the measuring tube of the alphatron. These particles collide with gas molecules and ionize them. These ions collect on a plate and are fed to an amplifier, the first stage of which is contained in the measuring tube. This is connected via a cable to the second stage of the amplifier and then to the indicating instrument, both of which are located in the instrument power pack. The small ion current ($10^{-10}$ to $10^{-13}$ amperes) is of course proportional to the total gas and vapour pressure in the vacuum system, and depends on the type of gas, so a calibrated curve or correction factor must be used.

**8.17 Vacuum plant**

Vacuum plant, whether for some industrial process or for laboratory and similar use, will consist of an assembly of:

(i) Suitable pumping equipment (which for high vacua will comprise vapour pumps backed by rotary pumps).

(ii) Instrumentation for measurement and control.

(iii) Suitable valves, pipework, traps, filters, etc.

(iv) Generally, a vessel which can be maintained under vacuum.

Such plant can be broadly divided into two groups:

(i) Those required to evacuate a vessel etc., whose contents contain comparatively small amounts of vapour, e.g. coating plants, laboratory equipment.

(ii) Those in which a process has to be carried out under vacuum and re-quires the removal of the large quantities of vapour (including water and process vapour), which are evolved from the contents of the vessel, etc., e.g. drying, impregnating and vacuum melting plants.

It should be realized that the pumping capacity of plants in the second group must be sufficient to deal with the enormous amounts of vapour evolved at the low pressure achieved. For instance 100 kg of water would have a volume in vapour form of 1,000,000 cubic metres at a pressure of $0 \cdot 1$ torr (and of $10^8$ cubic metres at $10^{-3}$ torr).

**8.18 Inspection aspects of high-vacuum plant**

*8.18.1 Inspection during manufacture*

Exercise of the usual inspection skills and techniques to ensure compliance with specifications and drawings will be required plus additional know-how relating to vacuum techniques.

To ensure that a vacuum system will operate satisfactorily it is essential that the connections between the different components are really leak-tight to high-vacuum standards. If they are not, then the high vacuum required may be unattainable, and many hours may be spent in pumping and in look-ing for the trouble. Even comparatively small leaks in a number of components may cause overloading of the pumps. Experience shows that the only removable connections which give the necessary tightness under high-vacuum conditions are smooth-faced flanges with rubber type seals (often 'O' rings in turned grooves) or metal gaskets. Bolted connections or bordered flanges, such as are used in pressure connections, are generally ineffective.

Inspection has to check that a very high standard of surface finish in achieved both on the flange and in the groove, which must be accurately machined to size and polished. A surface finish of better than 63 $\mu$in CLA

(1.5 $\mu$mm) may be specified. The seal must be of the correct material and hardness and dimensions, and its finish must be smooth and free from blemishes, inclusions, moulding 'flash', etc. Scratches *across* the flanges or the seal can cause a minute leak; concentric scratches or tool marks are not so serious. It is very easy to scratch the micro-finished surfaces during assembly or when changing components, and careful assembly is thus necessary. In some positions the 'O' ring may slip out of place, as it is not fully supported. Such 'O' rings and shaped seals (square, rectangular and sometimes trapezoidal in section) are made in a variety of rubbers (natural and synthetic) and plastics, according to operating conditions. Some 30% compression of the seal may be specified, and the groove must provide enough space to accommodate the deformed material. In some cases the compression is such that metal-to-metal contact is obtained (this is standard for 'O' rings and where minimum exposure of the seal to vacuum or operating conditions is desired).

Although not specifically intended for use on high vacuum work BS 6442 *Limits of surface imperfections on elastomeric toroidal sealing rings ('O' rings)* now gives some indication of the high standard of finish necessary to approach a leaktight seal. Two quality grades are specified: Grade N for general purposes and Grade S (Special) for applications requiring a higher level of quality (such as high-vacuum work).

The seal surface must be free from any crack, rupture, blister or embedded metallic foreign material. Various other imperfections are illustrated and must not exceed the dimensional limits given in a table (this necessitates taking fault measurements down to the order of 0·05 mm). There must be no flow marks which are essentially radially oriented, and such marks, indentations, etc. which are within the given dimensional limits must not interconnect or exceed a certain number or disposition.

This specification is applicable to 'O' rings having a cross-section up to 8 mm diameter (but larger sizes can be made).

*Dimensions of toroidal sealing rings ('O' rings) and their housings* are specified in BS 1806 (for up to some $15\frac{1}{2}$ in internal diameter and 0·275 in cross-section and working pressures to 1500 lbf/in$^2$) and in BS 4518 for metric sizes. The choice of material is left to the customer.

For high temperatures, special perbunan rubber can be used up to 80°C, and silicone and Viton rubbers to over 150–200°C; whilst PTFE might be used up to some 220°C, or where exposure to some particularly corrosive or difficult process fluid could occur, or down to the lowest temperatures.

For higher temperatures, metal gasket seals of tin, lead, aluminium, copper or gold (in this order) may be used. Such seals are also used on ultra-high-vacuum systems where baking is necessary in order to remove adsorbed and absorbed gases and vapours.

The methods of fabrication and the materials used in the construction of vacuum plant may have a considerable bearing on performance. For instance, the inspector should take care to ensure that no 'trapped volumes' which can cause a 'virtual leak' (see 11.7 and Fig. 11.2), are built into the plant.

Similarly, all materials give off gases and vapours when pumped, to an extent depending on their nature and finish, and these may be held within the substance (absorbed), or on its surface (adsorbed). The evolution of these 'occluded' gases and vapours may occupy much pumping time and capacity if unsuitable materials are incorporated in the plant. Furthermore, all materials possess a specific vapour pressure which will also tend to restrict pumping performance; in consequence materials having a low vapour pressure should be selected as far as possible when high-vacuum conditions have to be maintained. The presence of dirt and of extraneous substances likely to absorb vapours is inadmissible, and handling components with dirty or even bare hands is undesirable. Even the rubbers, etc., used for sealing can give off large quantities of vapour, and low-vapour-pressure rubbers and fully trapped metal-to-metal seals are desirable. Some solders have comparatively high vapour pressures, and soft soldering should be avoided in high-vacuum practice, in favour of brazing or welding. So should many plastics which readily absorb liquids, and will 'outgas' copiously.

It is claimed that an electro-polished finish, either alone or applied to a previously mechanically polished metal surface, improves vacuum performance by reducing the microscopic peaks and valleys of a mechanically polished surface so that there is less area for adsorbed gases, vapours and contaminants to cling to. Consequently a reduction in 'degassing' time results. Contamination by buried metal particles and polishing agents due to grinding and mechanical polishing is also eliminated.

Inspection should check that screw threads and sealing flanges, etc., are properly protected before electro-polishing, otherwise some $0 \cdot 001$ in ($0 \cdot 25$ mm) may be removed from their surfaces. Vessels, pipework and valves should be inspected generally to the requirements of Chapters 3 and 4, bearing in mind that they are for vacuum service.

## 8.18.2 Inspection during maintenance

Vacuum plant should undergo periodic inspection and maintenance. Rotary oil pumps can operate for long periods without attention on a 'clean' system which is rarely let down to air. However, if the system handles large quantities of vapours or contaminants, or if it is regularly cycled from atmospheric to high vacuum, then it will frequently require maintenance and cleaning. Contamination of the oil is the most frequent cause of trouble and results in a poor vacuum; flushing out and replacing is then necessary. It should first be ascertained by inspection and test that the poor ultimate vacuum is not due to leakage in the system, or to the malfunctioning of oil or exhaust valves, slipping of the driving belt, gumming up, corrosion, or seizing of parts due to dirt. Periodic scraping, cleaning and oil replacement should put matters right.

Inspection and maintenance of vapour pumps follows very similar lines. Letting the pump down to air whilst the pump fluid is hot must be avoided, as the latter may be either decomposed or otherwise affected; cleaning of the pump and replacement of the fluid is then usually necessary. The use of suitable isolating valves, and switching off the heater whilst leaving the cooling system operating, will help to avoid such trouble, but contamination of the pump fluid during use may eventually occur, resulting in poor performance. Consequently periodic checking of the fluid and cleaning or replacement as necessary, and cleaning of the pump should be undertaken. Other checks may be made on boiler temperature, pump fluid level, and coolant flow.

If cold traps are used in the vacuum system they should be cleaned periodically, and especially if an ice layer of some $\frac{1}{8}$ in forms. Traps using dessicants should be examined and recharged as necessary. Seals and gaskets should receive attention, especially if they are moved or moveable; static ones are often best left untouched, as if properly installed they rarely give trouble. Damaged seals, etc., should be replaced, and it is often policy to replace all seals which have been removed during maintenance. An appropriate grade of vacuum grease may be applied to some seals. Sealing grooves and surfaces should be inspected for damage and scratches.

## 8.19  Vacuum plant testing

The testing of vacuum plant has to ensure that the standard of leak-tightness is achieved, the ultimate vacuum required is attainable, and pumping rates are adequate.

### 8.19.1  Leak testing

This subject is dealt with in detail in Chapter 11. In order to avoid trouble it is as well to ensure that individual components are leak-tight to the required standard before assembly. A maximum permissible leak rate of $10^{-5}$ torr litre/second ($10^{-2}$ lusec) might be specified for good high-vacuum components; for medium-vacuum components perhaps 1 lusec, and for laboratory type components or measuring equipment 0.01 clusec might be desirable.

### 8.19.2  Ultimate vacuum

Vacuum pumps, and plant incorporating them, are tested to check that the specific ultimate vacuum is attainable, normally with a McLeod gauge.

When testing diffusion pumps a specially calibrated ionization gauge can be used, either on its own or in addition to the McLeod gauge, to register in the higher-vacuum range which may be attained. It is difficult to measure with accuracy pressures lower than, say, $10^{-5}$ torr with a McLeod gauge unless it has a large size bulb and a very small capillary tube. With most McLeod gauges a pressure of around $10^{-6}$ torr will result in the mercury sticking in the top of the capillary after taking a reading, i.e. a so-called 'sticking' vacuum. The McLeod gauge of course can only be used for taking periodic measurements, and not continuous readings.

When starting up large vacuum plants, connecting the two types of gauge can give useful results. The McLeod gauge will only register the partial pressure of the permanent gases present, whilst a thermal conductivity or an ionization gauge will record the total pressure of all the gases and vapours including those given off by the materials and components. The McLeod gauge will usually indicate a lower pressure. When the readings of the two instruments differ greatly, but this difference is reduced after a long period of pumping, it is an indication of dirt in the system or oil vapour or occluded gases given off from components, etc., rather than of leaks. The lower the McLeod gauge registers, the less likelihood there is of a leak.

### 8.19.3 Pumping performance and speed

The quantity of gas or vapour passing a given section of a pump or pipe line in unit time is termed the *throughput Q*; it can be measured as the product of pressure and the volume per second at the pressure at that section. Some commonly used units are litre torr per second (L torr/s); $\mu ft^3/h$; or in SI units Pa m$^3$/s. Conductance $U$ is the ratio of throughput of the gas to the partial pressure difference across the system in the steady state, a typical unit being the litre/second, and m$^3$/s.

*Pumping speed* at any point in a vacuum system is the ratio of the throughput to the pressure at that point.

$$\text{Pumping speed } S = \frac{\text{throughput } Q}{\text{pressure } p}$$

Since throughput is the product of pressure and volume per unit of time, pumping speed is expressed in units of volume per unit time, e.g. l/s (or L/s), ft$^3$/min, m$^3$/s, etc.

*Volumetric displacement* (swept volume) is the volume of air (calculated from dimensions) passed per revolution through a mechanical pump when the pressure at the intake and exhaust side is equal to atmospheric pressure.

*Free air displacement* is the product of volumetric displacement and number of cycles per unit time.

*Volumetric efficiency* is the ratio of the speed of a mechanical pump for air at a specified pressure to the free air displacement, usually expressed as a percentage.

The pumping speed stated by manufacturers is usually a measured speed and will depend on such factors as the pump design, the gas and/or vapour being pumped, temperature, the condition of the pump (cleanliness, presence of water, condition of oil, etc.), and in particular the pressure. The speed will fall rapidly as the pressure attained by the pump falls. When the pump's ultimate pressure is approached the speed will approach zero; and the maker's speed-pressure curves may show zero at this point. This is because the maker usually measures speed at various pressures by introducing a variable leak, and when this leak is shut off the ultimate pressure will be reached and the speed is then taken as zero. Actually the pump will still be pumping very slowly to remove occluded gases and vapours present in the system, but it will have reached equilibrium conditions (the gases then being removed at the same rate at which they are evolved).

Speed curves may be plotted on a log-log scale, in which case zero pumping speed cannot be shown, or a semi-log scale when the pressure scale only is a log scale. Makers usually specify the pumping speed of rotary pumps at atmospheric pressure and this may be called the free air displacement. This value of course depends upon the speed (in rev/min) at which it is operated.

A typical diffusion pump starts to operate when the backing pump produces a certain limiting value of low pressure. The diffusion pump speed rises, remains constant, and then falls as its ultimate pressure is approached. This pressure, if there are no leaks or sources of gas or vapour in the system, depends primarily on the vapour pressure of the pump fluid. This vapour pressure can be reduced by the use of a refrigerated trap but this also reduces the pumping speed.

Diffusion pump performance will vary with the type and condition of the pump fluid, the heat input, the amount of cooling water, the backing pressure, etc., and these factors should be carefully checked with the designed requirements. Clean pump fluid should be used for testing. The vapour pressure of mercury at room temperature is of the order of $10^{-3}$ torr, and in consequence a refrigerated trap (e.g. liquid nitrogen) is necessary in order to obtain low pressures. However, speed-pressure curves for mercury pumps are obtained without such a trap by using a McLeod gauge, which does not register the mercury vapour pressure.

It is often necessary to measure the *pump-down time* required by a pump or vacuum system to reach a specified pressure from atmospheric pressure. This will of course be greatly dependent on cleanliness, presence of water vapour, and leaks. Assuming conditions of a reasonably high standard the pump-down time may be estimated by using a formula or a graph.

### 8.20 Measurement of pumping speed

*8.20.1 Constant pressure (metered leak) method*

The speed of commercial vacuum pumps is usually measured by using a calibrated artificial leak; this method may be called the constant pressure method. Basically, atmospheric air is leaked into a pumped test chamber. The rate of air admission and the pressure in the chamber are measured, then;

$$\text{Pumping speed} = \frac{\text{atmospheric pressure} \times \text{flow rate}}{\text{pressure in test chamber}}$$

It will be noticed that the only throughput considered in this method (the top line of the equation) is that passing through the leak. It is important that the flow of air from the leak should not play directly on the pressure gauge, but should be at right-angles to it, or dispersed by a baffle.

*8.20.2 Constant volume (rate-of-rise) method*

With this method a calibrated leak is not required but the volume of the system being pumped must be known. A vacuum gauge and a needle valve are fitted to this volume, being located at right-angles to each other. A valve is required to isolate the pump from the system. The procedure is as follows:

(1) With the needle valve closed and the isolating valve open, pump down the system to its ultimate (equilibrium) pressure, and record this pressure.

(2) Close the isolating valve and determine the rate of pressure rise (due to outgassing and small leaks, etc.) using the vacuum gauge and a stop watch. (A rise of pressure to some ten times the ultimate value is usually suitable.)

(3) Open the isolating valve and pump down again to the ultimate value.

(4) Open the needle valve to admit air so that the pressure rises (whilst pumping) to some equilibrium value at which the pumping speed is to be determined.

(5) Again close the isolating valve and time the rate of pressure rise whilst the needle valve is admitting air. Then:

$$\text{Pumping speed} = \text{volume} \times \frac{\text{difference in rates of pressure rise}}{\text{differences in pressures}}$$

But using a clean system from which leaks have been virtually eliminated only one measurement of the rate of pressure rise is needed. The system is first pumped down to its ultimate or some suitable base pressure, the air leak needle valve is then adjusted to raise the pressure to a convenient operating value. The rate of pressure rise is determined by closing the isolating valve. Then:

Operational pumping speed

$$= \text{volume} \times \frac{\text{rate of pressure rise}}{\text{operating pressure} - \text{ultimate or base pressure}}$$

This equation gives the operational speed. Measured pumping speed is given by using the operating pressure as the denominator. The pumping speed will (by definition) be zero at the ultimate pressure.

### 8.20.3 Measurement of diffusion pump speeds

Diffusion pump performance figures published by manufacturers are often the result of different test procedures and there has been a tendency to employ the method giving the most favourable results. In fact, a pump could even be designed to take advantage of a particularly favourable method of testing. To prevent this, and to achieve some uniformity in the results obtained, the International Standards Organization (ISO TC/112 Meeting June 1965) agreed on a recommended test method for diffusion pump speeds (see also ISOR 1608: 1970). The test header has to be of the same diameter as the pump, and its dimensions and the position and arrangement of the pressure gauge and gas inlet are defined. The mean height of the header has to be $1\frac{1}{2}$ times its diameter, and the gas inlet tube is bent so that it faces away from the pump inlet (see Fig. 8.6).

When the pressure in the header has been brought to a constant low level gas is admitted at a constant measured mass flow (for not less than 15 min) and the resulting increase in equilibrium static pressure noted.

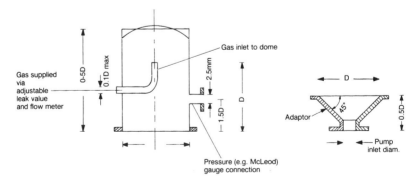

**Fig. 8.6  ISO test header fitted pump to measure pumping speed**
(volume rate of flow)

The pumping speed $S$ (in litres/s) is then evaluated from the ratio of measured gas flow $Q$ (in litre torr/s) and pressure $p$ (torr). Or using SI units:

$$S \text{ (expressed in } m^3s^{-1}) = Pa\ m^3s^{-1}/Pa$$

The speed is determined at a pressure (higher than the ultimate) of some $10^{-4}$ to $10^{-5}$ torr (some $10^{-3}$ Pa).

See Table 8.7 for some standards applicable to vacuum technology.

**TABLE 8.7**

*Some standards applicable to vacuum technology (see also Table 11.2)*

| Specification No. | Description |
|---|---|
| BS 2951 | Glossary of terms used in vacuum technology |
| ASTM E 294 | Vacuum chamber systems, effective test for pumping speed |
| ASTM E 295 | Method of measuring pumping speed, oil diffusion pumps |
| ASTM E 296 | Recommended practice for ionization gauge application to space simulators |
| ASTM E 297 | Methods for calibrating ionization vacuum gauge tubes |
| ASTM F 19 | Method for tension and vacuum testing metallized ceramic seals |
| *Sealing etc* | |
| BS 5543 | Vacuum technology – graphical symbols |
| BS 1399 | Rotary shaft lip seals |
| BS 1806 | Dimensions of toroidal sealing rings ('O' seals and their housings) |
| BS 4518 | Metric dimensions of toroidal sealing rings ('O' ring) seals and their housings |
| BS 4368 | Compression couplings for tubes |
| BS 5106 | Spiral anti-extrusion back-up rings and their housings |
| BS 5200 | Dimensions of hydraulic connectors and adaptors |
| BS 5380 | Hydraulic port and stud coupling using 'O' ring sealing and 'G' series fastening threads |
| BS 6442 | Limits of surface imperfection on elastomeric toroidal sealing ring ('O' rings) and their housings |

**References and further reading**

*Vacuum Technology*

Barrington, A.E. *High Vacuum Engineering*, Prentice-Hall, 1963.
Beck, A.H., *Handbook of Vacuum Physics*, Pergamon, Oxford, 1964.
Carpenter, L.G. *Vacuum Technology – An Introduction,* Hilger, Bristol, 1983.

Davy, J.R. *Industrial High Vacuum*, Pitman, 1951.

Dushman, S. *Scientific Foundations of Vacuum Technique*, Chapman & Hall/Wiley, 1962.

Engineering Equipment Users' Association,*Vacuum Producing Equipment*, Constable, 1961.

Holland, L. (et al.), *Vacuum Manual,* E & F Spon, 1974.

Lewin, G., *Fundamentals of Vacuum Science and Technology*, McGraw-Hill, 1965.

Pirani, M. and Yarwood, J. *Principles of Vacuum Technology*, Chapman & Hall, 1961.

Spinks, W.S.*Vacuum Technology*, Chapman & Hall, 1963.

*Transactions of the International Vacuum Congress* (1966 onwards), Pergamon Press.

*Vacuum*, An International Journal and Abstracting Service, Pergamon Press.

van Atta, C.M. *Vacuum Science and Engineering,* McGraw-Hill, 1967.

Weston, G.F. *Ultrahigh Vacuum Practice,* Butterworths, 1985.

Yarwood, J., *High vacuum technique,* Chapman and Hall, 1975.

*Seals and Sealing*

Flitney, R.K., Nau, B.S. and Reddy, D., *Seal Users Handbook*, 3rd edition, Brit. Hydraulic Research Assoc., Bedford, 1984.

*Seals and Sealing Handbook*, Trade and Technical Press, Morden, Surrey, 1986.

Summers-Smith, J. D. (editor), *Mechanical Seal Practice – for improved performance*, Mech. Eng. Pub., 1988.

# 9 Inspection procedures and processes

## 9.1 Inspection organizations

A broad classification of inspection organizations could be taken to include:

(1) Those operated by government and similar public bodies, or by large companies, to ensure that purchases are correct to requirements and, possibly, that value is obtained for the money expended.

(2) Government and similar inspectorates operated to ensure compliance with statutory requirements concerning such matters as the *Factories Act, Clean Air Act, Fire Precautions Act, Health and Safety at Work Act,* weights and measures, nuclear installations, etc.

(3) Those operated by manufacturing organizations to test and inspect their own products.

(4) Those operated by insurance companies primarily to enable them to undertake certain forms of commercial insurance.

(5) Those operated by consulting engineers, inspection engineers, etc. who undertake inspection work on a fee-paying basis.

Inspectorates of the first type mentioned above are concerned with the acceptance of supplies, and carry out inspection during and immediately after manufacture. Those of the second type may also be concerned with inspection during manufacture, although their primary function may be 'in-use' inspection. For instance, the Nuclear Installations Inspectorate (NII) was formed to assist in carrying out the provisions of the *Nuclear Installations (Licensing and Insurance) Act* 1959, which contains legislation to regulate the construction and operation of nuclear installations in the interests of safety.

The work of such inspectorates can often be divided into two fields:

(a) *Technical direction,* usually carried out by headquarters staff who decide how the work is to be inspected and the techniques to be employed.

(b) *Executive inspection,* carried out by inspection offices organized on a geographical or functional basis, which provide the inspectors to undertake the work as directed by (a).

The extent of inspection carried out depends on the nature of the product or service. If safety of life is involved, or where a single failure can have disastrous results, an extremely rigorous 100% inspection may be necessary, which would normally require the employment of a large number of government inspectors on, for instance, Defence contracts. Where an inferior part accepted into service can do no real harm, a more cursory inspection may be justified. To ensure high standards of safety at the minimum cost to the tax payer is a considerable problem, such as was faced by those responsible for aircraft inspection during the First World War. In the UK the Aeronautical Inspection Directorate (AID) evolved a system which was further developed between the wars and proved invaluable during the Second World War. This system forms the basis of many inspection organizations today, but it should be used in its entirety only when rigorous inspection is fully justified.

### 9.1.1  The AID 'approved firms' inspection system

In general, the AID system originally applied to those supplies on which safety of personnel or operational efficiency depended. Contracts were normally placed by AID only with firms whose inspection organizations had they approved, and it was a contract condition that the firm's own inspection staff carry out all inspection. AID staff were responsible for supervision and for final acceptance.*

The basic principles enforced by AID were briefly:

(1) Inspection must verify compliance with every specification and drawing requirement.

(2) There must be a complete chain of individual responsibility for inspection at each stage of progress.

(3) Identification of specific materials must be maintained from start to finish.

(4) Inspection must be fully and systematically recorded.

Special arrangements were made regarding the inspection of any usually minor items which had to be sub-contracted to firms not approved by AID. The 'approved firms' system was primarily devised for aeronautical work and related equipment; however other organizations often benefited from it or a similar system. It was a mark of distinction for a firm to be 'approved', and to put 'Air Ministry approved' or 'AID approved' on their literature.

During World War II, by the use of this 'approved firms' system having 'approved inspectors' employed by the company, AID could themselves adequately cover much meticulous inspection by the employment of comparatively few supervising inspectors. However, these AID employed

---

*In 1969 the AID became known as the Aeronautical Quality Assurance Directorate (AQD)—its new title reflecting more clearly its true function.

inspectors had to be of superior calibre, adequately trained to high technical or professional status. This system and its development is further considered, particularly in 9.4.1.

This was in direct contrast with other service inspectorates which employed large numbers of inspectors, many doing low-grade viewing work often of a 100% character, and often duplicating the work of contractors' staff.

### 9.1.2 Manufacturers' inspection organizations

Besides the 'approved firms' inspection organizations described above, which have, of necessity, to be set up and maintained by a manufacturer in order to obtain and retain this type of government contract, many other firms have an inspection organization of their own. This is to ensure the correct quality of their products, at least where it has been found to be a commercial necessity or advantage. In many firms the chief inspector may also be the chief of test; occasionally he may be in charge of quality control and assurance, and also deal with reliability. He holds an important position, usually with sufficient status for his decisions to be accepted by all and not reversed primarily in the interests of production. However in some firms his status may not be so high, and he may be subservient to works managers, production managers, superintendents, or even principal foremen. (AID/AQD did not allow this; they insisted that before a firm's chief inspector is approved he should be directly responsible to a director or other high official of the firm not primarily responsible for production.)

Some manufacturers' organizations have now been approved by various outside bodies to *assure* and certify the *quality* of their own products. Also, in comparatively recent years it has been found financially advantageous in many large organizations to use inspection techniques to find or predict trouble before it can develop seriously (i.e. to *control* quality). Thus appropriate preventative action can be taken, thereby saving much money which would have been lost because of plant shutdown, loss of expensive materials or even disaster. This concentration by management on the study of certain aspects of inspection and safety forms the subject of *loss prevention*.

### 9.1.3 Insurance companies' inspection

The oldest and most widely known insurance inspection organization is probably that operated by Lloyds of London. The 'cachet' 100 Al at Lloyds is the universally accepted symbol of excellent quality. Lloyds carry out inspection of much industrial plant and equipment and their work is not confined to marine activities. Oil refineries, chemical plant, nuclear and conventional power plant, pressure vessels, etc., are often built to their survey. Many other insurance companies undertake inspection, either preparatory to the issue and maintenance of insurance policies, or as an end in itself. Fees are naturally charged for the latter type of work.

Some insurance companies undertaking inspection have had their organizations approved by bodies such as the Pressure Vessel Quality Assurance Board (PVQAB) so that they can undertake the inspection (and quality assurance) of pressure vessels and components during manufacture in accordance with British Standards or other specifications (see 3.4.2 and 3.23).

### 9.1.4 Inspection by consulting engineers

Many of the larger consulting engineers not only design and engineer complete projects for a client, but also survey, test and inspect the various items at appropriate stages to ensure that all necessary requirements are complied with. Sometimes they, or a specialist inspection firm, carry out inspection only. Organizations of this kind also undertake the progressing (expediting) of orders. Although the two functions of inspection and progress are separate, one often reflects on the other. For instance, a visiting inspector can readily report back the progress of a job. Even if, owing to his rejections, the report is 'no progress', he can take steps to iron out troubles as they occur, thereby reducing delays and expediting delivery. Care is needed however to ensure that inspection does not suffer purely in the interests of rapid progress.

American practice, especially on oil refinery projects and in the petro-chemical industry, tends towards this combination of inspection and progress. The United Kingdom Atomic Energy Authority combined their inspection and progress departments in an endeavour to speed up construction and to avoid delays. Some large UK firms in the chemical and allied industries do likewise, but the UK government service inspectorates tend to keep strictly to inspection, leaving progress work to a relevant government production directorate.

### 9.2 Inspection planning

The inspecting authority should know as early as possible that it will be required to carry out the inspection of a project, contract or service. It should preferably have this knowledge well before any contract is placed and certainly before manufacture commences. It can then, where necessary, be represented at the project planning stage. Specifications and procedures can be drawn up with the knowledge that this particular inspecting authority will be involved, and the authority in turn can give advice on many matters, such as inspection clauses and methods of test. A close liaison between the responsible inspection engineers and the planners, designers, buying personnel and construction engineers can be built up during the preliminary stages and will prove invaluable later on when work is in progress, and teething troubles, tight delivery dates, etc., have to be dealt with.

Suitable staff will have to be earmarked for the inspection of the work, their numbers depending on its nature and magnitude. Suitable test equipment and methods will have to be provided, and if not readily available may have to be developed specially. It is essential that the test equipment should be ready for use when the first items are being manufactured. The question of who provides and pays for it will, of course, have to be settled.

The ordering or design authority should send to the inspecting authority as early as possible copies of the agreed specifications and drawings, as issued, and of the contract(s) and orders when placed. Background knowledge, where required, should be given before the placing of contracts, and afterwards as necessary. Quite likely, especially on new projects, the drawings will be issued in small batches as they are produced. With repeat orders for standard equipment, however, the drawings and specifications will generally be very much cut and dried and will be issued complete at the commencement of the contract.

In either case the inspecting authority will look carefully through the drawings and specifications and, in the light of its knowledge of the purpose of the project, will decide on the essential features which will be subject to inspection and test, and the stages at which these will take place. Sometimes the inspecting authority will be required to scrutinize and approve all the working drawings and/or calculations.

Main contractors should be notified at the earliest possible moment by the inspecting authority, in writing, of the designation and address of the responsible inspector. As many details as possible of inspection requirements should be given. These can be supplemented, if necessary, by later instructions and communications.

The main contractor will usually place sub-contracts for materials, components and, possibly, sub-assemblies. A suitable inspection clause has usually to be endorsed on these sub-orders and is arranged by agreement with the inspecting authority, who as a rule requires copies of such sub-orders, so that he can plan any necessary inspection action.

It is, of course, no use carrying out detailed dimensional inspection of an article and then later finding out that the material is unsatisfactory. Consequently, inspection and test of the raw materials must be planned. Many straightforward materials can be adequately covered by a certificate of quality from the manufacturers, plus perhaps a check test after delivery. Other more specialized materials and applications may warrant visits by an inspector to the makers' works and the witnessing of specified tests on the materials in their test houses.

It will be of great assistance to the inspecting authority if a copy of the ordering authority's production planning chart can be made available. When planning the various inspection stages during the processing and assembling of the equipment it is important to ensure that all dimensions which require checking are examined before they become obscured or difficult of access by reason of subsequent processing. Various gauges for checking dimensions and screw threads may have to be obtained. Processes such as welding, electroplating, metal spraying, etc., may be called for, which require inspection and tests perhaps involving radiological and other non-destructive techniques to ensure their effectiveness, and the inspecting authority will usually need to lay down, or agree, the detailed techniques to be employed. Stage and final assembly may be followed by stage and final testing, and again the inspecting authority will have to select or agree the tests required and the techniques to be employed to ensure that the requirements of the relevant specifications are met.

It should be possible for the inspecting authority to draw up an inspection schedule in the early stages and to distribute copies to all concerned.

As execution of the various contracts and sub-orders will be undertaken at places spread over a wide geographical area, planning will be necessary to ensure that inspection staff are deployed and available to undertake the necessary work at the appropriate time.

### 9.3  Recording the result of inspection

All manufacturing processes and tests must be carried out in accordance with the appropriate specifications or other governing documents, and to the general satisfaction of the inspector. This entails maintenance of adequate inspection and test records to ensure that evidence is available that each process and test has been properly conducted. The record system must clearly show not only the results of each test or inspection but also the identity of the inspector; this is indicated by means of a signature and/or an inspection stamp.

Obviously the record system maintained by any particular inspecting authority will comprise a large number of detailed facts recorded in log books, process charts, visit reports, test sheets, test reports, certificates, etc. Quite likely many of these details will never be referred to again. On the other hand, they might form vital evidence during subsequent enquiries and investigations, and they should not be destroyed prematurely. Details of defects and failures should be recorded and may be used to analyse their cause, the areas of responsibility and the necessary action to be taken.

Both test reports and test certificates are documents containing details of the *results* of tests. A further more concise document, which does not give detailed results, is very widely used, and is known as a *release note or inspection statement.* It can be used to convey from one firm or inspection organization to another the fact that the items detailed have been inspected to the requirements of the order and found to be satisfactory. Such a document would quote the contract, order and/or sub-order number, the quantity of goods inspected and approved, and the consignee and consignor. In addition the extent of inspection (usually complete to order or a particular specification's requirements, or occasionally limited to some stated degree) should be included, and, if applicable, a test report or certificate number and reference to any incoming release note. The document has to be stamped by an inspector, and contains a certificate stating that the goods enumerated have been inspected and tested to the specified requirements. This certificate has to be signed by or on behalf of the appropriate inspection authority.

A rejection note, giving reasons for non-acceptance and any other relevant detail, is also used.

### 9.3.1 Concessionary and modification procedures

Sometimes goods or parts which have been found not to comply with some specification, drawing or other requirement and in consequence have been (or will be) rejected, are considered by the supplier to be minor departures from requirements which would not affect the functioning, safety or interchangeability of the main equipment.

In such cases the supplier may apply in writing through the inspecting authority for a *concession* to accept a stated quantity of parts which depart from requirements to a stated degree. The inspecting authority after due consideration and, if necessary, consultation with the design authority, *may* then issue a concession form to the supplier.

Similarly, in cases where for instance a certain material is temporarily unavailable, the supplier may apply for a *production permit* to use a suitable alternative material. A permanent *modification* (to material, design or testing) requires alterations to drawings and documentation, and usually has to go through a written management procedure and be agreed by design and inspection before being implemented. In all the above cases the question of a decrease in price may arise, and full records must be kept. Details of concessions, etc. must be recorded on release notes or inspection statements.

### 9.3.2 Defect investigation

Many defects and failures are found by inspection, etc. at various stages during the processes of manufacture and they are rejected for rectification or scrap.

Occasionally, however, a defect or failure occurs in service, after final inspection and acceptance. In such cases, depending upon its seriousness, the appropriate authorities may call for a full investigation and report in order to find out the cause and to take appropriate remedial action, etc. AID took a very serious view of such troubles and had to determine whether it was a design or an inspection failure. If a design failure it was reported to the appropriate design branch. If an inspection failure, a defective inspection report (DIR) was raised. A procedure almost akin to a court-martial then followed to determine the reason for the failure, and the firm, the individual approved inspector/s and the supervising AID inspector responsible. Reprimands of varying severity, including disciplinary action, would then follow for any party or parties proved guilty.

## 9.4 Inspection procedures

From what has already been stated the general pattern of inspection emerges. Most manufacturing firms of any size will have an inspection and testing organization of their own to check and maintain the quality of their products. If so, any outside inspecting authority called upon to inspect a particular firm's products may make use of the firm's own inspecting organization. This does not, however, lessen its own responsibility for the correctness of accepted products. Consequently, the degree of reliability of a firm's own inspection organization is of great concern to an outside independent inspection authority. If satisfied in this respect, the authority may grant the firm's inspection organization some measure of approval to inspect on its behalf. The authority will, however, take steps to check periodically that its confidence has not been misplaced.

Should the firm have no inspection organization of its own, then the outside inspecting authority must provide all the inspection personnel and carry out all the inspection and testing required, possibly providing also any necessary test equipment and gauges.

With any actual inspection, the first step will be to see that the raw materials are adequately inspected. This is normally carried out at the material manufacturer's works, and any necessary test certificates are issued. The material is then despatched to the main contractor's works, or elsewhere if required, where it enters the 'goods inward' store. Associated with this store is usually a 'goods inward inspection', where all materials received are checked, correlated with test certificates, release notes, etc., and, if satisfactory, accepted for use. Manufacturing operations and processes are then carried out, controlled by appropriate inspection. Assembly can then take place, followed by appropriate inspection stages, any finishing processes, and final inspection and functional testing. Inspection of the packaging arrangements is often necessary, especially if plant and equipment has to be sent abroad.

Having agreed and laid down a proper inspection procedure, steps must be taken to see that it is clearly understood and followed by all concerned.

By and large the above procedures incorporate much of the AID system which developed the 'approved firms scheme' and extended it to cover process control.

If during its periodic checks the approving authority found anything that seriously caused it to lose confidence in a firm's inspection organization or a firm's ability to successfully produce equipment to specification, it could threaten 'withdrawal of approval'—which could mean ultimately no more contracts. So the wayward or offending firm would quickly have to 'pull up its socks'—or else!

In recent years a somewhat similar procedure of 'audit' has been developed to check on a quality assessed firm's continuing ability to supply correct products.

The following pages deal with how this 'approved firms' system has developed. Over recent years it has been documented by BSI, thus inaugurating and producing a QA scheme not only applicable to and used by most central and local government and other public bodies, but increasingly by most branches of industry. To understand its methods, and secure an entry in the Department of Trade and Industry's Register of Quality Assessed Manufacturers, would seem to be essential to the success of most industrial undertakings.

### 9.4.1 BSI and defence inspection/quality assurance procedures

In the 1960s the terms *quality assurance* and *quality control* came to be generally accepted as embracing more than *inspection*, which term may imply perhaps nothing more than end product inspection and test. *Quality control* is regarded as an integral part of *quality assurance*, which itself is defined by British Standards as 'all activities and functions concerned with the attainment of quality'.

Early in 1971, following the recommendations of the Raby Committee on Defence Equipment Inspection Policy, the Inspection and Quality Assurance Panel of the Confederation of British Industry made representations to the British Standards Institute which caused BSI to take account of 'several documents from various sources' and prepare a draft which eventually became BS 4891 — A *Guide to Quality Assurance,* which it was hoped would satisfy some of the needs of industry and commerce. This guide was based on Allied Quality Assurance Publication AQAP-1 *NATO Quality Control System Requirements for Industry,* which itself was developed from others and obviously incorporated the principles of the old AID system.

In April 1973 the UK Ministry of Defence in effect issued AQAP-1 slightly modified as their major defence quality standard DEF-STAN

05–21 *Quality Control System Requirements for Industry*—containing all-embracing requirements for a quality management system.

Two lesser levels of quality control and inspection were promulgated at the same time: DEF–STAN 05–24 *Inspection System Requirements for Industry* (based on AQAP–4) and (at a lower level) DEF–STAN 05–29 *Basic Inspection Requirements for Industry* (based on AQAP–9). In addition it was stated that DEF–STAN 05–21 and 05–24 required compliance with DEF–STAN 05–26 *Calibration Requirements for Industry.*

*Note:* These DEF-Standards are *mandatory* on defence contractors for certain types of work whereas BS 4891 is essentially a guide to industry.

A contractor wishing to undertake work on complex and critical products and to be responsible for design, development, manufacture and maybe installation and trials, must secure approval to DEF–STAN 05–21.

A contractor wishing to undertake work the design for which is already established (but conformance with requirements necessitates inspection at all stages) must secure approval to DEF–STAN 05–24. A contractor wishing to undertake lesser work where conformance with requirements can be adequately established by examination and tests conducted on the final article must secure approval to DEF–STAN 05–29. A contractor approved as complying with a higher level standard will be able to undertake work requiring compliance with a lower level standard.

Where the use of the above Defence Standards is inappropriate because acceptability of the items ordered can be adequately determined by the customer on receipt then no approval of the firm's inspection as such is necessary and MOD (PE) Form 248 will be used.

To secure approval a contractor is visited by a specialist quality assessment team to determine whether or not the management system could produce a quality product or service to the particular requirements. Much detailed work has to be gone into, advice offered and guidance given on any action needed to secure full compliance with requirements. Much paper will be consumed. A quality manual has to be produced. A contractor must make arrangements not only to control his own quality but also that of his suppliers. This procedure gradually came to be used not only by MOD and other Government Departments but by authorities such as CEGB and by industry using BS 4891 as a guide. (It was stated in 1976 that a CEGB team had fully evaluated 91 suppliers but about half did not meet the requirements.)

After approval has been given the inspecting/quality assurance authority will carry out such inspections and surveillance on contracts and orders as may be necessary. Periodically they will carry out a quality audit to ensure that the contractor is still complying with the provisions of his approval. The contractor's chief inspector will initiate similar surveys and the preparation of quality plans for specific products.

An inspector/quality assurance representative supervising a contract let to DEF–STAN 05–21 (or AQAP–1, or their derivatives) may find his involvement with the contractor extends further than usual and may include matters such as design, reliability, safety, supplier/vendor appraisal, and possibly installation and trials.

Certain categories of purchasing are exempt from the quality assurance/inspection arrangements described above. For instance, contracts and orders for electronic components within the extensive BS 9000 series (*General requirements for a system for electronic components of assessed quality*) are placed to the basic rules, procedures and relevant detailed specification/s of that series. With BS 9000 approved firms i.e. those listed in the BS 9002 *Qualified Products List* (now revised and renumbered as PD 9002), such components are made and inspected by the approved firm using statistical methods of quality control (see 9.4.3).

### 9.4.2 Introduction of BS 5750 Quality systems

Owing to misgivings in some sectors of industry about what was effectively the reissue of Defence Standards as British Standards covering quality management systems, a new document, BS 5179, was published as a series of guides to the operation and evaluation of quality assurance systems. But the growing demand (from many areas of industry) for the application of QA principles to contracts and for the assessment of suppliers' quality management systems led to the appearance of a number of QA standards produced by various large purchasing and third party organizations (covering a wide field). This highlighted the need for rationalization and resulted in the publication of BS 5750 *Quality systems* which specified requirements instead of recommendations. This standard was issued (in 1979) in three parts covering QA systems which in principle are similar to DEF–STAN 05–21, 24 and 29. In 1981 it was deemed necessary to issue Parts 4, 5 and 6 as guides to Parts 1–3 and this meant the supersession and withdrawal of BS 5179. Guides Part 4 and 5 were based on DEF–STAN 05–22 and 05–25 respectively.

Industry was encouraged to apply for QA approval to BS 5750 from a recognized authority for a specific type of work, it being government policy that good product quality was a critical factor in industry's drive to capture larger markets for their goods.

The Department of Trade and Industry's Quality Assurance Advisory Service (QAAS) operated by the Production Engineering Research Association (PERA) even arranged on request for their representative to visit factories employing 60 to 100 people to discuss with the firms' senior executives the outline of a QA scheme. Up to 15 man–days' work by a specialist advisor was offered and provided free, together with reports and recommendations aimed at helping the firm to obtain QA approval from a recognized authority. For companies of up to 500 employees financial assistance of up to 25% of the total costs of implementing the consultant's recommendations could be made available.

A Government White Paper, 'Standards, quality and international competitiveness', was issued in 1982 setting out policy and actions for the creation of a structure and facility for firms in pursuit of quality. The government wished to encourage the growth of independent third party certification schemes to BS 5750 and to endeavour to move away from multiple assessment of firms by different authorities; it was accepted that all large public purchasing organizations would acknowledge assessment against this standard (BS 5750) in place of any schemes previously operated.

The procedure for assessment is largely that already discussed earlier and relies on independent assessors and the production by the firm of a quality assessment schedule and other matters. It was considered that firms in the process industries would benefit from such assessment and approval.

BSI itself is one of the many independent 'third party' organizations which now operates QA rating assessment of suppliers (to BS 5750) and carries out surveillance/audit programmes and inspections of various products. It also issues a 'Kitebrand' certification mark to manufacturers listed as having received its approval to make products to specific British Standards.

Lloyds Register of Shipping operates a number of schemes whereby it surveys, assesses and if satisfied approves a manufacturer's quality control and assurance arrangements, rather than carrying out the traditional direct inspection by their own surveyors of individual components, materials and units as they are manufactured. There are differences in detail in the inspection schemes adopted depending on the nature of the products made, which range from oil engines, gas turbines, gears and refrigerating equipment to materials, fittings, freight containers, nuclear components and the construction of ships' hulls.

In general, after a firm's approval Lloyds surveyors carry out surveillance by regular visits to see that the standards of approval are maintained. All engines, equipment, etc. will then be eligible for a Lloyds Register certificate, but their surveyor may witness a final inspection and test.

CEGB, ICI and many other large purchasing organizations have carried out assessment and approval of their suppliers generally to BS 5750 to what is now generally known as Second Party Approval and in consequence have become familiar with their capabilities and shortcomings. However, it is possible for the QA organization of a firm which has been assessed and approved by one examining body to be rejected as unsatisfactory by a number of other authorities. Obviously it became necessary for the assessing officers to work to common standards, and this has led to training courses being run under the supervision of the Institute of Quality Assurance (IQA) who will now issue certificates to approved *assessors* and supervising *lead assessors* (see 9.45–6) enabling them to carry out this work.

*9.4.3 Assessing to the requirements of BS 5750 Quality systems*

It is the UK Government's intention that all government departments and agencies (and no doubt local government authorities) will eventually require their principal contractors and subcontractors to meet the requirements of BS 5750, Parts 1, 2 or 3, as also will many major buying firms and industries. This standard can be used:

(a) as a basis for evaluating the capabilities of a contractor or suppliers quality management system (either by a potential purchaser or by a third party)

(b) when invoked in a contract, to specify the appropriate QA requirements.

BS 5750 Part 1 Specification for design, manufacture and installation lays down the all-embracing quality management requirements which a contractor must satisfy before he can undertake complex work, specified principally in terms of the performance required or for which the design has not been established. The contractor may be responsible for design, development, manufacture, installation and trials, and for reliability matters and the use of new techniques.

Part 2 Specification for manufacture and installation lays down the quality/inspection requirements a contractor must satisfy before he can undertake work specified in terms of established design where conformance to specified requirements can be ensured by inspection performed during manufacture and, where required, installation.

Part 3 Specification for final inspection and test lays down the minimum quality system requirements when conformance to specified requirements can be adequately established by final inspection and tests on the finished material or services.

Parts 1–3 of this standard, read in conjunction with the guides to each part (published as Parts 4–6), and perhaps in conjunction with BS 4891 and what has already been stated in the present chapter of this book, should enable the reader to understand what is involved in the assessment of a potential contractor's quality management system prior to 'approval', and the continuing surveillance (and auditing) of an 'approved contractor'.

In an endeavour to simplify the somewhat legalistic procedure Table 9.1 has been prepared to show in outline what is required.

Some comments on the differences between BS 5750:1979 and for instance the old AID system already described might be helpful.

BS 5750 Part 1 in general calls for a more all pervading 'total' quality system than the 'inspection' organization envisaged by AID as being under the control of the firms' approved chief inspector. This system, besides inspection, embraces control of design, development, drawings and specifications; reliability and value engineering; investigation of new materials and techniques; analysis and use of defect data and consideration of

**TABLE 9.1**

*Quality requirements implied by BS 5750*

| Requirement | Part 1 | Part 2 | Part 3 |
|---|---|---|---|
| 4.1 Quality system | *Total* quality system to be established, documented and maintained. Documentation may include quality manuals, programmes and plans (see BS 4891) | Establish and maintain a documented inspection and process control system (including control of sub-contractors) to specified requirements. | Final inspection and test to specified requirements |
| 4.2 Organization | Top management representative (e.g. of director status) with relevant personnel responsible that *all quality* requirements are met to satisfaction of purchaser's representative. | Management representative (usually chief inspector) responsible to top management for *all inspection* matters to satisfaction of purchaser's representative | Supplier designates an inspection representative responsible for inspection matters to satisfaction of purchaser's representative. (The inspection rep. may also have other (non-inspection) duties) |
| 4.3 Review of quality system (audits) | Periodical review and evaluation to be made by supplier to satisfaction of purchaser's representative | As Part 1 | Check and calibration of inspection and test equipment as relevant |
| 4.4 Planning | Planning, documentation and control of all QA | NIL | NIL |

452

**TABLE 9.1** *continued*

| Requirement | Part 1 | Part 2 | Part 3 |
|---|---|---|---|
| | activities including design and new techniques beyond state of the art | | |
| 4.5 Work instructions | Develop, maintain and document instructions regarding performance of *all* work (including design and installation) | Establish written criteria for acceptable workmanship | NIL |
| 4.6 Records | Develop and maintain records of operation of total quality system and achievement of required quality, including sub-contractor's records, and maintenance of identity of materials, parts, etc. Also records of defects found, rejections made, etc. | Maintain documents of inspection and test procedures and process controls and records of conformance to specified requirements. Ensure issue of appropriate technical documents, including authorised changes, to all relevant personnel | Maintain records of conformance to specified requirements |
| 4.7 Corrective action | Analysis of work operations, concessions granted, materials scrapped, reworked, repaired or modified in | As Part 1 | NIL |

453

**TABLE 9.1** *continued*

| Requirement | Part 1 | Part 2 | Part 3 |
|---|---|---|---|
| | order to determine trouble and its cause (and the corrective action taken) | | |
| 4.8 Design control | Establish and maintain design (and possibly development) control, practice and procedure, including investigation of new techniques and materials; preparation and maintenance of drawings, specifications, and instructions; consideration of statutory requirements, health and safety, etc.; control of reliability and value engineering tasks, design review procedures, etc; identification of problem areas; use of defect data feedback | NIL | NIL |
| 4.9 Documentation and change control | Control all documents relating to requirements of | Covered generally by 4.6 Records Part 2 above | NIL |

**TABLE 9.1** *continued*

| Requirement | Part 1 | Part 2 | Part 3 |
|---|---|---|---|
| | this standard, including changes and matter covered generally by 4.6 Records, Part 2 above | | |
| 4.10 Inspection, measuring and test equipment | Provision, control, calibrate and maintain (generally to BS 5781 and specified requirements) all test equipment, etc. (including jigs, fixtures, templates and gauges, etc.) | As Part 1 | See 4.3 Part 3 above |
| 4.11 Control of purchased material and services | Supplier responsible for ensuring materials, etc. are ordered to clearly documented descriptions and conform to specified requirements, whether inspected by sub-contractor or himself. Monitoring at source and verification by purchaser's rep. at source or after receipt may be necessary. | Generally as Part 1 | The purchaser's representative may require technical data, test pieces, etc. for independent verification |

**TABLE 9.1** *continued*

| Requirement | Part 1 | Part 2 | Part 3 |
|---|---|---|---|
| 4.12 Manufacturing control | Incoming material to be segregated until documentary evidence of inspection available. Manufacturing and processing operations to be carried out to documented instructions. Workmanship to prescribed standards. Inspection and or monitoring after each operation as required | Manufacturing and in-process control inspection where necessary | NIL |
| 4.13 Purchaser-supplied material | Establish and maintain procedures for inspection, storage and maintenance, recording all details | As Part 1 | NIL |
| 4.14 Completed item inspection and test | Inspect and test finished product ensuring that any earlier tests are acceptable. Installation and trials work may be involved | As Part 1 (but not last sentence) | NIL (but see 4.1 Part 3) |

**TABLE 9.1** *continued*

| Requirement | Part 1 | Part 2 | Part 3 |
|---|---|---|---|
| 4.15 Sampling procedure | Check that any specified or required sampling procedure has been carried out | As Part 1 | NIL (but see 4.1 Part 3) |
| 4.16 Control of non-conforming material | Establish procedures for identification, documentation and possibly for repair work or concessions and re-inspection of non-conforming materials. Holding areas (quarantine and bonded stores) to be provided | As Part 1 | Non-conforming material to be identified and segregated |
| 4.17 Indication of inspection status | Establish system to identify and indicate all stages of inspection of material using stamps, tags, cards, records, etc | As Part 1 | Ability to distinguish between inspected and uninspected material |
| 4.18 Protection and preservation of product quality | Establish and maintain control of specified packing, preservation and | As Part 1 | After inspection arrange for protection during storage and transit, |

457

**TABLE 9.1** *concluded*

| Requirement | Part 1 | Part 2 | Part 3 |
|---|---|---|---|
| | marking, and any segregation and care (including checking for deterioration) necessary during any storage pending shipment | | including any specified packing and preservation and appropriate identification marking, etc. |
| 4.19 Training | Establish any training, certification, etc. needed by relevant staff | All relevant personnel shall have appropriate experience or training | As Part 2 |

*Note:* Table 9.2 co-relates these quality requirements with ISO 9000–9004 (and BS 5750:1987).

458

statutory requirements including health and safety; and possibly some involvement with installation and trials. For a large firm working in an area of advanced technology these requirements would necessitate the employment or assistance of a number of well qualified professional engineers, scientists and technologist—maybe answering to a special director. A smaller firm might be able to upgrade a suitably qualified chief inspector to fill this important new controlling position.

The chief inspector was always approved personally by AID after considering his qualifications and experience; he then appointed his own 'approved inspectors' informing AID for record purposes, and was responsible for seeing that they had appropriate experience and training.

Under BS 5750 Part 1 the supplier appoints the QA 'supremo' and staff (without apparently any direct approval from the purchaser, who may however appoint a purchaser's representative (the authorized inspecting body (AIB) acting (like AID) on his behalf to see that the system is effective).

The old AID inspector-in-charge acting as purchaser's representative at a high technology firm would often be given additional duties of a technical, design nature. If the firm was important enough a separate resident technical officer (RTO) might be appointed.

BS 5750 makes no mention of approved inspector's stamps, but their use may be implied by the requirements. Stamps at least distinguish between inspected and uninspected material, and with documentation provide not only for maintaining the identity of material but also the identity of the individual responsible for each and every inspection stage. For guidance on reliability BS 5750 refers to BS 5760 (see also 13.2).

BS 5750 Part 2 caters for the more general 'run-of-the-mill' inspection organization operated by firms to ensure that their products or services comply with all drawings, specification, process and test requirements and that identification of material and its inspection status is maintained from start to finish.

BS 5750 Part 3 caters largely for those firms supplying materials and/or services, or perhaps proprietary articles, to requirements specified by the purchaser, or maybe by the supplier, and which can be checked by final inspection and/or tests.

Following publication of the BS 5750 series (1979–81) it was rapidly adopted in a wide variety of industrial sectors and now forms a corner stone of the British National Quality Campaign and the reference basis of the Department of Trade and Industry's (DTI) Register of Quality Assessed UK Companies.

Many European and Commonwealth countries have their own national standards corresponding generally to BS 5750:1979, thus

France has NFX 50–111
Holland has NEN 2646

Norway has NS 5801/2/3

Australia has AS 1821/2/3

Canada has the CSA Z 299 series corresponding somewhat to BS 5750, but this has four categories (parts) instead of three:

CSA Z 299·1/Z 299·2 and Z 299·4 are similar to BS 5750 Parts 1–3;

CSA Z 299·3 is a category midway between BS 5750 Parts 2 and 3, and

CSA Z 299·0 gives guidance

The Canadian series seems rather more slanted towards the quality assurance of engineering plant than the more generalized BS 5750.

A general guidance document on quality systems somewhat similar to BS 5750 Parts 4–6 has been issued by the USA as ANSI/ASME Z 1·15/79.

Covering further ground, ISO Guide 48 contains guidelines for third party assessment and registration of a supplier's quality system and is a companion document to the ISO series, and broadly to BS 5750.

A somewhat similar, but more detailed specification sponsored by the American Society for Quality Control, entitled *Generic Guidelines for Auditing of Quality Systems*, has been approved as ANSI Q1–1986, and is adaptable to different industries and organizations.

ISO 8402 *Quality Vocabulary* has been proposed for adoption by British Standards and incorporation in BS 4778 *Glossary of terms used in quality assurance* as Part 1 International terms.

### 9.4.4 BS 5750 and International Standards

BS 5750 Parts 1–3: 1979, after a review by ISO and consideration of the experience of their use in the UK, were used as the basis for an International Standard on Quality Systems (the ISO 9000 series). Some changes in detail (and in language and syntax) were made and the new ISO series was issued simultaneously with a revised issue of BS 5750, which is a dual numbered British Standard.

The International Standards on quality systems (issued 1987) comprise:

ISO 9001 *Quality assurance in design/development, production, installation and servicing* corresponding to BS 5750 Part 1

ISO 9002 *Quality assurance in production and installation* corresponding to BS 5750 Part 2

ISO 9003 *Quality assurance in final inspection and test* corresponding to BS 5750 Part 3

ISO 9000 *Quality management and QA standards—Guidelines for selection and use* perhaps corresponding somewhat to BS 5750 Parts 4, 5 and 6 but adding further requirements

ISO 9004 Quality management and quality system element—Guidelines

Note that ISO 9000 and 9004 are intended as guidelines to complement the technical specifications (BS 5750 Parts 1–3) and to ensure that as far as possible customers' requirements are met.

ISO 9000 and 9004 have been issued as a dual numbered British Standard, BS 5750 *Quality Systems*, Part 0 Guide to principal concepts and applications, Section 1: Guide to selection and use; and Section 2: Quality management and quality system elements—guidelines.

The requirements of the new BS 5750 Part 1 (ISO 9001) are aimed primarily at preventing non-conformity at all stages from design through to servicing; Part 2 (ISO 9002) aims at preventing and detecting any non-conformity during production and installation and implementing the means to prevent its occurrence; Part 3 (ISO 9003) requires demonstration of a supplier's capability to detect and control the disposition of any product non-conformity during final inspection and test. Some of the comments made earlier regarding the 1979 issue (see p. 451 *et seq.*) have been covered directly or indirectly in the 1987 issue. For instance, inspector's stamps can be a method of segregating conforming from non-conforming items. It is stated that the requirements of BS 5750 Pt 1: 1987 (identical to ISO 9001) are very similar to BS 5750 Part 1: 1979 but a small number of additional quality system elements have been included, and other elements enhanced in the light of UK user experience; similarly with BS 5750 Parts 2 and 3. Any requirements in BS 5781 Part 1 Measurement and calibration systems have been incorporated (see Appendix to this book).

However, the paragraph titles, headings numbers and detailed wording in the revised international version of BS 5750 are in many cases expressed in a different manner and do not necessarily correspond with those in the older (English) issue, although the overall requirements are (as stated) similar.

Consequently it has been thought fit to leave Table 9.1 with the summarized details based on the older and perhaps more familiar 1979 paragraph headings and titles, and to update by including both 1987 and 1979 headings and clause numbers as may be relevant in Table 9.2, adapted from BS 5750 Part 0, Section 0·1:1987 which gives a cross-reference list of quality system requirements.

From this certain requirements additional to those in the 1979 standard will be evident; other requirements may differ in detail (but not necessarily in principle). Reference to a relevant clause in BS 5750 indicated in Table 9.2 should help, although in some cases the reference is brief and not very specific, whereas an essay might well have been written on each (perhaps with different interpretations on minor points, depending upon the particular author).

Some concern has been expressed (by experienced QA assessors and others) regarding the detailed interpretation of the QA system requirements in BS 5750: 1979 let alone the 1987 version (ISO 9000–9004) which

**TABLE 9.2**

*Cross-reference list of quality system requirements necessitated by ISO 9000, etc*

| BS 5750 Pt 1 & 4. 1979/81 | | | | Relevant clause in BS 5750:1987 | | |
|---|---|---|---|---|---|---|
| Clause | Short title | BS5750 Pt 0.2 Clause No. (ISO 9004) | Title | Part 1 (ISO 9001) | Part 2 (ISO 9002) | Part 3 (ISO 9003) |
| 4.1 | Quality system | 4 | Management responsibility (Quality system requirements, policy, organization, management representative & review) | 4.1 ● | 4.1 ◐ | 4.1 ○ |
| 4.2 | Organization | 5 | Quality system principles | 4.2 ● | 4.2 ● | 4.2 ◐ |
| 4.4 | Planning | 5.3 | Documentation of system-quality procedures, manuals and plans | 4.2 ● | 4.2 ● | 4.2 ○ |
| 4.3 | Review of QS | 5.4 | Auditing the quality system (internal quality audits) | 4.17 ● | 4.16 ◐ | — |
| | | 6 | Economics–Quality related cost considerations | — | — | — |
| 4.3 | Review | 7 | Quality in marketing (Contract review) | 4.3 ● | 4.3 ● | — |
| 4.8 | Design control | 8 | Quality in specification and design (Design control) | 4.4 ● | — | — |
| 4.8.1(j) | | 8.5 | Design review & verification | 4.4.5 ● | — | — |
| 4.11 | Purchased material | 9 | Quality in procurement (Purchasing) | 4.6 ● | 4.5 ● | — |
| 4.12 | Manufacturing and Document control | 10 | Quality in production (Process control) | 4.9 ● | 4.8 ● | — |
| 4.9 | | 11 | Control of production | 4.9 ● | 4.8 ● | — |
| 4.6 | Records | 11.2 | Material control & traceability (Product identification & traceability) | 4.8 ● | 4.7 ● | 4.4 ◐ |
| 4.17 | Indication of inspection status | 11.7 | Control of verification status (Inspection & test status) | 4.12 ● | 4.11 ● | 4.7 ◐ |

**TABLE 9.2** *continued*

| Clause | Short title | BS5750 Pt 0.2 Clause No. (ISO 9004) | Title | Part 1 (ISO 9001) | | Part 2 (ISO 9002) | | Part 3 (ISO 9003) | |
|---|---|---|---|---|---|---|---|---|---|
| | | | | **Relevant clause in BS 5750:1987** | | | | | |
| 4.14 | Complete item inspection and test | 12 | Product verification (Inspection & testing) | ● | 4.10 | ● | 4.9 | ◐ | 4.5 |
| 4.10 | Measuring and test equipment | 13 | Control of measuring & test equipment (Inspection, measuring & test equipment) | ● | 4.11 | ● | 4.10 | ◐ | 4.6 |
| 4.16 | Non-conforming material | 14 | Nonconformity (Control of nonconforming product) | ● | 4.13 | ● | 4.12 | ◐ | 4.8 |
| 4.7 | Corrective action | 15 | Corrective action | ● | 4.14 | ● | 4.13 | — | |
| 4.18 | Protection and preservation | 16 | Handling & post-production functions (Handling, storage, packaging & delivery) | ● | 4.15 | ● | 4.14 | ◐ | 4.9 |
| — | Work instructions | 16.2 | After sales servicing | ● | 4.19 | — | | — | |
| 4.5 | | 17 | Quality documentation & records (Document control) | ● | 4.5 | ● | 4.4 | ◐ | 4.3 |
| 4.6 | Records | 17.5 | Quality records | ● | 4.16 | ● | 4.15 | ◐ | 4.10 |
| 4.19 | Training | 18 | Personnel (Training) | ● | 4.18 | ◐ | 4.17 | ○ | 4.11 |
| — | | 19 | Product safety & liability | — | | — | | — | (use relevant safety standard, regulations, evaluation tests, etc. Issue necessary warning notices, maintenance manuals, etc) |

463

**TABLE 9.2** *concluded*

| BS 5750 Pt 1 & 4. 1979/81 | | | | Relevant clause in BS 5750:1987 | | |
|---|---|---|---|---|---|---|
| Clause | Short title | BS5750 Pt 0.2 Clause No. (ISO 9004) | Title | Part 1 (ISO 9001) | Part 2 (ISO 9002) | Part 3 (ISO 9003) |
| — | | 20 | Use of statistical methods (Statistical techniques) | 4.20 ● | 4.18 ● (use where appropriate) | 4.12 ◕ |
| 4.13 | Purchased material | — | Purchaser supplied product | 4.7 ● | 4.6 ● | — |
| 4.3 | Review of QS | 5.5 | Review & evaluation of the quality management system (Management review) [see note 4.17*] | 4.1.3 ● | 4.1.3 ● | 4.1.3 ○ |

1. The clauses & titles in columns 1 and 2 have been taken from Table 9.1. (page 327)
2. The main titles quoted in column 4 are taken from BS 5750 Pt.0. Sect.0.2:1987 (ISO 9004) but the titles in parentheses are from BS 5750 Pts.1, 2 & 3 (ISO 9001–3):1987
3. The clause requirements in BS 5750 Pts.1, 2 & 3:1987 are in some cases identical, but generally are more stringent in Part 1.
    ●   indicates full requirements
    ◕   indicates less stringent than Part 1
    ○   indicates less stringent than Part 2
    —   indicates requirement not present

464

purports to be 'very similar'. Contractors seeking approval may find that their interpretation of particular clauses differs from that of the assessing/ auditing body, and that with multiple assessments by different bodies (now frowned upon, but possible) further difficulties may arise. Revised guidance documents (e.g. BS 5750 Parts 4–6) in due course may help, but interpretation of internationalized legal documents keeps lawyers in business. Technical people should endeavour to see the objectives clearly and not be drowned in a flood of paperwork.

However (as was always the case) much depends upon the particular supervising inspector/assessor. The training of approved assessors should help towards giving them a consistent approach.

It has been suggested that a system of Enquiry or Code Cases along the lines conducted in connection with BS 5500 and the ASME Code for Pressure Vessels should be instituted. Any ambiguity or doubt arising as to the meaning of any clause, etc should be referred to a suitable committee and suitably publicized; their interpretation should be final and conclusive.

Some publications of interest are given at the end of this chapter.

*A final comment.* Effective quality assurance/inspection, although it requires proper documentation and paperwork, depends to a considerable extent on human factors not covered by rules and regulations. The staff, especially the controlling staff, *must have and exhibit* the qualities of enthusiasm, alertness, patience, broad vision and where necessary great attention to detail. Without these a quality assurance programme will be as flat as the paper on which it is written!

### 9.4.5  Register of quality assessed UK companies

Starting perhaps with the idea of the old AID List of Approved Firms (firms whose inspection organizations had received some form of AID approval), and with the growing demand from industry and government for quality, spurred on by the issue of BS 4891 and 5179, various large organizations, as has been stated, began to assess and, if satisfied, to approve the quality capabilities of their main suppliers (often at first imposing many of their own conditions). The issue of BS 5750, however, had a rationalizing effect on industry, who now use it as their main basis for assessment and approval.

Consequently the Department of Trade and Industry now issues a Register of Quality Assessed UK Companies, which is divided into sections according to the assessing authority. The bulk of the register is taken up by the list of companies approved by the Ministry of Defence (Procurement Executive) assessed generally to DEF–STAN 05–21 and 05–24 and 05–29. The BSI list contains those companies approved by them to make products to particular British Standards and to make use of the BS Kitemark. Also, BSI deals with the approval and listing of firms qualified to produce specific electronic components of assessed quality to the BS 9000/CECC and IEC Q

Systems, and now carries out inspections and Third Party assessments and certifications as an authorized inspection body (AIB).

Other sections of the register list firms approved by large purchasing organizations including British Gas Corporation, British Steel Corporation, British Telecom, British Rail, British Coal, Cable and Wireless, etc. These are now known as Second Party AIBs.

Other third party assessors (i.e. those independent assessors who are neither manufacturers nor purchasers, besides BSI include PVQAB, Lloyds, insurance companies, consultants, etc.

The largest list of companies assessed, approved and registered by any one purchasing organization is, as has been stated, that of MOD. Many of these companies owe their original approval to AID who also had a special form of approval for stockists and test houses. MOD continued to assess stockists generally to DEF STAN 05–31 mainly for metals traceable back to raw material batches or casts, or for products from quality assured sources, until 1982 when BSI took over this assessment and registration of stockists of assessed capability. However, in December 1987 MOD (who had of course inherited AQD, the successor to AID) announced that in future they would cease to carry out any further assessments and approvals of manufacturers, leaving this onerous duty to industry.

The assessments are made by a team from the organization concerned to the requirements of BS 5750 (Parts 1, 2 or 3) and any other relevant documents and requirements. Thus British Nuclear Fuels and the CEGB assess where necessary to the requirements of BS 5750 and 5882 whilst the PVQAB assesses also to BS 1113, BS 2790, BS 5500, BS 5169, BS 5045 Part 2 and BS 806 and any relevant material specifications.

British Standard products manufactured under quality systems assessed and accepted by BSI to BS 5750 and that are Kitemarked or safety marked with the BS emblem may be called 'Certified products' and provided with an appropriately worded certificate.

Manufacturers of electronic components approved to the product certification system of BS 9000/CECC/IECQ are recognized formally as having a quality system equivalent to that required by BS 5750.

### 9.4.6 Third party QA certification authorities

With the growth in the number of firms realizing the commercial advantage of obtaining approval of their QA arrangements, and in pursuance of government policy, there has been an increase in the number of third party organizations qualified and prepared to advise, assess, certify, register and periodically audit firms seeking approval to BS 5750.

Besides the large organization already mentioned, other specialist QA assessing bodies have been set up to cover the certification and periodical QA auditing of firms engaged in such diverse activities as pharmaceuticals, polymers, building and engineering services, packaging and electrical contracting.

Some of these assessing bodies have been sponsored and partly funded, at least initially, by the Department of Trade and Industry and appropriate trade organizations. QA auditor training is carried out by several organizations and this can lead to suitably experienced personnel being registered as assessors by the management board of the Registration Scheme for Lead Assessors of Quality Management Systems of the Institute of Quality Assurance.

By such means it is hoped that UK industry will increase its competitiveness both at home and abroad. Obviously, with the issue of foreign QA standards, such as those previously mentioned, similar QA schemes will be in being abroad; but it is hoped that the UK will retain its lead.

In order to ensure the continuing satisfactory performance of any organization, periodic reviews or audits must be made. BS 5750 Part 0, Section 0·2 (1987) states (in clause 5.5) that provision should be made by company management for independent reviews and evaluations of their quality system. These should be carried out by appropriate members of company management or by competent independent (i.e. apparently outside second or third party) personnel as decided by the company management.

Reviews should include:

(a) the findings of audits centred on various elements of the quality system (internal audits as required by clause 5.4.3 of the standard).

(b) overall effectiveness of the quality management system in achieving stated quality objectives.

(c) considerations for updating the QM system in relation to changes brought about by new technologies, quality concepts, market strategies and social or environmental conditions.

Findings, conclusions and recommendations reached as a result of a review and evaluation should be submitted in documentary form for necessary action by company management. Notice that BS 5750: Part 1 (1979) in clause 4.3 and the 1987 issue in clause 4.17 also refers particularly to internal audits, whilst Part 0.2 (1987) refers to *independent* review and evaluation . . . by company management *or* by competent independent personnel *as decided by company management*. It does *not* refer specifically to external audits carried out by independent bodies such as those necessarily arranged by company management to meet specific requirements (such as a company request for assessment by PVQAB), or one *imposed* on the company by legislation.

There can be a subtle difference in the meaning attached to the word independent. However, BS 5750 Part 0, Section 0.1. Clause 8.4—Pre-contract assessment—envisages the pre-contract determination of the suitability of an outside supplier's quality system being performed directly by the intending purchaser and/or user.

By agreement between purchaser and supplier pre-contract assessment (audit) may be delegated to an independent assessing organization (e.g. a third party assessor such as BSI).

It is becoming increasingly important to ensure the independence and integrity of QA Management and particularly of assessors.

### 9.4.7 Statistical methods of quality control

(i) A conference was held in 1932 by BSI, to meet Dr W.A. Shewhart of the Bell Telephone Co. of America and to discuss with him means whereby statistical methods could be applied particularly to the specification of quality. As a result a committee was formed, which included Dr B.P. Dudding with Dr E.S. Pearson FRS as secretary. It was decided to issue Dr Pearson's report as BS 6001 *The application of statistical methods to industrial standardization and quality control*; it was first published in 1935.

Perhaps one of the first applications of such methods to improving the quality and uniformity of mass produced articles was BS 161 *Tungsten filament electric lamps*, first published in 1934 which laid down sampling procedures to check for any lack of statistical uniformity in the variation of lamp quality.*

Further work on statistical quality control (SQC) was carried out during and after World War II by the military in America, Britain and Canada. Amongst other things this resulted in the publication of a standard entitled *Sampling procedures and tables for inspection by attributes* (known in the UK as DEF–131–A), which was then issued first as BS 9001 (now withdrawn) particularly for electronic parts of assessed quality and then as BS 6001 (for general use). A guide to this was published in 1972 as BS 6000 (see also Table 9.3). Electronic components are now dealt with by the extensive BS 9000 series.

(ii) BS 9000 *General requirements for a system for electronic parts of assessed quality* deals with an ambitious system of quality control of suppliers depending upon sampling inspection and tests to a statistically defined acceptable quality level (AQL). It was developed from existing military standards of the USA and DEF and CV specifications used in the UK and it is applied to most electronic components bought by the UK Government (civil and military). The organization of the system is now vested in BSI who use the Electrical Quality Assurance Department (EQD) of MOD as the supervising inspectorate.

---

*The current issue of BS 161 (1976 amended to 1981) departs from its original use of SQC. It introduces a new concept for whole product batch appraisal by checking manufacturers' claims for compliance. It does not deal with SQC as such.

## TABLE 9.3

*Some British Standards relevant to inspection and quality assurance*
(including statistical quality control—SQC)

| BS No. | Description |
|---|---|
| 600 | Application of statistical methods to industrial standardization and quality control |
| 2564 | Control chart technique when manufacturing to a specification with special reference to articles machined to dimensional tolerances (Practical guidance on use of Quality Control by Dr B.P. Dudding and W.J. Jennett) |
| 2635 | Drafting specifications based on limiting the number of defectives permitted in small samples |
| 2846 | Guide to statistical interpretation of data (in 7 parts) |
| 3518: Pt 5 | Fatigue testing: Guide to the application of statistics |
| 4778 | Glossary of terms used in quality assurance (including reliability and maintainability terms) |
| 4891 | A guide to quality assurance |
| 5882 | Specification for a total quality assurance programme for nuclear power plants/installations |
| 6143 | Guide to the determination and use of quality related costs |
| 5700 | Guide to process control using QC chart methods and cusum techniques |
| 5701 | Guide to number defective charts for quality control |
| 5702 | Guide to quality control charts for measured variables (revision of BS 2564) |
| 5703 | Guide to data analysis and quality control using cusum techniques Pts 1–4 |
| 5750 | Quality systems (in 6 parts) |
| 5760 | Reliability of systems, equipments and components (in 3 parts) |
| 6000 | Guide to the use of BS 6001. Sampling procedures and tables for inspection by attributes |
| 6001 | Sampling procedures and tables for inspection by attributes. Supplement 1: Sampling plans indexed by limiting quality (e.g. for 'isolated lots') |
| 6002 | Sampling procedures and charts for inspection by variables for percent defective (Provides 3 alternative methods of sampling (indexed by AQL). Recommended where test methods are expensive or destructive) |
| 9000 | General requirements for a system for electronic components of assessed quality |
| PD 9002 (previously BS 9002) | BS 9000, BS CECC and IEQC Containing also Qualified Products list<br>Part 2   List of approved firms<br>Part 3   Index to product codes |

**TABLE 9.3** *concluded*

| BS No. | Description |
|---|---|
| | Part 4   Component selection guide |
| | Part 6   Capability approvals |
| BS 9003 | Requirements for the manufacture of electronic components of assessed quality intended for long life applications |
| PD 9004 | BS 9000, CECC and IEQC–UK Administrative guide to procedures & the QA systems |
| BS 9010 onwards | Individual specifications for electronic components |

A manufacturer seeking general approval to make components of assessed quality has first to apply to BSI. He is then 'vetted' to ensure that his organization is satisfactory (in a similar manner to MOD approval as described previously). Then qualification approval is sought for the particular component/s desired. This necessitates stringent prototype testing of samples to an agreed specification (these tests are not carried out by the supervising inspectorate but by the component maker under the control of his chief inspector). After the test results and samples have been approved the manufacturer can then make and test these components. Acceptance of production quantities is carried out by his own inspection organization using source control methods of QA (any samples required being extracted from each batch and tested to specification). Deliveries are then made to a 'bonded store', whence they can be sold to any customer (government or commercial) as complying with the appropriate specification in the extensive BS 9000 series of several hundred specification. It should be noted that all operations are under the control of the firm's chief inspector, who will supply any test certificates and release documentation necessary, and that the customer does not have to carry out any inspection himself. However, continuing quality assurance supervision (including any periodic 'audit') is carried out by the BSI appointed inspectorate (in this case the EQD of MOD). It should further be noted that this system of inspection/QA procedure is applied internationally through CECC and IECQ* and is capable of development in other fields besides electronics.

(iii) *Process control charts to control quality.* By taking samples routinely during the manufacture of some articles and recording specific factor/s charts can be made which will help to control a process, so that corrective action can be taken if the process goes out of limits (or control). Hence these

---

*CECC–Electrical Components Committee of CENELEC (the Joint European Committee for Electrotechnical Standardization). IECQ–International Electrotechnical Commission–Quality

charts will enable production to be maintained along the correct lines and so will enable quality to be controlled. Consequently inspection after manufacture may be wholly or partly replaced. Various forms of charting are available:

(a) BS 5701 deals with control charts for counted attributes; i.e. whether a particular attribute, such as a dimension or a shape (perhaps checked by gauging) is right or wrong. The faults are counted and entered on 'number-defective' charts.

(b) BS 5702 deals with control charts for measured variables, i.e. a number of variable factors; one chart may be necessary for each variable.

(c) BS 5703 is a guide to data analysis and quality control using cumulative sum (cusum) techniques, which have advantages over traditional techniques. First, for a given sample size the chart gives a clear indication of any change occurring, and of the magnitude and location of that change in a process; second, the more effective use of data leads to cost saving. Sample sizes required for counted attributes (number–defective) techniques are some 25–50 whereas measured variables need some five samples. Cusum charts may be used for controlling counted attributes or measured variables, and are a comparatively new technique. Detailed explanations and methods of use are given in the relevant British Standards. Similar techniques can be used for statistical process control (SPC).

### 9.4.8 Other methods of quality assurance

Under the spur of foreign competition much thought has been given to many methods of improving, maintaining and assuring the quality of goods and equipment, but the British Standards etc. already mentioned represent the present 'official' position on these matters (Table 9.1 gives a list of British Standards relevant to inspection and quality assurance).

The BS definition of QA is '*all* activities and functions concerned with the attainment of quality' and traditionally an inspector's job has been to *reject incorrect* items. Quality control prevents production getting out of hand and *producing incorrect* items. Quality assurance embraces both inspection and quality control. The activities of Japan in this connection warrant close attention. In a few years Japanese goods have advanced from what were considered to be shoddy copies of Western products to highly sophisticated and reliable articles, which on their own merits have flooded the Western world to the detriment particularly of British domestically produced articles and exports.

This has been done by a combination of close study of, particularly, US and UK inspection and quality procedures and infinite attention to detail by Japanese industry (management *and* workers). It has almost become a matter of religion to attain and maintain quality. Circulation of literature relevant to QA has attained massive proportions. The conditioning of workers' minds before starting work, and the formation of quality circles to meditate on methods of improving work and quality are further examples. It is a well known fact (which the Japanese must know) that the first half-hour of work produces the most mistakes and accidents so why not have a period of relaxation exercises, meditation (or even prayer) before commencing work, thinking perhaps of the terrible results of any accidents, loss of jobs and prestige which might occur if faulty equipment should get into service. See also reference to the Japanese approach to QA e.g. *What is Total Quality Control? The Japanese Way*, by Ishikawa, Kaoru (Prentice-Hall 1985).

Another approach is the zero defects system, much tried and used in the USA and elsewhere, based on the idea of 'making things right first time' and a philosophy which includes *inter alia* pledged and signed personal statements by executives and workers. Each worker is requested to fill in a card detailing the errors that can be made on his job, and his suggestions for eliminating them. Recognition and awards are given for achievements, error-free days, etc. by individuals and departments. There is much publicity and bally-hoo from the top! It seems to work—improvements in quality and safety are recorded. But the pressure must be kept up, and an existing inspection/quality assurance department seems essential.

### 9.4.9 Quality circles

In Japan a quality circle is formed of 5 to 10 workers (who have volunteered), led perhaps by a foreman (or a person of higher or lower status). Similar circles exist in *all* departments throughout the whole plant or organization. Everyone from top management to the lowliest worker should cooperate, forming a company wide quality control (CWQC) scheme. Such circles form a ready means of communication between all levels and permit discussion and the use of initiative in solving problems in their own area.

Originally developed after World War II by an American sponsored study of statistical quality control (SQC) and organized by the Union of Japanese Scientists and Engineers (JUSE) quality circles spread like wildfire to cover all aspects of production (including design, technology and research and even planning, accounts, sales and personnel).

Education and training has enabled circle leaders (and many others) to understand the elements of SQC and to use where necessary the appropriate methods and charts. However activities now extend far beyond the mathematics of SQC and have produced amazing results. Much use is made of diagrams to display simply the statistical results of production, and to analyse defects and their causes (maybe trouble with materials, manpower, methods or machines) so that they can be eliminated. It should be noted that although SQC applies particularly to the mass production of small articles, the Japanese approach to CWQC covers the manufacture of all plant and equipment, large and small.

Perhaps there is an analogy between Britain in 1940 and Japan in 1945. Both countries then had to struggle for survival. Japan, with a large population to feed and employ, with little suitable agricultural land and few natural resources (like coal and oil), had to export or die. There was no room for arguments and considerations about 'them and us'. Everyone had to work together with a will in the national interest. To keep up enthusiasm QC conferences, quality months, standards months, etc. are held at intervals (like Britain's wartime savings campaigns, warship weeks, Spitfire collections, etc.). It is recorded that in one year some 80 conferences were held all over Japan, attended by over 60,000 QC leaders. Perhaps more than one in eight Japanese workers are engaged in some form of quality activity (often in their own time). Not only has quality been improved, resulting in increased customer satisfaction, but also there is increased job satisfaction and perhaps pride for the worker. As fewer incorrect parts, etc. are made less time and material is wasted and overall costs may well be substantially reduced.

### 9.4.10 Taguchi methods

From about the late 1970s, the Japanese engineer Taguchi developed methods of quality control based strongly on statistical concepts, a minimization of the total loss generated by a product, a continuing quality improvement programme including incessant reduction in the variation of product parameters about their target values and many other factors.

His methods seem complex and have been little understood outside Japan, but were taken up in the USA in the early 1980s by firms such as A T & T Bell Laboratories (ITT), Xerox and Fords with apparently startling quality improvement and reductions in cost (although some scepticism has been expressed in certain quarters).

Introductory papers and some details of Taguchi's methods may be found in Quality Assurance (the Journal of the Institute of Quality Assurance) Vol. 13, No. 3, September 1987. Further references include:

Taguchi, G & Wu, Y., *Introduction to off-line quality control systems*, 1980 (Central Japan Quality Control Assoc.—available from American Supplier Inst., Dearborn, MI)
Taguchi, G., *Off-line and on-line quality control systems* (Proceedings International Conference on Quality Control, Tokyo, 1978)

### 9.5 Manufacturing processes and their inspection

Some details of materials inspection and testing procedures are given in Chapter 2 and some manufacturing processes and their inspection are dealt with in Chapter 5; inspection requirements for a variety of items of plant and equipment are covered in other chapters. Some details of processes for joining materials, and for the inspection of these processes, will now be given, followed in Chapter 10 by a review of non-destructive testing techniques applicable to many processes and items of plant. Chapters 12 and 13 deal with inspection during commissioning and operation; many of the procedures and techniques used therein involve processes previously described.

### 9.5.1 *Joining of materials and components*

One important aspect of inspection during manufacture concerns the examination and approval of the techniques used in the joining of materials and components. Such joining may be carried out by a number of methods, according to the needs of design and particular circumstances, amongst which would be:

(i) Mechanical fastening, including the use of screws, nuts and bolts, hinges and rivets.

(ii) Physical bonding, ranging from surface adhesion by sticking, soldering, etc., to fusion welding.

Inspection of the methods in the first group largely consists of checking that detail parts, such as screw threads, are to specification, and that the connections have been well and truly made. Final examination of, for instance, riveted joints would check that the rivets are a good and complete fit in their holes, and that rivet heads are not malformed or the surrounding plate damaged by hammer blows, etc. Some process checking, such as for heat treatment of aluminium alloy rivets, may be necessary, but generally speaking, assuming satisfactory design calculations, much can be done by dimensional and visual inspection.

Inspection of the methods in the second group, however, cannot be adequately carried out purely by visual means. Effective process control is essential.

### 9.6 Inspection of soldering and brazing

The terms *soldering* and *brazing* are applied to processes in which a joint is made by the introduction of molten metal between the parts to be joined, without intentional fusion of the parent metal.

Inspection must check that firstly the parts to be joined have been cleaned by a suitable process, and that an approved flux is used. For soldering, the parts must then be thoroughly *tinned* at the proposed joint, and can then be joined by melting the proper grade of solder in contact with the parts, in the presence of the flux (by means of a non-luminous flame, a soldering iron or other suitable means). Afterwards it is often necessary to wash soldered parts in boiling water to remove any traces of a flux which may eventually cause corrosion. Parts which cannot be so washed, e.g. electrical and instrument equipment, are often soldered using a rosin type flux. The flux may be contained within the solder (e.g. BS 441 deals with flux-cored soft solder wire, and describes tests for freedom from corrosive action). Soft solders consist of tin and lead in various proportions with the occasional addition of other metals to lower the melting point.

The fluxes used for general engineering work include 'killed' spirits of salt (zinc chloride) for tin plate, brass, copper, gun metal, etc.; spirits of salt (hydrochloric acid) for galvanized steel and zinc; and stearin and ortho-phosphoric acid for aluminium and alloys. The addition of a wetting agent to the flux is recommended. It is possible to soft-solder stainless steel.

Silver soldering is carried out at a higher temperature than soft soldering and the solders used contain silver, copper and zinc and may have melting points of 650 to 800°C. The flux used may be borax or a proprietary one. Thorough washing in hot water after soldering is necessary.

Brazing is a form of high-temperature soldering using borax as a flux above 750°C, and a fluoride type from 600 to 750°C; the jointing medium (brazing or filler metal) is copper, brass or a copper or silver alloy, and may be in the form of powder, filings, wire, strip, etc. The surfaces to be joined must be closely fitted so that the filler metal can flow by capillary attraction. The process can be carried out satisfactorily on most metals, and will give joint strengths varying from a percentage of that of the filler metal to values in excess of this, where considerable alloying with a stronger brazed component has taken place. Inspection must ensure adequate removal of all residual flux. After removal of the flux residue the inspector should examine, if possible, both sides of the brazed joint to see whether the filler metal has penetrated and is visible on both sides. The pre-placing of prepared shapes or forms of filler metal in the correct position can help penetration and the achievement of high joint efficiency (which may be taken as 100% in visibly good cases).

Cracks in the filler metal or the adjacent base metal are cause for rejection. Dye penetrant inspection (see 10.8) can be used to check this. For the highest class of work a crack in the adjacent braze metal should not be repaired, but is a reason for scrapping.

Pin holes and rough or irregular surfaces in the braze metal should be rejected for rectification. Some standards, etc., dealing with soldering and brazing are given in Table 9.4.

It should be mentioned that the ASME Boiler and Pressure Vessel Code, under Section IX *Welding qualifications*, deals also with procedures for the approval of fabrication techniques for brazing, and the qualification testing of brazers and brazing operators.

## TABLE 9.4

*Some soldering and brazing specifications and publications*

| No. of specification or publication | Description |
|---|---|
| BS  219 | Soft solders |
| BS  441 | Purchasing requirements for flux-cored and solid soft-solder wire |
| BS 1723 | Brazing (deals with joint design and preparation, filler metals, flux and flux removal, inspection and testing of operators. Describes the blow pipe (torch), furnace, electric induction and resistance, vacuum, dip and salt bath processes) |
| BS 1724 | Bronze welding by gas (specifies workmanship, inspection and testing procedure, gives requirements for joints, filler metal, etc.) |
| BS 1845 | Filler metals for brazing (includes some for vacuum applications) |
| BS 3338 | Part 12: Sampling of solders |
| Aluminium Development Association Information Bulletin No. 23 | Describes materials and techniques for aluminium brazing |
| Tin Research Institute | Notes on soldering |
| American Welding Society | Soldering manual |

### 9.7  Fusion welding

In contrast with soldering and brazing, with welding the joint is made by bringing the respective portions of the parent metal to molten temperature and then causing them to fuse together, perhaps with the aid of pressure and/or the addition of suitable molten filler material.

The welding procedure is generally as follows.

The parts to be welded are heated along the line of the desired joint, and when the material is molten a filler rod, raised to melting temperature, is generally brought over the join, so forming a pool of molten material. This pool is then caused to run along the line of weld, melting ahead of it, and fusing the two parts together as they cool and solidify, so making a homogenerous joint.

A number of processes are in regular use in industry for the welding of both ferrous and non-ferrous metals. Other processes may be used for non-metallic materials. The choice of method depends on the material and thickness to be welded, quantities required, quality of weld demanded, etc.

An outline of these methods, such as would be necessary knowledge for the inspection and supervision of the processes, will now be given. This knowledge can be supplemented by reference to standard works and to the various codes and specifications, some of which are listed in Table 9.5. Other methods may be applicable to the welding and joining of plastics.

### TABLE 9.5

*Some welding standards*

(For standards dealing with non-destructive examination of welds see Tables 10.2, 10.5 and 10.6)

| BS No. | Description |
| --- | --- |
| 499 | Welding terms and symbols<br>Part 1: Welding, brazing and thermal cutting glossary<br>Part 2: Symbols for welding<br>Part 2C: Chart of British Standard welding symbols |
| 638 | Arc welding power sources, equipment and accessories (7 parts) |
| 709 | Methods of destructive testing fusion-welded joints and weld metal in steel |
| 1140 | Resistance spot welding of uncoated and coated low carbon steel |
| 1295 | Tests for use in the training of welders. Manual metal-arc and oxy-acetylene welding of mild steel |
| 1821 | Class I oxy-acetylene welding of ferritic/pipework steel for carrying fluids |
| 2630 | Resistance projection welding of uncoated low carbon steel sheet and strip using embossed projections |
| 2633 | Class I arc welding of ferritic steel pipework for carrying fluids |
| 2640 | Class II oxy-acetylene welding of carbon steel pipework for carrying fluids |
| 2971 | Class II metal-arc welding of carbon steel pipework for carrying fluids |
| 2996 | Projection welding of low-carbon wrought steel studs, bosses, bolts, nuts and annular rings |
| 3019 | TIG welding<br>Part 1: Aluminium, magnesium and their alloys<br>Part 2: Austenitic stainless and heat resisting steels |
| 3451 | Testing fusion welds in aluminium and aluminium alloys |
| 3571 | General recommendations for manual inert-gas metal-arc welding<br>Part 1: Aluminium and aluminium alloys |
| 4204 | Flash welding of steel tubes for pressure applications |
| 4206 | Methods of testing fusion welds in copper and copper alloys |
| 4360 | Weldable structural steels |
| 4677 | Class I arc welding of austenitic stainless steel pipework for carrying fluids (includes inspection and testing, procedure and welder qualification tests, acceptance requirements) |

**TABLE 9.5** *concluded*

| BS No. | Description |
|---|---|
| 4870 | Approval testing of welding procedures<br>Part 1: Fusion welding of steels<br>Part 2: TIG or MIG welding of aluminium and its alloys |
| 4871 | Approval testing of welders working to approved welding procedures<br>Part 1: Fusion welding of steel<br>Part 2: TIG or MIG welding of aluminium and its alloys |
| 4872 | Approval testing of welders when welding procedure approval is not required<br>Part 1: Fusion welding of steel (covers manual and semi-automatic welding)<br>Part 2: TIG or MIG welding of aluminium and its alloys |
| 5135 | Specification for process of arc welding or carbon and carbon manganese steels (includes procedures for approval, avoidance of cracking, lamellar tearing, acceptance levels, etc.) |
| 5289 | Code of practice for visual inspection of fusion-welded joints |
| 6265 | Resistance seam welding of uncoated or coated low carbon steel |
| 6503 | Hand-held blowpipes, mixers and nozzles using fuel gas and oxygen for gas-welding and cutting, etc (includes safety features) |
| PD 6493 | Guidance on some methods for the derivation of acceptance levels for defects in fusion welded joints. |

## 9.8 Oxy-acetylene welding

This method, which is cheap in cost and equipment, can be used where welds of the highest quality are not demanded and where corrosion problems are not generally encountered. Considerable distortion of the work may occur. The heat for welding is generated by the combustion of acetylene gas $(C_2H_2)$ in oxygen under controlled conditions using a simple blowpipe, the flame temperature attained being in the region of 3000°C. It should be checked by inspection that the flame is maintained as near neutral as possible, Fig, 9.1. In general an excess of oxygen produces a porous and oxidized weld, whilst an excess of acetylene causes a carburized weld of inferior corrosion resistance possibly of a brittle nature. However, some non-ferrous alloys, such as aluminium and magnesium alloys and Inconel, may require a slightly carburizing flame, whilst brass needs an oxidizing flame. A suitable approved flux is used for all metals other than middle steel. Filler rod is fed in separately as required; this rod may be flux coated.

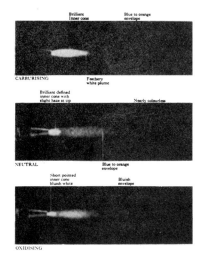

**Fig. 9.1 Carburizing, neutral and oxidizing flames.**
*(Welding Institute)*

## 9.9 Atomic hydrogen welding

In this method hydrogen gas passes through an alternating current arc struck between tungsten electrodes in the torch, and in so doing the hydrogen molecules ($H_2$) dissociate into single atoms (2H). Immediately outside the arc the atoms recombine to form molecules of hydrogen again. In so doing considerable heat is given out (the heat of re-association), forming an intensely hot 'flame' (about 3750°C). As the burning hydrogen atmosphere around the weld protects it from oxidation, extremely neat welds can be produced. Filler metal in the form of bare wire is added as required, the process being mainly used for steel and its alloys. The arc current may be some 12 to 50 amperes and the open-circuit voltage required some 300 volts.

## 9.10 Carbon-arc welding

In this method an arc is struck between a carbon rod electrode and the work. A source of direct current, usually provided by a special generator, supplies the arc, the carbon electrode being connected to the negative pole. The inspector should check that this connection is not reversed, nor must a.c. be used, as carbon would then be transferred to the weld, producing a hard, brittle weld, liable to crack, and impairing its corrosion resistance. The use of the correct grade of filler rod should be checked. These rods are usually specially coated with flux, which is necessary to prevent oxidation and porosity. Thick steel plates can be welded and a considerable volume of metal deposited. The arc temperature is high, and of the order of 3500 to 4000°C. Although stainless steel may be welded by this process it is not recommended that sizes larger than some 14 standard wire gauge should be so fabricated.

Welding by this process, and also by the atomic hydrogen process, is not so widely used today, having been largely superseded by the metallic-arc and inert-gas welding processes.

### 9.11 Metallic-arc welding

This method is possibly the most widely employed today. An arc is formed between a metal rod or electrode and the work, the rod being of the same of similar material. The heat of the arc, which may be slightly lower in temperature than that of the carbon arc, melts the metal immediately beneath it, and also the tip of the electrode, globules of which are forced to

**TABLE 9.6**

*Some standards for welding electrodes, rods, safety, etc.*

| BS No. | Description |
| --- | --- |
| 639 | Covered electrodes for the manual metal-arc welding of carbon and carbon manganese steels |
| 1453 | Filler materials for gas welding |
| 2493 | Low-alloy steel electrodes for manual metal-arc welding |
| 2901 | Filler rods and wires for gas shielded arc welding |
| 2926 | Chromium and chromium-nickel steel electrodes for manual metal-arc welding |
| 4165 | Electrodes wires and fluxes for submerged arc welding of carbon steel and medium-tensile steel |
| 4577 | Material for resistance welding electrodes and ancillary equipment |

**Standards dealing with welding safety**

| | |
| --- | --- |
| 679 | Filters for use during welding and similar industrial operations (Relates to eye protection) |
| 1542 | Equipment for eye, face and neck protection against radiation arising during welding and similar operations |
| 2653 | Protective clothing for welders |
| 6691 | Fume from welding and allied operations (Guide to sampling and analysis) |

cross the arc and are deposited onto the molten part of the work. This process can be used for material thicknesses varying from, say, 20 s.w.g. to plate many inches thick; most metals, including stainless steel, can be satisfactorily welded. Bare metal electrodes were originally used for metallic-arc welding, but these generally produce a sputtering arc and brittle welds, owing to atmospheric contamination. Consequently specially coated electrodes, which produce gas and slag and so protect the molten metal from the atmosphere, are now generally used (see Table 9.6). The inspector should check particularly that the approved grade of electrode for a particular application has been used. Heat drying of the electrodes may be necessary. For some applications, particularly for high-quality welds and for non-ferrous metals and stainless steels, the steady arc obtained from a special d.c. generator or rectifier is employed. The open-circuit voltage is some 60 to 70 volts and the electrode is usually connected to the positive pole, although when welding heavy sections, and also aluminium, the reverse connection is sometimes recommended as, when using d.c., more heat is generated at the positive pole. However, most metallic-arc welding, particularly of mild steel, is carried out using an a.c. supply, as a.c. equipment is cheaper in first cost and, when welding mild steel using coated electrodes and currents of the order of 200–300 amperes, gives results equally as good as d.c. welding. The open-circuit voltage is usually some 75–100 volts, generally obtained from the public supply mains via a transformer.

## 9.12 Submerged-arc welding

In this process the heat required for welding is generated by an electric current passing between the end of a continuous reel of bare wire, which forms one electrode, and the workpiece. The arc is struck and maintained underneath a layer of granular flux which is fed in automatically in front of the arc, completely covering the weld pool, the arc space, the tip of the electrode and behind it, so that the arc is invisible and the weld protected. The process may be manually operated or fully automatic, the flux and wire being fed in as the weld proceeds. The flux in contact with the weld fuses and then solidifies behind the welding zone. The remaining unfused flux is removed, usually by a suction hose, and used again. The fused flux contracts on cooling and is readily removed from the weld. This method is restricted largely to the automatic welding of heavy plates where the high cost of the equipment is justified; d.c. is normally employed, although a.c. may be used.

## 9.13 Inert-gas-shielded (argon-arc) welding

Two main variants of this type of welding are in use.

(i) Inert-gas-shielded tungsten-arc welding (TIG).

(ii) Inert-gas-shielded metal-arc welding (MIG).

The inert gas generally used is argon, sometimes mixed with oxygen, $CO_2$ or nitrogen. In the USA helium is normally employed. Consequently, as the molten metal is thus protected from attack by atmospheric oxygen and nitrogen, a good clean weld is produced. No flux is required.

An important application of argon-arc welding is in the production of high-quality welds in stainless steel, aluminium, etc. Generally speaking, a d.c. arc is preferred for these materials, but a.c. can be used, often with a high-frequency low-voltage current superimposed on it to aid arc initiation and prevent electrode contamination.

In the tungsten-arc (TIG) welding process an arc is struck between a tungsten bead electrode and the work, whilst the area is surrounded by the inert-gas atmosphere. Filler metal, when needed, is added separately in the form of a suitable bare wire. Manually operated or automatic plants are used. Material from the thinnest sheet to quite large plate can be handled with suitable equipment.

When using direct current the tungsten electrode is usually connected to the negative pole. The inert gas is fed from a cylinder via a reducing valve and regulator to the welding area, where it issues at low velocity around the electrode. For light-duty manual equipment the torch is air-cooled, but for heavier work and for automatic equipment water cooling may be necessary.

In the metal-arc inert-gas (MIG) welding process a bare wire is continuously fed into the arc at constant speed, through a pistol-like torch for manual operation, or via a suitable welding head in an automatic plant. The inert gas is also fed through this torch or head. Usually d.c. is employed, the

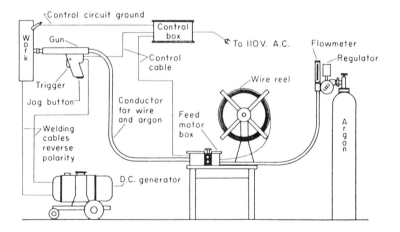

**Fig. 9.2  Schematic diagram of MIG welding equipment.**
*(Welding Institute)*

electrode being connected to the positive pole. A typical arrangement is shown in Fig. 9.2. Various automatic refinements can be fitted.

## 9.14 $CO_2$-gas-shielded metal-arc welding

The comparatively high cost of argon makes its use rather uneconomic for the commercial welding of ordinary steels, particularly outdoors. Consequently the $CO_2$-gas-shielded metal-arc welding process has been developed and has come into increasing use, particularly for the high-quality welding of abutting pipes during pipe-laying operations and for certain workshop and industrial applications.

This process is characterized by its economy, high welding speed and quality. It enables high metal deposition rates to be achieved, so cutting costs. Owing to the low hydrogen content of the deposited weld metal, the weld possesses very good mechanical properties.

$CO_2$ gas is fed from a cylinder (or possibly a liquid container in large installations) via a heater to a welding torch or gun, which is connected to a constant voltage d.c. rectifier unit, and fed by a reel of consumable wire. The arc is struck between the tip of this welding wire and the work, the work being connected to the negative pole. The welding wire is fed in semi-automatically. The gun may be air- or water-cooled, and an electronic timer unit may be fitted for spot, plug or tack welding.

The welding wire is of specially prepared steel, often containing small amounts of alloying elements such as manganese and silicon. It is electrolytically coated with deoxidized copper to minimize corrosion and to provide good electrical contact. For some applications, such as high deposition welding of thick sections, the wire may be cored with synthetic flux.

In general, the $CO_2$-gas-shielded metal-arc process can be used for high-quality ferrous welding, and the inert-gas argon metal-arc process for high-quality non-ferrous and some stainless steel welding.

The term metal inert-gas (MIG) welding is now taken to embrace both true inert-gas and $CO_2$ welding. Mixtures of various gases may be specified.

### 9.14.1 Modes of metal transfer

With normal MIG welding two principal modes of transfer of molten metal to the weld occur:

(i) In *spray* transfer, small droplets of metal are projected from the wire tip across the arc gap to the weld pool at constant current, and with sufficient velocity to overcome gravitational effects.

(ii) In *dip* transfer, metal is deposited somewhat irregularly during the periods when the wire dips into the molten pool and short-circuits the arc.

Metal transfer may also be *globular*, i.e. massive drops released relatively slowly.

In general, the modes of transfer often occur in combination.

If the inert gas helium is used for shielding, transfer is globular at all levels of current, but spray transfer can be produced by diluting it with argon (some 25%). Active gases like $CO_2$ and nitrogen behave much like argon.

Dip and globular transfer are not always satisfactory, and unfortunately the lowest current which produces good spray transfer may result in too high a heat input for unsupported thin material, and burn-through may occur.

### 9.15 Pulsed arc welding

A further development in MIG welding is to superimpose a pulse on the normal d.c. supply. By so doing, and by using an argon or argon-rich atmosphere, the spray transfer of droplets can be controlled and will only occur at the period of pulse or peak current. During the intervals between pulses a background current maintains ionization, but no metal is transferred. This means that, although metal is projected across the arc gap at a high current, the mean welding current is relatively low. The operator has control of the level of the background and pulsed currents; thus high deposition rates with comparatively low heat inputs are obtainable. This ability to weld with lower currents is of immense assistance in sheet metal work, particularly with thin gauges, as burn-through does not occur.

It has been found that pulse frequencies of 50 or 100 c/s give very satisfactory results.

Some other advantages claimed for controlled transfer pulsed arc welding are high-quality spatter-free welding, exceptional regularity of weld finish, consistent penetration, ability to weld in all positions, and reduced weld carbon content and improved alloy recovery with alloy and stainless steels.

### 9.16 Electrical resistance welding

In a number of welding processes, an electric current is passed through the materials to be joined, which are held together under pressure. Heat is generated by the passage of this current through the electrical resistance existing between the parts in contact, melting occurs, and welding takes place.

Electrical resistance welding can be sub-divided into several processes, including spot, seam, projection and flash or butt welding.

In *spot welding* the shaded tips of two electrodes (usually of copper) are brought together, so clamping between them the materials to be joined. At the appropriate moment a heavy but sharply controlled surge of current is passed between the electrodes, and welds the parts together by a small spot having the shape of the electrode tip.

Similarly in *seam welding* a series of spot welds are produced at regular intervals in line formation. The electrodes are disc-shaped and rotate as the material is welded, the current being controlled so that a timed pulse travels at intervals through the materials to be joined, so effectively stitching them together. As the weld is not continuous it may not form an absolutely tight joint, but by careful adjustment and control it can be made sufficiently tight for most commercial purposes. The inspector should therefore watch this point in applications where extreme tightness is desirable; it should also be noted that there will be a tendency for the trapping of chemical solutions, gases, etc., between adjacent welds, with the consequent risk of troubles such as corrosion.

In *projection welding* one or more projections are raised on the part or parts to be joined. These parts are arranged so that they can be clamped between specially designed dies which form the electrodes. When the machine is operated these projections are forcibly brought into contact with the other part or parts, weld current flows, and the projections soften and collapse under pressure, so forming individual welds. The dies are often faced with tungsten-copper inserts at the points of contact with the projections. Projection welding machines, which are of substantial construction, are often arranged so that they can also be adapted to heavy spot welding work.

Butt and flash welding are somewhat similar processes, butt welding being usually applied to components of somewhat smaller section. In *butt welding* the two pieces to be joined are held in clamps and then brought firmly together whilst a heavy current from the secondary winding of a transformer passes through them. This causes heating, the heat being concentrated mainly at the abutting faces. The material at these faces becomes plastic, and the applied pressure forces the parts together in a solid bond.

The abutting faces must be checked before welding to ensure they are flat and parallel, in order to obtain even heating and to avoid trapped crevices.

In *flash (or flash-butt) welding*, which is used to join comparatively heavy components of generally equal cross-section such as tubes and bars, the two pieces to be welded are solidly connected to a low-voltage a.c. supply, and are then brought into contact. The slight inequalities in finish, etc., of the ends is then relied upon to cause the current to pass through these small projections which are in contact. These quickly melt and flash away, the parts· are pushed closer together, flashing occurs again, and the metal ends rise to welding temperature. At the critical moment more force is applied (forging or *up-setting*), and the parts weld together, the current being cut off simultaneously.

## 9.17 Thermit welding

By mixing aluminium powder with powdered iron oxide and igniting it, a reaction is started and the heat generated is sufficient to raise the temperature theoretically to some 3600°C. This constitutes a convenient method of welding heavy sections of steel, such as rails, and for repairing industrial plant. The end portions of the pieces to be joined are contained in a mould, and this is generally preheated to red heat prior to the pouring of the molten steel resulting from the thermit reaction.

The inspector should ensure that the mould is thoroughly dry before the powder is ignited. The operator should wear goggles and protective clothing. The crucible for the molten metal should have a cover.

## 9.18 Ultrasonic welding and joining

Many otherwise difficult metals can be joined with the aid of ultrasonics. In some cases ultrasonic vibration makes the bond without the application of heat; in others, it assists fusion welding.

Soldering of aluminium can be successfully carried out, the tightly adherent oxide film being dispersed by ultrasonic vibrations, which are applied via the soldering iron.

## 9.19 Jointing of copper

Copper can be jointed by soldering with tin-lead alloys using a rosin or zinc and ammonium chloride based flux. The copper must be clean and free from grease and foreign matter. Brazing and silver soldering use higher temperatures, of the order of 600–900°C, and solders of various compositions of copper and zinc, or silver and copper, with or without small additions of other metals. Brazing materials however tend to cause some selective corrosive action in aggressive solutions due to the electrical potential between these materials and pure copper.

Welding of copper is regularly carried out by most of the usual methods, but trouble can arise if copper oxide is present. If the heating is prolonged and intense the copper oxide may migrate to the grain boundaries, causing serious embrittlement and possibly intergranular corrosion. Similarly a reducing oxy-acetylene weld flame on tough pitch copper can cause a reaction with the copper oxide present and lead to embrittlement and porosity in the weld metal. Consequently deoxidized and oxygen-free coppers (to such specifications as BS 6017) are subjected to a hydrogen embrittlement test to ensure their freedom from contained oxide. For best service results under exacting conditions inert-gas welding using deoxidized copper (or oxygen-free copper if high conductivity is required) should be employed.

## 9.20 Jointing of nickel

The jointing of nickel and its alloys can be carried out by most welding processes, with perhaps a preference for inert-gas tungsten-arc welding for use with light-gauge material. As-welded joints in nickel, Monel and Inconel match the tensile and corrosion-resisting properties of the annealed parent metals. However inspectors should note that heat treatment after welding is usually necessary for the other alloys in order to develop their optimum properties. Soft soldering has limited applications, but silver soldering is frequently used, care being taken to employ the recommended solders (BS 219) on materials in the annealed condition, to avoid stress cracking. High-temperature brazing can be used when welding is impracticable.

### 9.20.1 Embrittlement of nickel

Before any operation is carried out on nickel which involves heating it to a high temperature, such as welding, heat treatment, brazing, hot forming or forging, the inspector should carry out a thorough check to see that no trace of any sulphur or lead containing substance is present, either on or in the vicinity of the nickel. The substances involved could include oils, greases and lubricants, solders, paint and various marking compositions, whilst of course the furnace atmosphere should be essentially sulphur-free.

Should sulphur or lead be present they will combine with the nickel (and to a lesser extent with nickel alloys) at elevated temperatures and cause embrittlement, particularly at the grain boundaries, which can result in the formation of a network of cracks when the material is stressed.

In general, material so affected must be scrapped.

At room temperature nickel is strongly magnetic, nickel-copper alloy is slightly magnetic, and nickel-chromium-iron alloy is non-magnetic but begins to become magnetic below $-40°F$ ($-40°C$).

The inspector may find these facts of use in making a simple magnetic test to sort out the different materials.

## 9.21 Inspection of welding

The effectiveness of welding cannot be adequately verified merely by visual examination of the finished article. Consequently, welding inspection depends largely on supervision of the details of the process. A well-finished welded joint is a good sign, but this is not sufficient in itself.

The method adopted for ensuring weld quality is threefold:

(i) The competency of each individual welding operator is checked. Each is given a test piece to weld. These test pieces are then examined and tested. If satisfactory, the welder is given some measure of approval (or, in some cases, a particular piece of work with which the test piece is related receives approval).

(ii) The material of the electrodes or welding rods is specified (stating composition, diameter and, where relevant, the maker's approved type number). Details are given of any flux or shielding gas required. Inspection has to verify that these are actually used, and in the correct manner.

(iii) Techniques for the preparation of the material to be welded, for the actual welding, and for any subsequent treatment (such as stress relieving) and testing (such as radiographic examination), are laid down. Inspection has to verify that these techniques are followed; checks can be carried out at any other stages in and after the process if considered necessary.

Detailed particulars concerning these three requirements and of safety are given in many standards, codes and publications, not the least of which are those of the British Standards Institution. A selection of these is given in Tables 9.5 and 9.6.

### 9.21.1 Approval of welders and welding

Amongst other specifications, standards and codes giving details of procedure for the testing and approval of welders and welding operators, mention should be made of BS 4870, 4871 and 4872, and particularly of the ASME Boiler and Pressure Vessel Code, Section IX *Welding qualifications*. The ASME Code follows generally that of the American Welding Society's *Standard Qualification Procedure*, which forms the basis of many other codes and procedures.

In general, a welding procedure specification for each process, material, component, etc. is prepared (giving details of metals, electrodes, position of weld and its preparation, heat treatment, etc.), and submitted for approval. Test pieces to an approved drawing are then made to this specification or a particular application standard by the welder under examination, and submitted for test. The tests may include both longitudinal and transverse bend tests, tensile tests, and visual and macro inspection. For butt welds the bend test may consist of bending through 180° over a former, four times the weld thickness in diameter, without cracking. For fillet welds the test piece may be broken by hammer blows and examined.

(*Note.* Fillet weld sizes are usually given on drawings in terms of leg dimensions, i.e. lengths parallel with the members being joined. The ASME Code (and others), however, gives sizes in terms of throat dimensions (i.e. the perpendicular distance from the root to the hypotenuse of the largest

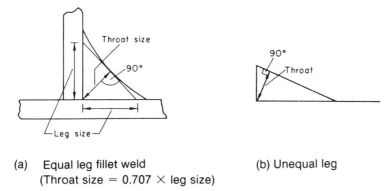

(a)    Equal leg fillet weld                    (b) Unequal leg
(Throat size = 0.707 × leg size)

**Fig. 9.3.    Fillet weld dimensions.**
**The minimum throat area is normally used when making load calcu-**
**lations.**

right-angled triangle that can be inscribed within the fillet weld cross-section), in order to facilitate load calculations (see Fig. 9.3).)

The examination of welded joints by sectioning is often carried out, one procedure being detailed in an Appendix to the ASME Code, but it is not now considered a substitute for spot radiography in pressure vessel inspection.

A specimen, large enough to provide a full cross-section of the joint, is cut out from the weld, ground or filed smooth, and then etched in a suitable solution (such as hydrochloric acid and water) to reveal any defects. The specimen must not show any cracks or lack of penetration, but a certain amount of porosity and of slag inclusions is permitted.

Specimens may be marked or otherwise identified with relevant details and kept for reference.

The holes left in the welded component must be closed by a welding procedure approved by the inspector.

The destructive and non-destructive testing of welds (including radiographic examination) is dealt with in BS 709, BS 4870, and particularly in BS 5500 and BS 1113 (see Chapters 3, particularly 3.14 and 3.15).

BS 709 *Methods of Destructive testing fusion welded joints and weld metal in steel* gives details of routine approval tests normally required by application standards (such as BS 1113) and covers transverse and weld tensile tests, bend tests, fillet weld fracture tests, nick break and impact tests, macro-examination and now includes an intercrystalline corrosion test (see also BS 5903), a fracture toughness test ($K_{1c}$/COD test—see 2.8.1 and BS 5447, BS 5762 and PD 6493) and a test of hardness gradient across a weld. Dimensioned drawings of test pieces, specimens, etc. are given in this standard or in the appropriate application standard (somewhat as in Fig. 3.10).

## 9.21.2 *Inspection of welding techniques*

Information regarding the preparation of the material to be welded, and of the actual welding operations and inspection is given in great detail in many codes and specifications (e.g. see 3.8.2 and 3.9 and Chapters 3 and 4 and BS 4870). In general, prior to welding, the faces and edges of material should be examined for laminations, blisters, seams and scabs, and heavy scale, grease, paint, etc., should be removed. Warped and damaged material should be rejected. Edge preparation, bevel angle, dimensions and fit-up should be checked. The gap between abutting edges should not normally exceed $\frac{1}{16}$ in. (1·6 mm).

Some coated electrodes are subject to deterioration in store and may have to be dried in an oven before use. Low-hydrogen type coatings are particularly susceptible to moisture absorption. The presence of moisture tends to produce porosity and cracking.

During welding, the specified procedure should be seen to be carried out, and inspection at various stages may be necessary, e.g. after the first run of weld metal; any cracks or inadequate fusion or other defects can then be remedied. Details such as the number of welding runs, the current strength, etc., can be checked.

After welding, a visual inspection is carried out and tests may be made by non-destructive methods, including radiography, dye penetrants, magnetic particle inspection and ultrasonics (Chapter 10).

The control of distortion is a problem which will greatly concern the inspector and, even if he secures undistorted fabrications after welding, processes such as galvanizing, which are carried out at high temperatures after welding, may cause further trouble.

A welder and/or a welding technique proved satisfactory with one material will not necessarily be satisfactory with another, even similar, material. Even a skilled welder may need much practice before he becomes competent and can produce satisfactory test pieces when using some difficult materials. For instance, close attention to detail is needed particularly to ensure satisfactory welding of high-yield steels such as grades 50B and 50C of BS 4360; the 'fit up' for fillet welds is particularly important. A fabricator's equipment, operators, procedures and 'know how' may have to be assessed to determine his competence to undertake such work. To prevent hydrogen embrittlement with this high yield strength type of steel, basic (low hydrogen) electrodes are necessary. These must be baked immediately before use (possibly to as high as 400°C) in order to restrict porosity and cracking. The inspector may have to check the carbon equivalent of the steel, calculated from the formula given in BS 4360.

*9.21.3  Visual examination of welds*

The inspector should carry out visual inspection of the actual welds to ensure:

(i) Freedom from under-cut, overlap, cracks, craters, blow holes, spatter, burning and marked irregularities.

(ii) Correct profile (including size and shape of reinforcement and sealing run, leg length in fillet welds, etc.). Gauges may be used.

(iii) Correct fusion between weld and parent metal.

(iv) Good appearance—a smooth even finish and freedom from pockets, etc., will avoid the possibility of stress concentrations leading to cracking.

(v) Smooth joins where new electrodes have been started.

(vi) Good penetration at root of weld, as judged from the bead on the underside (in the case of a butt weld) prior to the application of the sealing run.

Extension of the visual range by optical instruments and aids is permitted. See also BS 5289, *Code of practice for visual inspection of fusion welded joints.*

*9.21.4  Acceptable levels of weld defect*

Illustrations of typical weld defects are given in BS 499. Acceptance levels for defects in fusion welded joints are often given in relevant applications specifications (e.g. BS 5500 or an ASME Code (see 13.16)); they may also be the result of mutual agreement between purchaser and manufacturer. See also PD 6493 *Guidance on some methods for the derivation of acceptance levels for defects in fusion welded joints* (BSI (1980))

*9.21.5  Inspection of welding in stainless steel*

All of the above inspectional points apply equally to stainless steel welding. In addition, when dealing with austenitic stainless steels the inspector must be alert to the possibility of so-called 'weld decay' (see 2.13). The material must be checked (or certified) to ensure correct stabilization. Welding rods or electrodes must also be stabilized, and those used in the electric-arc welding process must be niobium (columbium) stabilized. Disintegration tests should be carried out as necessary on welded test pieces.

One form of disintegration test using a cross weld piece is shown in Fig. 9.4. In this test, weld A is made first, followed by weld B, and then the sample is boiled in a copper sulphate, sulphuric acid solution for 72 hours. It is then bent at a radius $R$ from 5 to 8 times the thickness of the material. Any tendency to disintegration will be shown by cracks in the weld deposit at the positions indicated; also, if struck, the test piece will have lost its characteristic steel 'ring' (see ASTM A393 *Recommended practice for*

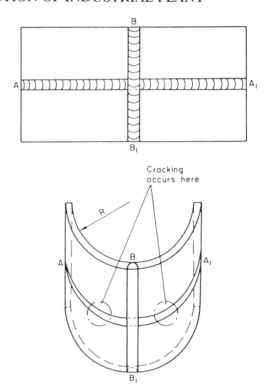

**Fig. 9.4  Stainless steel weld decay test.** (Welding Institute)

*conducting acidified copper sulphate test for intergranular attack in austenitic stainless steel; also BS 5903 Method for determination of resistance to intergranular corrosion of austenitic stainless steels: copper sulphate – sulphuric acid method* (Monypenny Strauss test).

Care must also be taken to avoid the possibility of zinc embrittlement (see 5.9) during welding operations. The action is similar to that of nickel embrittlement (9.20.1), but in this case seemingly any trace of zinc present at high temperature will interact with the nickel content of the stainless steel to produce cracks and failure.

*9.21.6 Inspection of spot welding*

The effective inspection of spot welding is difficult to achieve without destructive tests on a large percentage of welds and expensive non-destructive testing of the remainder (or a large percentage of them). Quality control of the process can and does help, but even so, individual spot welds may be below standard.

BS 1140 *Resistance spot welding of uncoated and coated low carbon steel* requires that the components to be spot welded shall be free from grease, scale, rust, paint, dirt or excessive pitting. Edges etc. must be free from burrs or other defects likely to interfere excessively with interface contact when the components are brought together during welding.

Weld test pieces, consisting of two equal metal strips welded together by one spot weld in their centre to form a cross, are specified. Type tests using a given procedure are carried out for shear, cross tension and torsion, plus a visual and metallurgical examination.

Routine production tests on similar test pieces or on actual components are carried out at the beginning and end of each shift and whenever any change of material, component or machine setting is made. These tests consist of a visual examination and a peel (slug) test or a torsion test. In general, for the shear, cross tension and peel tests all welds must 'pull a slug' on fracture (i.e. take part of the mating metal with them). For torsion test the weld should be assessed by the maximum torque or angle to failure. The standard of defects permissible, and acceptance requirements generally, are subject to agreement.

A method of assessing weld quality by utilizing the amount of thermal expansion of a spot weld during its formation, has been developed by the Welding Institute. Briefly the thermal expansion caused by the heat of the weld is accommodated by the separation of the electrodes. Although the machine may be set to give a fixed effective weld current (and therefore a fixed amount of expansion), unpredictable variations will occur due to such things as voltage fluctuations, surface resistance variations, electrode wear and shunting of part of the weld current. Consequently the amount of expansion (or head movement) during welding is a measure of the quality of an individual spot weld. The slope or rate of thermal expansion is an even more effective measure of quality.

(See D.N. Waller, 'Head movement as a means of resistance welding quality control', *British Welding Journal*, March 1964; 'The BWRA spot welding quality monitor', *BWRA Bulletin*, Sept. 1964.)

### References and further reading

*Inspection procedures*

*Feigenbaum, A.V., Total quality control*, McGraw-Hill, 1961.
Grant, E.L. and Leavenworth, R., *Statistical Quality Control*, McGraw-Hill, 1980 (5th rev. ed.).
Hutchins, D., *Quality circles handbook*, Pitman, 1985.
Institute of Quality Assurance, *Guide to the preparation of a Quality Manual*, 1979.

I. Mech. E., *Quality circles—practical experiences*, Mech. Eng. Pub., 1982.

Juran, J.M. et al., *Quality Control Handbook*, McGraw-Hill, 1974.

NDT Centre, Harwell, *Quality Technology Handbook*

Robson, Mike, *Quality Circles - a practical guide*, Gower, 1988 (2nd. ed.).

Price, F., *Right first time: using quality control for profit*, Wildwood House, Gower, 1986.

Shewhart, W.A., *Economic control of quality of manufactured products*, Macmillan, 1931.

Shingo, S., *Zero quality control: source inspection and the poka-yoke system* (translated from the Japanese), Productivity Press, Stamford, Conn., 1985.

Society of Motor Manufacturers and Traders, *Guidelines to statistical process control*, London, 1986.

Stout, R., *Quality control in automation*, Kogan Page, 1985.

Wadsworth, H.M. and others, *Modern methods for quality control and improvement*, Wiley, 1986.

*Some welding publications*

The Welding Institute, Cambridge:

Advances in welding processes
Pulsed TIG welding
NDT aspects of the significance of weld defects (1972)
Significance of defects in welds
Arc welds, production and inspection
Faults in metal-arc welds in mild and low-alloy steels (wall chart)
Argon arc welding of aluminium alloys
$CO_2$ welding
Control of distortion in welded fabrication (1976)
Standard data for arc welding (1975)
Health and safety in welding and allied processes
Weld decay in austenitic stainless steels (1975)
Brittle fracture of welded structures (1971)
Quality control and NDT in welding (1975)
Welding processes (1975)
Toughness of heat-affected zones (1975)
Fitness for purpose of welded constructions (1982)
Fatigue strength of welded constructions (1969)
Weld symbols of drawing (1982)
TIG and plasma welding (1979)

American Welding Society (Miami, Florida)

Welding inspection
Standard methods for mechanical testing of welds

HMSO
Safety, Health & Welfare, New Series No. 38, Electric-arc welding
Memorandum No. 1704, Dangers connected with acetylene gas and oxy-acetylene welding
Aluminium Development Association, Information Bulletin
No. 19, Aluminium welding

Burgess, N. T. (editor) *Quality assurance of welded construction*, Applied Science Pub., 1983.

Davies, A.C., *Science and practice of welding*, Cambridge U.P., 1977.

Engineering Equipment Users Assoc., *Welding of plastics materials, thermal and chemical*, 1977.

Gray, T.G.F and Spence, J., *Rational welding design*, Butterworth, 1982.

Kanazawa and Kobayashi, *Significance of defects in welded structures*, Univ. of Tokyo Press, 1975.

Ott, E.R., *Process quality control*, McGraw-Hill, 1975.

*Welding and fabrication in the nuclear industry*, Conference proceedings, Thomas Telford, 1979.

# 10 Non-destructive testing techniques

## 10.1 Introduction

Non-destructive testing (NDT) may be said to include all those inspection techniques which do not reduce the suitability of a specimen for service or detract in any way from its acceptability. The most widely used methods include radiographic, ultrasonic and magnetic techniques, and crack detection using fluid penetrants. Such methods find increasing application both during production and in service as an aid to assessing and maintaining higher standards of quality. Success in their use, however, depends heavily on intelligent application and discriminating interpretation of the results. As it is essential that the inspector who may be faced with NDT should know enough of the principles involved to ensure that the tests are carried out properly, and to give an intelligent decision on the result, a broad review of these techniques will be given. It is emphasized that *detailed* knowledge of NDT techniques and of the equipment and its operation, and *detailed* interpretation of the results are properly the province of the specialist technician. The inspector, however, after any necessary consultations, has to give the decisions regarding acceptability. More detailed information on NDT can be obtained from the specialist works listed at the end of this chapter.

Some applicable standards, codes of practice, etc., are listed in Tables 10.2, 10.5, 10.6, and others which include NDT requirements for specific items are dealt with particularly in Chapter 3 and 4.

It will be found that, even where a standard relating to NDT exists, quite often interpretation of the results is left entirely to the inspector, surveyor or technician. He can, quite likely, call upon specialist advice, such as that of a metallurgist, but the decision as to acceptance is his. With a perfect inspector this would be tolerable, but, as is well known, the standards of inspectors and what they will or will not accept vary over very wide limits. A manufacturer consequently may take a considerable risk, almost like

496

signing a blank cheque, if he accepts a contract to an inadequate specification which leaves too much to the discretion of the inspector, who may be inexperienced, or perhaps over-meticulous, in his rejections.

There are of course difficulties in specifying limits for acceptable faults, especially with borderline cases, and rightly something should be left to the skill of the inspector. However, some specifications do now lay down some detailed standards of acceptance. For instance, considerable research has been done on the influence of discontinuities on the static and fatigue strength of welds, and this has enabled limits to be set in some cases where a certain measure of discontinuity is acceptable. Previously the inspector may have demanded completely 'clear' radiographs before acceptance, when such a high standard was only justifiable for work of the highest class, where possibly some dangerous hazard had to be considered.

In most industries such extremely high standards are not usually necessary or economic. Pressure vessels, for instance, may be fabricated to the ASME Code (see Chapter 3), which gives limits of permissible defects. Large numbers of these vessels have been made for arduous refinery service, etc., and few, if any, are known to have failed owing to such permissible defects.

Before commencing the review of scientifically based NDT techniques it is important to remember that such testing basically examines specific areas in great detail and is only complementary to older methods of NDT which (by definition) include the use of the sense of sight, hearing, smell, touch and taste. A good experienced inspector, by wide ranging use of his senses (particularly sight), can detect faults and so prevent failure in a wide range of engineering plant, and this must be a prerequisite to more detailed NDT. Some inspectors even seem to have a sixth sense for detecting trouble!

Most serious accidents or breakdowns are the result of:
(i) lax fabricating operating practices and/or bad housekeeping,
(ii) deterioration of plant and equipment.
Much can be detected without the use of sophisticated NDT equipment but by the five (or six!) senses of an experienced inspector:

He can see quite a lot.
He can hear unusual sounds.
He can smell unusual odours.
He can touch and feel unusual vibrations.
He can taste something unusual (sometimes).
He can sense and feel something is wrong (rarely).

Of course the use of optical instruments, microphones, feeler gauges, etc. can aid the senses where necessary. This seems to be recognized by Table 3.4 of BS 5500 for unfired pressure vessels, which states that vessels fabricated to construction category 3 require only a visual examination but adds in clause 5.6.4.3 that aids to visual examination (including penetrant and magnetic particle methods, etc.) may be used, and that guidance on acceptance criteria thus revealed is given in BS 5289 (see 9.21.3).

## 10.2 Radiological inspection techniques

Radiological techniques depend upon the use of:
 (i) X-rays produced by a suitable tube.
 (ii) Gamma rays produced by a radioactive material.
 Such rays are ionizing radiations in the electromagnetic spectrum which have the power of penetrating matter to an extent which increases as their wavelength decreases. The degree of penetration achieved is restricted by the absorption characteristics of the material concerned, and this restriction increases with the thickness and atomic number of that material. Thus, a thin portion, or a void, will pass more radiation than a thicker portion. Some device, often a photographic film, is required to indicate or record the relative extent of this penetration, so that a shadowgraph picture can be obtained.

The modern X-ray tube, a highly evacuated vacuum tube of glass and/or metal, contains an electrically heated filament supplying electrons by thermionic emission, which are accelerated by an extra high voltage and so made to bombard a tungsten target or anode. This bombardment causes the generation of a spectrum of X-rays at the target, having an intensity and wavelength distribution dependent on the voltage and the target material. The higher the voltage the shorter is the minimum wavelength of the X-ray spectrum emitted and the greater its penetrative power. Short-wavelength rays are known as hard X-rays, and longer ones as soft X-rays. Suitable focusing arrangements enable the X-rays to be directed at the object under test. As some 90% of the energy supplied to the tube is dissipated as heat, cooling by water, oil or otherwise is invariably required. A diagrammatic arrangement of an X-ray tube with a typical circuit is shown in Fig. 10.1.

A milliammeter inserted in the tube circuit to read the electron beam current will give a measure of the intensity of the X-rays emitted; their penetrative power will be a function of the peak voltage employed. X-ray inspection equipment is generally supplied having peak voltages of some 120, 200, 250, 400 and occasionally 1000 kV or more. These will permit examination of, say, steel having thicknesses ranging from some 1 in (25 mm) at 120 kV to 6 in (150 mm) (at 1000 kV).

Gamma rays were first used for industrial radiological inspection work around 1925, the naturally occurring radioactive element radium being employed. This was supplemented after a few years by radon (the gamma-emitting gas given off by radium). Today these have largely been supplanted by various artificially produced radioactive isotopes, which are available

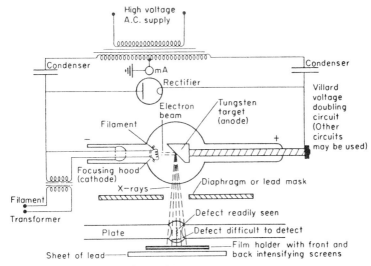

**Fig. 10.1  X-ray examination of a weld.**
Defects in line with the plane of the X-rays are readily seen.
Those at right-angles to this plane are more difficult to detect.

generally in cylindrical form of some 2,4 or 6 mm diameter. The principal advantage of gamma-ray radiology is the elimination of the costly X-ray equipment and its necessary cooling arrangements and high-voltage electricity supplies. It can thus be used for remote site work. For some duties, however, X-rays may be more effective.

The emission from a gamma-ray source falls off exponentially with time and eventually reaches a low level. To give a measure of this falling off the term 'half-life' (or half-value period) is used to express the time taken for the emission from a given source to decay to half its initial value.

The electromagnetic spectrum emitted by a given gamma-ray source is not, as with X-rays, a continuous one covering a comparatively wide range of wavelengths with varying intensities, but consists of a number of lines of differing intensities at discrete wavelengths. Consequently it is difficult to compare the results obtained by gamma rays with those obtained by X-rays. Generally speaking the intensity of gamma-ray sources is less than that given by X-ray machines, and longer photographic exposure times are required when using them. Some details of the main gamma-ray sources in industrial use are listed in Table 10.1. When not in use these sources have, of course, to be kept in suitable containers of lead or other heavy material to prevent any radioactive hazard. Gamma-radiography is not generally recommended for aluminium and its alloys for thicknesses up to 50 mm. X-ray techniques should normally be employed. However, thulium 170 and more recently ytterbium 169 have been so used for thin sections of both steel and aluminium.

## TABLE 10.1
*Gamma-ray sources*

| Source | Peak kV | Half-life | Approximate X-ray equivalent (kV effective) | Typical radiographic use | |
|---|---|---|---|---|---|
| | | | | (in) | (mm) |
| Cobalt 60 | 1750 | 5·3 years | 1250 | 2 to 6 steel | 50–150 |
| Caesium 137 | 1000 | 33 years | 700 | $\frac{1}{2}$ to 4 steel | 25–100 |
| Thulium 170 | 120 | 129 days | 100 | $\frac{1}{16}$ to $\frac{1}{2}$ steel and aluminium | 2–12 7·5–35 |
| Ytterbium 169 | 400 | 31 days | 300 | $\frac{1}{4}$ to $\frac{1}{2}$ steel and aluminium | 2–10 3–30 |
| Iridium 192 | 850 | 74 days | 600 | $\frac{1}{2}$ to 3 steel | 12–75 |
| Radium C | 1500 | 1600 years | 1000 to 1750 | 2 to 6 steel | 50–150 |
| Radon | 1750 | 3·8 days | 1000 to 1750 | 2 to 10 steel | 50–250 |
| Tantalum 182 | 1700 | 120 days | 1200 | 2 to 6 steel | 50–150 |

Although gamma-ray equipment is readily portable and relatively cheap and easy to use, and for some jobs is the only practicable means of radiography, it should be realized that the area emitting radiation when using isotope sources (usually 2, 4, or 6 mm in diameter and length) is much larger than that in X-ray equipment under similar circumstances. Therefore, in general, X-rays give better definition and contrast than gamma sources. Conventional X-ray equipment of extra high voltage (say over some 500 kV), and therefore of great penetrating power, is very expensive and often bulky, and gamma-ray equipment has tended to be used in its stead. However equipments producing X-rays by linear accelerator and betatron techniques at voltages of the order of 31 MV have been increasingly employed for thick plate radiography (up to at least 200 mm).

Amongst the methods available for indicating or recording the results of radiological tests are:

(i)   A fluorescent screen (fluoroscopy).
(ii)  A photographic film or plate (radiography).
(iii) A radiation intensity counter (nucleonic gauging).
(iv)  An electrostatic plate (xeroradiography).

The first two methods, particularly the second, are widely used in inspection work.

*Fluoroscopy.* Fluorescent screens can be used for the rapid 'screening' of components, etc., where no permanent record is required. The object under examination is placed between an X-ray tube (gamma rays are not normally used as they do not give a bright enough image) and a screen coated with some material such as cadmium or zinc sulphide, cadmium tungstate, etc.

which fluoresce when excited by the radiation. Thin parts of the object will permit bright illumination of the screen and vice versa. Fluoroscopy is used for the detection of relatively coarse flaws and defects, checking for the presence or position of components in sealed packages, containers, etc., and searching for foreign bodies, hidden objects, etc., in a variety of commodities. In some of these applications it is amenable to automation techniques, the articles for examination being arranged to travel on a moving belt. Sometimes it is advantageous to arrange for the article to be rotated during examination. A photograph of the image as seen on a fluoroscope may be termed a fluorograph.

*Radiography.* A radiograph is taken when it is desired to make a critical examination and to keep a permanent record which can be examined at leisure. The ionizing radiations, either X-rays or gamma rays, after passing through the object under test are allowed to fall on a photographic film, which becomes exposed in accordance with the radiation pattern and can be developed in the usual photographic manner.

*Nucleonic gauging.* As the intensity of all ionizing radiations is attenuated by passage through a material to an extent which depends on the thickness of the material and its density, it is possible to measure thickness by placing a suitably calibrated radiation intensity counter (see 6.17.3) on one side of the material and a suitable ionizing source on the other, Fig. 10.2.

A high-energy gamma source is required for the measurement of substantial thicknesses of steel, etc. The thickness of thin layers or coatings backed by a material of higher density can be measured by the 'backscattering' method, Fig. 10.3, and commercial beta-ray gauges may be employed.

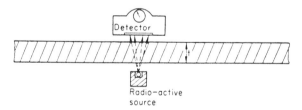

**Fig. 10.2 Nucleonic gauging–thickness gauge**

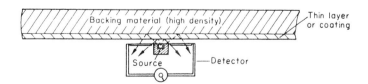

**Fig. 10.3 Nucleonic gauging–coating thickness gauge, back-scattering method.**

Such nucleonic gauges have wide application in sheet, strip and tube manufacture, latex coating, etc. They can also measure such parameters as density, liquid/solid ratio, etc., and are readily adapted to automatic control of the process.

*Xeroradiography* employs a re-usable dry plate to record the image. It uses static electricity to arrange a fine powder on a specially coated aluminium plate, so producing an image varying in contrast similarly to that of a conventional radiograph. This image is available for scrutiny within seconds, instead of possibly taking an hour for developing as with a conventional photographic film. A permanent record can be made, if desired, by normal photography of the plate.

BS 2600 covers radiographic examination of fusion welded butt joints in steel. Part 1 deals with methods for steel from 2 – 50 mm thick; and Part 2 with those for steel from 50 – 200 mm thick.

No attempt is made to specify which of several techniques described should be used for a particular application, and whether X-rays or gamma-rays should be employed. This is a matter for agreement, and depends *inter alia* upon the thickness of material to be penetrated (see Table 10.1) and the type of film used. The use of Ytterbium 169 and Thulium 170 enables gamma-rays to be used down to thicknesses of 2 mm, which is also around the lower limit for X-rays. However thulium gives inferior results to ytterbium, whilst at these small thicknesses a good X-ray technique will give a better flaw sensitivity. Below 5 mm thickness the intensifying screens (generally of lead) specified for use with most techniques should be omitted to improve image quality.

Recently some high power linear accelerator X-ray equipments have been miniaturized by using a 3 cm wave length carrier (instead of the more normal 10 cm wave length) and this has enabled them to be used as semi-portable units for the inspection of thick section items of plant (up to say 300 mm) whilst in service. For instance they have been used to check the correct (and incorrect) operation of large valves on power plants whilst in use; and by operating the linear accelerator at the end of a flexible wave-guide they can be used for the in-service inspection of water-filled piping in-cluding the detection of the development of cracks, perhaps due to intergranular stress corrosion cracking (IGSCC).

## 10.3 Radiographs and their quality

Inspection authorities generally require radiographic proof of the quality of fusion-welded pressure vessels and of important castings and components. Such bodies as the American Society of Mechanical Engineers (ASME), the American Petroleum Institute (API), Lloyds Register, the Aeronautical Inspection Directorate (AID) and British and foreign Admiralties pioneered and insisted upon such radiological inspection, and by so doing have succeeded in raising the standard of welding achievable in industry. A selection of some of the inspection codes and specifications applicable is given in Table 10.2.

**TABLE 10.2**
*Some standards dealing with radiology*

| Specification No. | Description |
|---|---|
| BS 499 | Welding terms and symbols |
| | Part 1: Glossary for welding, brazing and thermal cutting (includes sections on testing weld imperfections) |
| | Part 3: Terminology of and abbreviations for fusion weld imperfections as revealed by radiography |
| | (Covers use of abbreviations and a method for reporting and locating defects on radiographs) |
| BS 2597 | Glossary of terms used in radiology |
| BS 2600 | Radiographic examination of fusion-welded butt joints in steel |
| BS 2737 | Terminology of internal defects in castings as revealed by radiography (Interpretation of casting radiographs) |
| BS 2910 | Methods for radiographic examination of fusion-welded circumferential butt joints in steel pipes |
| BS 3971 | Image quality indicators for industrial radiography (including guidance on their use); (deals with wire and step/hole and duplex-wire types) |
| BS 4031 | X-ray protective lead glasses |
| BS 5650 | Apparatus for gamma radiography |
| BS 5288 | Sealed radioactive sources |
| ASTM E52 | Industrial terminology for use in the radiographic inspection of castings and weldments |
| †ASTM E71 | Reference radiographs for steel castings up to 2 in thickness |
| †ASTM E94 | Recommended practice for radiographic testing |
| ASTM E98 | Reference radiographs for the inspection of aluminium and magnesium castings |
| ASTM E99 | Standard reference radiographs for steel welds (Contains 35 radiographs covering types and degrees of severity of discontinuities) |
| †ASTM E142 | Controlling quality of radiographic testing (Deals with penetrameters) |
| ASTM E155 | Reference radiographs for the inspection of aluminium and magnesium castings, Series 2 |

**TABLE 10.2** *concluded*

| Specification No. | Description |
|---|---|
| | (Contains 25 radiographs covering discontinuities in castings) |
| ASTM E170 | Terms relating to dosimetry (Part of a projected ASTM Handbook on Dosimetry) |
| †ASTM E186 | Reference radiographs for heavy-walled ($2$-$4\frac{1}{2}$ in) steel castings (Contains 3 sets each of 40 plates) |
| ASTM E192 | Reference radiographs for investment steel castings for aerospace application (Contains 16 plates of reference radiographs and a nomenclature for reference in acceptance standards) |
| †ASTM E242 | Reference radiographs for appearances of radiographic images as certain parameters are changed (Shows the effect of changes by means of 4 composite illustrations complied from 36 radiographs) |
| ASTM E272 | Reference radiographs for high-strength copper-base nickel-copper alloy castings |
| †ASTM E280 | Reference radiographs for heavy-walled ($4\frac{1}{2}$ to 12 in) steel castings |
| ASTM E310 | Reference radiographs for tin bronze castings |
| ASTM E390 | Reference radiographs for steel fusion welds (a 3-volume document illustrating discontinuous welds) |
| ASTM E446 | Reference radiographs for steel castings up to 2 in (51 mm) thickness |
| British Admiralty BR 1783 | Standards terms for detects shown by weld radiographs |
| British Welding Research Association (now the Welding Institute) | Classified radiographs for defects in aluminium X-ray and gamma-ray precautions |
| International Institute of Welding TC5 | Collection of reference radiographs of welds (Also covers recommended practice regarding image quality indications) |
| Deutscher Normenausschuss DIN 54110 | Guidance for the evaluation of the quality of X-ray and gamma-ray radiographs of metals |
| DIN 54111 | Guidance for the testing of welds in metallic materials with X-rays and gamma-rays |

†Indicates ASTM standards adopted by ASME for us in their Boiler and Pressure Vessel Code, Section V. As included in this code they are prefixed by the letters S (e.g. SE 94) and may have modifications, additions or restrictions placed upon their application.

Generally such standards also call for proof that the technique employed is capable of revealing deviations from the normal of some 2% or less of the maximum thickness of the item under test. In order to assess this, a thin step-like wedge of the same material as the item may be placed alongside the weld or component and its image examined on the finished radiograph; the thinnest step thickness just discernible is noted as a measure of sensitivity. This wedge is known as a *penetrameter* or *image quality indicator* (IQI). The design of the British Welding Research Association (BWRA) step-hole type is shown in Fig.10.4. Other types made from graduated wires (see Fig.10.6). separate small plates or a combination of these, or from graded ball bearings, or the ASME pattern, as shown in Fig. 10.5, are in use. It is possible that if more than one type is used on a job they will give different values of sensitivity. Consequently the inspection authority should obtain agreement on the type and method of assessing image quality to be used.

The International Institute of Welding recommended that only two types of IQI should be used, based on the step (wedge/hole) and wire type designs. Fig.10.6 shows a wire type (to DIN 54110), consisting of seven wires of diameters increasing from 0.6 mm × 0.2 mm to 1.8 mm, set in a material of low X-ray absorption, suitable for ferrous metals up to some 100 mm thick. It is placed on a weld with the wires lying across the seam, and the sensitivity is given as the percentage ratio of the diameter of the

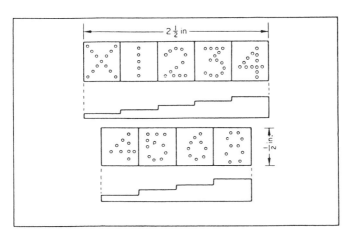

**Fig. 10.4   BWRA step-tyre penetrameter.**
Material is the same basically as the specimen under test.
In model 1 the step thicknesses are 0·005 in, 0·010 in, 0·020 in, 0·030 in, 0.040 in; and the drill holes are 0·025 in in diameter.
In model 2 the step thicknesses are 0·040 in, 0·050 in, 0·060 in, 0·080 in and the drill holes 0·050 in in diameter.
Model 1 is used for thickness less than 1½ in, Model 2 for 1½–3 in thickness.

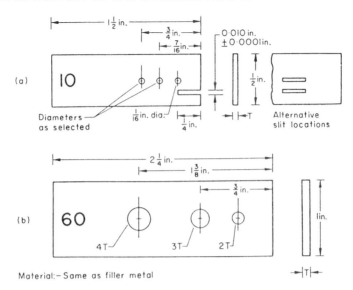

**Fig. 10.5  ASME design penetrameters (image quality indicators).**
(a) General design for up to $\frac{1}{2}$ in weld thickness.
(b) General design for over 4 in weld thickness.

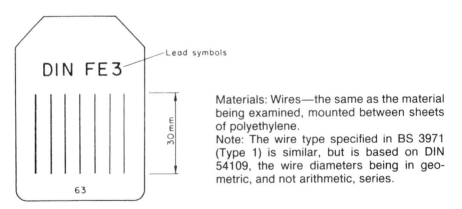

Materials: Wires—the same as the material being examined, mounted between sheets of polyethylene.
Note: The wire type specified in BS 3971 (Type 1) is similar, but is based on DIN 54109, the wire diameters being in geometric, and not arithmetic, series.

**Fig. 10.6  German wire type image quality indicator (DIN 54110).**

thinnest wire visible on the radiograph to the maximum thickness of the weld. The lower this figure the higher the sensitivity. Other wire sizes are used for different materials and thickness.

BS 3971 *Image quality indicators for industrial radiography* deals with wire-type (known as type I and shown in Fig.10.7) and step/hole type (known as type II and shown in Fig.10.8) patterns, but the latter are not of the BWRA type. Both types are for use on materials from 3 mm to 250 mm thick.

The latest issue of this standard now specifies a third type (type III) (see Fig. 10.9), the duplex-wire type developed by the Central Electricity Research Laboratories. This has certain advantages and can often (by agreement) be used in conjunction with an indicator of the other types (types I or II).

When viewing a radiograph showing a duplex wire type of IQI the largest element (pair of wires) the image of which has just merged from that of two separate wires into the single form is taken as the criterion of discernibility. There is no direct relationship between the sensitivity value as given by indicators of types I or II and the criterion of discernibility (expressed as unsharpness (mm) = diameter (d) of wire + distance between wires (a) in element) given by a type III indicator.

For work of the highest quality (e.g. boilers and pressure vessels) defect discernment, as expressed by penetrameter sensitivity, should be of the order of not greater than 1·5% of the metal thickness for up to 50 mm and not greater than 1·25% for thicknesses up to 20 mm when using wire type penetrameters.

Models A, B and E $\simeq$ 6, thickness of letters $\simeq$ 2
Models C and D $\simeq$ 12.5, thickness of letters $\simeq$ 4

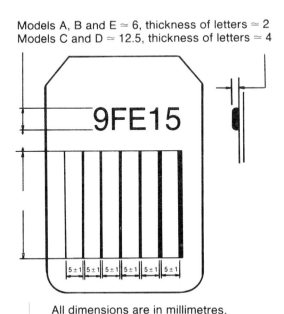

All dimensions are in millimetres.

**Fig. 10.7   Wire-type image quality indicator (type I).**

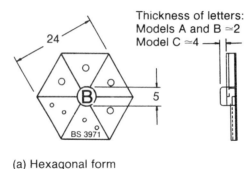

(a) Hexagonal form

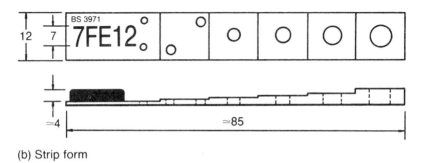

(b) Strip form

All dimensions are in millimetres.
*Note.* Holes/steps are not to scale.

**Fig. 10.8  Step/hole-type quality indicator (type II).**

When using step/hole type penetrameters the sensitivity should not exceed 3% for thicknesses up to 50 mm and 2·5% for thicknesses exceeding 50 mm.

The above figures are similar to those given in Section A of Table 7 of BS 3971, which is quoted in BS 5500 as being the maximum acceptable percentage sensitivity. An appendix provides detailed guidance on the use of each type, including sensitivity and *unsharpness* values.

## 10.4 The interpretation of radiographs

Having obtained a radiograph, whether by X-rays or gamma rays, its interpretation is a matter of considerable technical knowledge and experience on the part of the technician concerned. Guides to the interpretation of defects show up by radiography are given in various publications, codes and standards, but much must be left to the 'know-how' of the technician,

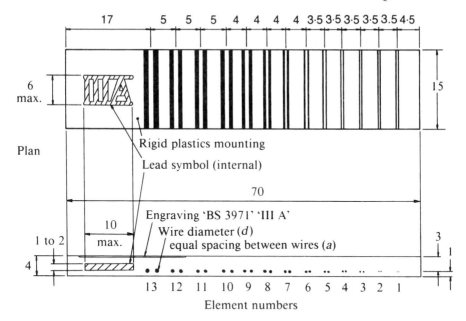

Plan

Side elevation

All dimensions are in millimetres

*Note 1: Construction.* 13 metallic elements (pairs of wires of circular section) mounted in a rigid plastics materials. Wire diameters (range from 0·05 to 0·80 mm). The spacing in each pair is one wire diameter. The element dimensions are graded with a common ratio of 1·25. Elements 1 to 10 are platinum and elements 11 to 13 are tungsten.

*Note 2: Tolerances.* Wire diameter: ± 5%. Wire length: ± 1·0 mm. Wire/gap positioning in each element: ± 10% or ± 0·05 mm, whichever is smaller. Centreline spacing of elements and overall length of image quality indicator: ± 10%. Overall width of image quality indicator: ± 1·0 mm. Plastics mounting thickness: ± 0·5 mm.

**Fig. 10.9  Duplex wire-type image quality indicator (type IIIA) for use with steel (or its equivalent) up to 90 mm thick (type IIIB is for thicknesses above 90 mm).**

especially in doubtful and not clearly defined cases. Once the cause of any particular image or defect on a radiograph has been ascertained, it is usually the responsibility of the inspector, and not the radiographic technician, to decide whether the component is acceptable or not. He may of course seek advice, but the responsibility for the decision is rightly his.

In general, X-rays show up defects more sharply than gamma rays, and this must be taken into account when interpreting results. Consequently personnel changed from one method to the other will tend to under- or over-estimate the seriousness of defects. However, if the penetrameter image shows clearly and the technique employed is correct, then the obvious defects will be seen. The less obvious defects may need the experienced technician for identification and assessment.

It should be realized that in practice radiography does not show up *all* defects. Locked up stresses, of course, remain hidden. Small inclusions and cavities (particularly the former) may not be detectable unless larger than, say, $1/2$–1% of the specimen thickness. Again, unless the radiation passes generally along the plane of a defect, such as a crack or lamination, it may miss it.

Orientation of the source in different locations, tube shift and stereoradiographic techniques will help to detect and locate a defect. In particular it should be mentioned that the radiographic appearance of a discontinuity changes as the radiation energy is varied, an increased voltage, for instance, reducing the degree of contrast obtainable between different thicknesses. With constant energy, radiographic appearance becomes less distinct as the section thickness is increased. Optimum conditions may be obtained when the finest grain film and the lowest radiation energy is used consistent with a given specimen thickness and exposure time (see ASTM Standard E 242). Consequently, to produce optimum results, a good knowledge of radiographic techniques and variations thereof is required.

Whilst much may be left to the discretion of the inspector as regards acceptance standards, and many specifications infer that no defects shown up by radiography are acceptable, a few specifications and codes now give some guidance on the degree of defects acceptable on welded joints.

Thus, the ASME Code for pressure vessels, whilst rejecting cracks and lack of root fusion, allows a certain amount of porosity and slag inclusions as do certain British Standards, such as BS 5500 (see 3.16).

The British Admiralty Class A Standard and American Ordnance Specifications for welds provide somewhat similar guidance. ASTM Standard E 71 *Reference radiographs for steel castings up to 2 in thickness gives* guidance, by reference to standard radiographs, on recognition of discontinuities and their differentiation as to both type and severity level, so enabling purchasers to select standards representing minimum acceptability. Two sets of reference radiographs are provided: one for relatively low-energy radiation (X-rays up to 400 kV and iridium 192), and one for high-energy X-rays and gamma rays. In each set 31 radiographs illustrate seven different types of discontinuity (lettered A to G) of various severity levels or classes (numbered 1–6, 1 being the least severe). For each part examined the severity level or class should be specified for each type of discontinuity. Other ASTM reference radiographs provide similar guidance (see Table 10.2).

In the chemical and petroleum industries it is common practice to give limits of acceptance for radiographs of plant and equipment. Such limits can readily be achieved by the competent fabricator without any significant or unpredictable increase in cost, which quite often accompanies the introduction of radiographic examination to a standard where limits are not specified, and where consequently the vagaries of different inspectors have to be allowed for. The standard specifications of the American Petroleum Institute, in particular API 650 *Welded oil storage tanks* and API 1104 *Field welding of pipelines*, which specify such acceptance limits, should be mentioned in this connection as they are in almost universal use in these industries.

Although European practice tends to make extensive use of various American welding standards it should be mentioned that the International Institute of Welding publishes a somewhat similar collection of European reference weld radiographs for steel and light alloys which set out to interpret and grade defects in all types of weld. It states however that they are not meant to be acceptance standards, but just a basis of comparison as regards the nature and amount of various defect. Five degrees of defect are given, ranging from those colour-graded black (showing few or no defects), through blue, green and brown to red (showing severe defects) (see Table 10.3). Thus, by prior agreement between the manufacturer and purchaser, an acceptable standard can be laid down. For example, it may be agreed that welds should not show defects worse than those indicated in the green reference radiographs.

**TABLE 10.3**

*International Institute of Welding's colour grading of weld radiographs*

| No. | Colour | Radiographic interpretations |
|---|---|---|
| 5 | Black | Homogeneous weld or a weld with a few small scattered gas cavities |
| 4 | Blue | Very slight imperfections as regards homogeneity in the form of one or more of the following defects: gas cavities, slag inclusions, undercut |
| 3 | Green | Slight imperfections; as previously listed for Blue with the addition of incomplete penetration |
| 2 | Brown | Marked imperfections; as previously listed for Green with the addition of lack of fusion |
| 1 | Red | Gross imperfections; as previously listed for Brown with the addition of cracks |

## 10.5 Supervision of radiographic inspection

Radiographic work should be carried out in accordance with some specified or approved technique. This technique will usually lay down such details as:

(i) The type of film to be used.

(ii) The use to be made of lead foil screens to give clear-cut radiographs and prevent unwanted scattered radiation; or of intensifying screens, which and fluorescent screens placed on either side of the film, to assist image formation.

(iii) The type of radiation:

(a) If X-rays, the peak voltage, which may vary from, say, 120–2000 kVp. (*Note.* Although penetration increases with voltage, an increased voltage will reduce the degree of contrast obtainable between different thicknesses.)

(b) If gamma rays, the source (see Table 10.1). The strength of a source is expressed in curies, and most are rated at a few curies. Cobalt 60 may however be used up to 2000 curies.*

(iv) Exposure time.

(v) Distance between the source and film. A large source will be placed at a greater distance than a small one, and the distance specified is always a minimum (it should be some 16–25 times the specimen thickness). The film should be as close as possible to the specimen.

(vi) Precautions necessary against the effects of stray radiation, both on personnel and on the film. The Ionizing Radiations Regulations (6:18) deal with personnel protection (see 6.4).

(vii) Film density (see BS 1384 *Measurement of photographic transmission density*).

(viii) Sensitivity as measured by a penetrameter.

(ix) Film processing details. Scratches and defects on the film caused by handing and processing must not be confused with defects in the component under examination.

(x) The system for marking up and identification of radiographs (required by specifications such as BS 5500: clause 5.6.6.1.1. (see also Figs 3.11 and 3.15.3).

When the radiograph has been taken and processed, it can viewed as a transparency in a viewing lantern suitably illuminated, preferably in a darkened room, using a magnifying glass where required. A rough assessment as to whether a radiograph shows up any serious defects may be required immediately, but this is usually followed by a critical examination and report in which the various flaws and points of interest shown are marked by arrows and annotated on the radiograph in white ink or china marking pencil. This marking up, identification and interpretation of defects, etc., is done by the technician or by the inspector, or usually by both in conjunction. The sentencing of the component is however the inspector's duty. A list of symbols which have been used for the marking up of

---

*If SI units are employed note that 1 curie $= 3\cdot7 \times 10^{10}$ becquerels

**TABLE 10.4**
*Abbreviations for weld defects which may be used for the marking up of radiographs*

| Defect in the weld (or adjacent parent metal) | Typical industrial symbol | BS symbol | IIW symbol |
|---|---|---|---|
| **Internal imperfections** | | | |
| Crack, longitudinal | CR/L | KL | $E_a$ |
| Crack, transverse | CR/T | KT | $E_b$ |
| Crack, edge | | KE | |
| Crack, crater | | KC | |
| Incomplete penetration at root of weld | IPR | LP | D |
| Lack of fusion | LF | | C |
| Lack of side fusion | | LS | |
| Lack of root fusion | | LR | |
| Lack of inter-run | | LI | |
| Inclusion (slag or other foreign matter) | | IN | $B_a$ |
| Inclusion, linear (slag line/s) | S/L | IL | $B_b$ |
| Inclusion, oxide | | IO | |
| Inclusion, tungsten | | IT | |
| Inclusion, copper | | IC | |
| Worm-holes (pipe) (caused by entrapped gas) | Pip | WH | $A_b$ |
| Crater pipe (due to shrinkage) | | CP | |
| Gas pore | | GP | |
| Porosity (or cluster of gas inclusions) | P | | $A_a$ |
| Porosity, uniform | | PU | |
| Porosity, localized | | PG | |
| Porosity, linear | | PL | |
| Elongated cavities (at root of weld due to unstable arc conditions) | | EC | |
| Burn through (hole in weld run) | | BT | |
| **Comparatively minor surface imperfections** | | | |
| Pitting (surface) | pit. | SPT | |
| Undercut | u | SUC | F |
| Incompletely filled groove | i.g. | SGI | |
| Exposed slag | e.s. | | $B_a$ |
| Excessive dressing (grinding) | e.g. | SED | |
| Chipping or tool mark (slag inclusions due to bad chipping) | c.m. | SMT | $B_d$ |
| Torn surface | t.s. | STS | |
| Grinding scratch | g.s. | SMG | |
| Hammer marks, etc. | h | SMH | |
| Weaving faults (slag inclusions due to incorrect weaving techniques) | | | $B_c$ |
| Fault at electrode change | | | $B_e$ |
| Fault at junction of seams | | | $B_f$ |
| Excess penetration bead | | SXP | |
| Root concavity (suck back) | | SRC | |
| Shrinkage groove | | SGS | |
| Spatter | | SSP | |

radiographs is given in Table 10.4, together with British Standards and the International Institute of Welding's recommended symbols.

In first-class work, such as that of plant in which a failure could result in a dangerous hazard, any of the major internal defects tabulated can result in rejection of the weld, possibly for rectification, and the radiograph can be marked 'R' in the top right-hand corner. Blow holes above $\frac{1}{16}$ in diameter and (1.5 mm) and oxidation can also result in rejection. Isolated cavities (gas pores) or inclusions may be acceptable up to $\frac{1}{32}$ in (0·75 mm) diameter, and perhaps in groups of not more than four separated from each other by at least four times their diameter. 'Worm-holes' (piping) have to be located, perhaps by the tube shift method, and cut out. A 'clear' radiograph (absence of defects) can be suitably marked. Comparatively minor surface imperfections on or adjacent to the weld, or other defects, can be marked on the radiograph as tabulated in Table 10.4, and such defects will be considered on their merits. Acceptable radiographs can be suitably marked.

A welding report (possibly in tabular form) could give concise details of the techniques employed, together with symbols showing the types of defect, their location and the classification of the relative importance of these defects in accordance with the colour grading of the International Institute of Welding.

Thus, in accordance with BS 499: Part 3, the coding

$$2—PL—9: 4—LR—0·5$$

would indicate that a radiograph revealed the existence of linear porosity 2 in from the reference mark and extending over a length of 9 in and also lack of root fusion at a distance of 4 in from the reference mark and extending for 0·5 in. Note that BS 499 Part 3 1965 has been withdrawn and superseded by Part 1 1983 but the BS symbols have not been incorporated in it. For convenience, they have been included here in Table 10.4. (Marking and identification are requirements of pressure vessel codes, etc (e.g. BS 5500).)

### 10.6 Ultrasonic inspection techniques (for applicable standards see Table 10.5)

Ultrasonic methods depend on the generation of waves or vibrations beyond the audible range (greater than some 20 kc/s (kHz)), and their transmission through the object under test. These waves may be used to detect internal defects by:

(i) *Transmission techniques*, in which a detecting unit on the far side of the object under test will give a reduced output when a flaw lies in the path of the wave, and thus can be used to show a shadow or absorption effect. Continuous waves having frequencies of the order of 10 Mc/s (MHz) may be

**TABLE 10.5**

*Some standards dealing with ultrasonic inspection*

| Specification No. | Description |
|---|---|
| BS 661 | Glossary of acoustical terms |
| BS 2704 | Calibration blocks for use in ultrasonic flaw detection (Deals with the manufacture and use of five types of calibration block, recommendations for special purpose calibration blocks including the BSI/BWRA block employing shear waves) |
| BS 3683 | Glossary of terms used in non-destructive testing |
| | Part 4: Ultrasonic flaw detection |
| BS 3889 | Non-destructive testing of pipes and tubes |
| | Part 1: Methods of Automatic Ultrasonic testing for the detection of imperfections in wrought steel tubes |
| BS 3923 | Methods for ultrasonic examination of welds |
| | Part 1: Manual examination of fusion-welds in ferritic steels |
| | Part 2: Automatic examination of fusion welded butt joints in ferritic steels |
| | Part 3: Manual examination of nozzle welds |
| BS 4124 | Ultrasonic detection of imperfections in steel forgings |
| BS 4331 | Methods for assessing the performance characteristics of ultrasonic flaw detection equipment |
| | Part 1: Overall performance: on site methods |
| | Part 2: Electrical performance |
| | Part 3: Guidance on in-service monitoring of probes |
| BS 5996 | Methods of testing and quality grading of ferritic steel plate by ultrasonic methods |
| BS 6208 | Methods for ultrasonic testing and for specifying quality levels of ferritic steel castings |
| †ASTM A388 | Ultrasonic inspection of heavy steel forgings (Describes the use of the resonance method and longitudinal pulsed waves) |
| ASTM A418 | Ultrasonic testing and inspection of turbine and generator steel rotor forgings |
| †*ASTM A435 | Ultrasonic testing and inspection of steel plates (Describes the use of $2\frac{1}{4}$ Mc/s longitudinal waves over a grid) |
| *ASTM E113 | Ultrasonic testing by the resonance method |
| †ASTM A577 | Ultrasonic angle beam inspection of steel plate |
| †ASTM A578 | Straight beam ultrasonic examination of plain and clad steel plates for special applications |
| †ASTM B548 | Ultrasonic inspection of aluminium alloy plate for pressure vessels |

**TABLE 10.5** *concluded*

| Specification No. | Description |
| --- | --- |
| ASTM E114 | Ultrasonic testing by the reflection method using pulsed longitudinal waves included by direct contact |
| ASTM E127 | Fabricating and checking aluminium alloy ultrasonic standard reference blocks (for pulsed longitudinal waves) |
| *ASTM E164 | Ultrasonic contact inspection of weldments (Describes the use of a plate reference block for shear waves) |
| †*ASTM E213 | Ultrasonic inspection of metal pipe and tubing for longitudinal discontinuities |
| †ASTM E214 | Immersed ultrasonic testing by the reflection method using pulsed longitudinal waves |
| †ASTM E273 | Ultrasonic inspection of longitudinal and spiral welds of welded pipe and tubing |

* ANSI approved Z.166 standards series
† Adopted by ASME (see footnote to Table 10.2)

necessary and in some applications they are frequency-modulated. Fig. 10.10 shows a typical application which continously monitors sheet steel as it comes from the rolls.

(ii) *Reflection technique*, in which the waves are reflected back by the defects and detected by a receiver near to or incorporated in the transmitter. Continuous wave transmission for reflection techniques has been abandoned in favour of pulsed waves operating in a similar manner to that employed in radar, the echo being received back by a suitable receiver or combined transmitter/receiver.

Ultrasonic testing is now much used for checking important castings, forgings, plates, and components, both metallic and non-metallic, to ensure freedom from hidden defects, so possibly saving time and money in machining and preparing items which subsequently prove to be faulty. It may be used for the *location* of any defects present, or simply to *sort out* quickly defective components which can then be examined in detail by other methods. It is also much used for the examination of welded joints, either on its own or in conjunction with the radiological examination required by the various inspection codes. In some cases ultrasonic methods may have advantages over radiology but generally they are complementary. They will readily detect laminations in plate, whereas with radiology this may be difficult. They can often be used for quick scanning, and consequently lend themselves to automated inspection techniques. Hidden

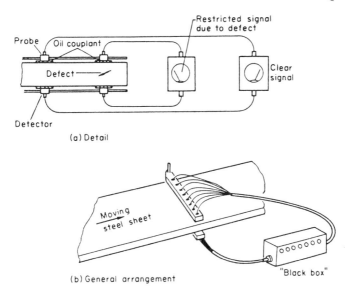

Fig. 10.10 Ultrasonic monitoring of steel sheet—transmission technique (diagrammatic only).

boundary layers (including those in plastics and laminates), unbonded surfaces between rubber and metal, etc., can be detected. Defects in ceramics and rubber can be found and the quality of concrete can be tested. Thickness measurements, such as those of pressure vessels and tube walls, can be made.

## 10.6.1 Methods of presentation

The beam of ultrasonic waves is projected into the material under test by means of a transducer or probe in which high-frequency electrical energy is converted into mechanical vibrations. In the reflection technique the waves or vibrations are echoed or reflected back from the opposite side of the material and picked up by the receiving transducer and converted back into electrical energy. Any defect or obstruction in the path of the beam of ultrasonic vibrations will also cause an echo to be reflected back. These electrical impulses may be displayed on the screen of a cathode-ray tube (see Fig 10.11) which has an adjustable time base connected to its X plates. The time scale (displayed on the X axis), by virtue of the distance travelled by the ultrasonic waves in unit time, is also a distance scale and thus can be used to locate a defect. The transmitter is triggered off by the time base at the instant it commences to move the spot over the screen. At this same instant the transmitter also delivers a pulse to the receiver amplifier and

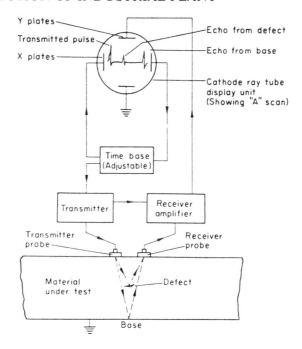

**Fig. 10.11 Basic diagram of ultrasonic flaw detector.**

thence to the Y plates, so giving a representation of the transmitted pulse on the screen. The ultrasonic reflection from the opposite side of the material under test, and an echo from any defect in the material, are picked up by the receiver probe and fed through the receiver amplifier to give representations on the screen, as shown in Fig.10.11. By measuring the horizontal distance to scale the thickness of the material and the location of the defect can be ascertained. This screen representation is known as 'A' scan or A-scope presentation.

In another presentation, known as the 'B' scan, the CRT display is turned clockwise through 90° so that the time base is vertical, with the transmitter marker pulse at the top and the base echo (if any) at the bottom. In this method the probe is moved along the surface of the material under test, say from left to right as in Fig.10.12(a). The pulses, projected downwards, search through the material until a defect is found. The signal due to this flaw is made to brighten the CRT trace, which previously had been biased back to invisibility, and in consequence bright spots will appear on the screen in positions which will indicate defects. The CRT screen is of the type which has an afterglow so that the spots persist long enough to enable them to be identified. This type of B-scope presentation is shown in Fig.10.12(b).

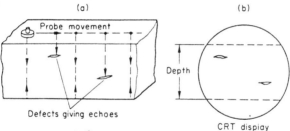

**Fig. 10.12  B-scope presentation.**

In a further presentation, the 'C' scan, the vertical and horizontal sweeps on the CRT correspond with the movement of the probe across the width and along the length of a surface such as a steel plate, Fig.10.13(a). Pulses are directed downwards from the probe into the material. It is arranged that any defects they encounter are shown up by a brightening on the CRT screen, thus giving a fluorescent pattern plan view of these defects as seen from the surface, but not of course indicating their depth, Fig.10.13(b).

Other methods of presentation may occasionally be used, e.g. as in the radar plan position indicator (PPI), in which the 'C' scan is presented by a single rotating sweep on the CRT.

The probe may consist of a quartz crystal transducer having a fundamental or harmonic frequency of the desired ultrasonic value. Its mechanical vibration must be communicated to the object under test via the medium of the liquid, a paste or some similar material (called the couplant). Even the thinnest air gap will interfere with the transmission. With articles of complex shape, or with large-scale production testing, an immersion technique may be employed, the ultrasonic waves passing between transmitter, object and receiver via a liquid (usually water), Fig.10.14. With continuously operating production plants some degree of automation is possible, alarms being fitted to indicate flaws, and if required graphical records can be taken automatically.

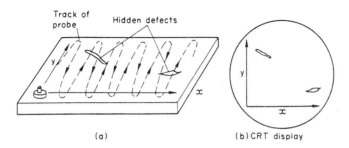

**Fig. 10.13  C-scope presentation.**

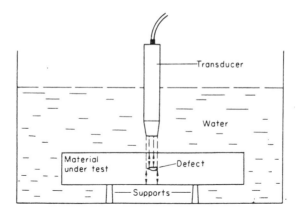

**Fig. 10.14 Ultrasonic immersion technique.**

*10.6.2 Modes of vibration*

When ultrasonic waves are applied to an object they will set its particles vibrating, and the resulting wave motion in it may travel in a variety of modes, sometimes simultaneously.

The principal modes of vibration, listed in decreasing order of use in ultrasonic testing, are:

(i) Longitudinal (or compressional) waves, in which the particle motion is in the same direction as the beam propagation.

(ii) Transverse (or shear) waves, in which the particle motion is at right-angles to the direction of propagation.

(iii) Surface waves in which the particle motion is along and/or slightly beneath the surface of the object.

Longitudinal waves can be produced by the direct application of a transducer to the surface of an object, and are used to detect defects lying largely in beam at right-angles (normal) to the surface; they may miss a defect lying largely parallel to the beam, Fig.10.15.

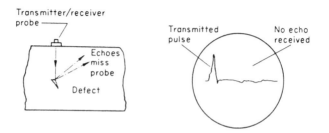

**Fig. 10.15 How a longitudinal wave may miss a defect.** A thin defect parallel to the beam may produce no echo at all.

It is advisable to use one mode only when carrying out a test. However, a mode can change when a beam impinges on an oblique surface, and to complicate matters these different modes have different velocities. Special wedges, often of Perspex, can be interposed between a transducer probe and the object under test to change, for instance, a longitudinal mode to a transverse mode: they can also eliminate an unwanted mode. If the angle of the wedge exceeds a certain value a surface wave also appears and eventually predominates. Steerable probes, perhaps consisting of two wedges and a rotating ring, so arranged that the wedge angle can be varied, can be usefully employed to test components of shapes which would otherwise present difficulties, Fig.10.16.

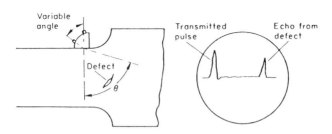

**Fig. 10.16 Showing use of a variable-angle probe.** $\theta$ = Angle which may be swept by the beam.

Welds can be examined by scanning with shear (transverse) waves having an angle between 35° and 70° to the normal and a frequency up to 5 Mc/s; A-scope presentation is usual, Fig. 10.17. Other methods may be employed, using two probes which may be separate transmitting and receiving probes. With all ultrasonic testing maximium indication is obtained when defects lie in a plane at right-angles to the beam, and the technique adopted must take this into account.

The ultrasonic examination of welds in austenitic steels presents difficulties. Shear wave techniques cannot be used, and it is only recently that some progress has been made in obtaining meaningful inspection results using longitudinal waves together with special purpose probes. When using normal probes the beam propagated through certain weld metal can be substantially deviated from its expected path. The sizing of defects still presents difficulties.

*10.6.3 Ultrasonic thickness measurement*

Most ultrasonic thickness measuring instruments operate on the resonance principle. Usually continuous ultrasonic waves are generated by a variable

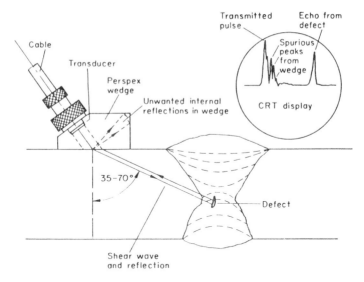

**Fig. 10.17 Ultrasonic testing of a multilayer butt-weld using shear waves and a single transmitter/receiver probe.**
Note the bending of the beam which occurs when passing at an angle from one material (Perspex) to another (steel).
Note also the spurious peaks on the CRT display resulting from the unwanted internal reflections in the wedge; special wedge designs can reduce these.

frequency oscillator, and these are applied via a transducer or probe to the part whose thickness it is desired to measure. This part is thus set into vibration, and by adjusting the applied frequency it can be set into resonance. This will occur when the frequency ($f$) is such that its wavelength ($\lambda$) is equal to twice the thickness ($t$) of the part. If $V$ is the velocity of the wave in the test material, then:

$$f = \frac{V}{\lambda} = \frac{V}{2t}$$

and

$$t = \frac{V}{2f}$$

Under these conditions, a wave, after travelling through half a wavelength, will reach the boundary defining the thickness of the part and will be reflected back to reach the probe just as another wave is emerging, i.e. it will be in-phase, and augment or resonate with the original transmission. If the frequency is increased gradually resonance will be lost, and when $3 \times \lambda = 4t$ the reflected signal will arrive completely out of phase with the original transmission and will oppose or cancel it. A further increase of frequency, such that the wavelength is equal to the thickness, will again give rise to resonance, and further resonances will occur at harmonics of the fundamental resonance frequency. The increase of signal indicating resonance can be applied to a meter, 'phones, or a cathode-ray tube. Knowing the exact frequency generated at any particular dial setting, and checking for resonance with standard test blocks (see BS 2704), it is possible to measure the thickness of plates, etc., with fair accuracy.

Knowing the frequency of two adjacent harmonics $f_1$ and $f_2$ the thickness $t$ can be calculated as follows:

$$t = \frac{V}{2(f_1 - f_2)}$$

Accuracy may be between 0.2% and 0.5%, and could reach ±0.1% under ideal conditions; however, it can be considerably less with some materials and is particulary dependent on the standard of surface finish.

*Pulsed reflection techniques* can be employed, particularly for greater thicknesses. The ultrasonic waves travel from the top surface and are reflected back from the bottom surface of the material, their transit time being equal to twice the material thickness divided by the velocity of the waves in this material (which must be known accurately, or the equipment must be calibrated using a known standard thickness test piece). The transit time must be large compared with the time length of the pulse and this limits the minimum thickness which can be measured to some 0.2 in. Frequencies of the order 1 Mc/s are used when testing metals, with a pulse repetition frequency of from 50 to 1000 c/s. Accuracy of thickness measurement may be some 1 to 2%.

## 10.6.4 Operational notes

In all cases of ultrasonic measurement and inspection supervision should be such as to ensure that:

(i)   Regular checks are carried out on the apparatus using standard test blocks and/or blocks containing known defects.

(ii)  The surface examined or in contact with the probe is smooth, clean and free from scale (otherwise spurious results may arise).

(iii) Probes, wedges, etc., are effectively coupled by a suitable liquid to the object under test.

(iv)  When seeking defects a second test is carried out with the ultrasonic beam at right-angles to that in the first test, as some cracks or defects may be parallel to the first beam and cause little, if any, reflection.

(v)   When seeking very small flaws and discontinuities the wavelength used must be of the same order as the size of the defect; hence frequencies of several megacycles per second (megahertz) may be required.

*10.6.5 Assessing for quality by ultrasonics*

Advances in the understanding and application of ultrasonic techniques have been made over the past decade, including the introduction of automatic testing of welds and tubes and particularly in the examination of steel plate for discontinuities and its quality grading. With these advances the skill and training of the operator and his ability to assess results becomes of increasing importance, and it is usual to expect that he, like a welder, should have some form of qualification and/or approval.

The techniques of ultrasonic testing were covered to some extent in BS 4336 Part 1A *Ultrasonic detection of laminar imperfections in ferrous wrought plate*, but grading of the plate from the results of testing presented difficulties. Developments led eventually to the replacement of BS 4336 by BS 5996. *Testing and quality grading of ferritic steel plate* by ultrasonic methods, 1980. Plate material is examined by the pulse echo method with an A-scope presentation using a compressional wave probe, scanning being from one side of the plate only, the back wall echo having previously been adjusted to full screen height. All indications (defect echoes) on the screen that are 50% or greater of the reduced back wall echo — or cause a 50% or greater reduction in back wall echo are defined as discontinuities, for further investigation. Some seven test procedure techniques are described, those used being generally at the discretion of the producer. Automatic scanning is permissible.

Tables are given by which the areas of discontinuities and the total defect area, etc, can be assessed for laminations (L) and inclusion clusters (C). At present four quality grades (1,2,3 and 4) for either of these defects are designated, the highest number representing the smallest area of defects in the plate. Edge discontinuities are assessed according to a table into quality grades E and ES (ES being the better quality).

The present highest quality plate would be designated L4, which would include testing to L4, C4 and ES. Individual tests (e.g. edge testing only (to E or ES)), or combinations thereof may be specified in particular orders (e.g. LC2E means L and C are both to the same grade number (2); however LC3 to the higher grade (3) also includes E). Verification and calibration of the equipment should be carried out in accordance with the requirements of BS 4331.

The ultrasonic testing of ferritic steel castings (not austenitic) and their assessment for different quality levels is covered in BS 6208, the methods described being suitable for the examination of castings of at least 30 mm thickness. The equipment uses an A-scope presentation and operates over a frequency range of at least 1–5 MHz with a gain control calibrated in steps of 2 dB or less. Calibration is carried out using the procedure described in BS 4331 Part 1 and with reference blocks complying with BS 2704.

After a preliminary examination and a scan to locate both planar and non-planar discontinuities (i.e. discontinuities having either two or three dimensions as determined by the techniques used), these discontinuities are assessed for size (length and area). Four quality levels (of length and area) are tabulated in the standard (quality levels 1–4).

Quality level 1 requires complete freedom from any ultrasonic indication displaying planar characteristics; non-planar discontinuities in the outer zone of a casting may go up to a total area of 5000 mm$^2$ and 12,500 mm$^2$ in the middle zone. Quality level 4 permits the greatest extent of discontinuity and may go up to 50,000 mm$^2$ in the mid-zone for non-planar defects.

BS 4124 *Ultrasonic detection of imperfections in steel forgings* describes four methods for U/S detection using A-scope pulse echo equipment. Such methods are complementary to magnetic particle and dye penetrant methods and can be used on much greater thicknesses of material than is possible with radiography.

These methods include (i) the assessment of defects by comparison with artificial defects formed in test pieces (e.g. flat bottomed holes and notches, etc), (ii) the distance gain size (DGS) diagram technique, (iii) and (iv) 20 and 60 dB drop techniques.

By such methods the depth, location and size of an imperfection can be established.

This specification does not give acceptance levels for such imperfection; these have to be agreed between the parties concerned.

Ultrasonics may be used for manufacturing and in-service inspections where geometry or difficulty of access precludes or reduces the effectiveness of the use of radiography. Even so, original design should take into account the necessity for effective methods and ease of access for NDT. France has developed an ultrasonic in-service inspection vehicle or robot to crawl inside a nuclear reactor and monitor it for surface and internal defects, periodically throughout its lifetime. It is called MIR (Module d'Inspection des Réacteurs Rapides), and is fitted with built-in propulsion, and a TV navigation camera to seek and track welds, and a TV camera to inspect and record them. Other automated NDT scanners for pipe and vessel inspection are under development in the USA and eleswhere.

### 10.7 Magnetic inspection techniques (for applicable standards see Table 10.6)

*Magnetic particle inspection* can be carried out on ferromagnetic materials and components to detect the presence therein of surface and some sub-surface discontinuities, flaws and particularly cracks. The methods employed depend on the magnetic properties of the defect being different from those of the normal material. In one technique a magnetic field is *continuously* maintained in and around the part under test; during this time any differing

## TABLE 10.6
*Magnetic and fluid penetrant inspection standards*

| Specification No. | Description |
| --- | --- |
| **Magnetic techniques** | |
| BS 3683 | Glossary of terms used in non-destructive testing |
| | Part 2: Magnetic particle flaw detection |
| | Part 5: Eddy current flaw detection |
| BS 3889 | Non destructive testing of pipes and tubes |
| | Part 2A: Eddy current testing of ferrous pipes and tubes |
| | Part 2B: Eddy current testing of non-ferrous tubes |
| BS 4069 | Magnetic flaw detection inks and powders |
| BS 4397 | Methods for magnetic particle testing of welds |
| BS 4489 | Method for assessing black light used in non-destructive testing (used in fluorescent magnetic particle and penetrant testing) |
| BS 6072 | Method for magnetic particle flaw detection |
| ASTM A275 | Magnetic particle testing and inspection of heavy steel forgings |
| † ASTM E109 | Standard method for magnetic particle inspection (dry powder) |
| ASTM E125 | Standard reference photographs for magnetic particle indications on ferrous castings (Contains a collection of reference photographs covering types and degrees of discontinuities detectable by the dry powder method) |
| † ASTM E138 | Method for wet magnetic particle inspection |
| ASTM E215 | Electromagnetic testing of seamless aluminium alloy tube (A guide for eddy current testing, with an appendix on fabrication and application of reference standards) |
| ASTM E216 | Measuring coating thickness by magnetic or electromagentic methods |
| ASTM E243 | Electromagnetic (eddy current) testing of seamless copper and copper alloy heat exchanger and condenser tubes |
| ASTM E309 | Eddy current testing of steel tubular products with magnetic saturation |
| SAE 1960 | Recommended practice for cleanliness rating of steels by the magnetic particle method |
| SAE AMS 2640E | Magnetic particle inspection (aeronautical materials) |
| US MIL-6868 (USAF) | Magnetic particle inspection (aeronautical materials) |
| T.O.33B2-1-1 | Magnetic particle inspection (aeronautical materials) |

**TABLE 10.6** *concluded*

| Specification No. | Description |
|---|---|
| **Liquid penetrants** | |
| BS 3683 | Glossary of terms used in non-destructive testing |
| | Part 1: Penetrant flaw detection |
| BS 4124 | Non-destructive testing of steel forgings |
| | Part 3: Penetrant flaw detection |
| BS 4416 | Method for penetrant testing of welded or brazed joints in metals |
| BS 4489 | Method for assessing black light used in non-destructive testing (used in fluorescent magnetic particle and penetrant testing) |
| BS 6443 | Method for penetrant and flaw detection |
| † ASTM E165 | Methods for liquid penetrant inspection |
| ASTM A462 | Methods for liquid penetrant inspection of steel forgings |

†Adopted by ASME (see footnote to Table 10.2).

magnetic properties are looked for. In a second method, a magnetic field is applied and then removed, so magnetizing the part. Any differing magnetic properties are then sought for in the residual magnetism.

Magnetic techniques were first used in the 1920s for detecting cracks in heavy castings, forgings, turbine blades, etc. The most usual method adopted is to distribute magnetic particles over the article under test, either during or after magnetization. These particles may be in the form of a dry powder (of iron or iron oxides), or more usually wet powder in the form of what is know as magnetic ink. This ink consists of magnetic power suspended in paraffin (kerosene) usually with some additives.

The magnetic particles will tend to cling to places where there is no continuous magnetic path, e.g. where there is an air gap, however slight, due to the presence of a crack. Free magnetic poles are formed at such places, and also at other defects which interrupt the magnetic path (such as non-metallic inclusions, etc.). Defects are thus observed by visually inspecting the component for evidence of clinging particles after it has been magnetized and immersed in them. The addition of a fluorescent substance to the particles aids inspection if an ultra-violet lamp is used.

Defects are most readily detected when the lines of magnetic flux are at right-angles to them and to the surface. Hence it is customary to test a component in two different planes, Fig.10.18.

The following main methods of magnetizing the component can be employed:

(i) *Magnet method* (magnetic flow method). The component is placed

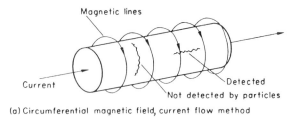

(a) Circumferential magnetic field, current flow method

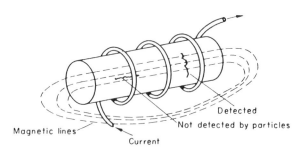

(b) Longitudinal magnetic field, coil method

**Fig. 10.18   Magnetic particle flaw detection.**
Maximum sensitivity is obtained when the plane of the defect is perpendicular to the magnetic flux. Thus current flow magnetization (a) does not reveal transverse defects. These may be detailed, however, by a complementary operation such as lengthwise magnetic flow as in the coil test shown in (b).

between the poles of a magnet, closing the magnetic circuit. An electromagnet is usually employed, but a permanent magnet of sufficient strength can be used.

(ii) *Coil method.* The component is placed inside a coil or solenoid, but does not form part of a continuous magnetic circuit.

*Note.* In these two *magnetic flux* methods free poles appear at either end of the component, besides at defects.

(iii) *Current flow method ('prod' type).* A heavy current is passed through the component by attaching substantial copper contacts (prods) to it. Alternatively the prods may be passed through a hole in the component and connected together to give the same effect as a coil *(threading bar method).*

(iv) *Induction method.* The component is magnetized by a.c. induction, a circulating current being induced in it.

*Note:* In these two *current flow* methods no free poles will appear except at defects or gaps.

In the first three methods d.c. or a.c. can be used, although d.c. is normally used for electromagnets. In methods (ii) and (iii) d.c. (preferably pulsed or rectified) is generally more sensitive than a.c. for detecting defects below the surface. The current is often only applied momentarily, the powder usually being applied before, but sometimes after, magnetization.

### 10.7.1 Operational notes

(i) The effectiveness of the results obtained is dependent on the skill of the operator, and experience in interpreting the minute dark lines of heaped-up powder at any defects. False indications may occur at corners and sharp changes of section, due to flux leakage. 'Ghost' marks may also appear owing to careless handling of magnetized components. Large rounded sub-surface cavities may not be noticed owing to the diffuse indication given.

(ii) *Demagnetization.* After a component has passed a magnetic flaw detection test it must be demagnetized if specifically called for, as otherwise it could cause trouble by attracting ferrous particles, inducing electric currents in moving parts, or interfering with magnetic compasses, etc. This demagnetization can be carried out most effectively by subjecting the component to a field having a reverse direction to that of the original, and gradually reducing its value.

Alternatively, the component may be placed inside a solenoid or coil fed with alternating current, and this current is then reduced gradually from a high value to zero. More usually the alternating current continues to flow at its full value whilst the component is passed through the coil and gradually withdrawn well away; twisting the component in all directions during the operation will help the process.

The inspector should check that demagnetization has been effectively carried out by, for instance, noting the difference between the deflection caused by the component on a compass needle and that caused by a known unmagnetized component. Sometimes limits of permissible residual magnetism are laid down.

It should be noted that if a component has to undergo heat treatment after magnetic flaw detection then this heating will automatically demagnetize it, if carried out at a temperature above the Curie point of the material.

### 10.7.2 Eddy current testing

Magnetic particle flaw detection as described above is only applicable to ferromagnetic materials, but other magnetic techniques can be employed.

The alternating magnetic field produced by a coil fed with alternating current can be arranged to 'cut' a component of electrical conducting material and to induce eddy currents in it. Variation in these induced currents can be used to detect flaws in the component. A typical application is the eddy current testing of tubes (see 4.4.6 also ASTM E215).

### 10.7.3 Thickness measurement

The measurement of thickness, particularly of coatings on a metal base, can be made by magnetic or electromagnetic techniques. The coating may be electrically conducting or insulating. If the base material is magnetic then an instrument which measures magnetic flux, or attraction between the detection unit and the base, can be calibrated to indicate coating thickness.

An electromagnetic instrument that measures the effect of lift-off, and/or conductivity, and/or permeability, in changing the apparent impedance of an eddy current inducing coil, can be calibrated to indicate coating thickness and used for magnetic and/or non-magnetic base materials.

These techniques may not be accurate, or may not give a suitable response for some combinations of coating, base or electrical conductivity. The supervisor or inspector must therefore ensure the suitability of the technique employed, and check that calibration has been carried out against carefully set up reference standards. The instrument response is usually converted to thickness measurement by a calibration curve.

## 10.8  Liquid penetrant inspection techniques (see Table 10.6)

The use of penetrants as a method of inspecting for the presence of cracks and flaws is of considerable value as it provides a ready means of detection without the use of complex apparatus.

The method has developed from the practice of detecting defects by immersing castings, components, etc., in a heated mixture of kerosene (paraffin) and lard oil. The components are then dried and cleaned, covered with chalk, and allowed to cool. On cooling, the oil in any defects, cracks, etc., seeps out and stains the chalk surface, tending to build up a ridge of chalk at any deep defects. This method still has its uses today but suffers from lack of contrast between defects and background, and some lack of sensitivity. It has consequently largely been superseded by modern penetrants.

Basically, all surface defects should be detectable by visual inspection, and much can be done with the aid of magnifying glasses, low-power binocular microscopes, etc., perhaps assisted by etching or electro-polishing. The main difficultly is knowing where to look, and this increases as the degree of magnification increases. Consequently, any method of drawing attention to the location of a defect is of value, and modern fluid penetrants do just this.

Visible red dye penetrants give a good contrast on a white blackground and have the power to penetrate deeply into quite minute cracks. Before use however the component must be suitably cleaned by a method which ensures the removal of any material clogging a defect, and which does not itself result in the filling of any crack with the cleaning fluid. Various methods, including detergents and vapour degreasing, are employed. After cleaning, the component must be thoroughly dried. The penetrating liquid is then applied and allowed to soak for some 5 to 20 minutes, so permitting penetration of any defects. The surplus fluid is then removed by wiping and/or the use of a suitable solvent or emulsifier, followed if necessary by a water rinse, care being taken that the penetrant is not removed from any defects by too vigorous washing. After drying, the components are coated or sprayed with a developer of white composition. This tends to draw out the dye penetrant from any cracks or defects, leaving a brilliant red outline of the defect on the surface in major cases, and perhaps a dotted chain outline for minor defects. A pre-determined time is allowed for the indication of any defect to develop. Most will show up almost immediately, but fine defects may take some half-hour to appear. The indications will remain for several days at least.

By replacing the red dye in the penetrant by a fluorescent material the components can be viewed under ultra-violet light, when any defects will appear generally as vivid yellow or green fluorescent markings against a purple background.

A 'black light' source is used $(2000°–4000 \text{ Å})^\dagger$, giving an illumination of 90 to 100 ft candles (measured as described in ASTM E165*); a 100 W mercury vapour lamp is normally adequate); a 'black light' filter suppresses the ultra-violet end which would damage the viewers' eyes over long periods of inspection.

Acceptance requirements may vary considerably. Serious defects will be obvious, and generally speaking linear defects (cracks, laps and fissures) having a length greater than twice their width, and chains of four or more rounded defects in line separated by $\frac{1}{16}$ in or less (edge to edge), may have to be rejected, except where the specification quotes otherwise.

Many minor differences exist in the composition of penetrants, developers, rinses, etc., and in the techniques employed. Some users prefer fluorescent and some dye penetrant methods. Perhaps the main advantage of the dye penetrant method is that it can be carried out on site or in any location without the need for special lighting. A disadvantage is that its use may not be practicable on rough surfaces, whereas here a fluorescent penetrant can give good results.

Penetrants can be applied to detect not only surface porosity, but porosity through a material, i.e. leakage. Surface porosity will be indicated by a series of fine dots, increasing in size with the amount of porosity. Leakage is detected by applying the penetrant to one side and examining the

---

*A different, indirect, method of assessment given in BS 4489 recommends not less than 50 lux (1ft candle = 10·76 lux).
$^\dagger$One Ångström unit (Å) represents a wavelegth of $10^{-8}$ cm.

other side after a time interval. For more sensitive leak detection a vessel or tank, for instance, may be filled with suitable penetrant and put under pressure (possibly that due to its own weight). This method is used for checking leakage from welded containers. The indication will build up with time and show, in the case of fluorescent penetrant, a brilliant spot at the location of the leak.

## 10.9 Surface finish and its inspection

In practice the surface of any manufactured part always departs from an absolutely smooth and perfect texture. The imperfections take the form of a succession of hills and valleys which may vary in both height and spacing, and the characteristics of which, in appearance and feel, are often dependent on the particular manufacturing process employed. Thus, the imperfections on a surface produced by a machine with a single point cutting tool will tend to be uniformly spaced and directional; those resulting from plain and cylindrical grinding will tend to be irregularly spaced but directional; and those resulting from abrasive processes such as lapping and honing will tend to be irregular and non-directional. Superimposed on these may be more openly spaced variations, resulting from faults in the machining process.

For many applications surface texture variations and finish may be of little importance. For a comparatively few applications an extremely high standard of surface finish is essential. For such applications it is often desirable to specify the lowest standard of surface texture which is acceptable. Consequently it must be possible to assess the standard of surface texture achieved.

This can be done by two principal methods:

(i) By actual measurement using a suitable instrument.

(ii) By qualitative assessment; sight and/or touch is used to compare the finish achieved with that of a reference specimen or specimens produced by the same process.

Most instruments in general use for the *measurement* of surface texture are designed to respond to surface irregularities through the agency of a stylus. This is traversed across the surface on a skid which follows the general contour, thus providing a datum, but the stylus moves vertically relative to the skid owing to surface roughness. The movements of the stylus are amplified, recorded graphically and possibly analysed. The method of measurement generally employed is described in BS 1134 *The assessment of surface texture.* Part 1 methods and instruments provides a basis for numerical evaluation of the texture of a surface which ensures compatibility of results when using different instruments. Part 2 gives general information and guidance.

Two parameters are used, both now internationally recognized (in ISO/R 468), which provide a numerical value for the measurement of surface texture. The main parameter is that previously known as CLA (centre-line-average) height and now designated internationally as $R_a$. It gives a measure of the arithmetical average value of the height of the departure of the whole of the profile, both above and below its centre line in a plane substantially normal to the surface. The secondary parameter gives a measure of average total height of surface irregularities and is designated $R_z$. This is similar to that known as PVA (peak-to-valley height). $R_a$ values can be determined graphically or by direct reading electrical instruments. $R_z$ values may be determined graphically, by the 'ten-point height' method (the average peak-to-valley distance calculated using the five highest peaks and the five deepest valleys within the sampling length). The values may be expressed in micro-inches ( $\mu$m) or micrometres (0·001 mm). BS 1134 gives a table of 13 preferred $R_a$ values ranging from 0·5 $\mu$in (0·0125 $\mu$m) for the finest work to 2000 $\mu$in (50 $\mu$m). This table also gives the ISO roughness grade number (extracted from ISO/R 1302) ranging from N1 (corresponding to 1 $\mu$in) to N12 (corresponding to 2000 $\mu$in). The generally similar American Standard ANSI B. 46. 1 *Surface roughness, waviness and lay* uses the term 'arithmetical average' instead of CLA ($R_a$).

If the surface texture has a directional quality its numerical value ($R_a$ or $R_z$) should be measured approximately at right angles to this 'lay'. As an alternative to using a direct reading instrument (possible with $R_a$) a recording instrument can be used to 'plot' the profile of the surface, and the value $R_a$ or $R_z$ can then be enumerated graphically. Athough there is no direct relationship between the two the value of $R_z$ may be some 4 to 7 times that of $R_a$.

The CLA ($R_a$) value is used in the UK, the Commonwealth generally, and in the USA. Some countries (including the USA until 1955) used the root mean square (RMS) value, whilst some Continental European countries (including Sweden) use the peak-to-valley height value ($R_z$) to express surface finish.

In order to *assess* the standard of surface finish it is now common practice to use sets of reference specimens exhibiting various grades of roughness as produced by different machining and other processes. These specimens may be flat ground or cylindrically ground, or may represent turned, bored, milled, cast or polished surfaces etc; they are covered by BS 2634 *Roughness comparison specimens* (equivalent to ISO 2632).

Each is marked with its normal $R_a$ value and if required its ISO roughness number, etc. By their use operators and inspectors gain a knowledge of how the feel and appearance of various surfaces are related to $R_a$ (CLA) index numbers, and by, say, using two specimens, one having the required value and the other half that value, it is possible to manufacture and inspect to a required standard of surface finish with a fair degree of confidence.

BS 6393 *Calibration specimens for use with stylus instruments used for the measurement of surface texture* deals with the characteristics of the specimens required to check the accuracy of *measurement* of such stylus instruments.

## 10.10 Thermal and other methods of NDT

Amongst the many unconventional methods of NDT which may be applied to specific problems mention should be made of techniques using the 'heat pattern' of the item under test to show up some abnormality.

One such technique which shows promise has been developed by the Central Electricity Research Laboratories as a method of detecting corrosion and blockages in boiler and heat exchanger tubes without the complete shut-down and possible dismantling necessary when inspecting tube bores internally by optical, mechanical or even ultrasonic methods. A tube with water flowing through it is heated externally. 'Hot spots' occur on the tube wall at positions where there are internal patches of corrosion products or deposited debris; they result from the poor conductivity of the corrosion product (e.g. magnetite) or debris, even though the tube wall thickness has been reduced. Conversely, thin patches of wall, without corrosion products, will show up as cold spots. Failure could occur in service at such spots.

By inducing a comparatively small temperature rise by means of a heater applied momentarily to the outside of a tube on test and then scanning the tube as it cools down owing to the flow of water, using a sensitive infra-red camera, these hot spots (and cold spots) can readily be detected. Many tubes can be scanned in the one operation and the result shown on a cathode-ray tube display.

Similarly, if the tube is blocked either partially or completely, the reduced water flow rate results in a generally reduced heat-transfer rate along the tube length. This blocked condition can be revealed by heating only a small area of the tube at a convenient place and observing the subsequent cooling rate with, for example, a simple contact thermocouple instrument.

### 10.10.1 Infra-red thermography

The Central Electricity Generating Board is amongst other organizations now using *infra-red thermography* to asses plant conditions and hence to carry out routine and non-routine maintenance and repair work.

One use is regular condition monitoring of insulated pipework and boiler surfaces. These are insulated with blocks of material cut and shaped to fit.

Any gaps in between these blocks, due to poor installation or to movement, etc. during operational use owing to vibration, etc. will allow heat to escape. This escape is readily detected and photographed by the thermal imaging equipment. Seeing that steam at temperatures up to 565°C may pass through the boiler and turbine pipes (and boiler flue temperatures can be higher) whilst exterior surface temperature should not exceed 50–55°C, the loss of heat energy can be considerable and the thermal stress set up may cause mechanical failures. By referring to these thermal records maintenance operations can be planned. Every boiler installation is shut down for a statutory inspection every three years and major maintenance repair and replacement may be carried out then, followed by a final inspection using infra-red thermal imaging equipment which will readily show up any poor workmanship, etc.

The electric power industry also uses infa-red equipment mounted in a helicopter for routine checking of the thousands of kilometers of overhead conductor lines for heat-emitting faulty electrical connections. Similarly, possibly annually, each sub-station may be surveyed with a hand-held thermal imaging instrument. Corroded and otherwise faulty connections may then be found and corrective action taken possibly at the next scheduled maintenance period.

Many other industrial uses for thermal imaging equipment suggest themselves, such as the location of unwanted fires and hot spots, and the detection of spontaneous combustion in coal stock piles.

*10.10.2 SPATE technique*

It has been known for many years that the adiabatic elastic deformation of a body is accompanied by a small change in temperature and that there is a linear and reversible relationship between the change in the sum of the principal stresses and the temperature changes produced. Any discontinuities, faults, etc. show up as local regions of higher stress where heat is generated or absorbed. With most engineering metals and materials tension will cool and compression will heat the affected area of the structure. Rubber, some plastics and carbon fibre may have the reverse effect. The SPATE (stress pattern analysis by measurement of thermal emission) technique uses infra-red radiation to measure local temperature changes remotely, and thus can provide details of the associated stresses. Hence it can be used for NDT, the detection of defects, stress analysis, fatigue studies (including welds), material and component testing, etc. Generally speaking the structure under stress is subjected to a constant amplitude cyclic loading and the resulting small induced thermal radiation changes emitted from its surface are collected by an optical system which scans the surface and are imaged upon a high sensitivity detector which correlates and derives the magnitude of the peak-to-peak changes in stresses. Instrumentation can be arranged to display various options, such as a 'stress map' of the structure. Compressive and tensile stresses may be distinguished (see Fig. 10.19).

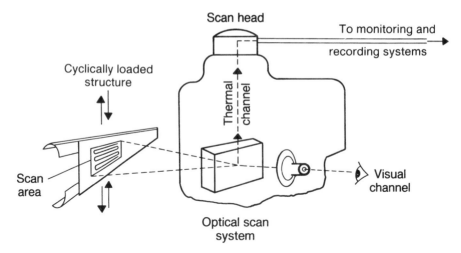

**Fig. 10.19 Schematic of SPATE system.**

## 10.11 Optical methods of NDT

These can be used on their own or in conjunction with other techniques. Magnifiers, microscopes, etc. have their obvious uses.

### 10.11.1 Polarized light

Light becomes polarized if passed through a Nicol prism, a crystal of calcite cut diagonally in two and then cemented together, the properties of which were investigated by William Nicol in 1828. By a process of double refraction one of the two polarized beams is removed by total reflection.

For well over 50 years strains in glass and intricate glasswork have been readily detected by viewing through polarized light. Areas of serious strain, liable to crack, show up like a Turner sunset. Such affected areas or components can be carefully annealed and then re-checked to see whether the strain has been reduced or eliminated. This process of NDT has been little exploited over the years but its development for checking other materials (e.g. plastics) has been receiving some attention (but see Appendix A.8).

### 10.11.2 Optical fibres

The use of optical fibres as sensors for the detection and monitoring of cracks is an interesting development. Optical fibres are suitably bonded to the surface of a structure. If a crack develops immediately beneath a fibre this will crack also and the light transmitted down the fibre will become attenuated and can be detected and recorded remotely. By the use of suitable polymers for protection and bonding monitoring can take place over a temperature range of some −196°C to 120°C and in undersea conditions.

### 10.11.3 Closed circuit television

This is often used for the visual inspection of areas not readily accessible to personnel, such as within nuclear reactors and other hazardous plants, and in the offshore industry to supplement inspection, etc. carried out by divers.

### 10.11.4 Photography

Photography is often also adapted for the visual inspection of remote areas, as it can give increased resolution and contrast, enabling defects to be identified and the information can be stored for perhaps corrective action at the next maintenance or shut-down period. Dimensional positioning information can be obtained by viewing stereoscopically two photographs taken from different positions. There is a complication with photography of nuclear installations as radiation will fog photographic film. This problem can be overcome by a system (developed by the CEGB) whereby the unexposed film is loaded into a shuttle which is then 'shot' pneumatically to the previously located camera, exposed and then returned within less than two seconds. A special camera can be manipulated (without film) to a previously set programme of some 30 photographs. Other special cameras can be developed for the accurate measurement (three-dimensional) of creep (± 0·01mm) over small areas such as in steam headers.

### 10.11.5 Holographic interferometry

These techniques can be applied to non-destructive testing. The specimen under test is given a small deformation by applying a controlled mechanical force, or if appropriate by changing the internal pressure. Double exposure of a holographic photographic plate before and after the change of force can produce a system of interference fringes which can map out surface displacements, measure strain and perhaps indicate weak areas. A reflection holography technique can be used to reveal the propagation of internal cracks in socket-fusion plastic pipe joints due to artificially accelerated fatigue. The photographic plate is supported over the joint by a special holder with four feet, which contact the cylindrical wall of the pipe. The application of a change of pressure in the pipe produces a deformation. Illumination of the pipe joint by a laser beam through the photographic plate will produce interference fringe patterns which can be interpreted to measure deformation and strain, and the propagation of cracks, etc. Laser interferometry can be used for the remote measurement of vibration. Light is scattered back from a spot on the surface, under test, which is illuminated by a laser. In general holographic interferometry, inspection, etc. can be developed to complement many visual inspection processes such as defect and stress measurement, monitoring and detection of faults.

## 10.12  Radar type techniques of NDT

Conventional methods of detecting and locating buried pipes and cables (such as are used for military mine detecting) cannot detect non-metallic materials. Radar techniques can be and have been applied to such matters as searching for buried pipework both metallic and non-metallic, perhaps to replace the very old but often imprecise practice based on 'water divining'. But as with divining some difficulties and problems still remain, especially with plastics. However by using low frequencies (around 1GHz) a downward looking radar has been developed by British Gas and gives considerable promise.

## 10.13  Sensing pigs

Many kilometres of pipelines and pipework are in service and subject to deterioration. Testing and inspection to discover incipient faults may be essential especially in hazardous installations. However periodic pressure and leak testing would necessitate taking the installation out of service. In 12.11.14. reference is made to the use of 'pigs' for inspecting the inside of a pipeline using illumination and a camera. British Gas have developed such 'pigs' for use with an on-line inspection service. These pigs, propelled perhaps by the flow of the liquid, travel down a pipeline and in effect 'smell' out defects and potential defects, variations in wall thickness (corrosion), depth of burial and perhaps cracks by the use of various sensors (magnetic, ultrasonic and TV camera sensors, etc. are amongst those which have or can be used), coupled with tape recording and analysis by computer.

British Gas have a network of some 17,000 km of large diameter high pressure (up to some 70 bars) pipelines at risk, and which must be inspected by methods including the use of 'pigs'. Even an annual inspection of some 10% of this network is a mammoth task.

## 10.14  Acoustic emission

When materials are under stress it has been shown that they can give audible evidence of their distress (in other words they groan!). Research has shown that regions of high stress can be so detected; the structural integrity, for instance, of a pressure vessel under hydrostatic test can be checked. However the results as yet do not allow quantitative, but only qualitative interpretation. Corelation of acoustic emission indications with simultaneous indications from other NDT techniques show promise that acoustic testing can become a useful tool. On-line monitoring of pressure vessels and plant etc. whilst in service can show the formation of and continued growth of fatigue cracks and defects, and should be of great value during in-service inspection. (For acoustic leak detection see 11.11.)

On-line crack detection and monitoring of the underwater and splash zone areas of off-shore structures can be undertaken by acoustic emission, using suitable transducers, without the removal of marine growth or the use of a diver and has given good results.

### References and further reading

Abrahams, *Ultrasonic examination of circumferential butt welds in pressure pipins,* Brit. Inst. of Non-destructive Testing, 1973.

Archbold, E. *The history of a holographic non-destructive test procedure,* Cambridge Univ. Press, 1976.

Berger, H. (ed), *Non-destructive Testing Standards – A Review,* American Society for Testing and Materials, STP 624, Philadelphin, Pa., 1977.

Dean, G.D. Ennos, A.E., and Quinn, G.B., 'Detection of cracks in a plastics pipe joint by reflection holography', *Plastics & Rubber Processing and Application,* vol.5, no.3, 1985, pp. 229–238.

Filipczynski et al (ed. J. Blitz), *Ultrasonic Methods of Testing Materials,* Butterworth, 1966.

Halmshaw, R., *Non-destructive Testing,* Edward Arnold, 1987.

Hogarth, C.A. and Blitz, J. (eds), *Techniques of Non-Destructive Testing,* Butterworth, 1960.

Institute of Chemical Engineers, *Guidance notes on use of acoustic emission testing in process plants,* Rugby, 1985.

International Institute of Welding, *Handbook of Radiographic Apparatus and Techniques,* Commission V.

International Institute of Welding, *Handbook on the Ultrasonic Examination of Austenitic Welds.*

International Institute of Welding, *Handbook on the Ultrasonic Examination of Welds,* Doc. IIS/IIW/527/76.

Iwadate, T. et al. 'Fracture Analysis of a $2\frac{1}{4}$ Cr-1 Mo steel test vessel and its correlation to acoustic emission'. Paper C110/80, 4th International Conference on pressure vessel technology, 1. Mech.E./ASME/Japan Society M.E., 1980.

Lamble, J.H. (ed), *Principles and Practice of Non-Destructive Testing,* Heywood, 1962.

Lucia, A.C. et al., 'Continuous monitoring of fatigue cracks growth in pressure vessels by acoustic emission', Paper C107/80, 4th International Conference on pressure vessel technology, I. Mech.E./ASME/Japan Society M.E., 1980.

Mountain, D.S. and Webber, J.M.B., 'Stress Pattern Analysis by Thermal Emission' 4th European Electro-Optics Conference, Utrecht, Oct. 1978.

Nichols, R.W. and Dau, G.J., 'Non-destructive Examination of Pressurised Components' Proceedings of International Seminar in conjunction with a conference on structural mechanics in reactor technology, Elsevier, 1984.

Oliver, D.E. and Webber, J.M.B, 'Absolute calibration of the SPATE technique for non-contacting stress measurement', SESA Conference Montreal, 1984.

Oliver, D.E. and Webber, J.M.B. 'Use of sensitive temperature transducers to produce stress maps of cyclically loaded structures', SESA Conference, 1983.

*Review of current Ultrasonic Non destructive Testing Developments in the UK*, UKAEA Harwell, 1975.

Rockley, J.C. *An Introduction to Industrial Radiology*, Butterworth, 1964.

Spanner, J.C. 'Acoustic emission – some examples of increasing industrial maturity, ASTM E-7 NDT Committee, Florida, 1979.

Silk, M.G. Stoneham, A.M. and Temple, J.A.G., *The Reliability of Non-destructive Inspection – assessing the assessment of structures under stress*, Adam Hilger, Bristol, 1987.

Szilard, J. (ed), *Ultrasonic testing (non-conventional testing techniques)*, Wiley, 1982.

UK Elec. Supply Ind. Standard 98.10, *Manual ultrasonic testing of welds in ferritic steel sections*, 1981. Part 1 Butt welds in ferritic steel sections greater than 10 mm thick. Part 2 Nozzle, branch stub etc.

Watson, J. and Britton, P.W., 'Applications of holography to underwater inspection'. Proceedings Subtech 83: Design and Operation of Underwater Vehicles, London, 1983.

Colloquium on Optical Techniques for NDT organized by IEE & British Institute of NDT January, 1986, which includes some of the above references.

Further information on related NDT subjects can be found in the proceedings of the 1st, 2nd and 3rd International Seminars on:

NDE in Relation to Structural Integrity, 1980.
Advances in NDE for Structural Integrity, 1982.
NDE for Pressurised Components, 1984.

All are published by Elsevier.

# 11  Leak-testing techniques

## 11.1  The growing importance of leak testing

To ensure safe and reliable operation much engineering and industrial plant
and equipment has to be gas- or liquid-tight. Obviously vessels and
equipment subjected to large pressure differentials must be leak-tight,
especially if their contents are above atmospheric pressure and are in any
way toxic or otherwise dangerous. With equipment under vacuum, any 'in-
leakage' may spoil a process, and if the equipment is not continuously
evacuated the vacuum may well soon be lost. This is particularly so with
high-vacuum techniques—quite a small leak will prevent the attainment
and maintenance of the required high degree of vacuum.

Often clauses requiring the equipment to be 'free from leaks' are
encountered in specifications, etc. In general these are pointless unless the
degree of leak-tightness is specified. With engineering materials it is
extremely difficult to construct and maintain equipment capable of passing
the leak rate tests sometimes necessary today. The degree of leak-tightness
required may depend on the expected life of sealed components, their size,
the effect of in-leakage on contaminating the contents, etc. With equipment
which is intended to be continuously pumped to a low pressure, it will
depend on the gas handling capacity of the pumps and the ultimate vacuum
required. Quite often the degree of leak-tightness required on a vacuum
vessel will be such that it would take many years for the pressure to rise
appreciably.

To prove whether or not plant or equipment is leak-tight to the specified
standard a *leak rate* or *proving test* must be carried out. Should the specified
leak rate be exceeded it is then necessary to find the source of the leak or
leaks and carry out repairs. Some methods of test are only suitable for the
location of leaks, others can be used for measuring leak rate, and some can
be adapted for both.

It is important to realize that leaks may be temporarily masked by dirt, paint, grease, etc., on the surface of a vessel or component. Therefore testing should in general be carried out with surfaces clean and dry and free from paint and surface coatings. This is of particular importance with vacuum plant. Again, surface defects and blemishes, inclusions, poor welding, etc., may cause leaks to develop in equipment after it has passed its initial leak tests. The difference between real and 'virtual' leaks in vacuum systems should be appreciated (see 11.7.2).

## 11.2 Leak rate

The tightness of a vessel can be expressed in terms of the mass flow of fluid passing through any leaks in it. With a gas obeying the ideal gas equation at constant temperature the product of pressure times volume is proportional to mass. Hence leak rate is proportional to:

$$\text{Rate of pressure change} \times \text{volume of plant}$$

The internationally agreed unit of leak-rate until recently was the torr litre per second (torr L/s). (1 torr = 1 mmHg = 1000 μmHg; 760 torr = 1 standard atmosphere, see 8.6 and Table 8.6.) Thus unit leak rate would indicate a rate of flow of 1 L/s streaming through the leak at a pressure of 1 torr; or expressed another way, a rate of pressure change of 1 torr/s due to leakage into an isolated plant volume of 1 litre.

As an example, consider a vessel of 100 litres volume evacuated to a pressure of 0·1 torr (mmHg) and then isolated from the pump. If after 15 minutes the measured pressure in the vessel is found to be 0·3 torr—an isolation pressure rise of 0·2 torr—then:

$$\text{Leak rate} = (0.2) \times 100)/(15 \times 60) = 0\cdot0222 \text{ torr L/s or } 2\cdot2 \times 10^{-2} \text{ torr L/s}$$

Torr-litre per second units are rather large. Consequently other units for leak rate will be encountered.

In the UK, particularly for vacuum work, the lusec, in which pressure change can be expressed colloquially in 'microns' (μm) of mercury (1 μmHg = 0·001 mmHg), has been widely used. Thus:

1 lusec = 1 litre μmHg per sec (loosely Lμ/sec) = 0·001 torr L/s
= 1 millitorr L/s
1000 lusecs = 1 torr L/s
1 clusec = 0·01 lusec

The leak rate in the above example would thus be 22·2 lusecs.

In the USA some much used units of leak rate are the micron cubic foot/hour, and the atmospheric cubic centimetre/second, signifying flow rates of 1 ft³/h at 1 μmHg pressure, and 1 cm³/s at atmospheric pressure respectively.

With the introduction of SI units and the acceptance of the newton per square metre as the SI unit of pressure (now called the pascal), SI units are gradually being adopted for high vacuum pressure measurement (see 8.6 and Table 8.3), and as a basis for expressing leak rate.

Hence using SI units, leak rate (being proportional to pressure × volume ÷ time) can be expressed in terms of:

$$\frac{N}{m^2} \times \frac{1}{s} \times m^3 = \frac{Nm^3}{m^2s}$$

or $Pa^{-1}$ $^3s^{-1}$ $m^3$

It will be noticed that the expression can be reduced to $Nms^{-1}$ which equals the watt (the SI unit of power, indicating that a leak is an expenditure of energy).

However, much of the present high vacuum technical data and literature makes use of the torr.

To convert to and from pure SI:

1 torr litre per second (torr L s⁻¹) = 0·133 Pa m³ s⁻¹ = 1.333 mbar Ls⁻¹
1 Pa m³ s⁻¹ = 7·5 torr Ls⁻¹ = 10 mbar Ls⁻¹

Table 11.1 gives some leak rate conversions which should be useful to the inspector when dealing with the many different units he will encounter in specifications and the technical literature. The leak rate of a water can or bucket might be of the order of 10 lusecs, and that of a chemical plant 1 lusec (which is equal to $133 \times 10^{-6}$ Pa m³ s⁻¹, or should we say 133 microwatts?)

The leak rate of vacuum process plant, perhaps continuously pumped, might be 1 clusec (1·33 μW) and hermetically sealed items 0·01 clusec ($10^{-4}$ lusec). The leak rate of a glass electronic valve etc., if measurable, might be $10^{-8}$ lusec ($1·33 \times 10^{-12}$ Pa m³ s⁻¹ or 1·33 pW); although equipment with such a leak rate would generally be regarded as 'vacuum-tight', this valve would eventually become 'soft' and useless.

Note: all the above leak rate units are currently in use, with additions of mbar Ls⁻¹, Pa Ls⁻¹, atm cc/s and other units with time intervals of seconds, minutes or hours. UK industrial practice has in general changed from units using torr (not now accepted for legal use by EEC) to those using bar (accepted apparently temporarily by EEC) perhaps prior to going over to pure SI (i.e. Pa m³ s⁻¹) which is used particularly in academic circles. Industry, while preferring to use mbar Ls⁻¹, will graduate equipment in any other leak rates specified.

**TABLE 11.1**

*Pressure–volume leak rate unit conversions*

| | mbar Ls$^{-1}$ | torr Ls$^{-1}$ | atm cm$^3$ sec$^{-1}$ | Lusec |
|---|---|---|---|---|
| 1 mbar Ls$^{-1}$ = | 1 | 0·75 | 0·987 | 750 |
| 1 torr Ls$^{-1}$ = | 1·333 | 1 | 1·316 | 1000 |
| 1 atm cm$^3$ s$^{-1}$ = | 1·013 | 0·76 | 1 | 760 |
| 1 Lusec = | 1·333 × 10$^{-3}$ | 0·001 | 1·316 × 10$^{-3}$ | 1 |
| 1 atm ft$^3$ min$^{-1}$ = | 478 | 358 | 472 | 358 × 10$^3$ |
| 1 Pa m$^3$ s$^{-1}$ = | 10 | 7·5 | 9·87 | 7·5 × 10$^3$ |
| 1 Pa Ls$^{-1}$ = | 0·01 | 7·5 × 10$^{-3}$ | 9·87 × 10$^{-3}$ | 7·5 |

| | atm ft$^3$ min$^{-1}$ | Pa m$^3$ s$^{-1}$ | Pa Ls$^{-1}$ |
|---|---|---|---|
| 1 mbar Ls$^{-1}$ = | 2·097 × 10$^{-3}$ | 0·1 | 100 |
| 1 torr Ls$^{-1}$ = | 2·795 × 10$^{-3}$ | 0·133 | 133·3 |
| 1 atm cm$^3$ s$^{-1}$ = | 2·12 × 10$^{-3}$ | 0·101 | 101 |
| 1 Lusec = | 2·79 × 10$^{-6}$ | 133 × 10$^{-6}$ | 133 × 10$^{-3}$ |
| 1 atm ft$^3$ min$^{-1}$ = | 1 | 47·8 | 478 × 10$^2$ |
| 1 Pa m$^3$ s$^{-1}$ = | 2·097 × 10$^{-2}$ | 1 | 1000 |
| 1 Pa Ls$^{-1}$ = | 2·097 × 10$^{-5}$ | 0·001 | 1 |

Many small leaks are complex, the escaping gas following a devious path through the structure of a material. Other small leaks may be simple, like a pinhole in a car tyre inner tube.

It is sometimes desirable to equate leak rate ($Q$) with the diameter ($D$) of an equivalent finite hole (such as a pinhole). Assuming molecular flow and a vessel wall thickness of some 2 mm then:

$$D = \frac{Q1/3}{35\cdot6}$$

For a leak rate ($Q$) of 10$^{-5}$ torr litre/sec

$$D = 6 \times 10^{-3} \text{mm}$$

(This is about one-eighth of the diameter of a human hair.)

### 11.3  Effect of test pressure on leak rate

For a given leak (through an equivalent finite hole) the rate of flow will increase with the pressure differential. Consequently, particularly for pressurization methods, the pressure differential must be specified.

When testing vacuum vessels and equipment, however, the pressure differential is generally one atmosphere (or thereabouts), and is taken as such.

The leak rate will vary as the square of the pressure differential generally for viscous flow when the pressures on both sides exceed 1 torr (mmHg). For very small leaks, however, where the physical dimensions are comparable with the mean free path of the gas molecules, the leak rate tends to vary as the pressure differential.

### 11.4  Effect of type of gas on leak rate

The leak rate will also depend on the nature of the leaking fluid, owing to differences in diffusion and flow characteristics. Thus water, penetrating oils, air, hydrogen, etc., can have greatly differing leak rates when subjected to the same pressure differentials. The leak rate of hydrogen (a very penetrating gas) through a given aperture will be about twice that of air. Oxygen and helium are slightly less penetrating than air.

### 11.5  Leak location by pressure methods

*11.5.1  Pressure testing*

In practice some comparatively simple tests are applied to many items of plant to check whether any major leaks are present. A hydraulic pressure test may be carried out, and the exterior surface of the vessel or component examined for any seepages of fluid. A suitable wash of paint, etc., applied to suspected surfaces, and the segregation of certain items by the use of shut-off valves, etc., may help in locating leaks.

If conditions permit, the equipment to be tested can be pressurized with air and immersed in water. The formation of a string of bubbles will indicate the location of a leak. It is an advantage if a wetting agent (such as Tepol) is introduced into the water to reduce its surface tension. Immersion in paraffin (kerosene) or alcohol, and/or pressurizing with a gas of lower viscosity than air (such as hydrogen), will enable quite small leaks to be located (sensitivities up to 100 times greater than with air and water may be achieved).

If immersion is impracticable, the surface to be tested can be covered with a soap or detergent solution (*after* the pressure has been applied), when the resulting bubbles due to leaks should readily be discernable. *Caution.* The danger inherent in pressurizing with air or gas must be realized. The plant should be regarded as a pressure vessel and designed, constructed and tested accordingly (see Chapter 3). A pressure regulator with an over-pressure safety device, such as a bursting disc (to BS 2915 *Domed metallic bursting discs and bursting disc assemblies*) or a safety valve, should be fitted.

Note that pressure-testing methods, when used on plant intended for vacuum service, are open to criticism because it is possible for a leak to have a directional bias. However, it is often an advantage first to pressure-test certain items of vacuum plant before final vacuum tests, as it can simplify leak finding. Instead of pressurizing the *inside* of the item under test pressure may be applied to the *outside* to drive a fluid or a tracer gas into the interior of any leaking item.

On release of the pressure (and possibly the application of vacuum) any fluid or gas which has leaked in will bubble or ooze out and can be detected by sight or various other methods.

Such methods are widely used for leak testing relatively small components such as electronic devices, semiconductors, radio-active sealed sources, etc. Dye penetrants are particularly useful for devices with glass or transparent walls where the dye, can be detected inside.

Depending upon the method used, leaks of the order of $10^{-2}$ to $10^{-5}$ Pa m$^3$ s$^{-1}$ can be located.

### 11.5.2 Search-gas methods

Many methods of leak detection depend on pressurizing the inside of the plant under test with a search or tracer gas (usually introduced into the pressurizing air, and consequently of low concentration). A suitable detector of this gas is then moved slowly round the outside of the pressurized equipment and any points at which the search gas is leaking out are thus shown up.

(a) *The halide torch method.* An organic halogen vapour (usually a compound of chlorine, fluorine or occasionally bromine or iodine) is introduced into the plant under test (usually mixed with air). A primus-type paraffin burning blow torch (or a Tilley lamp) is used as the detector. The air supply for this torch is taken via a length of flexible metal tube which is used to probe slowly the surface of the plant under test. Should a leak be present then the halogen vapour will pass through it and enter the tube and so reach the torch. This torch will normally burn with a non-luminous flame, but the presence of the halide vapour produces a green coloration turning to bright blue in the case of a large leak. This method when used by a skilled operator can readily locate leaks down to the order of 2 lusecs ($2.66 \times 10^{-4}$ Pa m$^3$ s$^{-1}$), but it has largely been replaced by the halogen diode detector.

(b) *Halogen diode leak detector* (see Fig. 11.1). This method depends on the positive ion emission from a heated platinum anode when this is exposed to a halogen (halide) vapour. A sampling probe attached to a 'gun' is slowly moved over the surface under test and sucks in air, which is passed over the heated element. Should this air contain halide vapour (e.g. from a leak), the resulting increase in ion emission is amplified and is shown on a meter, or is used to increase the repetitive rate of a flashing lamp or of the note from a loudspeaker. This type of halogen leak detector is comparatively simple and cheap, and under favourable conditions considerably less time is taken in locating leaks than with any other method at present in use.

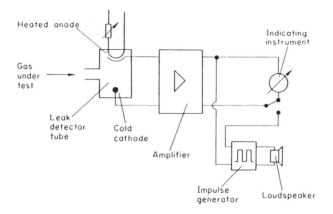

(a) Circuit diagram

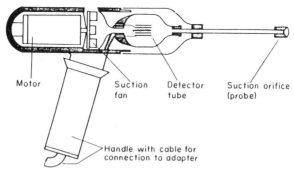

(b) Construction of the leak sniffer

**Fig. 11.1  Halogen leak detector.** (*Leybold.*)

Although not meant primarily to be a quantitative instrument leaks of less than one clusec can be detected.

When testing refrigeration equipment and other items which may already contain a halogen compound, operation is easy. For other applications a quantity of Freon or Arcton, or of some other halogen compound such as carbon tetrachloride, or trichloroethylene, is injected into the system as a tracer gas. It has been stated that a leakage of Arcton amounting to 300 mg per year can be detected with absolute certainty (a leakage of less than $10^{-5}$ torr L/s or $1 \cdot 33 \times 10^{-4}$ Pa m$^3$ s$^{-1}$).

The pressure need only be something over atmospheric, although higher pressures can be used. When slowly probing over a surface a leak is indicated, for instance, by a rapid increase in 'ticking', like a Geiger counter; it can readily be pin-pointed. Small leaks of halide vapour are readily detected, but should large concentrations be encountered for any appreciable length of time the detector may vary widely in sensitivity and become erratic. The sensitivity recovers generally when operated in fresh air, but the element may become 'poisoned' and need reactivation, or occasional replacement. Frequent sensitivity checks are desirable, using a standard reference leak (see 11.6.5). Should the test area become contaminated with halogen vapour (even small amounts), then it will not be possible to achieve reliable results until the area has been thoroughly ventilated. Smoking (or other vapours, even bad breath!) in the test area is undesirable. The plant under test should be clean and dry and free from oil vapours, etc., and obviously cleaning by carbon tetrachloride or trichloroethylene is not permissible as their residual vapours persist for a long time and will give spurious results. (Purified commercial benzene may be used.)* Leak detection in confined spaces may be difficult; it may be necessary to use very dilute gas/air mixtures until the major leaks have been eliminated. Leak detection should not be carried out when explosive vapours, etc., are present, owing to the high-temperature detector.

(c) *Thermal conductivity leak detectors.* By pressurizing with a search gas and probing the outside of the plant or vessel for leaks it is possible to arrange for any escaping gas to be drawn over a hot-wire element heated to about 200°C. The gas/air mixture changes the temperature and hence the resistance of the element and thus unbalances a bridge circuit containing a reference element exposed only to air. The out-of-balance current is amplified and gives a leakage indication on a meter, or by an audible response. The arrangement is similar to the Pirani vacuum gauge, 8.15.

Various search gases can be used, but for good sensitivity they should possess a thermal conductivity differing considerably from air. Argon and carbon dioxide, having thermal conductivities less than air, can be used, but

---

*All three solvents mentioned must be used with discretion because of their toxicity. Safer substitutes are desirable.

hydrogen and helium are the most sensitive (leaks of the order of $10^{-5}$ torr L/s can be detected).

(d) *Infra-red absorption leak detector.* The plant under test is pressurized with a search gas, usually nitrous oxide (occasionally carbon dioxide). The probe, which is connected by rubber tubing to the detector, is moved slowly over the plant surface, first rapidly drawing air (and any search gas from leaks) through it and the analyser (to rapidly show up any large leaks); then the speed of pumping air is reduced to obtain increased sensitivity. This however slows up the response so that the delay before a leak at the probe gives an indication may be as much as 15 seconds.

In the analyser, the gas from the probe is passed through one of two identical parallel tubes, the other containing a reference atmosphere. Both are traversed by identical infra-red radiation. The differential heating effects of the emergent beams on a pure sample of the search gas causes the deflection of a thin diaphragm, to an extent which can be measured electronically.

Leaks down to the order of $10^{-5}$ torr L/s ($1 \cdot 33 \times 10^{-4}$ Pa m$^3$ s$^{-1}$) may be detected, but as the speed of probing at maximum sensitivity is some 1 inch per minute leak location is tedious.

There is a certain overlap between the absorption characteristics of nitrous oxide, carbon dioxide and water vapour. Consequently if nitrous oxide is used as the search gas the presence of the other two is undesirable. The normal background quantities present may be taken into account by adjusting the zero of the instrument accordingly, but any variation in these quantities will produce spurious results. Care should be taken therefore to prevent the addition of carbon dioxide or water vapour to the test area atmosphere, and this includes breath exhaled by operators in the vicinity of the probe.

For leak location by penetrant methods, see 10.8; using ammonia and $CO_2$, see 7.6: by mass spectrometer (pressure method), see 11.10.3.

## 11.6 Leak rate measurement by pressure methods

Some methods of locating leaks are also adaptable to measuring leak rate. Search-gas methods generally can be so adapted, but accuracy may not be high.

### 11.6.1 The isolation pressure-drop method

This is perhaps the simplest basic method. The plant or component under test is pressurized above atmosphere to the required pressure (due precautions having been taken) and is then isolated by shutting a valve (which must itself be above suspicion as regards leakage). A sensitive pressure gauge or element is then used to measure the drop in pressure ($p$) over a given time ($t$). If the volume of plant, *including that of the trapped volume of pipework, etc., up to the isolation valve*, is $V$, and if the temperature and barometric pressure remain constant throughout the test (which they probably will not) then the apparent leak rate will be $pV/t$, expressed in the appropriate units. A variation on this method is to place the component, pressurized with air, etc., inside an evacuated chamber and to measure the rate at which the pressure drops, as before.

For accurate leak rate measurements using pressure-drop methods account *must* be taken of any change of temperature or of barometric pressure during the test. For an account of an accurate method of measuring the leak rate of 'dry boxes' by pressure drop, see 6.6.

### 11.6.2  The volumetric flow rate method

The plant or component is pressurized by a constant pressure source to the required value, indicated by the pressure gauge. When steady conditions have been reached a flow meter is used to measure any air (or gas) required to maintain the constant pressure, so enabling the leakage rate to be evaluated.

In its simple form again this method suffers from inaccuracies, and it is assumed that all readings are taken at times of similar ambient temperatures. In practice this is difficult to arrange, as an appreciable period of time is required for the test, during which temperature changes will affect the dimensions of the plant, and both of these will affect the pressure within it; changes in atmospheric pressure will also have their effect.

In both methods it is possible for the pressure in the plant to *rise*, and even then it may be leaking slightly (see 6.6)

### 11.6.3  Search-gas methods

Leak rate can generally be measured by pressurizing the plant or component with the search gas, placing a hood or container over it, and passing the contents of this hood (and thus any search gas due to leakage) over the detector element. Alternatively, it may occasionally be desirable to pressurize the hood and to pass the contents of the plant (including any search gas due to leakage) over the detector element. Owing to the slow rate of diffusion of search gas through the surrounding air any detector using a slow sampling rate (as most do) will not give a measurable response in a time short enough to be practicable. The infra-red detector can however employ a higher sampling rate and thus it is used for the direct measurement of leak rate.

### 11.6.4  Infra-red absorption leak rate measurement

Four variations of method may be encountered:

(a) *Flow measurement—plant pressurized.* The plant is pressurized with the search gas (e.g. nitrous oxide) and isolated; a hood is placed over it. Clean, dry air, forced under the hood and over the exterior of the plant at a suitable sampling rate, passes through a flow meter, and then through the infra-red detector. If this detector indicates that $n$ parts per million of search gas are present (having leaked from the plant), and the absolute pressure at the detector (approximately atmospheric) is $p$ torr (mmHg) and the flow as indicated by the flow meter is $q$ litres per second, then the leak rate will be $pqn \times 10^{-3}$ lusec (microtorr L/s).

(b) *Flow measurement—hood pressurized.* An alternative in which the hood is pressurized and the air is passed through the plant.

(c) *Accumulation or integration procedure—plant pressurized.* This procedure can be adopted when greater sensitivities are required, as the leaking search gas builds up to a greater concentration. The plant or component is pressurized (with nitrous oxide) and put into a collapsible container or hood, which is initially full of air. During the period of the test any search gas which leaks from the component will accumulate in the container. After the test time has elapsed this air and search gas is expelled through the infra-red detector, which measures the concentration of gas.

If this should be $n$ parts per million, and the period of test has been $t$ seconds (perhaps one hour), whilst the volume of free air in the container is $V$ litres, the absolute pressure at the detector being $p$ torr (mmHg), then:

Leakage rate $= pVn/t$ microtorr litre/second ($pVn/t \times 10^{-3}$ lusec) (A slight variation on the method described is to circulate continually the contents of the hood through the detector in a closed circuit during the test. The leak rate is then obtained from the rate of increase in concentration of the search gas.)

(d) *Accumulation or integration procedure—hood pressurized.* This is an alternative in which the hood is pressurized instead of the plant.

*11.6.5 Other search-gas methods using pressurization*

These can be adapted to check approximate leak rates (perhaps on a pass/reject basis) of specified areas or components by comparing the response of the detector with that made when it is connected to a standard calibrated reference leak.

For instance, when a halogen leak detector fitted with a leak rate meter is used, it must first be calibrated using a standard leak. This consists of a specially made capillary containing the search gas (Freon) which leaks out to the atmosphere at a known rate. The detector sensitivity control is adjusted so that when the probe sniffs at the standard leak the detector leak rate meter reads the same value as that of the standard leak.

As the response of most detectors to leakage is not linear it is essential that the value of the standard leak should be approximately the same as that of the leak being evaluated, if reasonable accuracy is to be achieved.

## 11.7  Inspection and testing of vacuum equipment for leakage

### 11.7.1  Preliminary remarks

In a vacuum system quite small leaks can attain greater significance than they would in a pressure system owing to the low pressures involved. This is understandable when it is realized that 1 cm$^3$ of air at n.t.p. will have a volume of 760 litres at $10^{-3}$ mmHg (torr), and of no less than 760,000 litres at a pressure of $10^{-6}$ mmHg. Such volumes would seriously overload most vacuum pumps (and of course in the high-vacuum range a vapour (diffusion) pump has to be backed by a suitable rotary pump—see 8.10). Consequently the joints in a vacuum system must be given very careful attention. Soldering, brazing and welding must be inspected to ensure the highest quality.

Furthermore, designs and methods of fabrication which may lead to small trapped volumes or pockets of air, dirt etc., within a vessel should be avoided, as these will gradually leak out under vacuum conditions and give the symptoms of a slow, minute leak which it will be practically impossible to trace. Consequently such points should be carefully watched. For instance, a screw in a blind hole under vacuum will provide a souce of contaminating air giving the effect of a leak for many hours of pumping (see Fig. 11.2(a)).

A crack in a normal weld which permits slow leakage from a trapped volume into the vacuum space is almost impossible to locate. By using tack welding on the atmospheric side, so leaving a path to the atmosphere, the leak can however be located by the methods to be described (Fig. 11.2(b)).

Demountable joints should be of special construction, usually employing 'O' rings in properly designed grooves. Inspection of 'O' rings to ensure the removal of moulding 'flash', and of grooves and contact surfaces to ensure a smooth finish will pay dividends (see 8.18.1). The use of varnishes and jointing compounds usually proves unsatisfactory in the long run, and the use of paint, purposely or inadvertently, to cover up minute leaks is a positive menace.

### 11.7.2  Detection of leaks in vacuum systems—real and 'virtual' leaks

Generally speaking the detection of leaks is carried out in two stages:
  (i) Tracking them down to particular sections or units of the plant.
  (ii) Locating them precisely.
By shutting off appropriate valves one at a time and thus isolating

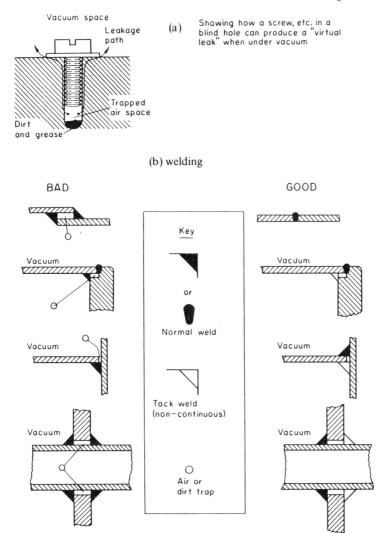

(a) Showing how a screw, etc. in a blind hole can produce a "virtual leak" when under vacuum

(b) welding

**Fig. 11.2 Examples of good and bad design in vacuum equipment.** (Edwards High Vacuum)

different sections from the pumping system any large leaks can be tracked down by observing the vacuum attained in each case. If necessary the rate of pressure rise is measured (see 11.9.2).

Having established the presence of a leak in a certain section, the next step is to examine all joints for tightness and to check that all 'O' rings are in good condition. Very often 'O' rings become damaged or receive cuts owing to improper trapping or by mishandling. They may also deteriorate in use, or even in store. On some plants, especially where conditions are onerous, it is the practice to change 'O' rings, and similar seals and gaskets, every time a particular item is dis-assembled. If checking the joints, etc., fails to stop the leak then it may be located precisely by one of the methods described in what follows.

Before doing so however it is necessary to be certain that a real leak exists and not an apparent one, often due to 'outgassing'. Long periods of pumping sometimes do not succeed in producing the expected high degree of vacuum, and so the many circumstances which might prevent it being attained should be considered. What are sometimes known as 'virtual' leaks are due to outgassing from the walls of the vessel, etc., and even more so from any porous material, particularly rubber, plastics, etc., and from any partially trapped enclosures containing air, grease, water, oil, etc., which may be present. All of these can slowly release vapours for long periods, but those due to outgassing from the walls, etc., which can swamp a small leak at first, should gradually tail off after a reasonable period of pumping (maybe some hours). The application of heat, if permissible, will accelerate the release of vapour. Water or any volatile contaminant in the pump fluid may prevent proper operation, and the pumps may have to be isolated and checked, and if necessary cleaned.

## 11.8 Leak location by vacuum methods

The methods used for leak locating (and proving) on pressurized systems have their counterpart in systems tested under vacuum. However the techniques employed tend to be more complex and involve a knowledge of vacuum technology.

Many of the methods require the use of search gas in 'probing' for leaks. The general method is as follows. Search gas from a cylinder via a regulating valve is supplied at a suitable rate to a probe or applicator which is moved slowly by hand over the suspected areas of the plant under test. This plant is maintained dynamically under a high degree of vacuum by a suitable pumping system. When a leak is probed the search gas will pass through it into the plant and then into the vacuum system, where it will be detected and indicated by a suitable instrument. When search gas is applied to a leak the 'response time' of the detector should be reasonably fast, and conversely when it is removed the 'clearing time' for the detector to return to its initial condition should not be too long.

### 11.8.1 Backing-space technique

Some pressure gauges, etc., used in vacuum systems are dealt with in

Chapter 8. When used for leak detecting purposes they are placed in one of two basic positions:

(a) On the high-vacuum side, in the vessel being tested (or in the line between this vessel and the pump). These connections give the shortest response times.

(b) On the fore-vacuum side, in the 'backing' line or space between two pumps operating in series.

The use of this second position, known as 'backing-space technique', is of particular importance if small leaks are involved under high-vacuum conditions, as it gives an amplification of any pressure changes occurring.

If two vacuum pumps connected in series are evacuating a vessel, as in an electrical series circuit, the current flow will be the same in all parts. Therefore even if the two pumps are of different types and pumping rates the mass flow under conditions of equilibrium will be the same throughout the system. Thus if the first pump has the higher volumetric pumping speed it will try to evacuate gas initially of mass $\propto p_1 V_1$ into the backing space. But the second pump cannot cope with this high rate of flow, so the pressure in the backing line will rise to some value $p_2$ such that the mass flow through this second pump at its reduced volumetric flow is the same as that through the first pump.

Hence any change of pressure occuring on the 'fine' side (such as might occur when leak probing) will be magnified considerably on the backing side (perhaps by 10 to 100 times).

If a very sensitive detector is fitted in the backing space between a diffusion and a rotary pump the fluctuations in pressure arising from the rotary pump will upset results. This defect can be overcome by inserting the sensitive detector between two diffusion pumps. The secondary pump is of smaller throughput, and is often built into systems specifically designed for leak detection. The pumping speed from the backing space (interspace) is varied by a throttle control valve, and maximum sensitivity is achieved with the smallest opening (and consequently the highest pressure in the inter-space). A limit is set however by the maximum outlet pressure at which the pump can still operate, and also by the maximum operating pressure of the detector.

### 11.8.2 *Electrical discharge methods* (see Table 11.2)

In glass vacuum systems the traditional method of leak location is to probe the suspected area with the point of a high-frequency Tesla spark coil operating at around 4 megacycles/second. The presence of a leak is indicated by the characteristic colour of the discharge excited in the system due to the presence of gas (such as air or nitrogen which give a pinkish colour). The actual location of the leak is indicated by the entry of the spark into it. Quite often the spark will enter and open out a minute leak, and,

**TABLE 11.2**

*High-voltage discharge tube as a vacuum leak detector*

When used as a leak detector, the following table gives the colours that can be observed using various probe gases (operated at 30 kV, 4 Mc/s).

| | | | |
|---|---|---|---|
| Air | Reddish pink | Argon | Deep red |
| Oil | Blue or green | Neon | Blood red |
| Water vapour | Transparent blue | Carbon dioxide | White |
| Methylated spirit | Grey blue | Sodium | Yellow |
| Nitrogen | Yellow (red gold) | Potassium | Green |
| Oxygen | Lemon | Mercury | Greenish-blue |
| Hydrogen | Rose-pink | Chlorine | Light green |
| Helium | Violet-red | | |

(*Courtesy Genevac Ltd*)

especially in inexperienced hands, it will make its own quota of sizeable leaks!

A glass gas discharge tube connected to a metal vacuum system (often as a vacuum indicator) can be used for rough leak tests, a pink discharge generally indicating a leak. By probing suspected areas with a suitable search gas and noting any changes in the colour and/or appearance of the discharge it is possible to locate leaks. Gases such as hydrogen, carbon dioxide and methane can be used. Alternatively, suspected parts can be covered with methylated spirit, trichloroethylene, etc., or a solvent such as acetone, but these are not generally recommended as they may temporarily block a leak. The discharge tube is often placed in the backing space to make use of the resulting amplification.

*11.8.3 Hydrogen Pirani leak detector* (see also 8.15)

Thermal conductivity gauges of Pirani type used for pressure measurement can be adapted for leak detection using a suitable search gas. Of all gases hydrogen has the highest thermal conductivity; if it passes through a leak into the Pirani gauge it results in increased heat losses from the filament and a consequent change of resistance and of indication (due to an apparent pressure increase). Being of low viscosity hydrogen will readily pass through a leak, but owing to its low molecular weight it is rapidly pumped away. Other gases of higher molecular weight and good thermal conductivity may also be used for probing and may give quite sensitive results. These gases include helium, argon, carbon dioxide, halides and even town gas.

The Pirani gauge head is usually inserted in the backing space. It is necessary to locate and rectify large leaks before using the gauge.

A thermocouple or a thermistor type gauge head may be used instead of the Pirani type, although the latter is considered the more sensitive. The gauge can be used at pressures up to 10 torr (mmHg), but the best sensitivity is obtainable at pressures below $0 \cdot 1$ torr (mmHg), when leaks down to the order of $10^{-5}$ torr L/s ($1 \cdot 33 \times 10^{-4}$ Pa m$^3$ s$^{-1}$) can be detected using hydrogen and a differential Pirani arrangement. In this, two identical gauges are used. One is sensitive to both hydrogen and background pressure fluctuations, and the other to background pressure only, the hydrogen being excluded by means of an adsorbent (e.g. charcoal) or some other trap.

*11.8.4 Ionization gauge leak detectors* (see also 8.16)

Ionization gauges of both the hot cathode and the cold cathode (Penning) type are used as a leak detectors, and are particularly useful in the high-vacuum range where they have sensitivities somewhat higher than the Pirani gauge. They are not suitable for pressures greater than about $10^{-2}$ torr (mmHg). A cold trap can (as with other gauges) be inserted in the system so that the gauge will record partial gas pressure and not be affected by condensable vapours.

The sensitivity of a hot cathode ionization gauge, particularly, can be increased by fitting a stabilized gauge control unit with a 'backing off' device. The value of the standing ion current due to the prevailing pressure conditions can then be reduced ('backed off'), and the very small changes in this current due to small pressure changes can then be measured by shunting the sensitive meter fitted, and/or by using an amplifier.

Small fluctuations in system pressure (such as those due to cyclic pump fluctuations) will tend to limit sensitivity, but these fluctuations can be reduced by making use of 'backing-space technique' (see 11.8.1) and by the use of a charcoal cold trap. The refrigerant used in the trap can be solid carbon dioxide or liquid nitrogen (rather than liquid air or oxygen). Most gases and vapours will be condensed and adsorbed in the charcoal, but any hydrogen or helium (used in leak probing) will readily pass through and be detected. (These remarks also apply to the Pirani gauge.)

Any search gas having an ionization probability differing from air can be used, for example hydrogen or argon, but propane or calor gas gives good results.

Leaks down to the order of $10^{-8}$ torr L/s ($10^{-3}$ clusec) can be detected using a differential arrangement and the various refinements.

A special thermionic cathode diode leak detection gauge, or a normal hot cathode triode ionization gauge connected as a diode, can be used for leak testing. The electronic emission is affected by traces of oxygen or hydrogen, but quickly recovers. Consequently by using oxygen or hydrogen as a probe gas and by watching for changes in electron emission under steady conditions leaks can be observed. The emission is decreased by oxygen but increased by hydrogen. Leaks down to some $10^{-7}$ torr L/s ($1 \cdot 33 \times 10^{-6}$ Pa m$^3$ s$^{-1}$) may be detected.

## 11.8.5 *Halogen diode leak detector* (see 11.5.2(b) and Fig. 11.1)

The head of a halogen diode leak detector can be connected into the 'backing space' of a vacuum system and used to indicate leaks. To locate a leak, the plant under test is sprayed from the outside with the search gas, usually Arcton (Freon). When a leak is probed the gas penetrates it, enters the vacuum system and passes to the detector head. Here it results in an increase in ion current and a consequent indication on an instrument and/or loudspeaker, etc. Leaks down to the order of some $10^{-6}$ torr L/s may be detected, although much depends on the operating conditions.

Precautions must be taken to ensure that no halogen-containing solvents are used to clean any plant which is to be leak-tested, as their residues will persist for long after the plant has been so cleaned and will give an indication on the leak detector which could be mistaken for a leak. Purified commercial benzene* may be used for cleaning purposes.

It is necessary to run the detector unit for some considerable time so that it settles down to stable conditions. For new units, or those which have not been in use recently, up to three hours running may be desirable. Normally about $\frac{3}{4}$ hour should suffice, although large leaks may be detected after about ten minutes.

As the search gas (Arcton) is a condensable vapour it can consequently contaminate the rotary pump oil when passing through it, and so it may be desirable to use a gas ballast arrangement (see 8.8).

## 11.8.6 *Palladium window or barrier leak detector*

Hydrogen gas will pass through a thin sheet of heated palladium metal, which however remains impermeable to other gases. By using this metal as a 'window' between a vacuum system and an ionization gauge, hydrogen can be used as a search gas to detect leaks in the vacuum system. Any hydrogen entering via a leak will then pass through the heated palladium window and will be detected by the ionization gauge. The actual gauge head is in the form of a sealed-off high-vacuum triode thermionic valve in a glass envelope. The filament heats the cathode which gives off electrons which bombard the paladium-capped anode, thus maintaining it at a temperature of around 800°C. If any hydrogen passes through the palladium and encounters the electron stream, positive ions will be formed and will travel to the ion collector. The increase in positive ion current above the background level is then amplified by a d.c. amplifier and gives an appropriate indication.

Spurious results and lack of sensitivity may occur unless certain precautions are taken. A cold trap should be inserted between the gauge

---

*A less toxic solvent may be desirable. (See *HSE Toxicity Review TR4-Benzene*)

head and the vacuum system to prevent any pump oil or water vapour from reaching the hot palladium, where dissociation could take place. Large leaks should first be eliminated by other methods before using the palladium method, as the presence of large quantities of air may affect the heated palladium. The window should occasionally be 'cleaned' by passing a controlled amount of hydrogen through it.

The palladium leak detector is often connected in the backing space between two diffusion pumps of a vacuum test system. It can detect leaks down to the order of $10^{-5}$ lusecs. For the highest sensitivity, mercury vapour pumps may be used to avoid any irregularity in the hydrogen background due to oil dissociation; vapour from cleaning solvents should also be avoided.

### 11.8.7 Mass spectrometer leak detector

Generally speaking the most sensitive method of detecting leaks, especially in high-vacuum equipment, is to make use of mass spectrometer techniques.

The mass spectrometer was adapted and developed for leak testing during the Second World War, particularly in the United States for the Atomic Bomb Project. Today this highly complex and expensive technique has been developed into a comparatively small and relatively inexpensive instrument, and is produced in quantity by several manufacturers as a leak-detecting tool (see Fig. 11.3).

The original American mass spectrometer leak detectors used helium as the search gas, and this is usual today, although other gases such as hydrogen and argon can be used with specially designed equipment.

This search gas, if it passes through a leak, will enter the ion source of the mass spectrometer and is then detected. The basic principle is as follows:

Electrons emitted as a beam from the hot filament of the ion source are accelerated electrically through the ionization chamber and collide with any gas molecules present. The positive ions thereby produced are accelerated by a negative potential arranged at right-angles to the electron beam. They leave the ion source and are then acted upon by a powerful magnetic field arranged at right-angles to the ions. The combined effect causes the ions to move in curved paths. The radius of curvature ($r$) of any single ion will depend upon the mass ($m$) of that ion, and is given by:

$$r = \sqrt{\frac{2\,Vm}{H^2 e}}$$

where  $H$ = magnetic flux density,
  $V$ = ion accelerating voltage,
  $e$ = ion charge.

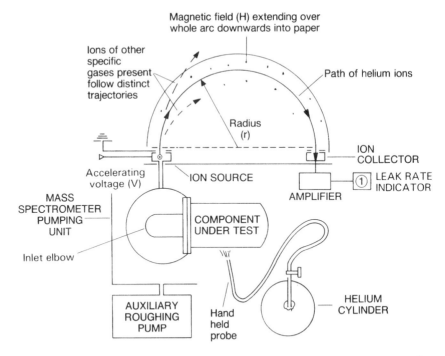

*Notes*  1. When pumped down to vacuum very little residual gas will be left in the component other than any air or helium which has entered through a leak.
2. The ion source is connected in the 'backing space' of the mass spectrometer unit (see 11.8.1)
3. The accelerating voltage is set so that only helium ions will enter the ion collector (see text).
4. By adjusting the accelerating voltage the ions of other gases, such as hydrogen or argon, can be made to enter the ion collector; hence such gases may be used for leak detection
5. Similarly a mass spectrometer can be used for analytical purposes by first ionizing the molecules of any material (see 2.11)

**Fig. 11.3   Schematic diagram of a mass spectrometer tuned to detect leaks using helium**

Consequently the ions of each particular gas present will have their own specific radius of curvature. If helium of mass 4 (from the leak) is present, then all these helium ions will arrive at the same spot. In the helium mass spectrometer leak detector an ion collector plate is arranged at this spot, and the ion current collected will depend on the amount of helium present and hence on the magnitude of the leak. This ion current is amplified and used to operate some suitable indicator. The ions of any other gases or elements present will travel on different radii and will not affect the indication.

This method of sorting out and analysing the ions from a test sample forms the basis of special designs of mass spectometers used in analytical work (see 2.11).

Similar arrangements are possible for connecting up a mass spectrometer as for other methods of leak detection. The plant or equipment under test is usually evacuated by a separate pumping system. The evacuated mass spectrometer, which has its own pumping system, is then connected to the equipment under test by opening the appropriate valve; its pumping system may then be shut off if this is possible whilst still maintaining a low enough pressure. The outside of the equipment under test is then probed systematically by spraying the search gas from a fine nozzle. If at any point there is a leak, the search gas will pass through and enter the mass spectometer, giving an appropriate indication. When using helium or hydrogen as the search gas the probing should start at the top and work slowly downwards, because these gases are light and will rise and might otherwise give a false leak location by entering a leak at a higher level which has not yet been probed. A liquid nitrogen cold trap is usually placed in the line between the plant under test and the mass spectrometer to prevent condensable vapour contaminants reaching the ion source; this is essential if hydrogen is used. A further trap is required if mercury vapour diffusion pumps are used.

## 11.9 Leak rate measurement by vacuum methods

The measurement of the leak rate of vacuum plant by vacuum methods can be carried out by static or dynamic testing. The isolation pressure rise method is a static test and is the basic method of measuring leak rate on vacuum equipment. It suffers from the disadvantage that if accurate results are required it is slow and tedious.

The simplest dynamic test is perhaps the volumetric flow rate (pumping) method. This however does not give accurate results and is limited to pressures of the order of 25 torr (mmHg) and above, and so cannot be used for medium- or high-vacuum work. Dynamic leak rate testing in these latter ranges invariably makes use of a search gas.

### 11.9.1 Volumetric flow rate method

The plant or assembly is connected to a suitable vacuum pumping system and evacuated down to the specified pressure (first checking for and rectifying any major leaks which may be present). The throughput (output) from the pump is passed through a gas-measuring device or flowmeter. After the pump has been running for some time and steady conditions have been attained, i.e. when flow rates taken at intervals do not vary by more than about 10%, the mean of the last two readings can be taken as the leak rate. It is often desirable to repeat the test, by allowing air to enter the plant and by taking fresh readings, averaging the results. Barometric pressure and temperature may have to be taken into account. Generally speaking however it is an inaccurate method and the smallest leak detectable is only of the order of 1 ft³/h at atmospheric pressure (6 torr L/s).

### 11.9.2 Isolation pressure rise method

The plant or component under test is connected to a suitable vacuum pumping system and evacuated to a high degree of vacuum (which is usually specified). It is then isolated from the pump by an isolating valve, which must have been previously checked for tightness and which must itself have a negligible leak rate (and certainly one which is very small in comparison with the maximum permitted for the plant). The pressure inside the plant is then measured by means of a suitable gauge connected thereto, and it is again measured after a suitable time interval (say $\frac{1}{2}$ to 1 hour). Any pressure rise during this time will be an indication of leakage. A series of pressure readings are then taken at regular intervals (which may extend over many hours) until the rate of pressure rise with time becomes steady. Steady conditions are such that successive leak rate measurements do not differ by more than 10% at the very most. The average of the last two readings may be taken as the basis for the computation of leak rate.

Unless special precautions have been taken, such as cleaning and the previous outgassing of the component under test, evacuation to a lower pressure than around $10^{-1}$ torr (mmHg) may lead to a large evolution of gas and vapour from the walls of the component which will give (possibly for some hours) an apparent leak rate greater than the real value. The use of a McLeod vacuum gauge (which is not affected by water vapour, etc., evolved from the walls) is of course an advantage. Alternatively, or in addition, a cold trap can be inserted between the vessel and the gauge in order to freeze out these vapours.

As an example of the method, if the plant under test has a volume of 100 litres and is evacuated down to a pressure of 0·1 torr, and then 15 minutes after isolation is found to have increased in pressure to 0·2 torr, its initial leakage rate will be:

$$\frac{(0\cdot2-0\cdot1) \times 100}{15 \times 60} = \frac{10}{900} = 1\cdot1 \times 10^{-2} \text{ torr L/s or 11 lusecs}$$

This method of test is by its nature slow and tedious, particularly if the specified maximum leak rate is small and evacuation to a pressure lower than, say, $10^{-1}$torr is required. Many hours can be spent in testing components, especially if they happen to be borderline cases as regards leakage. Out gassing and minor transient troubles on the tightness and functioning of the test equipment can readily nullify hours of testing. In such cases adequate cleaning of the component (perhaps with trichloroethylene), methodical step-by-step checking of the vacuum-testing equipment, and prolonged pumping prior to isolation (possibly with the application of heat) will be desirable.

The first readings after isolation are in general disregarded, as they will be higher than later readings—owing to outgassing. Only when equilibrium conditions have been established is it safe to evaluate the leak rate. Quite often the isolating valve will be reopened and a further period or periods of pumping will be necessary to remove accumulated outgassing in an endeavour to prove a component.

In view of the very long period of testing which may be required there is a preference to use dynamic methods of leak rate measurement, in which pumping continues during the test, rather than this static method in which pumping is stopped during the test.

An arrangement of a high-vacuum test unit can be used for leak rate measurement as well as for leak detection (see Fig. 11.4). Pressure is measured by means of a Pirani gauge connected in a bridge circuit which is balanced at some datum pressure (and voltage). The out-of-balance currents at all other pressures are then read on a sensitive mirror galvanometer, and give a measure of the relative pressure. A typical method of procedure when testing a component with this equipment would be:

(a) Determine the volume of the component in litres.

(b) Determine the volume between the closed isolation valve and the component. (This is known as the 'dead volume'.)

(c) Clean the component thoroughly, dry and mount on the manifold flange, using a suitable unrestricted method of connection and a rubber gasket. (Obviously care is needed to prevent leaks.)

(d) Start up the vacuum pump, checking each stage before going on to the next, until eventually the test unit is proved satisfactory up to the isolation valve.

(e) Evacuate the component until the degree of high vacuum required for the test is obtained (this may be specified, for instance, as better than 50 'microns' Hg (0·050 torr)), and then continue pumping for some considerable period to remove occluded vapours and outgassing as far as possible.

(f) At intervals close the isolation valve, and with the bridge balanced just prior to isolation (i.e. with the bridge-balancing voltage set), time the travel of the galvanometer spot across its scale with a stop watch as the bridge becomes unbalanced owing to leakage and possibly outgassing.

(g) By calculation, or by reference to a chart, this time in seconds for a full-scale deflection is then converted into the pressure rise (in say microns/hour).

It may for instance be arranged that during the actual test the galvanometer is shunted in such a way that full-scale deflection means a pressure rise within the component of exactly one micron of mercury.

Then, if $T$ = time for full-scale galvanometer deflection (seconds):

$$\text{Observed rate of pressure rise } (R_a) = \frac{1 \cdot 0 \times 3600}{T} \text{ microns Hg/hour}$$

(h) When this pressure rise becomes sensibly constant (as shown by successive values not differing by at most 10%), the average of the last two readings is used to evaluate the leak rate. However this observed rate of

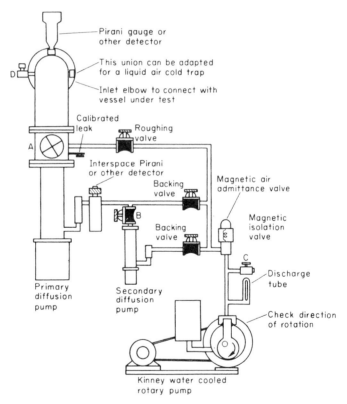

A Main isolation valve
B Interspace pressure control valve (Throttle)
C Manual air admittance valve (Roughing line)
D Manual air admittance valve (Inlet elbow)

**Fig. 11.4   Schematic diagram of a high-vacuum test unit.**

pressure rise ($R_a$) arises from the total volume of the plant or component ($V_c$) plus the 'dead' volume ($V_d$). For greater accuracy the equivalent or true rate of pressure rise ($R_t$) for the plant only can be calculated from the observed value by applying a correction factor as follows:

Equivalent rate of pressure rise ($R_t$) =

$$\text{observed rate of pressure rise } (R_a) \times \frac{(V_c + V_d)}{V_c}$$

Sometimes the leak-test requirement is specified as a maximum rate of pressure rise, in which case $R_a$ (or $R_t$), expressed in the appropriate units, is the information required. (If expressed in microns Hg/hour, then divide by 3600 to give microns Hg/second.) More often however it is specified as a leakage rate (in torr litres per second or equivalent).

Consequently the observed leak rate ($L_a$) can be found approximately from:

$$L_a = R_a \times V_c$$

and the equivalent or true leak rate ($L_t$) of the plant from:

$$L_t = R_t \times V_c$$

or, using the observed rate of pressure rise:

$$L_t = R_a \times \{(V_c + V_d)/V_c\} \times V_c = R_a \times (V_c + V_d)$$

*Note 1.* Should the dead volume when tested on its own show any appreciable pressure rise (which is clearly undesirable), its leak rate can be measured and calculated:

$$\text{Leak rate of dead volume} = \frac{\text{observed rate of pressure}}{\text{rise of dead volume}} \times \text{dead volume}$$

In this case the corrected leak rate for the plant can be found by subtracting the leak rate of the dead volume from the leakage rate ($L_t$) as obtained above.

*Note 2.* If it is desired to differentiate between outgassing and true leakage, without using a cold trap in the gauge line, it is sometimes possible to arrange to lower a substantial hood over the component under test. But firstly a normal isolation pressure rise test is carried out. The hood is then lowered, sealed at its base and evacuated to around the same pressure as the component. A further pressure rise measurement is then made, and, since there is now no pressure difference between the inside and outside of the component, this pressure rise is due to outgassing alone. The true leak rate can then be evaluated from the arithmetical difference between the two pressure rise measurements.

This method is sometimes used for the routine production leak rate testing of comparatively small components.

### 11.9.3 Infra-red detector method (see also 11.5 (d))

The infra-red gas analyser can be adapted for vacuum leak detection and leak rate testing. The principle is essentially the same as that described earlier for pressurization methods but the instrument is specifically designed for vacuum applications. The infra-red detector is one method by which the leak rate can be readily measured without recourse to comparison with a standard leak. It is able to test under dynamic conditions with a sensitivity of around $10^{-1}$ lusecs or, using the semi-static technique described below, down to around $10^{-4}$ lusecs ($10^{-7}$ torr L/s). Nitrous oxide (laughing gas) or carbon dioxide is used as the search gas.

The component under test is evacuated and surrounded by an envelope of nitrous oxide for a period of say one hour, during which the isolation valve on the fine side is closed; also the analysis tube is kept under vacuum and its zero adjusted. The backing pump valve is then shut, and the isolation valve opened so that the contents of the component are compressed by the diffusion pump into the backing space. Any search gas which has entered the component through leakage is consequently detected by the analysis tube. Assuming that the reading of the tube corresponds to a partial pressure of the search gas of 5 microns Hg and that the volume of the backing space is $\frac{1}{2}$ litre, then the leak over a test period of one hour will be $5 \times \frac{1}{2} = 2\frac{1}{2}$ microns Hg litres, and the leak rate will be:

$$\frac{pV}{T} = \frac{5 \times \frac{1}{2}}{3600} = \frac{2 \cdot 5}{3600} = 7 \times 10^{-4} \text{ lusecs (or } 9.3 \times 10^{-6} \text{ Pa m}^3 \text{ s}^{-1})$$

If the period of isolation used to begin with is only, say, some minutes then the partial pressure reading on the infra-red detector will perhaps be almost negligible, and the pressure reached in the backing space may be less than the critical backing pressure of the diffusion pump. To increase these readings, and consequently the sensitivity, further tests with increased periods of isolation are necessary.

Obviously the shortest period of isolation compatible with sufficiently accurate results is required.

The infra-red absorption detector responds not only to the search gas but to outgassing products such as hydrocarbons, hydrogen, carbon dioxide and water vapour. It is considered that these will seriously affect the results if the resultant pressure rise in the backing space on opening the isolation valve exceeds 50 times the recorded partial pressure caused by the search gas.

## 11.10 Search-gas (dynamic) methods of leak rate testing of vacuum equipment

### 11.10.1 General method

A search gas is almost invariably employed in dynamic methods of high-vacuum leak rate testing. When used it is necessary to compare the response of the detector with that obtained from a calibrated reference leak before the leak rate can be evaluated, the one major exception being the infra-red absorption method described in 11.9.3. The reference leak itself must previously have been calibrated by some absolute method, usually the isolation pressure rise method.

The search gas must differ from any which may be present in the equipment under test, the process it is used with, or its surroundings. Also it must not cause any harmful effects or be otherwise incompatible with the materials employed. The choice of gas depends on the detector system. Most of the detectors used for leak location can be adapted for leak rate testing.

The component under test should be completely surrounded by the search gas. In general, two methods are possible: (1) the components, whilst remaining connected to the vacuum pumping system and the detector, are surrounded by a hood or container which is then evacuated and filled with search gas; (2) a flexible envelope is placed over the component whilst under test and search gas is then fed into this envelope. In both methods search gas will then pass through any leaks in the component and be indicated by the detector system, the magnitude of the indication being compared with that of the standard reference leak in order to evaluate the leak rate.

There are two alternative positions for the reference leak (see Fig. 11.5). In both cases the leak is connected (via a valve) between the plant under test and the pumping system and detector, but in position 1 the far side of the reference leak is in the search-gas atmosphere under the hood or envelope, whilst in position 2 it is in free atmosphere. In position 1 search gas is applied to the hood in the normal way. A reading on the detector is taken, firstly, with the valve to the reference leak open. This reading represents leakage through the plant *and* the reference leak (call this reading A). The valve is then closed and a further reading taken. This reading (B) represents the leakage through the plant only. If the indicator response is linear, the leakage through the plant will be:

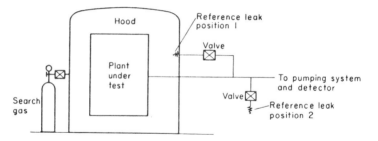

**Fig. 11.5 Positions for reference leak.**

B/(A − B) × value of reference leak (expressed in the appropriate units)

In position 2, with the valve open, search gas is applied to the reference leak and a reading (C) taken. With the valve closed, search gas is then applied to the hood and a reading (D) taken.

If the response is linear, the leakage through the plant will be:

$$D/C \times \text{value of reference leak}$$

When taking the readings it is necessary to wait until the search gas has had time to diffuse through, or to clear from, the reference leak and the reading has settled down. It is also desirable to repeat readings A and C as a check.

Position 1 gives the most accurate results, but only when the detector response is linear (e.g. in a mass spectrometer and some ionization gauges).

Position 2, when used with a non-linear detector, will show whether the plant leak rate is greater or less than that of the reference leak.

*11.10.2 Measurement of leak rate by the halide diode*

The halogen diode leak detector can be used to evaluate leak rates on vacuum systems. The same general arrangement is used as for vacuum leak detection (11.8.5 and Fig. 11.1), except that a hood is placed over the plant under test. The plant is evacuated to the required degree of vacuum. The hood or envelope and the reference leak are adequately purged to ensure that the search-gas concentration is as intended. The hood, if strong enough, is evacuated before feeding in search gas.

The detector is switched on and allowed to become stable. Readings of the detector are then taken by one of the methods given in 11.10.1 and the leak rate evaluated. Equilibrium must be restored between readings.

As the detector gives a non-linear response, a quantitative result is only possible when the leak rate is of the same order as that of the reference leak. It is essential to check with a reference leak before and after each test as the element is liable to show changes in sensitivity during the test.

### 11.10.3 Measurement of leak rate by mass spectrometer

The mass spectrometer leak detector system (11.8.7) can be adapted for leak rate testing to a high degree of accuracy.

To check for the presence of leaks and to measure leak rate, the plant or component under test is completely shrouded by a removable hood, or placed in a separate vessel, into which is admitted an atmosphere of the search gas (usually helium). To connect the mass spectrometer leak detector (which has its own high-vacuum pumping system) it is best to use backing-space technique when testing at pressures below $2 \times 10^{-4}$ torr.

Any leakage of search gas will be indicated by the mass spectrometer, the magnitude of this indication being a measure of the leak rate. The instrument is calibrated by using a standard reference leak, usually a glass device containing a minute hole of which the leak rate has been ascertained accurately by laboratory methods.

The reading of the mass spectrometer indicator when this calibrated leak is connected is then used as the standard by which other leak rates are evaluated. As the instrument has a linear characteristic (unlike most other indicators) it is possible to determine accurately leak rates which differ appreciably from that of the reference leak. The positions available for this leak and the method of evaluating the leak rate have already been dealt with in 11.10.1.

If need be, production testing of components may be carried out by suitably marking the indicator scale with 'accept' and 'reject' regions.

Sealed components which must remain leak-tight are sometimes filled with a quantity of helium gas. They can then be tested at any time by placing them in an evacuated chamber connected to a mass spectrometer leak detector.

Components can also be tested by pressurizing with the search gas and using a mass spectrometer leak detector connected through a fine valve to a flexible tube which is used to probe the surface of the component for leaks. The amount of air (together with any leakage gas) entering the probe must be kept small enough for the pumping system to cope with.

The mass spectrometer leak detector can measure leak rates down to the order of $10^{-10}$ torr L/s ($1 \cdot 33 \times 10^{-9}$ Pa m$^3$ s$^{-1}$), although special instruments are available to detect leaks of even lesser magnitude.

BS 5914 *Calibrating leak-detectors of the mass-spectrometer type used in the field of vacuum technology* is identical with ISO 3530 and is restricted to leak detectors not capable of detecting leaks smaller than $10^{-12}$ Pa m$^3$ s$^{-1}$ ($7\cdot5 \times 10^{-12}$ torr L/s). Leak rates smaller than this will be influenced by other factors such as 'virtual leaks' which are due to the evolution of gas or vapour from within the system under test.

### 11.10.4 Thermal conductivity gauges (see also 11.8.3)

Gauges of the Pirani type, with suitable galvanometers and perhaps amplifiers, can be used for leak rate testing in conjunction with a search gas and a calibrated leak. Should hydrogen be used as the search gas the use of a flexible shroud containing hydrogen will obviously involve a danger hazard and should be restricted, especially if large components are involved. If a non-metallic shroud is used it should be of anti-static material; a metal shroud should be earthed.

Carbon dioxide can be used as a search gas with good results.

As thermal conductivity type gauges have a non-linear characteristic, a quantitative result can only be obtained when the leak rate is of the same order as that of the reference leak. The gauges are liable to be affected by draughts, and any necessary shielding should be arranged, as required.

### 11.10.5 Ionization gauges (see also 11.8.4)

Gauges of this type can be adapted for leak rate testing. A variety of search gases are used, including propane. Cold cathode ionization gauges of the Penning type can measure down to the order of $10^{-6}$ torr L/s, whilst the hot cathode type can measure down to around $10^{-7}$ torr L/s, and can be used with oxygen as a search gas. The response of a hot cathode triode ionization gauge is substantially linear, and that of a cold cathode gauge is linear at low pressures. Consequently it is possible to evaluate leak rates dissimilar to that of the reference leak. The hot cathode diode gauge however has a non-linear response, and so can only give a quantitative result with a reference leak of the same order of magnitude.

### 11.10.6 The palladium window detector

This form of ionization gauge described in 11.8.7 is readily adaptable for leak proving. Production testing of components is carried out on a specially designed pumping system connected to palladium barrier detector which, when used in conjunction with a calibrated leak, can measure leak rates down to the order of $10^{-8}$ torr L/s ($1\cdot33 \times 10^{-7}$ Pa m$^3$ s$^{-1}$). The detector has a linear characteristic which makes it possible to determine leak rates that differ from that of the reference leak.

## 11.11  Acoustic leak detection

Non-destructive testing by acoustic emission methods have been described in Chapter 10. Acoustics can be applied to the detection of steam, gas and water leaks, e.g. the leaks will make a 'hissing noise', the loudness of which will be a measure of the magnitude of the leak.

A suitable microphone placed in a strategic position can be used for continuous monitoring. A leak will announce and/or record itself by a noise above the normal background level. By such methods early warning of trouble is given so that according to the magnitude of the leak, action can be taken say to shut down the plant immediately, or perhaps to continue until repairs can be arranged with the minimum of consequential damage.

Equipment of this type has been developed and is used on large boiler plants, etc. with display units connected to many microphone channels covering the whole plant. Most installations (such as those of the CEGB) make use of microphones and air-borne noise encompassing a 40–50 decibel range. Other developments making use of piezo-electric transducers fixed to the structure (perhaps via a waveguide) may be used and may give increased sensitivity and be capable of specialized applications. The size of a leak (and its leak rate) can be estimated.

**TABLE 11.3**

*Some standards applicable to leak testing*

| Spec. No. | Description |
| --- | --- |
| BS 2520 | Barometer conventions and tables |
| BS 2951 | Glossary of terms used in high-vacuum technology |
| BS 3636 | Methods for proving the gas-tightness of vacuum or pressurized plant (Deals with 17 methods for proving, and 20 for leak location) |
| BS 5914 | Methods of calibrating leak detectors of the mass-spectrometer type used in the field of vacuum technology |
| ASTM E425 | Definition of terms relating to leak testing (ANSI approved) |
| ASTM E432 | Guide for the selection of a leak testing method (ANSI approved) |
| ASTM F 78 | Calibration of helium leak detectors by use of secondary standards (Deals with mass spectrometer leak detectors) |
| ASTM E427 | Recommended Practice for testing for leaks using the Halogen Leak Detector |
| ASTM E493 | Tests for leaks using the Mass Spectrometer Leak Detector in the Inside-Out testing mode |
| ASTM E498 | Testing for leaks using the Mass Spectrometer Leak Detector or Residual Gas Analyzer in the Tracer Probe Mode |
| ASTM E515 | Testing for leaks using Bubble Emission Techniques |
| ASTM F97 | Test for hermeticity of electron devices by dye penetration |
| ASTM F98 | Test for hermeticity of electron devices by a bubble test |

# 12 Inspection during commissioning and operation

## 12.1 The design background

When a plant is to be designed for the manufacture or processing of a particular product, some choice is usually possible concerning the operating processes to be employed, throughput (and whether for continuous or discontinuous working), materials of construction and protective finishes, operating and/or economic life, cost range, methods of instrumentation and control, etc.

If the particular type of plant has been made previously, details of its design, manufacture and operation will be on record and the choice will be generally the same as before, with perhaps a few improvements. If the plant is of a new type, or embraces new features or possibly is unique, then the designers, engineers, chemists, etc., should use all available knowledge and experience in trying to make the right decisions. Consultations with scientists, works safety officers and inspection engineers may prove helpful. The decisions cannot however be completely right first time. Consequently, with a new type of plant, laboratory and process trials and tests on materials and components for suitability, compatibility with one another, corrosion resistance, etc., will be necessary. Some environmental testing may be desirable. It may be thought necessary to build a small-scale pilot plant and to try things out before becoming committed on all items of the full-scale plant. Things which seem right in theory may show snags on laboratory testing, and even if satisfactory in the laboratory may run into troubles at the pilot plant stage. These may then be ironed out, but when the full-scale plant is built much interest will centre in its commissioning trials.

## 12.2 Plant commissioning—inspection and acceptance

When the new plant is approaching completion, steps should be taken to prepare it for commissioning. Much can be done to smooth out installation and commissioning by the use of a systematic inspection and test system put into force *from the beginning.* If all items of consequence have been ordered to a specification (which should not be too elaborate, but must be *clear* where requirements are important), and inspection at works, etc., is delegated to a competent organization which can *readily refer back* all departures from specification and is responsible for ensuring that proper tests, etc., have been carried out and recorded, then items on delivery to site will satisfy the design requirements.

It is now often customary, especially with chemical plant, for the inspector also to carry out progressing duties at the various manufacturers' works to ensure the arrival of plant and equipment on site at the appropriate time.

There is a danger here, however, that pressure on securing delivery may result in troubles, faults, important tests and other matters being side-stepped. This must *not* occur—all such matters must be reported and dealt with.

On delivery all items should be checked for transit damage, for evidence of prior works inspection (if required) and possibly for general suitability, correctness of fixing centres, etc. Items not cleared by inspection *must not* be accepted for use on site.

If the design is new or untried, and snags are likely to arise and/or alternative ways of doing things are possible, then a really effective liaison must exist between inspection, design and site engineers; and one not confined to or restricted by paperwork, which—although important—is only secondary.

Preparations will have been made on site to install the various items ordered from outside. Buildings, ducting, pipework, etc., will have been erected to the designers' requirements. Building and civil work, and most site installation work, is not usually covered by plant inspection as such, but is generally under the supervision of clerks of works of the various trades, acting on behalf of the site engineer or agent. Some overlap of particular items may be necessary, hence the necessity of a good liaison to ensure that nothing is overlooked. For instance, civil pipework, etc., might well be inspected at works by the inspection organization and erected on site under the site engineer's supervision; but a complex process vessel or piece of machinery may not be acceptable until certain finishing operations and special tests have been carried out on site. In some cases, however, the same inspection organization may be responsible for overseeing all the work, both at manufacturers' works and on site.

In any case, the various items of plant and equipment will be erected on site in their appropriate positions under supervision. Pipework, valves, electrical equipment and circuits, and instruments will be connected up and tested. Quite often detailed drawings for these connections will not be available, only diagrams, and the installation and checking of the various circuits, etc., may be an exacting task. A pipework, etc., layout model can be a great help.

It is in the process of connecting up that many mistakes can occur. For instance a certain type of valve may be fitted in the wrong place. Mild steel bolts or parts may be fitted where stainless steel should have been used, and vice versa. Gaskets may be incorrectly fitted or of the wrong type. Leaks may be present in pipework perhaps due to incomplete tightening of bolts, etc. It should be remembered that microscopic leaks can exist in plant under certain conditions even through apparently solid material (see Chapter 11). For some plants a high degree of leak tightness may be required and leak rate tests may be specified.

Site weld inspection, including radiological examination of pipe joints, etc. must be carried out methodically to recognized standards (e.g. see 4.25). In particular, the requirements of radiation safety and of the Ionizing Radiations Regulations, etc. (see 6.18) must be observed as it has been reported that radiological inspectors working under site conditions are often exposed to greater levels of radiation than under factory conditions.

On electrical equipment, etc. pre-commissioning tests should include:

(i) insulation resistance (taking care that low energy low voltage circuits are not damaged by excess voltage);

(ii) earth electrode resistance measurement;

(iii) earth loop impedance;

(iv) setting and operation of protective devices.

It may be necessary to check that the area is gas-free. Any electrical equipment for installation in a hazardous zone should be checked to see that it is of the correct type and has the correct documentation. Drawings should be available showing the limits of each hazardous zone, with the gas group, temperature class, and location of each item (see 6.10–11).

Finally a check on the instrumentation and control system, carried out on a loop-by-loop basis, may be required and will probably call for the use of specialist inspection staff. Any relevant test sheets and certificates will be made out and certified.

The preparation of a detailed commissioning programme showing the sequence of operations and testing against a time background, and listing agreed working procedures and schedules, safety instructions documentation required, etc., can be of considerable value. A 'permit-to-work' system, and a pressure vessel register should be prepared in advance, and used as necessary during commissioning.

When snags have been sorted out and all seems satisfactory, it may be desirable to carry out a 'dummy run' using perhaps water or other fluids and materials in place of the proper process materials (which may be expensive, toxic, or of such a nature that it is unwise to use them until the installation is clearly in a fit state). This dummy run will enable details of operations, etc. to be checked. It may then be necessary to clear and clean the plant, checking that all foreign bodies, materials, etc. have been removed, and then perhaps to purge it, or parts of it, with suitable liquids or gases prior to the introduction of the proper process materials. The nature of these materials may necessitate the adoption of special precautions, and any safety equipment and instrumentation should be in position ready for immediate use.

Services such as steam, water, gases and electricity will have to be got ready and equipment gradually warmed up or started. If the plant is a continuous process plant a complete run will be undertaken for a specific period; if not, then trial runs will have to take place separately on its components. At first, no doubt, the runs will not be at full output. Records will be made of relevant instrument readings throughout the plant, of the process and raw materials, and of the product output and analysis, etc. Erratic or faulty behaviour of particular items will be noted, as well as the ability of the component parts to stand up to loading corrosion, etc. during the period of the trial. Faults and snags will, as far as is possible, be corrected.

Pressure vessels and pipework installations must be pressure tested and examined for faults under working conditions. In particular bellows expansion joints must be examined after their first full movement and checked for any unanticipated movement, leakage, etc. and for satisfactory behaviour of supports and foundations (see 4.6.3 and 13.6.3). During pressure testing any valves in the system should be in the fully open position (or bypassed).

If any specific requirements or guarantees have been made regarding the performance of the plant then the commissioning trials will normally have to show that these can be met.

During the period of the trials the staff who will have to operate and maintain the plant when it is in normal service will be standing by or assisting the site and technical staff, contractors' representatives and inspection and test personnel who are conducting the trials, so that operating techniques, snags, etc. can be seen and discussed.

Obviously such people as the project engineer and his design and other staff, and the site engineer and his clerks of work will be present; however it is probably best if the engineer who is to run and maintain the plant, and who has been making himself familiar with it during construction, should be the one primarily responsible for commissioning and acceptance.

Eventually, when mutual agreement has been reached regarding the attainment of a satisfactory standard of operation and performance, the plant will be 'taken over' from the various contractors by the management.

Drawings, data sheets, operating and maintenance instructions, test reports, etc. will be handed over. Any items which for various reasons cannot be immediately delivered or cleared must be listed, together with the agreed action to be taken on them.

Certificates of completion and acceptance, and any other relevant paperwork, including QA documents, will be signed by the various parties involved. Clearance of outstanding financial matters may then be settled.

Should mutual agreement regarding acceptance not be possible then protracted legal proceedings may arise, which could involve inspection in much searching of records and preparation of evidence. For instance, in one case, a main contractor sub-contracted work to its own drawings but specified a final hydraulic test. The work was satisfactory to drawing but failed on hydraulic test and was rejected. It was eventually ruled legally that (despite the main contractor's drawings having been used) the sub-contractor was at fault and he had to meet replacement and other financial costs.

Most contracts for industrial and chemical plant and for its installation contain a clause guaranteeing materials, workmanship and/or satisfactory performance for a stated period of time (e.g. six months, one year or more). Possibly during this period the contractor may be required to replace faulty parts free of charge, or to send workmen to iron out difficulties or to put the plant in order. Sometimes a special servicing clause or separate contract may be negotiated in which, usually at an agreed price per year or per visit, the contractor undertakes to keep the plant in order.

Further reading on commissioning exists as follows:

Institution of Chemical Engineers, *Commissioning of chemical and Allied Plant*, Rugby, 1974.

BS 6739 *Code of Practice for instrumentation in process control systems: installation design and practice*, 1986.

Eng. Equip. and Materials Users Association, *Code of Practice for site radiography*.

CCIP/1 *Instrumentation installation testing procedure*, Energy Industries Council.

CCIP/4 *Colour coding of cables*, Energy Industries Council.

API RP550 *Manual on installation of refinery instruments and control systems*.

## 12.3 Pre-service cleaning

Pre-service cleaning can usefully be applied to much process and industrial plant, steam and heat exchanger equipment, etc. A boiler can be said to be in proper condition chemically when its internal surfaces are coated with a thin homogeneous film of magnetite (magnetic iron oxide). This film is produced by the reaction of water on hot chemically clean steel surfaces under the correct reducing conditions. A typical pre-commissioning or periodic cleaning schedule might be as follows:

(1) Flush the system by high-velocity water to remove coarse debris left over during construction, which could block or damage valves, etc. or act as a source of corrosion.

(2) Degrease the system by an initial alkaline boil-out. The presence of oil reduces heat-transfer rates and can lead to tube failures.

(3) Clean by a static soak in weak hydrochloric acid solution.

(4) Steam to exclude air.

(5) Preheat and acid-clean using a hot inhibited solution of citric acid, which must be circulated at reasonable velocity, and then drained and flushed.

(6) Boil out with a reducing agent to passivate surfaces so that they will not corrode unless wetted and left exposed to atmosphere.

(7) After inspection the plant can then be put into commission.

Should the system be cleaned using chemicals, or perhaps steam, inspection should ensure that any items such as control valve discs are suitable for withstanding the operation. If not they should be removed, bypassed or temporarily replaced.

## 12.4 In-use inspection—legislation

Many items of chemical and process engineering plant are subject to government legislation relating to their use, safety and inspection. This legislation dates mainly from 1882 when the *Boiler Explosions Act* was passed, enabling the Board of Trade to conduct investigations into nearly all boiler explosions. This Act defines a boiler as 'any closed vessel used in generating steam or for heating water or for heating other liquids or into which steam is admitted for heating, steaming, boiling or other similar purposes'. It is thus a broad definition embracing many items of industrial and chemical plant.

In general, in the event of a boiler explosion, a report had to be made within 24 hours to the appropriate Ministry, which might then conduct a legal enquiry. If negligence was proved, severe financial penalties could be inflicted. Official accident reports are published which help engineers and others by drawing attention to the underlying causes. No rules or regulations regarding safety or inspection as such are detailed in this Act, but it is up to the owner, usually by employing a 'competent person' as inspector (see below) to ensure that he has not neglected any relevant safety precaution, including recognized design standards, proper methods of operation and maintenance, and adequate periodic inspection.

The next legislative steps were provided by the *Factories and Workshops*

*Acts* of 1901 to 1929, followed by the *Factories Acts* of 1937, 1948 and 1961 (see Chapter 14). Here again, the owner is made responsible for the safety of plant, and only a few detailed technical regulations are laid down, such as the provision of certain fittings and the maximum periods between thorough examinations.

Where inspection of plant is required, statutory prescribed reports embodying certain standard questions may have to be completed. The form of these reports follows similar lines to that instituted by engineering insurance societies over the years.

Then came the HSW *Act* 1974 which among many other matters requires (under Section 2(d)) as far as is reasonably practicable as regards any place of work (or working environment) under the employer's control, the *maintenance* of it in a condition that is safe and without risks to health. Also (under Section 14) the Health and Safety Executive or any other person may be directed to investigate any accident, occurrence or other matter, or set up an official inquiry into any such matter.

As with the *Boiler Explosions Act*, if an accident occurs it must be reported by the responsible person forthwith to the enforcing authority and/or the appropriate government department, followed by a written report on the form approved by the Health and Safety Executive within 7 days (see Reporting of Injuries, Diseases and Dangerous Occurrences Regulations (SI 1985 No. 2023) which now replaces these requirements in the *Boiler Explosions Act*).

If negligence is suspected, or there has been any failure to conform to the regulations, then legal proceedings (with their possible penalties) will no doubt be taken. The competency of the 'competent person' will be investigated at such an inquiry.

The official view is that such a person should be independent of the owners and experienced in the work involved (he may, for instance, be a qualified inspection engineer, perhaps of an inspection or insurance society).

The procedure for compiling one of the statutory prescribed reports on plant is that the inspection engineer or 'competent person' carries out the necessary physical examinations and inserts the results in the report. These are then checked by a senior engineer who is responsible for assessing the safe working pressures or loads from design calculations and by considering the condition of the plant. He will insert on the report any qualifications regarding the use of the plant, details of any repairs or modifications necessary, and any safety requirements which should receive attention. The certified report is then sent to the owner who must ensure that any work required by it is carried out and that the plant is only used in strict accordance with the conditions laid down in the current certificate. The report must be retained in the appropriate register on the plant site and be available for inspection at any time by the Government Factories Inspector, who may check that its conditions have been fulfilled. This Factories Inspector, or the certifying authority, may stop the operation of any prescribed plant or unit if at any time it is considered to be in an unsafe condition.

The *Health and Safety at Work Act*, 1974, a 'blanket' or enabling Act, through the Health and Safety Executive now exercises authority over most of such legislation (see Chapter 14).

## 12.5 Statutory periods of examination under the Factories Act

Thorough examination of certain items of plant must be undertaken by a competent person at stated maximum periods under the provisions of the *Factories Acts* and associated legislation. These periods may be summarized as follows:

(1) *Steam boilers: Examination of Steam Boilers Regulations* (SI 1964 No.781 as amended by SI 1981 No. 687)

(a) *An individual boiler*—14 months (except as below).

(b) *A water tube boiler* not over 21 years since it was first taken into use, and of which the drums and any headers are of fusion-welded or solid forged construction, and which has an evaporative capacity of not less than 50,000 lb/h of steam—26 months.

(c) *A boiler in a group of water tube boilers* of which the drums and any headers are of fusion-welded or solid forged construction and for which a period of 21 years has not expired since it was first taken into use, and being of a group in which (i) each boiler has an evaporative capacity of not less than 25,000 lb/h of steam; and (ii) the total evaporative capacity of all the boilers is not less than 100,000 lb/h of steam—26 months.

(d) *A boiler which is a waste heat boiler or heat exchanger* with fusion-welded longitudinal and circumferential seams or a *superheater* of fusion-welded construction and which is an integral part of a continuous flow installation in a chemical or oil refinery processing plant—26 months.

(2) *Steam receivers and condensers*—26 months.

(3) *Air receivers*—26 months (except those of solid drawn construction which may be extended to a thorough examination interval of 4 years).

(4) *Water-sealed gas holders*, at least once in every period of 2 years (see 6.8).

(5) *Various construction regulations* (see Table 14.2) which in addition to the periods stated below, may require daily inspections of such matters as excavations, shafts, tunnels, unfenced machinery, and weekly inspections of scaffolds, certain hoists, automatic safe working load indicators on cranes, etc.

(a) *Hoists and lifts*, at least once in every period of six months (12 months for continuous and hand-operated hoists).

(b) *Chains, ropes and lifting tackle*, at least once in every period of 6 months (every 3 months under the Dock Regulations 1934).

(c) *Cranes and other lifting machines*, at least once in every period of 14 months (some may additionally require a major inspection every 4 years).

(6) *Breathing and reviving apparatus*—monthly.

(7) *Fire alarms* (factories and offices)—every 3 months.

(8) *Power presses and their safety devices*—12 months for those with fixed fencing, otherwise 6 months (Power Press Regulations 1965).

(9) Exhaust ventilation—every 6 months (Grinding of Metals Regs. 1925).

(10) Dosimeters, etc.—every 14 months (Ionizing Radiation Regs 1985, see 6.18).

Besides the specific items of plant mentioned above, which must be examined periodically under the provisions of the *Factories Act*, the *Health and Safety at Work Act*, 1974 under Section 2 (2) and 40 introduces in effect a requirement for the examination of all plant and systems of work which, when allowed to continue in use unchecked, could lead to unsafe conditions. Presssure systems, particularly bellows expansion joints, must be regularly examined. Consequently some organized system of periodic checking must be introduced to show, *so far as is reasonably practicable*, plant is maintained safe for use. These periodic checks would include where appropriate any hydraulic proof tests and any other tests (such as NDT) considered necessary in the interest of safety. Such examination could be carried out by a 'competent person', perhaps employed by the operating organization, or by an independent inspector employed by a consultant or an insurance company. In any legal proceedings instituted for an offence against statutory requirements the onus of proving what is reasonably practicable, etc. falls up on the accused.

If the HSE inspector can be satisfied that certain provisions of the *Factories Act*, etc. cannot reasonably be applied he may grant a certificate of exemption. This certificate will describe in detail the item of plant, equipment, etc. concerned, and its use. It will prescribe the conditions under which the exemption is granted, usually detailing sometimes elaborate inspection and testing requirements which must be satisfied before the item is first taken into use, and then the periodic inspection and testing required during use and/or after repair.

Typical items of plant which have been granted exemption certificates are specialized boilers and air receivers. The schedule of conditions may state:

The boiler/air receiver, etc. . . . shall be thoroughly examined by a competent person in the manner specified . . . before being taken into use . . .

Subsequent examinations . . . after a period not exceeding 18 months . . . will include the following tests and examinations . . .

After 21 years ... the following tests and examinations will be necessary ...

Tests may include the measurement of thickness of any part, hydraulic testing, and the use of ultrasonic, radiographic or other-NDT or electronic devices ...

A full report on a prescribed form must be made of every examination by a competent inspector (perhaps of a boiler inspecting company) ..., countersigned by the Chief Engineer ... and submitted to the Health & Safety Executive, etc.

(See also 14.5, para. 25)

## 12.6 Corrosion of plant

One of the most important aspects of plant inspection is the detection of corrosion and the taking of steps to avoid or reduce its effects. A few years ago it was estimated that corrosion costs this country some £600 M a year in plant failure, lost production, maintenance and material replacement. (A similar National Bureau of Standards report estimated the annual cost to the USA as 10 billion dollars.) Obviously, anything which inspection can do to reduce this colossal figure will be well worth while. To do so effectively requires a knowledge of the mechanism of corrosion, the capabilities and limitations of available materials of construction, of design features and fabrication techniques which may limit corrosion, and of inspection techniques which can be adopted.

Corrosion is a complex phenomenon and does not necessarily follow a set pattern. Theoretical considerations alone do not always allow the pattern to be predicted, and a practical approach, such as can be obtained from inspection data obtained during use, can be invaluable. A fund of experience is available regarding the behaviour of different materials under various conditions, their relative corrosion rates and the economics of material selection. All metals, even gold and platinum, corrode under certain circumstances; the problem is often that of selecting the most economical material and protection for the environment in question. Even so, a material selected may not prove entirely satisfactory. The limited amount of corrosion products evolved may be of a type which contaminates, discolours or otherwise upsets a process. For instance, minute particles of metal (such as copper) dissolved by limited corrosion may be deposited elsewhere in the system and there cause a more serious (and perhaps unsuspected) attack, difficult to diagnose (this can occur in steam and hot water systems). Other unpredictable side effects may occur.

Consequently, an inspector will *always* be on the look-out for corrosion and for the existence of conditions which might lead to it.

Laboratory tests, pilot plant runs and commissioning trials may have given some data concerning corrosion resistance. More reliable data and actual measurements of rates of corrosion over longer periods can, however, be obtained by periodic checks whilst the plant is in use, or during planned maintenance. Test plugs, corrosion spools or test coupons are placed in suitable areas of the plant. By close examination of these (and of parts of the plant itself), coupled with weight loss tests at periodic intervals (say, every 500 or 1000 hours if possible, or at least during periodic maintenance) the relative corrosion resistance of the materials under actual working conditions can be determined.

Two units are in common use for measuring the rate of corrosion when it is uniformly distributed over a surface, as would be the case under normal conditions of attack. These are (i) loss of thickness in inches penetration per year (ipy) and (ii) loss of weight in milligrammes per square decimetre per day (mdd).

These units are convertible as follows:

$$\frac{\text{mdd} \times 0 \cdot 001437}{\text{relative density of material}} = \text{ipy}$$

When corrosion is not uniform, the cause should be sought, and on pitted samples the maximum depth of penetration should be measured. Pitting can usually be avoided or restricted by correct design or choice of material (for instance, by the avoidance of stagnant areas, differential aeration, etc.).

Records should be kept of the environmental conditions appertaining to each sample, such as position in plant, materials to which it is exposed, temperature, pressure, concentration, degree of agitation or aeration, any known impurities present, etc.

As the initial rate of corrosion is usually greater than the final rate, quoted corrosion rates should preferably state the duration of time over which they have been averaged. It is often unwise to extrapolate for a long period ahead.

In chemical plant subject to uniform attack, a metal would have good corrosion resistance to a particular medium if its corrosion rate was less than 0·005 ipy; a corrosion rate of 0·005 to 0·05 ipy would be tolerable in some cases for tanks, pipes, etc., whilst a corrosion rate of greater than 0·05 ipy would generally be unsatisfactory.

Steel in sea water corrodes at perhaps a little over 0·005 ipy.

## 12.7 The mechanism of corrosion

The corrosion of a metal may be defined as 'the destruction of metal or alloy by chemical or electrochemical change, or by physical dissolution'. The corrosion of non-metals may be referred to as chemical attack.

Because of its importance to inspection, the inspector should possess some knowledge of the complex and still in some respects debatable mechanisms of corrosion; specialist works such as those listed below may be consulted. Corrosion protective finishes and their inspection have been dealt with in Chapter 5 and cathodic protection in 4.29. Some literature on corrosion appears at the end of this chapter.

### 12.7.1 Dry corrosion—oxidation

Oxidation, the combination of a metal with oxygen, is an example of chemical change, and takes place readily at high temperatures, but less readily at room temperature where, generally speaking, an oxide surface film tends to isolate the metal from further attack, particularly in dry, pure air. The presence of minor constituents and/or impurities in the metal can influence oxidation, maybe accelerating or retarding it. For instance, the presence of chromium, silicon or aluminium in steel increases its high-temperature corrosion resistance, and generally its mechanical properties also. Traces of vanadium or molybdenum may increase corrosion resistance at the expense of mechanical properties.

If the oxide film is loose, porous or tends to flake off, then oxidation will continue and the metal will waste away. Some constituents or processes help to anchor an oxide film and prevent further corrosion. Aluminium and its alloys can be prevented from further corrosion by 'anodizing', a process of anodic oxidation whereby a controlled film of oxide is formed electrolytically on the surface of the material (see 5.13).

Other forms of dry corrosion may occur in atmospheric conditions which contain such gases as sulphur dioxide, carbon dioxide and monoxide, chlorine, fluorine, etc. A surface film may develop which may be more or may be less protective. In porous materials penetration may take place to such an extent that intergranular deposits are formed, which embrittle the material and make it susceptible to shock.

### 12.7.2 Electrochemical corrosion

Most corrosion processes are due to complex electrical or electrolytic mechanisms. If conditions are damp or involve immersion in some aqueous media, then electrochemical corrosion results from the formation of short-circuited cells in which the electrodes consist of the anodic and cathodic areas of metal and the electrolyte is the corrodent in contact with them. This electrolyte allows current to flow between anodic and cathodic areas (owing to positively charged metal ions entering the electrolyte at the anode), resulting in the corrosion of the anodic area of metal.

Electrochemical corrosion can take place between areas of the same metal surface which may differ metallurgically or chemically, or because of inclusions or defects in this surface. This is known as 'local action'. Local action cells can be set up also by variations in environment (including variations in liquid concentration, aeration or temperature, or even stress).

The magnitude of the corrosion will depend also on the nature of the aqueous medium or electrolyte. Absolutely pure water (including pure ice) will not allow corrosion current to flow, but water will generally contain varying quantities of salts, air and other dissolved matter. Oxygen from the air at a wet surface takes up electrons in a cathodic reaction and, as a result, metal from the anode is eaten away and enters the liquid as cations (positively charged ions) which migrate towards the cathode.

The strength of the corrosion current often depends on the supply of oxygen to the area where the cathodic reaction takes place. If this oxygen supply is diminished then corrosion may be reduced. A more concentrated solution may be more or may be less corrosive.

By introducing a salt, so that the cathodic and anodic products become insoluble, an insoluble film is produced which tends to *inhibit* further corrosion. Chromates and nitrites are commonly used as inhibitors, particularly to restrict the attack on iron in water.

### 12.7.3 Galvanic corrosion

More severe electrochemical corrosion generally occurs when two dissimilar metals are in contact via a conducting fluid (electrolyte), and it may be serious if the metals are widely spaced in the 'electrochemical series'. In practice, the 'galvanic series', as in Fig. 12.1, which is an arrangement of metals and alloys in accord with their actual measured potential in sea water, is of more use in assessing galvanic corrosion, as it gives the actual e.m.f. developed between any pair of metals. In general, the 'base' or anodic metal (the one higher in the chart) suffers corrosion whilst the 'noble' or cathodic metal is protected and sometimes unharmed.

The actual anodic and cathodic areas on a steel surface can be detected by observing the colour changes caused by applying phenolphthalein and potassium ferricyanide. The hydrogen evolved at the cathode will cause a sufficient concentration of hydroxyl ($2OH^-$) ions in the electrolyte to turn the phenolphthalein pink; whilst the ferrous ions going into solution at the anode will turn the potassium ferricyanide a deep blue.

Salt-laden moisture is a good electrolyte and favours corrosion. A large area functioning as a cathode may lead to a severe attack on a small anodic area. Thus steel rivets in copper sheeting immersed in salt water will be severely corroded and may actually fall out, whilst copper rivets in steel sheeting may stay in good condition for a long period. Damp packaging or other material bridging dissimilar metals can give rise to serious corrosion. The presence of naturally formed films or deliberately applied coatings will limit current flow and thus restrict corrosion.

Where dissimilar metals have to be bolted together consideration can sometimes be given to the provision of an insulating washer. Welds between dissimilar metals may set up corrosion problems, both galvanic and those due to unremoved fluxes and hygroscopic residues therefrom.

## 12.7.4 Acid corrosion

In acid solutions the main cathodic reaction results in the evolution of hydrogen, generally where the metal has a negative normal electrical potential, or where there is a high pH value (hydrogen ion concentration).

Generally speaking, the 'noble' metals do not liberate hydrogen when placed in acid, whereas 'base' metals do and are subject to attack.

Strong oxidizing acids, such as nitric and concentrated sulphuric, may produce films on metal surfaces which under certain conditions give some protection. Perversely, however, the metals may be more strongly attacked by dilute acid. Consequently, it may sometimes be found that steel and cast iron are used for storing concentrated sulphuric acid, and aluminium for concentrated nitric acid.

Iron-nickel-chromium alloys are much used for resisting acids (and alkalis). The mechanism is not clearly understood but the presence of oxygen (or other oxidizing agent) in the liquid and the formation of a film of chromium, etc., on the surface which resists attack are believed to be contributory.

## 12.7.5 Intergranular (crystalline) corrosion

Corrosion may occur with certain materials, notably stainless steel and Duralumin, when exposed to various forms of chemical attack, and will take place along the grain or crystal boundaries of that material. Generally grain boundary material of limited area, acting as anodes, is in contact with larger grain areas acting as cathodes. The incidence of attack is of much greater moment than if it occurred uniformly, as by penetrating inwardly along grain boundaries it causes a much greater decrease in strength and can readily cause failure in service. The subject of intercrystalline corrosion of stainless steel and of the associated 'weld decay' and of the methods used to combat it has been dealt with in 2.13. Inspection must ensure that such methods are always used and must be alert to detect signs of such corrosion near weld joints.

## 12.7.6 Stress and fatigue corrosion

It has been found that if a stress acts continuously in a corrosive environment it can produce cracks which would not otherwise occur. These cracks may follow intergranular boundaries or may be along paths of weakness, or possibly at random. Consequently, failures may occur in service. In a specific corrosive environment steel, brass, aluminium-magnesium alloys, and aluminium alloys containing copper, zinc or manganese are subject to stress corrosion cracking, as is also stainless steel, particularly when used with chloride-containing solutions.

If a corrosion crack appears at the bottom of a crevice or crack it will readily spread if the stress continues. Annealing before fabrication and stress relieving after welding help to avert this trouble. Cold-worked materials may be particularly susceptible.

Somewhat similarly, corrosion fatigue may occur in the presence of alternating or fluctuating stresses, such as vibration, in a corrosive environment, and may appear in almost any corrodible material. Allied to this is fretting corrosion which may occur at the surface of closely fitting parts when they are subject to vibration.

Much is not understood about the mechanism of stress and fatigue corrosion, but it seems that they occur more particularly at high temperatures and in materials where the granules are disarranged. Correct heat treatment (if properly specifiable) is perhaps a solution, whilst the careful selection of materials and use of protective treatments can help.

The presence of nitrates in a plant, or even in industrial cooling water which will usually contain some nitrates especially following water treatment, can set up *nitrate stress corrosion cracking* when in contact with mild steel. The severity of the attack depends upon the degree of concentration of nitrate, a high stress, a low pH value, and a temperature above about 80°C. A suitable paint coating may give some protection from low concentrations of nitrate.

Creep was discussed in 2.7. There is a very rapid increase in creep rate with temperature. With overheating, perhaps by abnormal operating conditions or a fire, the effects of creep with stress and chemical process fluids can cause distortion and corrosion, and perhaps creep cavitation of stainless steel.

### 12.7.7 Localized corrosion (pitting)

In some cases of corrosion the attack may be confined to a relatively small area or areas, owing perhaps to a scratch or break in a surface film or scale permitting the underlying metal to act as an anode, and/or to the formation of local action cells. Oxygen is normally present in the liquid and the attack takes the form of 'pitting'. Isolated pits can become quite deep. Pitting may occur readily during a shut-down, owing to stagnant conditions.

Pitting sometimes occurs when a high-velocity liquid impinges on a surface, and is sometimes known as 'corrosion-erosion' or 'impingement attack'. Similarly, 'cavitation-erosion' resulting from the formation and collapse of vapour bubbles at a dynamic metal-liquid interface (as in propellers, pump impellers, etc.) may cause a series of pits.

## 12.7.8 Dezincification

The so-called dezincification of brass is an example of a type of corrosion which can occur with some alloys. With brass, the zinc corrodes preferentially leaving a porous residue of copper and corrosion products which may retain the shape of the original article but of course has little strength.

For zinc embrittlement, see 5.9.

## 12.8 Plant inspection after a period of operation

All plant should be inspected after a period of use, or after repair or modification. Deterioration may have occurred and in any case the effects of service, corrosion, etc., can be profitably studied.

Plant not subjected to any appreciable corrosion and not required to be inspected by statute or otherwise should be inspected at least *every five years*. In addition, particularly with outdoor plant, it is desirable to make a visual examination of supports, etc., at least once *every year*; a vulnerable point is where structural steel emerges from foundations.

Any item of plant which is out of service for some time should be thoroughly inspected before being put back into use.

Amongst features to which attention should be directed are:

(1) *Corrosion*, and measurement of corrosion rate (see 12.6), minimum plate thickness, etc.

Plate thickness measurement has generally involved drilling holes through the relevant part and physically measuring the thickness still left, afterwards welding up the holes. Modern ultrasonic techniques of thickness measurement (see 10.6) may avoid dismantling or taking out of service, though some practical difficulty is encountered in detecting and interpreting corrosion and pitting, e.g. inside the numerous small tubes in heat exchangers, etc. (For a thermal method of detecting such corrosion see 10.10.) In such plant, the maintenance of streamline rather than turbulent flow will help.

Corrosion rates can be estimated with the aid of data obtained from vessels in similar service, but should be checked with the results of actual measurement. In general, if corrosion exceeds 10% of the wall thickness per year, inspection should be at least yearly; for lesser corrosion rates, at longer intervals.

The various forms of corrosion mentioned in 12.7 should be searched for and any necessary action taken, particularly if periods of overheating during operation are suspected. Serious overheating or a local fire may necessitate the careful inspection and possible replacement of stressed or corroded components.

(2) *Weld condition.* Rough or undercut welds may form crevices. Welds may deteriorate. Crack detection by magnetic particle or liquid penetrant

methods may be desirable. Particular attention should be paid to any welds which cross or are in the immediate vicinity of main seams.

The inspector should be alert for signs of intercrystalline corrosion (or weld decay) in austenitic stainless steels (see 2.13 and 9.21) and should carefully examine the vicinity of all welds, though if the plant was originally correctly fabricated and inspection and process control was adequate no defects should develop. Tapping with a hammer and listening for the absence of the characteristic steel 'ring' may help.

(3) *Surface condition* of working areas, presence of embedded inclusions, contaminants, etc.

(4) *Accumulation of materials* (solid, semi-solid or liquid) and waste matter in crevices, corners, etc. (trapped spaces should be avoided as far as possible to limit this and stagnation effects).

(5) *Vessel drainage provision* during shut-down. (Dished ends fitted with a draincock are more effective than flat bottoms.) As flushing out is usually necessary during maintenance, supports, baffles and interior components should not form traps but should allow for easy cleaning and drainage. Any crevices or dirt traps should be welded up.

(6) *Sharp edges and corners* should be avoided; they may lead to trouble or physical injury, and on stressed parts may lead to cracks.

(7) *Overstressing*. Actual environmental conditions, or design weaknesses, may lead to visible distortion and strengthening may be necessary. A dimensional check may be helpful.

(8) *Dissimilar metals in contact*, particularly in the presence of liquid, should be reviewed for corrosion and in the light of a chart of electrochemical potential (Fig. 12.1).

(9) *Stray electric currents* through chemical plant may cause corrosion and other troubles. In general, electrical equipment should not be earthed directly to chemical plant.

(10) *Periodic pressure testing* (see 3.20 and 12.5) is a statutory requirement on pressure vessels, etc. Other items, pipework, etc., may be so tested, and in some cases particular items of plant should be periodically leak-tested (see Chapter 11).

(11) *Gaskets, seals and tube-to-plate joints* should be examined for condition and the possibility of leakage. Where operating temperatures have been high the behaviour of the materials and the possibility of creep should be considered.

(12) *Lagging of vessels and pipework* should be checked and, if need be, possibly extended. Exposed items may need protection against frost. The top of a heated vessel should be well lagged and the unit kept above the dew point to avoid condensation in any vapour space.

Corrosion hidden beneath lagging should be looked for and dealt with. Dripping of process liquids and water on to lagging may cause considerable trouble. The checking, repair and, if necessary, the removal of asbestos

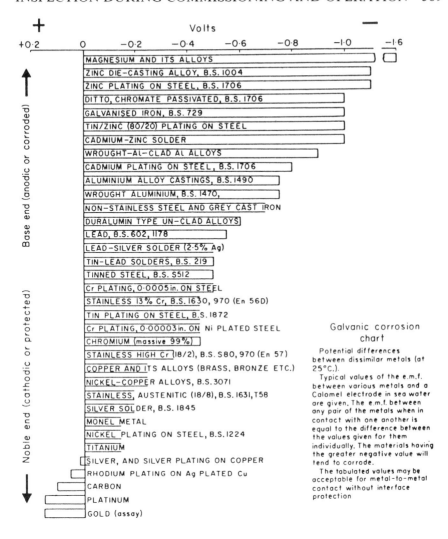

Fig. 12.1  Galvanic corrosion chart.

lagging should receive particular attention (see 6.16). Prior permission for its removal must be obtained from HSE so that proper precautions and supervision can be arranged.

(13) *Ease of access* is important in relation to time saving on inspection and maintenance of plant and equipment.

(14) *Wear.* Surfaces, etc., subject to abrasion and wear should be examined. Bearings may have to operate under severe conditions; perhaps oil lubrication is prohibited; dry bearings or even PTFE bearings may be failing and needing replacement more often than expected.

(15) *Protective finish, painting* (see Chapter 5). The interior or working surfaces having been dealt with, consideration should be given to the condition of the exterior finish. This has generally to give atmospheric protection, but more severe environments may have to be guarded against.

(16) *Electrical services.* The inspector should check and report, after any maintenance, repair and modification work has been carried out, as to:

(a) whether the integrity of the system has been maintained;

(b) whether any corrosion has taken place;

(c) whether any deterioration of insulation has occurred and been remedied (checking particularly flexible cables);

(d) whether any loose connections have been tightened;

(e) whether any withdrawn equipment has been safely isolated/removed and its cable terminations made safe.

A typical inspection schedule for checking electrical equipment installed in a potentially hazardous area after repair, modification or periodic maintenance is given in Table 6.6 (taken from BS 5345 by courtesy of BSI).

Alterations and additions to this schedule can be made to suit particular equipments. Thus for flameproof motors, etc., details could be given of gap dimensions.

Inspection schedules and registers for other types of equipment besides electrics can be made and kept.

(17) *Instrumentation and control.* Instruments should meet their design specifications and operate in a reliable and consistent manner. Typical reasons for failure are incorrect rating of components, lack of appropriate environmental testing, inadequate inspection during manufacture, and deteriorating and intermittent electrical wiring and connections. These last must be examined frequently, especially if exposed to corrosive atmospheres.

Valves should be tested periodically and opened at least monthly, and equipment such as pressure gauges, thermometers, weighing machines regularly checked.

(18) *Defects, damage or corrosion* discovered either will be repaired or may perhaps call for reducing the allowable working pressure or conditions, or scrapping. Minor defects in plates, cracks in welds and the like can usually be repaired by chipping out to sound metal and depositing weld metal according to the relevant construction code. Sometimes small cracks

can be stopped by drilling holes at their extremities to reduce stress concentration. Repairs should be carried out to ensure compliance with the original specification. Repairs to pressure systems should comply with BS 3351.

(19) *Safety precautions in inspection and repair.* Before beginning welding or cutting work in tanks, drums and the like, check for any residual or trapped liquid; if in doubt, treat as flammable. Cleaning out is best done with live steam.

Fumes produced by working inside a vessel must be effectively removed, or a respirator worn; oxygen must not be used for breathing. Special care is needed when breaking joints or with frozen pipelines.

Generally, clearance certificates, permits-to-work, etc. are required by statutory or local regulations, before any person is allowed to enter, inspect or work in any dangerous or potentially dangerous area (including those involving electrical equipment). These must be signed by a competent person, and their issue may involve the removal of keys, interlocks, etc. in order to prevent danger arising whilst work is in progress. If the space cannot be certified as isolated and sealed from danger, then the person must wear a breathing apparatus (as defined in the *Chemical Works Regulations*) and a life belt with a rope attached in charge of a man in touch with any necessary assistance. The breathing and rescue apparatus must be inspected at least once a month and generally after each occasion on which they are used, and the results recorded in a register. (See also Chapter 14, particularly 14.5, paras 23 and 24.)

(20) *A plan of all service installations* should be available and kept up to date.

(21) *Records.* A permanent record of all inspections should be kept in a register and give all relevant details. A general inspection report on the ability or otherwise of the chosen materials to meet all operating conditions, including those of starting-up, stand-by and shut-down, may be required, together with suggestions for improvements.

Huge quantities of documentary records are nowadays associated with every type of large-scale engineering project, many of these documents relating to safety and quality assurance, including inspections during construction, commissioning, operation and maintenance. Chemical plants have to maintain readily accessible records of every item of equipment in use and every process carried out. In many cases copies of documents have legally to be kept readily available on the spot. For instance, a currently valid test certificate must be kept with every crane or lifting device, whilst a modern nuclear power station generates not only a large amount of electricity but an enormous amount of paperwork, including some 4–5 million quality assurance documents relating to its construction alone. Throughout its operational life (and perhaps after) many more such documents will be added to the collection and have to be kept constantly available.

An off-shore platform is said to produce (besides oil or gas) some 10 million pages of engineering documents, of which some 1·5 million having operational relevance must legally be stored on the platform.

Obviously in many cases some computer-type storage and retrieval system is essential. It is hoped that the alert inspector will not be drowned by this paperwork (or by the collapse of his project), but rather that the action recorded, required or implied by these documents will bring safety and success!

## 12.9 Maintenance

Maintenance has been described as the essential means of perpetuating the design intention; alternatively, as the process of sustaining a service in all its material needs. This second definition is perhaps the more embracing, as it includes design, provision, storage, distribution and servicing.

Inspection can aid maintenance all along the line. To begin with, it must ensure that the plant and equipment as originally provided is such that its construction and performance fulfils the design intention, so that maintenance can afterwards see that this is perpetuated. Inspection has also a role to play in checking for deterioration during storage, distribution and use.

Maintenance may involve inspection, cleaning, adjustment, repair and modification. It may introduce hazards not only to maintenance personnel but to the plant and its operatives. It is essential that the integrity of the plant should be not impaired, i.e. that the designers' intentions and specifications should be maintained, even after repair. A problem may arise when carrying out a modification to plant originally made to a specification which is now obsolete or obsolescent. In general the old original specifications should be worked to, but snags may arise or the originally specified material may no longer be available. In such cases expert advice should be obtained, possibly from the design authority. (For example pressure vessels may have been made to BS 1500 or 1515 now superseded by BS 5500, or flameproof electric motors may have been made to BS 229 now superseded by BS 5501 Part 5.)

Safety precautions must be observed and documented during maintenance and a permit-to-work system employed to ensure that equipment, vessels or areas are not worked on or entered until certified safe. (See Chemical and Allied Process Industries' Training Board Information Paper 16A (1977) and HSE Tech. Data Note 47, Entry into confined spaces (1975) based on Chemical Works Regulations CWR7 (192) and *Factory Act* 1961 Sect. 30 and 12.8.19 of this book.)

When inspection or maintenance work is required on any items of plant the instructions given must identify *precisely* the item and its location. The method used may make use of drawings, descriptive labels, numbered tags, coloured pipework, and standards and codes of practice (see Table 4.9).

Repainting is often necessary during maintenance. A danger arises here if pipework, etc. is repainted but not in the original colour, perhaps inadvertently or because the colour code for the particular service has changed (see 4.14). Confusion due to such action has been the cause of serious accidents (see various HM Inspector of Factories Annual Reports). Similarly, materials used in maintenance should be obtained from a bonded store to ensure that they are of the correct specification. Here again, material colour coding may be used. Isolation of pipelines, electrical equipment, etc. must be methodically done and recorded before any maintenance work is started. Cleaning or purging of equipment and pipelines may be necessary (see 12.3). The safety provisions given in 14.4, 14.6 and 14.7 may be applicable. Pumps should be checked for leakage at seals and for bearing trouble.

Particular care is necessary when pressure testing old pipelines and vessels, and suitable precautions must be taken, such as securing end caps, etc. which might be blown off like a projectile. Many accidents, sometimes fatal, have occured.

Regular inspection and check testing of protective devices, instruments and fire protection equipment should be carried out on a routine basis and any necessary repairs, adjustments or replacements made.

It should be realized that, although proper maintenance is essential to safety, it is responsible for some 21% of all fatal factory accidents—caused mainly by work on machinery, plant and roofs, and lack of proper safety precautions (see HSE booklet 'Deadly Maintenance' (HMSO), 1985)).

*12.9.1 Maintenance—planning and execution*

The servicing aspect is perhaps the one most usually thought of as maintenance, and here inspection has generally to decide what has to be done, and to check that it is done satisfactorily. Any deterioration in condition or performance must be put right, or kept within agreed limits.

This servicing (or maintenance) aspect can be broadly divided into two categories: (i) planned (which includes scheduled) maintenance; (ii) unscheduled maintenance.

Planned maintenance must be carefully thought out, and the pattern of events, likely faults, etc., foreseen as far as possible.

Unscheduled maintenance deals with events, faults, etc., as and when they occur, without any previous planning other than perhaps the provision of equipment and manpower for use should they be required; e.g. it would deal with random and largely unexpected failures.

## 12.9.2 *Planned maintenance*

A system of planned maintenance—the determination of the most economic way of carrying out individual maintenance work—can be built up for any particular plant, using modern techniques of work study, inspection, scheduling, planning and statistics.

Three basic planned maintenance procedures may be adopted:

(i) *Breakdown maintenance*, a system of *knowingly* operating a particular plant or equipment until a fault occurs, which, although apparently somewhat crude, is occasionally the most economic. Obviously, it cannot be adopted if the breakdown could cause dangers or the loss of valuable material, or have undesirable side effects.

(ii) *Scheduled preventative maintenance*, a system involving the inspection, adjustment, repair or replacement of plant or equipment at predetermined intervals, in an attempt to prevent or reduce the chance of trouble. Generally speaking, such a system involves the periodic shut-down of the plant (or items) thereof, which may be inconvenient and costly when such plant normally runs continuously or for long periods. However, it is the most widely used system for the planned maintenance of all forms of engineering plant.

(iii) *Condition based maintenance*, a system whereby the plant is monitored by some technique or techniques which will detect any deterioration or incipient failure in sufficient time to permit suitable maintenance, repair or replacement action to be taken. Allied with this may be a system of 'designing out' failures, as far as statistically possible by using components, etc. which have been assessed and inspected and selected to have a 'life' greater than the planned period of operation of the plant. Operating experience and periodic design audits may also highlight components subject to frequent faults; such components could possibly be redesigned to eliminate such failures.

A close study of the economic and safety aspects of the plant, or parts of it, is necessary before deciding which system/s to adopt. Certain components such as electric lamps of generally known life can be economically replaced in bulk in certain areas during scheduled maintenance periods. The techniques employed in condition monitoring include:

(i) those regarded as non-destructive testing (including thermography, optical methods, acoustic emission, etc — see Chapter 10),

(ii) those based on vibration measurement, particularly of rotating machinery,

(iii) the evaluation of debris due to wear found in lubricating systems, filters, etc., and

(iv) the study of any change in the performance of pumps, machines and other components by instrumentation (often of a basic kind, even the use of the human senses only; but sometimes by expensive high technology 'beyond the state of the art' equipment if warranted by the circumstances).

(v) micro-processor and computer based techniques can be used to process effectively and quickly the mass of data obtainable from condition monitoring and provide failure prediction reports, etc.

The subject is further considered in Chapter 13.

### 12.9.3 Operation of defective plant

When it is known, by inspection, testing or otherwise, that a particular item is defective, or is deteriorating rapidly, it is a question for close consideration whether it should be allowed to run for a further period, with the consequent risks attached, until appropriate remedial or replacement action can be taken, or whether it should be immediately taken out of service.

### 12.9.4 Scheduled shut-downs

The frequency of shut-down is often based on past practice. A particular item might be allowed 1000 running hours, after which it must be shut down and examined, and/or renewed, perhaps involving complete stripping of a machine. A complete plant might be given a thorough inspection and overhaul annually or as required by statute. A study of operational records and of inspection reports after shut-down will help to decide the optimum frequency. Improved instrumentation and inspection techniques could perhaps be introduced.

When plant is shut down it is not earning money, and overhead charges of course continue—it would be salutary to know the cost of an hour's shut-down for particular items! Consequently, organization and methods should be adopted to shorten the time, bearing in mind the labour available, its hourly cost (including overtime), and the cost or repair or, alternatively, replacement of defective items. Again, inspection techniques can assist in rapidly sorting out the work to be done, and deciding whether particular items should, for instance, be repaired or replaced. On some plants the duration of a scheduled annual shut-down may extend, justifiably, to one month, in order to get the work done economically; in other cases such a duration would not be permissible and vigorous measures would have to be taken or, alternatively, the installation of a duplicate plant considered.

### 12.9.5 Good housekeeping

Perhaps a final word: inspection and maintenance is not something which is only carried out periodically—it is a perpetually continuing process, and like a woman's work is never finished! Good housekeeping (which includes cleanliness) is often vital, especially in some high-technology plants where 'hospital conditions' are not out of place. Tidiness (a place for everything and everything in its place!), clean paintwork and safe floors, removal of rubbish, absence of dust (thick dust on electrical equipment can cause excessive temperature rise), neat colour coding and identification systems, good lighting and pleasant conditions—all these can pay dividends.

One laboratory dealing with oxygen equipment experienced trouble eventually traced to a plague of exceedingly minute 'red spiders' from the adjacent countryside. They seemed to pass through all barriers in large numbers. They got into small crevices in oxygen regulators and many other items of plant and equipment—nothing would stop them. Being 'combustible' they could even cause minor explosions when suddenly encountering high pressure oxygen! Consultation with the 'agricultural experts' led to the purchase and planting of a hedge of red roses outside the laboratory. This solved the problem—this particular species of mite was allergic to roses (presumably red) and would not pass them!

(See also BS 6869 *Code of practice for procedures for ensuring cleanliness of industrial process measurement and control equipment in oxygen service.*)

### 12.10  In-service inspection of hazardous plant

Much of what has been said hitherto regarding inspection of plant after the requirements of construction standards and codes have been met (i.e. in-use or operational inspection) may be called *recommended practices* to ensure efficient service and good management. However with plant of a hazardous nature certain regulations and rules for examination, testing and inspection must be regarded as *mandatory*, either to satisfy legislation or particularly outstanding safety requirements. Many chemical plants come into this category and have received the attention of, or have been scheduled by the Health and Safety Executive and/or other recognized bodies. See for instance the control of Industrial Major Accident Hazards Regulations (SI 1984 No. 1902) and other Regulations in Table 14.2. Amongst such mandatory rules, standards or codes attention might perhaps first be drawn to the ASME Boiler and Pressure Vessel Code Section XI 'Rules for Inservice Inspection of Nuclear Power Plant Components' (first published in 1971). This is an example of the great attention to detail considered necessary in the hope of ensuring 'as far as is reasonably practicable' that plant will continue to operate safely, and is applicable in principle to many hazardous plants besides those for nuclear power. But of course nothing in this life can be guaranteed and the most an inspector can do regarding any hazardous plant or activity is to be constantly alert in the carrying out of his duties and tests to the latest available information. Any sign of possibly approaching danger must be reported and action taken. For instance, after carrying out in-service tests of pumps ASME Sect. XI requires an analysis of the results to assess any deviation from earlier tests. This analysis must be completed within 96 hours. Any deviation has to be classified as falling either within an *alert* or an *action required* range: within the first alert range the period between tests is halved until the cause of the deviation is discovered. For those classified as *action required* the pump is declared inoperative until the condition has been corrected. Again, with certain valves, tests have to be carried out at specified intervals and leakage rates compared with previous measurements and with the specified permissible leakage rate. Any deviation may require action along the lines previously indicated. Requirements are laid down for system pressure testing of class 1, 2 and 3 components (see 3.28), the period between inspections, the test pressure, system leakage tests and other details being specified.

The techniques of visual inspection and non-destructive testing (described in Chapter 10) are employed for various types of hazardous including nuclear plant and their components. The duties and required qualifications of inspectors, inspection agencies and non-destructive examination personnel are often specified. Records of all in-service tests, reports and relevant documents have to be kept for at least the service lifetime of the component or plant.

In-service non-destructive examination results have to be compared with the recorded results of the original construction and other prior in-service examinations. Components whose examination either reconfirms the absence of flaw indications or reveals flaw indications that do not exceed the currently listed acceptance standards are acceptable for continued service. Changes of indications from prior examinations are recorded and those which do not meet current acceptance standards have to be repaired to the extent necessary to meet such standards. (It was reported that recent 100% radiographic and other periodic NDT examinations showed that welding carried out some quarter of a century ago on the early British Magnox reactors was still completely acceptable even to modern standards (see *IEE Journal* E & P Oct. 1985).) Detailed requirements are laid down for the removal of any defects found and for the procedures to be adopted for repairs by welding etc. After repair, of course, components must satisfy all current test requirements. Pressure and containment vessels (whether of metal or concrete), and certain pipework must be condition monitored throughout service life. Obviously some methods of periodic pressure and non-destructive testing cannot be used in the normal way where there is a possible presence of a hazard (such as radioactivity). However, certain forms of sensor etc. may be fitted initially to remotely monitor particular parameters perhaps continuously.

Neither the ASME Code Section XI nor BS 5500 for Pressure vessels covers tests for leakage of radioactivity. Where necessary such tests may be carried out by continuous monitoring of all areas and possible outlets, and by monitoring of personnel after each shift, etc.

Records may have to be kept for several years at least 50 in the case of personnel exposed to radiation, and any leakage beyond the currently acceptable limits (see 6.19) must be reported to the Health and Safety Executive. Radiation leakages slightly beyond permissible concentrations often become front page news items.

It is presumably thought (and hoped) that if mechanical construction and in-service inspection is carried out rigorously to an accepted code, serious troubles will not occur, leaks will not happen (but practically everything leaks!—see Chapter 11) and any faults which may develop will be detected before they become dangerous (such things as brittle fracture, (see 2.8) which can develop with explosive rapidity, must not be allowed to occur!). Much responsibility rests on the shoulders of the inspector. It is hoped that, with access to all the currently available relevant information, he should make his decisions without fear or favour, irrespective of pressure from management, politics or any other quarter.

All hazardous chemical plants should be designed, constructed and inspected (during construction and operation) along somewhat similar lines to those mentioned above to ensure, as far as is reasonably practicable, that faults and troubles do not develop, and that leakage of any dangerous material does not occur beyond the generally agreed international maximum permissible limits (see for instance HSE *Guidance Notes* EH40 and 42). Any relevant application standards, codes, and regulations may give some detailed information.

To this end it is regarded as good practice (and it may be required or inferred from current or projected legislation, especially that appertaining to the HSE's activities regarding major hazards) to identify the hazards and to monitor the environment in and around a hazardous plant in order to demonstrate that no harm is caused to life etc. in its vicinity. The results of this monitoring are then compared with the internationally agreed maximum permissible limits for the substances relevant to the plant's operations, and checked with previous readings to see whether there are any significant changes. Any appropriate action may then be taken.

Occupational exposure limits for airborne substances hazardous to health are given in HSE *Guidance Note* EH 40/85 which is revised annually. Exposure limits are given as control limits or as recommended limits (which are used as criteria by HSE inspectors) and may be expressed in parts per million (ppm) and/or mg/m$^3$, either as a long-term (8 hours) or a short-term (10 minutes) value. (See also HSE *Guidance Note* EH 42—Monitoring strategies for Toxic Substances.)

The results may also usefully be compared with readings obtained before the plant came into operation, if such readings are available. Such monitoring is particularly valuable in the case of nuclear plants, and is usually carried out for both radiation and contamination (fallout on surfaces, etc.) at places at a radius of 5, 10, 15 and 20 miles from the plant. Samples of milk, water, grass, soil, etc. are also examined, perhaps at fortnightly intervals.

Any effluent discharged from a hazardous plant should also be monitored. It may be necessary to send samples to and obtain the permission of the relevant licensing authority for the discharge of stated levels and quantities of specific effluent.

But although the highest standards of design, construction, inspection, calculation, maintenance and operation may have been met, troubles perhaps augmented by human failings can arise in any undertaking and it is considered prudent for management (pressurized no doubt by the HSE and legislation) to draw up plans of action to deal with any major accident or foreseeable on-site hazards to all workers on site, and, preferably in cooperation with the local authority, to all people living within a certain distance of the plant, together with instructions as to what they all should do in an emergency. The borderline between what is foreseeable and what is statistically extremely unlikely (but not impossible) can and will cause difficulties in planning.

Well designed and competently operated plant should give little trouble and the UK chemical industry in the past generally has had a good record. Occasional lapses occur and perhaps leakages somewhat beyond the permissible limit may take place; but its is hoped that there is always a factor of safety with these limits and the authorities (such as the HSE) will deal with such incidents. However, design, inspection, etc. has to cater for the possibility of an accident due perhaps to bad management, human error or a chain of exceptional circumstances. The Flixborough explosion (June 1974) which caused 28 deaths, some 100 casualties and damaged almost 2000 dwellings, and the much greater Bhopal (India) disaster (December 1984) which resulted in the release of a toxic cloud and reputedly caused over 200,000 casualties, including some 2500 deaths, are cases in point. The permissible leakage of radioactivity from nuclear plant is discussed in 6.20 *et seq.*

Many steps taken in design, construction, inspection and operation of hazardous plants with the object of preventing serious accidents are covered in standards, codes and regulations. In-service inspection (including maintenance and alterations) must be tailored to meet this object, making use of all possible techniques including failure and fatigue analysis studies. Fatigue and brittle fracture are potentially prime causes of failure of many vessels and structures. However they are almost completely amenable to prevention by the application of suitable measures and techniques involving design, construction and treatment. There is an extensive literature on the subject.

Fatigue life may be calculated by carrying out an analysis (see for instance BS 5500 Appendix C) or predicted by the use of fracture mechanics.

Brittle fracture crack arrest constructions may be used; these involve placing some obstruction (such as low stress and/or tough material) across the path that a crack would follow. Crack Opening Displacement (COD) tests to BS 5762 may be carried out (see 2.8.1).

*12.10.1 In-service inspection and maintenance of hazardous electrical gear*

The *Health and Safety Act* 1974 and its associated *Factories Act* and Electricity Regulations (see Chapter 14) require that measures be taken to safeguard personnel and prevent any danger arising from electrical equipment.

Electrical installations, although they may be dangerous under certain conditions, are not normally regarded as hazardous unless installed in a hazardous area (see 6.9.2). However, installations for the production of metals or non-metals by means of electrical energy are amongst those which come under the Control of Industrial Major Accident Hazards Regulations (SI 1984 No. 1902). The owner has, *inter alia*, to take adequate steps to identify and prevent such accidents and to limit their consequences to persons and the environment.

Also under the Reporting of Injuries, Diseases and Dangerous Occurrences Regulations (SI 1985 No. 2023) an electrical short circuit or overload attended by fire or explosion resulting in the stoppage of the plant involved for more than 24 hours must be notified and reported to the relevant enforcing authority.

Statistics seem to show that perhaps electrical testing and operating personnel are subject to the greatest danger, and that switchgear would seem to be the most dangerous equipment. Consequently, warning notices should be displayed together with copies of the relevant electricity regulations, etc. Switchgear, in large and small sizes, may control energy amounting to many thousands of kilowatts (or even MVA). The switches may be operated very frequently or only rarely, and then perhaps automatically under fault conditions. If their rupturing capacity is inadequate to break such a fault they may explode and perhaps cause a fire. Switchgear can and will deteriorate, perhaps due to the surrounding environment, deteriorating insulation, or the burning of contacts. It is also subject to hazards due to lightning strikes (thunderstorms) and other abnormal external circuit operating conditions. Internal or external fault conditions may frequently cause failure of any associated current and potential transformers. A circuit breaker must be able to interrupt the maximum likely short circuit current without sustaining serious damage. Its designed rupturing capacity is a statistical property and can be established by a number of tests (see also BS 5311). Failures under normal operating conditions are rare; but when called upon to operate frequently under heavy loads (say 30 times per day), or perhaps due to poor maintenance, deterioration, fatigue, loosening of nuts and bolts, breakage of parts, etc, or to abnormal external conditions, a severe fault may cause a heavy destructive explosion. With an oil circuit breaker this could lead to a fire. Also, with oil, continued arcing causes the formation of explosive gases, including hydrogen and methane, and the deposition of carbon particules on insulators, etc, which itself may cause a flashover. Hence the need for regular replacement or filtering of oil.

Within a year of installation (or sooner in the case of frequently used switchgear) or after operating and breaking a heavy fault current, a thorough inspection should be carried out. But first a signed permit-to-work must be obtained, guaranteeing the isolation of the equipment. Then the switch mechanism should be examined and operated, checking for correctness of movement. Any necessary tightness of connections, fixings, etc., clearances, burnt contacts, insulation resistance and condition, and general cleanliness should be checked. If the switch is designed to operate under insulating oil this should be checked for contamination, and then perhaps tested at high voltage for electrical strength.

Indoor switchgear seldom required to operate on load may be found in perfect condition and a quick visual inspection yearly may suffice. Other heavily used switchgear in a severe environment may require a more thorough and frequent examination and perhaps overhaul and replacement of parts. A schedule can be prepared covering all switchgear, and depending upon experience the intervals between checks can be laid down for each item. A possible scheme might be:

(i) Yearly – carry out visual inspection. Lubricate mechanism as necessary.

(ii) Every five years – take down and examine mechanism thoroughly. Check insulation and any insulating oil.

(iii) Every ten or 15 years – overhaul and replace any necessary parts, including oil.

Depending on the findings at each of the above checks any further or necessary action may be taken. In some cases more frequent examinations may be necessary. Advice from the manufacturer may include the number of (i) normal and (ii) short-circuit operations after which overhaul is recommended.

More sophisticated switchgear may require additional precautions. Air blast circuit breakers need to be isolated from the source of high pressure air as well as from the electricity supply before being worked upon. The air receivers are pressure vessels and there are statutory requirements to inspect, test and certify these periodically (see 14.5, para 26). It may be convenient to schedule the inspection and maintenance periods for such switchgear to coincide with those for the pressure vessels. It may be desirable to avoid hydraulic testing of these vessels and to use pneumatic tests, as the presence of water in the switchgear is undesirable.

Sulphur hexafluoride ($SF_6$) circuit breakers have come into increasing use in recent years. This gas is used to blast and extinguish the arc when the circuit breaker is operated. It also acts as a good electrical insulator. In one type of circuit breaker the movement of the operating mechanism also moves a piston which forces $SF_6$ gas through a nozzle to blast out the arc. In another (larger) type the $SF_6$ gas is stored in a high-pressure cylinder and on operating the circuit breaker, is blasted through a nozzle to extinguish the arc. This gas is then collected by a compressor and returned to the high-pressure cylinder.

Pure sulphur hexafluoride is a colourless, odourless, tasteless and apparently non-toxic gas, five times heavier than air. But (with such a chemical composition) it is not surprising that the products and impurities formed during arcing are toxic if inhaled in sufficient quantity, and solid fluoride powders may produce skin irritation. If a pungent, unpleasant odour arises and the nose, throat and eyes are affected, personnel should quickly get into fresh air. If it is necessary to remain to carry out work respirators or air breathing apparatus should be worn.

Inspection and maintenance should be carried out with such due precautions when working on and cleaning equipment containing or exposed to $SF_6$ breakdown products, particularly the filters used to absorb them. Protective clothing, rubber gloves, goggles, and respirators etc. should be worn. It should also be remembered that $SF_6$ gas will collect in spaces, enclosures and trenches at low level, and as it does not support life, unprotected personnel entering therein could be asphyxiated.

Besides the usual checks on the electrical parts of this switchgear, the movement may be operated pneumatically or hydraulically and this system will need inspecting, together with any pressure containers (the pressurized $SF_6$ storage cylinders may also need checking, although this is surprisingly not yet a statutory requirement). The $SF_6$ gas system should be checked. Large leaks may be audible, or they can be found by using a soap solution; small leaks can be found with leak detection equipment (see Chapter 11). The $SF_6$ gas should be sampled and tested periodically (see BS 5209 *Testing of sulphur hexafluoride taken from electrical equipment* which details methods of testing, and nature of impurities and their effect on assessing, for further service). Some $SF_6$ circuit breakers have gas heaters fitted to the high-pressure $SF_6$ gas system to prevent the gas liquefying; these heaters should be checked for correct operation. It is important to ensure that $SF_6$ breakdown products, etc. do not become heated.

A further development of $SF_6$ switchgear is the rotating-arc circuit breaker. The arc is drawn across the face of the field coil and then rotates rapidly under magnetic action within the confines of a tube. The vortex set up causes $SF_6$ gas to flow through the tube which helps to extinguish the arc, and removes arc-contamination products away from the contacts. As no separate gas jet or 'puffer' is necessary a suitably welded 'sealed for life' gas tank may be provided and the equipment is then relatively 'maintenance-free'. (Sealed circuit-breakers operating under vacuum have also been developed to be virtually 'maintenance-free'.)

Modern metal-clad substations using $SF_6$ switchgear and busbars, disconnectors and auxiliary equipment all housed in metal enclosures filled with pressurized $SF_6$ gas can be built into about one-eighth of the space which would be required for a normal air-insulated open substation. High power high voltage substations of this type can be constructed in valuable but small city-centre locations to supply high density loads. Consequently some 15 large generating stations which were needed in the London area to supply the capital's needs have now been largely replaced by compact $SF_6$ substations. These city-centre substations are fed from the national grid and interconnected by 400 kV underground cables cooled by polyethylene pipework supplied with water from an adjacent river and a canal.

Oil-immersed and cooled transformers are the most widely used type for normal distribution purposes but they carry a fire risk under fault conditions and normally require the installation of expensive fire-fighting equipment. In special cases air blast cooling has been used. Other transformer cooling media including immersion in silicones, complex esters and paraffinics which are less flammable than oil are used in certain locations, but under catastrophic fault conditions they may produce gases of an explosive nature. Polychlorinated biphenyl (PCB) was thought to be ideal for high fire risk areas, but is now regarded as a hazard and unacceptable for environmental and health reasons. $SF_6$ cooled units may be used, but are expensive. A recent development undertaken in conjunction with the Electricity Council is to use a new halocarbon fluid called Formel NF, which is totally non-flammable; transformers using it can be reduced in physical dimensions (compared with oil) and are hermetically sealed in a rigid tank tested to ensure it can operate over the pressure range 2 bar absolute down to a vacuum of 0·15 bar absolute. (For further details see Electricity Supply Standard ES1 35–14.) Such transformer units are regarded as 'maintenance-free'.

Some details regarding electric cables for use in hazardous environments and/or to maintain circuit integrity under fire conditions are given in 12.10.2 (see also BS 6141).

Armoured cables are included in BS 6346 *PVC insulated cables for electricity supply*, and in BS 5467 *Armoured cables with thermosetting insulation* (the insulation may be crosslinked polyethylene (XLPE) or hard ethylene-propylene rubber (HEPR)).

BS 6724 *Armoured cables for electricity supply having thermosetting insulation with low emission for smoke and corrosive gases when affected by fire* has been issued to provide cables suitable for operation at maximum sustained conductor temperatures at 90°C and to give lower levels of smoke and corrosive products under fire conditions than cables to BS 5467 and 6346. Type tests for smoke emission are described.

In general, cables may be armoured with aluminium wire or strip, galvanized steel wire or perhaps phosphor bronze.

In general during maintenance most electrical equipment will require periodic checks for insulation resistance (generally not less than 1 megohm when tested at 500Vd.c.), continuity of circuits and perhaps a high voltage flash test (generally at twice the rated voltage plus 1000V with a minimum of 2kV).

Operating tests on no load and full load may be checked. Some control circuit functioning tests may be carried out when the main power supply is isolated.

Clear instructions for the installation, operation and maintenance of electrical equipment should be supplied by the manufacturer, and indeed is required by legislation (e.g. see HSW Act 1974 and the Consumer Protection Act 1987).

### 12.10.2 Offshore platforms

Structures fixed offshore in connection with oil and gas operations in such places as the North Sea are required to withstand a particularly hostile environment in all weathers. They house much industrial plant and equipment, some of which will have to operate in hazardous areas, as defined by a recognized code (such as that of the Institute of Petroleum — see 6.10). In addition (under the *HSAW Act* 1974) personnel have to be provided with suitable accommodation, etc. and a safe place of work for both drilling, production and maintenance operations.

The legal requirements regarding offshore installations (oil rigs etc.) and their equipment in hazardous areas are in general governed by:

*The Petroleum (Production) Act* 1932
*The Pipelines Act* 1962
*The Continental Shelf Act* 1964
*The Mineral Workings (Offshore Installations) Act* 1971
*The Health and Safety at Work Act* 1974

The Offshore Installations (Construction and Survey) Regulations 1974 require all installations to have a Certificate of Fitness and to be regularly surveyed by appropriate certifying authorities. The HSW Act Sect.6 (3) 'requires the article to be safely installed.'

The government-appointed inspection authorities include:

Lloyds Register of Shipping
Bureau Veritas
Det. Norske Veritas
American Bureau of Shipping
Offshore Certification Bureau

In addition, Government Department of Energy (Petroleum Engineering Division) inspectors check and oversee the inspection/certifying surveyors, while their Pipelines Inspectorate enforces relevant parts of the *Pipelines Acts* in respect of pipeline operation and maintenance. In some cases the requirements of European surveyors may have to be met. Consequently it is safe and normal practice to specify equipment that has been tested and approved by a recognized authority and to inspect it not only during manufacture but during installation and use by an approved inspection authority. The existence of a properly organized QA scheme (such as that complying with BS 5750 Part 1) covering the whole field of offshore operators, contractors and suppliers is a prerequisite for any successful commercial undertaking.

During construction the materials, workmanship, techniques and procedures used (particularly welding), test methods (including NDT), etc. should be subject to inspection under the supervision of an authorized inspection body to ensure compliance with design and specification requirements.

As with pressure vessels, nuclear reactors, etc., owing to the serious consequences of failure due to brittle fracture, it is necessary to use steel of sufficient toughness, correctly treated to guard against the initiation of fast fracture during service, and to withstand fatigue (including corrosion fatigue) and occasional very high loadings due to storm or abnormal conditions. Generally speaking steels to BS 4360 having specified Charpy V-notch impact values may be selected for the designed minimum operating temperature. It may be necessary or desirable to carry out and record the results of a fracture mechanics test on weldments to demonstrate adequate toughness, and these data may be of great value in assessing the significance of fabrication defects or cracks found during in-service inspection. Crack opening displacement (COD) tests to BS 5762 may be carried out at a temperature not higher than the minimum design temperature (for the North Sea generally $+4°C$ for submerged parts and $-10°C$ for other parts) to assess such areas, and also to determine the maximum tolerable flaw size (using the procedure given in PD 6493).

Generally speaking the testing of welds and welding procedure approval, post-weld heat treatment and standards of acceptability of welds are similar to those specified in BS 5500 for unfired pressure vessels (see Chapter 3, Part 1). Specifically for steel offshore pipelines reference should be made to BS 4515 which was originally based on API Standard 1104 *Field welding of pipelines*; design, materials and methods of construction are covered by BS CP 2010 Parts 1 and 2 (see also 4.25).

BS 4515 *Process of welding of steel pipelines on land and offshore*, besides dealing with approval and testing of welding procedures and welders, production welding, and inspection and testing (including all types of NDT), gives alternative methods of acceptance criteria:

(i) Criteria based on quality control (as in most welding standards). In general no planar defect must exceed 25 mm (or such smaller value as may be specified) or a continuous accumulation of defects of 100 mm. Cracks are not permitted, whilst acceptance criteria for such defects as root penetration concavity and undercut, incomplete root penetration, lack of root fusion, porosity, inclusions and defects of profile are tabulated.

(ii) Criteria based on engineering critical assessment (ECA):

(a) full ECA e.g. as given in BS PD 6493; where data derived from using fracture mechanics (see BS 5447 for plane strain fracture toughness ($K_{lc}$), or BS 5762 for COD testing) is available this may be used to establish acceptable flaw sizes;

(b) a simplified ECA approach based on a paper by Carne and Harrison of the Welding Institute, Cambridge.

An appendix to BS 4515 gives recommendations for hyperbaric welding (i.e. welding under water at depths down to some 200 m or more carried out with a hydrogen-controlled arc-welding process and within a chamber from which the water has been displaced by air or an inert gas). All diving operations by welders and inspectors, etc. must comply with the Diving Operations at Work Regulations SI 1981 No. 399 and the requirements of the Chief Inspector of Safety, Department of Energy, including the Code of Practice for the Safe Use of Electricity under Water. The maximum open circuit voltage in the chamber for the welding circuit must not exceed 60 V d.c., the only live uninsulated surfaces being the welding electrode and the workpiece. The chamber must be continually vented to remove smoke and fumes. Heat-resisting masks fitted with ultra-violet/infra-red filters must be provided, together with all necessary surveillance cameras, NDT and monitoring equipment.

Records of design and construction, including drawings, calculations, quality control reports, inspection and test results, material specifications and sources, with details of any concessions granted, minor defects accepted (and their location), possible problems, etc. should be available on the platform to enable in-service inspections to be carried out with full knowledge of suspect areas, high stress regions where fatigue cracking could occur, etc.

To assist in-service inspection personnel in their endeavours to maintain the safety of the structure it may be desirable to instal complex monitoring equipment perhaps with sensors fitted permanently to such parts of the structure where it is considered that critical or dangerous strains or attitudes might develop due to extreme conditions of loading, temperature and the hostile environment.

Other inspection equipment, including selected NDT equipment, should of course be available, but much will depend on the intelligent use of man's five senses. Visual inspection will have to be extended by the use of diving equipment and possibly underwater television and cameras (see also Chapter 10 (NDT)). Inspection of the structure in the 'splash zone' (i.e. between some 10 metres below the lowest tide level and the highest tide level plus the crest level of the highest expected wave) is particularly important. Inspection should ensure the maintenance of the integrity of protective coatings and paint, etc. to prevent corrosion. The continued effectiveness of any cathodic protection system if fitted (see 4.29.3) will have to be checked. Any incipient surface cracks found during in-service inspection may be ground carefully away in an attempt to improve the fatigue life of a welded joint.

The inspection and testing of any concrete structures and components should comply with BS Code of Practice 110–117. Non-destructive methods of testing concrete are given in BS 4408.

Apart from the continual in-service inspection necessary to ensure safety and detect any damage or deterioration an inspection schedule should be drawn up covering regular inspections of all areas, above and below water. Annually a comprehensive inspection to record changes, deterioration, the state of repair work, safety arrangements, etc. should be undertaken. Reports from these inspections should enable a programme of repair and maintenance work to be undertaken. At intervals not exceeding 5 years a major survey should be carried out to determine particularly whether the structure can continue in further service.

Regarding electrical equipment, it seems, surprisingly, that in the UK there are no legal requirements as such to use and instal approved electrical equipment, etc. in a hazardous area. But the *HSW Act* 1974 Section 6(1), (2) and (3) requires *inter alia* that it must be safe under normal operating conditions, and tested to prove safety. Compliance with appropriate standards and codes of practice (BS and otherwise) and use of approved equipment is one way to satisfy the relevant inspectors, or a court of law in the event of an accident, that 'every reasonable step' has been taken to ensure safety.

British electrical equipment for use in hazardous areas is normally approved by BASEEFA (see 6.9.2) who issue the necessary certificates. BASEEFA can also arrange for such equipment to be certified to European (CENELEC) standards.

Equipment made outside the UK may carry certificates showing test and approval by foreign organizations but before using them on British installations the inspector will have to make sure that the foreign standards, codes of practice, etc., utilized comply with current UK standards. However the International Electrotechnical Commission (IEC) has over the years made steady progress in the standardization of electrical apparatus for use in explosive atmospheres.

Before installation offshore, approved equipment must be checked to ensure that it has not suffered mechanical damage due to abuse or transit, or to the hostile environment to which it may have been exposed offshore, and to see that it can be correlated with its certificates and paperwork to ensure it is correct to requirements. Instruments, particularly those of a delicate nature, should be carefully checked for damage, especially that due to any breakage of their transit packaging or occurring *after* removal of packaging and before or during installation. Records seem to show an inordinate number of faults (out of calibration, deranged, broken, etc.) found in instruments which were certified as perfectly good when tested at works.

It must be emphasized with all approved equipment that it cannot be assumed that it will necessarily be satisfactory and safe when installed. The 'conditions of use' often seen on certificates, the relevant codes of practice and maker's instructions should be studied carefully during installation and subsequent maintenance. Doing all 'that is reasonably practicable' in this manner will help to satisfy the legal requirements of health and safety.

Electrical equipment for installation offshore must be able to withstand salt water, oil, a wide temperature range, and perhaps abrasion and much other abuse. In the event of an emergency it must not contribute further to the danger to personnel (this applies particularly to electric cables). Some equipment must continue to function during an emergency—for example emergency lighting systems and control cables for essential circuits.

The basic design standard used for electric cables is perhaps BS 6883 *Specification for elastomer insulated cables for fixed wiring in ships*, to which may be added further specific requirements including those of IEC 92–3 and Ministry of Defence DG ships range. The cable insulation may be polyvinyl chloride (perhaps to BS 6346) or perhaps silicone or ethylene propylene rubber (EPR) sheathed with a heat-resistant, oil-resistant and flame-retardant (HOFR) compound. Protective armouring with a galvanized steel or phosphor bronze wire braid with perhaps overall lead sheathing to prevent contamination, may be specified.

However, most if not all cables will burn in a fire if the temperature and oxygen conditions are suitable, and in doing so they can produce harmful choking and killing fumes and dense smoke as in the Falklands campaign. The fact that to some extent they are flame-retardant when tested to a particular specification perhaps disguises what can actually happen in a really fierce fire. PVC and CSP, for instance, give off hydrochloric acid (HCl) gas, whilst these and other materials give off carbon monoxide and carbon dioxide. HCl gas also has a harmful effect on delicate electronic equipment. It is a difficult problem to find cable materials which retain their desired electrical properties under severe fire and other environmental conditions, and a compromise is usually necessary. The inspector should check such details as the materials oxygen index (see BS 2782 Part 1 Method 141A–D), temperature index, flame propagation and smoke and gas emissions, using available specifications and information (e.g. those in Tables 6.2 and 6.3). See particularly BS 6387 *Performance requirements for cables required to maintain circuit integrity under fire conditions*; BS 4066 *Tests on electric cables under fire conditions*; and BS 6425 *Test methods for gases evolved during combustion of electric cables*.

Cable fires in many restricted industrial locations (e.g. underground, including tube railways) are a great hazard. Mica glass-taped and mineral-insulated and sheathed cables (BS 6207) can be used in some instances, where circuit integrity must be maintained under fire conditions, and can be tested to BS 6387 to simulate actual fire conditions. However mineral-insulated metal-sheathed (copper) cables may be subject to corrosion and fatigue, although normally maintaining integrity for longer periods than PVC etc. Asbestos-braided wires and cables have been much specified in the past, but they now have their own problems.

*Recommendations for the electrical/electronic equipment of mobile and fixed offshore installations* (includes tests on completed installations), IEE/Peter Peregrinus Ltd, 1983.

### 12.10.3 In-service inspection of nuclear plant

The owners and operators of nuclear installations and power plants in the UK, USA and elsewhere are required by law to carry out periodic (and may-be continuous) in-service inspection of nuclear plant and components in the interests of health and safety.

In the UK the main regulatory authority is the Nuclear Installations Inspectorate (NII) of the HSE.

Perhaps a major difference between the in-service inspection of nuclear plant (including any resulting repairs necessary) and other industrial plant, is the almost military procedure and discipline considered necessary.

First, the rules must be obeyed in detail. In the UK these rules are largely contained in the site licence granted by the authorities (basically the NII of the Health and Safety Executive with DoE and MAFF for radiation and waste disposal matters) under the provisions of the *Nuclear Installations Act*, and they are enforced basically by the Nuclear Installations Inspectorate; any deviation from the rules may result in severe disciplinary action (perhaps involving up to two years' imprisonment and/or a heavy fine).*

Included in the site licence is an agreed maintenance schedule detailing the action necessary to inspect, ensure and prove that all items of the plant are and remain in a safe condition at all times. Also, in addition to the statutory requirements of the *Factories Act* (as amplified by the *HSW Act*) which lay down the maximum period between inspection and overhaul of certain items of plant, there is in the licence an agreed maximum period of time that the plant (and/or other specified items of plant) can be allowed to run before it is shut down for a programme of inspection, testing and overhaul. Following this, the plant (or particular items) must be sentenced as to whether or not it can continue in service, and if so, for how long.

---

*The enactment of the Ionizing Radiation Regulations 1985 (see Tables 6.10 and 6.11), which harmonized radiological protection standards throughout the EEC and adopted SI units of radiation, prompted the CEGB to produce revised Radiological Safety Rules incorporating these regulations, and applicable to all their establishments from July 1986. This meant they had to carry out a 'crash' training programme for all affected staff.

Second, with nuclear plant, any repairs or modifications must be carried out strictly in accordance with a previously authorized and agreed code. Consequently no sudden *ad hoc* ideas, modifications, changes in operational methods, etc.—maybe at the whim or inspiration of somebody—are permissible. To ensure compliance with these criteria all work of any kind must be checked and tested and approved so that any which may have been inadequately conceived or executed cannot lead to an increase in risk such as that of a radiological hazard.

Third, many items involving high technology may be incorporated into the control and safety systems and will need specialized knowledge for checking and maintenance (unnecessary interference may for instance cause trouble). Some of these items will be contaminated or within radiation areas, and will need highly disciplined procedures for their maintenance (see BS 4247). Normal operational checks can be carried out, and will be familiar to the operator; abnormal operational and emergency procedures must be approved and their consequences must be understood by the operator (and the inspector).

An emergency supply or supplies of electricity for essential services, possibly from a generator which comes into operation automatically when needed, is a normal requirement in most power stations and is essential with nuclear stations. In particular, emergency and foolproof systems to maintain other essential supplies such as cooling water, etc. are necessary with nuclear power.

Specially designed simulators may be used in the training of operators to help them to understand and carry out normal and abnormal operations, response to station alarms and actions during fault conditions, etc. Multi-faults may be simulated so that their relative priorities may be assessed. One of the conditions of the site licence is that arrangements must be made for dealing with any accident or emergency, including the release of any significant amount of radioactive material. An annual emergency exercise has to be carried out and witnessed by the Nuclear Installations Inspectorate.

One of the most troublesome possibilities of failure is the loss or reduction of coolant (particularly in a PWR), or loss of feed water supply to the steam generator. Many safety devices and rigid operational procedures to prevent human error are necessary to reduce the possibility of such a failure.

In the USA (and maybe elsewhere) the regulatory authority bases its inspection requirements largely on the ASME Code Section XI Rules for In-service Inspection of Nuclear Power Plant Components which lays down details and frequency of inspection for specific components of particular types of reactor, criteria for fault evaluation, repairs, etc. This code is augmented by the issue of Inspection and Enforcement Bulletins, Regulatory Guides, reports and documents by the US Nuclear Regulatory

Commission and other bodies, which often go beyond ASME requirements (the ASME Code may be amended later if necessary to cover some such matters).

As a result of experience at the Three Mile Island accident (March 1979) and particularly of in-service inspection at Nine Mile Point Power Plant and elsewhere some amendments became necessary. Cracks had been found in service in large diameter stainless steel pipes and some difficulty had arisen in sizing the depth of such cracks using ultrasonic testing; *different inspection teams had given different results.*

A 'crash' programme was arranged whereby some 18 inspection teams using various techniques sought to locate and size flaws artificially put into a number of pipes. The flaws were afterwards measured by destructive means. Only about one-third of the teams showed adequate performance in locating and sizing the depth of crack to within some 70% of its correct size. A training programme for inspectors was put in hand and every team had (and now has) to demonstrate the effectiveness of its ultrasonic testing technique in accurately detecting and sizing faults such as intergranular stress corrosion cracks before being allowed to operate in the field. As a result it can be said that a properly trained inspection team can detect and size cracks adequately and that perhaps the crack-tip opening displacement technique is the most useful.

So in the 1983 issue of the ASME Code the flaw evaluation procedure for intergranular stress corrosion cracking in stainless steel piping was revised. In Europe somewhat similar investigations under the auspices of the OECD's Nuclear Energy Agency using 28 inspection teams had shown that using the procedure based on the 1974 ASME Code satisfactory detection using ultrasonics was only achieved for defects over 50 mm in size. The NII confirmed that it was possible to obtain unacceptably poor results. Later defect detection trials organized by UKAEA (circ. 1985) however have demonstrated a high intrinsic capability of ultrasonic techniques to obtain good results.

Understandably a nuclear reactor pressure vessel (RPV) must be produced and maintained to the highest standards of quality laid down by the appropriate specification (usually BS 5500 or the ASME Pressure Vessel Code) plus any extra requirements imposed by the designer or relevant regulatory authorities.

In-service inspection *must* detect (usually by ultrasonic testing) the onset of any cracks (above a critical size), or crack extension due for instance to fatigue, high stresses (due perhaps to over pressure), thermal shock and/or differential expansion. Such cracks may lead to early failure of the vessel.

'Cold overpressurization' and 'pressurized thermal shock' (due usually to mal-operation) are particularly severe classes of fault; measures to reduce the failure risk from these may be taken in an emergency (perhaps by increasing cooling water temperature), or they may be incorporated in the design (perhaps to be triggered automatically). There is evidence that up to 2 mm of stable crack growth may be safely permitted.

Many RPVs have an inner stainless steel lining or cladding (see 5.7) which is welded on by a special process (perhaps by automatic submerged-arc welding). Cracks may occur here, and must be eliminated. They may be due to hydrogen present in the cladding being driven into the underlying steel; their formation may be prevented by suitable heat treatment. Failure of a vessel may be due to 'plastic collapse' of ductile uncracked material. The mechanism of rapid crack propagation interacts with plastic collapse and a method of predicting failure when both are involved has been developed by CEGB. (The R6 method—see CEGB/S/558 (Harrison, R.R. et al. 1980).)

The integrity of tubes in a reactor or RPV may be affected in service by corrosion. Measures may be taken to prevent or inhibit this corrosion. Inservice inspection and maintenance may be carried out by specially designed robotic equipment.

In-service inspections and NDT examinations of all UK nuclear plants were instituted from the inception of operations and have continued routinely, being carried out by the holder of the nuclear site licence (the licensee) under the supervision of NII.

Something has been said elsewhere regarding the careful and painstaking in-service radiographic and other NDT examinations carried out on the early UK and CEGB nuclear plants with generally satisfactory results. But today, even if a minor crack is found (which is the object of the exercise in order that it may be repaired) it often becomes front page news.

The early Magnox reactors were expected (at the design stage) to have a useful, safe life of 20 to 25 years. But following successful operation and the accumulation of further information on oxidation, creep, radiation effects on materials, etc. the licensees indicated their wish to continue to operate beyond 20 years.

Consequently the licensees accepted the requirement to carry out a comprehensive long-term safety review (LTSR) based on day-to-day monitoring and thorough biennial inspections (including NDT testing using many advanced techniques), all subject to assessment by NII.

The first CEGB Magnox station to be subject to a LTSR was Bradwell, which commenced operating in 1962. The CEGB, starting in 1982, began submitting review papers of their inspections and findings to NII and continued until 1987. Some 45 detailed review papers covering some 13 main areas required assessment by NII. Amongst the subjects covered were reactor pressure circuit integrity and safety, effect of oxidation and corrosion on the integrity of the steel restraining system for the graphite core, boiler tube integrity, boron ball shut-down sytem, NDT examination of those parts of the refuelling machine pressure vessel components where access is reasonably practicable, monitoring of plant for ageing effects, etc.

The CEGB's safety case was vitally concerned with demonstrating that no significant defects could exist in pressure circuit welds. NII had to confirm that the plant was still operating to at least its original design criteria, and to compare it with modern standards, where necessary introducing reasonably practicable improvements.

Referring to HSE's publication, *Bradwell Nuclear Power Station. The findings of NII's assessment of the CEGB's long term review*, (HMSO, 1987), this states that the substantial completion of NII's detailed examination has not disclosed any reason for thinking that the plant is unsafe to operate or diverges substantially from its original design intent, and that CEGB has made a good case for extended operation to April 1992. However certain key requirements are listed which, where practicable, should be completed by specified dates. Extended operations would be subject to agreement on these matters (including consideration of a seismic analysis—see 3.30) and the usual monitoring and periodic inspections (perhaps increased in scope and frequency).

As a result of the Three Mile Island scare and the Chernobyl disaster (augmented by the American shuttle inquiry) very considerable thought and research must now be directed towards the in-service inspection of nuclear plants in order to foresee trouble before it really develops.

Operational techniques must be carried out methodically in an attempt to avoid human error.

The various inspection and operational teams, etc. must be able to demonstrate their effectiveness not only to the higher regulatory authorities, but must be seen to do so by the general public.

Accidents still occur in normal chemical plants, sometimes with disastrous results. Research to prevent these and nuclear accidents of even greater potential danger must be undertaken if nuclear power is to be accepted by the public so that it can contribute to man's power supply after fossil fuels have been exhausted.

But obviously, existing plants must be continually subject to searching and stringent inspections (audits) to assess and obtain assurance of their continuing quality and operational safety.

## 12.10.4 Nuclear safety audit

It will be noticed that BS 5882 *A Total QA Programme for Nuclear Installations* requires, under Clause 18, that a system of internal and external audits (spot checks) must be carried out by an independent auditing organization to verify compliance with all conditions and aspects of the programme (see 9.4.6 and 13.10).

In the UK the premier independent organization for carrying out an audit on a nuclear installation is HM Nuclear Installations Inspectorate. (Although generally termed a safety audit it of necessity also involves inspection of plant.) Other organizations may carry out perhaps limited audits or reviews from time to time.

The documented results of an audit must be reviewed by the top management of the company being inspected (particularly with a NII audit) and they *must* take any necessary corrective action to an agreed time scale. Such an audit of BNFL, Sellafield's existing spent Magnox fuel reprocessing plant (which occupies a large part of the site) was commenced by NII in February 1986 following a flurry of minor incidents and much adverse publicity and public concern regarding the safety of the installation. Their report was published in December 1986 (HSE HMNII *Safety Audit of BNFL Sellafield*, 1986, 2 vols, HMSO) and the action required had to be completed within a year.

The Sellafield audit and the inspections involved probably constituted one of the most thorough-going and critical in-service examinations ever carried out on any major plant in the UK and the detailed report is worthy of study. A few comments may perhaps be attempted here.

First, the legal requirements. As with any UK nuclear installation the plant operator has to comply with the conditions attached to the Site Licence granted to BNFL in 1971 when it took it over from UKAEA (which did not—and does not—need a licence). There are at present some 70 conditions attached to the Sellafield site licence (including operational safety assessments of the various plants).

Legally, three main Acts control a UK nuclear installation:

(a) The *Health and Safety at Work Act* 1974 and its many relevant Regulations, including particularly the Ionizing Radiation Regulations 1985 (see Chapter 6).

(b) The *Nuclear Installations Act* 1965, including particularly the Nuclear Installations (Dangerous Occurrences) Regulations 1965 and additional requirements imposed by DoE in 1977 and 1982 for reporting specified matters and dangerous occurrences, including:

(i) Exposures to radiation or contamination exceeding twice the maximum annual permissible limits.

(ii) Any examination, inspection, maintenance or test that may reveal a significantly unsafe operation or condition of the plant.

(iii) Any abnormal occurrence leading to a release or spread of radioactivity inside or outside the plant.

The site licence required the setting up by BNFL of a nuclear safety committee, and this has been established as the North West Area Safety Committee (NWASC). It includes senior members of BNFL and Sellafield staff and safety, medical and UKAEA members. Some 20 sub-committees have been formed to 'consider and advise' (*Note:* The committee has no 'input' from outside the nuclear industry.)

Under the Safety Representative and Safety Committees Regulations

1977 of the *HSW Act* 1974 (see 14.2) a Joint Health and Safety Committee (JHSC) has been set up under the chairmanship of a works general manager. This committee provides a forum for consultation between management and trade union appointed safety representatives; it has established various sub-committees. (*Note:* There are no trade union representatives on the NWASC, which is essentially a committee of engineers and scientists.)

Under the requirements of BS 5750 and BS 5882 a comprehensive QA organization is in being, charged with assuring both plant and product quality and performance (see 9.4.6). It has to review continually its own activities and is itself subject to independent audit.

As a QA organization must by definition be independent of production matters and control, being primarily interested in quality and safety, whilst the NWAS and JHS Committees are primarily advisory, it has been suggested that the QA organization, whilst giving its own QA decisions, could well review independently relevant matters for the committees so that the best advice could be available to management for executive action.

One is cognizant of the large number of people, rules, regulations, etc. involved in advising, controlling and even warning those responsible for taking executive action in, particularly, a nuclear installation. In addition management may be under stress and diverted by close public scrutiny, incidents, uncertainties (even lack of morale), and difficulties (including lack of decision regarding disposal of the waste accumulating on the site). Some may say there is too much red tape. Regulations and red tape are essential to ensure the safety of the workers and the public, and the success of the project, but it must be realized that an excess unsympathetically applied, may tend to strangle any enterprise. The criticism is made that management does not lead, but tends to shelter behind committees and paperwork. Clear management decisions are needed and a dedication to safety (and good housekeeping) that is characteristic of the best parts of the chemical industry has yet to be achieved. Perhaps in an attempt to deal with radiation leaks and hazards it seems that conventional hazards and faults may have been neglected.

In their inspection of the plant and equipment, some of which was ageing and corroding, NII found that some 17% of the items were those commonly found in any industrial plant, such as poor labelling and identification, neglected pipe-bridges, inadequate protection (from a variety of hazards), unsatisfactory location, trouble due to pump failures and ventilation defects, leaks (sometimes unsuspected) and deterioration to an extent that the designer's intentions were not maintained; insufficient staff and equipment were available for the adequate monitoring of hazards.

Criticism was made of maintenance arrangements, particularly that they were often limited to immediate needs and that production was sometimes resumed after the annual shut-down for maintenance before all the planned work had been completed. (This is not unknown elsewhere in industry.) It must be pointed out that the Magnox power stations (which the plant exists to service) are approaching the end of their planned life. However NII rightly emphasized that even should nuclear power to be phased out tomorrow the plant would still be required to operate for some further ten years. One source of trouble and potential defects is the current lack of national agreement on the means for future disposal of radioactive waste (nobody wants it whatever elaborate schemes for its relatively safe disposal are dreamed up). Consequently Sellafield has (temporarily?) to store on site some 90% of the radioactive waste ever produced in the UK, and it requires constant monitoring and attention (it is somewhat akin to having to store sewage, human bodies, hospital refuse and germs, dangerous drugs, etc. instead of disposing of them as soon as possible).

Although realizing that the plant poses a potential risk to employees and the public, and that one recent incident could have posed a danger to workers but did not because the designed protective systems came into operation, NII criticized other protective systems as being unsatisfactory.

BNFL are required to report certain dangerous occurrences. The most serious are those which are likely to cause death or injury as a result of radiation, criticality or fire. Such occurrences may be known as Category A incidents; however none have taken place at Sellafield during the period 1979–86.

BNFL have established a system of radiological incident reports (RIR) ranging from Categories A (serious) to D (for minor incidents)—Categories B and C are reportable to HSE whilst Category D are not necessarily reportable off-site. During the period 1979–86 some 672 incidents were recorded for the whole of the Sellafield site, of which some 87 (13%) were for the reprocessing plant proper, plus some 30% for associated plants. Of the reportable incidents 30% were Class C incidents (i.e. minor ground leak or a radiation dose somewhat greater than the annual or quarterly permissible limit; or a fire or explosion which *may* affect the safe condition of the installation) and reportable only to HSE under the conditions of the site licence; and 3% were Class B incidents (i.e. a major leak or escape of radioactive material, or a radiation dose uptake of greater than twice the maximum annual permissible limit) and reportable both to HSE and the Secretary of State.

Five incidents, which occurred in 1986 before or around the time the audit was instituted and received much publicity, were investigated again in detail. All five incidents fell into the lower two categories of severity (i.e. categories C and D). There was no effect on the public, although some workers received radiation doses at or near the annual limit. One incident involved a fire in a waste disposal trench. No one was contaminated. In each case the worst possible eventuality that could occur was imagined to assess its potential effect on members of the public. In only two cases could it be remotely imagined that the public could have been endangered.

The report concludes with a number of immediate requirements, which BNFL have now carried out. Further requirements to be implemented include decontamination, decommissioning or refurbishment of old plants, more systematic monitoring, completion of quality assurance arrangements and procedures (including those for plant operation) and improved arrangements for training. It contains material, as may be relevant, applicable to many industries involved in the attainment and maintenance of quality and safety. It covers most normal industrial hazards—it does not cover those which might occur due to major 'acts of God,' terrorist activities or warfare. Within the alloted time 'period NII announced that BNFL had satisfactorily implemented all outstanding requirements.

## References and further reading

*General*

I. Mech. E., *Condition monitoring of machinery and plant*, Mech. Eng. Pub., 1985.
I. Mech. E., *Pressurised water reactor in the UK* (Design, safety, licensing and construction in the light of the Three Mile Island accident) Mech. Eng. Pub., 1982.
I. Mech. E., *Fatigue and Crack Growth of Offshore Structures* (provides guidance in inspection requirements), Mech. Eng. Pub., 1986.
I. Mech. E., *Tribology Offshore* (includes reliability and machine monitoring) Mech. Eng. Pub., 1985.
I. Mech. E., *Heat and fluid flow in Nuclear and Process Plant Safety,* Mech. Eng. Pub., 1983.
I. Mech. E., *Decommissioning of Radioactive Facilities*, Seminar, Mech. Eng. Pub., 1984.
I. Mech. E., *Mechanical Reliability in the Process Industries*, Mech. Eng. Pub., 1984.
I. Mech. E., *Mechanical Reliability—A Systems Approach,* Mech. Eng. Pub., 1987.
Royal Society of London, *Fracture mechanics in design and service: living with defects* (conference papers on industrial operating experience are particularly relevant), Phil. Trans. A. 299, 1981.
I. Chem. Eng., *Preparation of plant for maintenance*, 1983.

*Condition Monitoring '84*, (ed: Jones, M.H.), Proceedings of International Conference, Swansea: Pineridge, 1984.
*Condition Monitoring in Hostile Environments*, Seminar Proceedings, (ERA Report No. 85–0118), ERA Technology Ltd, Leatherhead, 1985.
*Condition-based maintenance*, (seminar co-sponsored with I. Chem. E and Inst. of Metals), I. Mech. E., 1987.

Fordham-Cooper, W. *Electrical Safety Engineering*, Butterworth, 1986.

Grothus, H., *Total preventative maintenance of plant equipment*, Executive Enterprises Pub., N.Y., 1976.

Jardine, A.K.S. (ed.), *Operational Research in Maintenance*, Manchester Univ. Press, 1970.

Mann, L. (ed.), Maintenance management, Lexington, Mass., 1984.

*Quality assurance for the offshore industry*, Oyez Sc. and Tech. Services, 1983.

White, E. N., *Maintenance planning, control and documentation*, Gower, 1979.

Willows, R.A., *The evaluation of an integrated condition monitoring maintenance scheme*, (technical steel research Report EVR 9285, EEC); obtainable HMSO, 1985.

*Welding*

Welding Institute, *Welding in offshore constructions*, 2 vols conference papers, Cambridge, 1974.

Welding Institute, *Underwater welding for offshore installations*, seminar conference papers, Cambridge, 1976.

Welding Institute, *Detection and measurement of cracks* (papers from a discussion meeting), 1976.

Welding Institute, *Fatigue of welded structures* (a reference work of papers from an international conference), 2 vols, 1971.

Welding Institute, *Procedures and recommendations for the ultrasonic testing of butt welds (covering calibration, defect location, recognition and sizing)*, 1971.

BS 6235 *Code of Practice for fixed offshore structures* (becoming obsolete).

*Corrosion*

*Corrosion Prevention Directory*, HMSO, 1978.

*Control of corrosion on offshore steel pipelines*, RP-06-75, NACE Tech. Practices Committee, Houston, Texas.

*Control of corrosion on steel fixed offshore platforms*, RP-01-76, NACE Tech. Practices Committee, Houston, Texas.

Evans, U.R. *Corrosion and Oxidation of Metals: Scientific Principles and Practical Applications*, Edward Arnold 1960, (Also supplementary volumes starting with No. 1, 1968).

Evans, U.R. *Introduction to Metallic Corrosion*, 2nd edn., Edward Arnold, 1963.

Donovan, P.D., *Protection of metal from corrosion in storage and transit*, Ellis Horwood, Chichester, 1986.

Fontana, M.G., *Corrosion engineering*, McGraw-Hill, NY and London, 1986.

Hancock, P. *Corrosion of Alloys at High Temperatures in Atmospheres Consisting of Fuel Combustion Products and Associated Impurities*, 1968, Institution of Chemical Engineers: Corrosion Survey Report (1973).

Inter-Service Publications (H.M. Stationery Office):

La Que F. L. and Copson H. R. (eds), *Corrosion Resistance of Metals and Alloys*, Reinhold, 1963.

Rance, V. E. and Cole, H. G. *Corrosion of Metals by Vapours from Organic Materials*, 1958

Rance, V. E. and Cole, H. G. *Corrosion and its Prevention at Bimetallic Contacts*, 3rd edn., 1963.

Shreir, L. L., *Corrosion*, Newnes Butterworth, 2 vols. 1976.

Stewart, D. and Tulloch, D.S., *Principles of Corrosion and Protection*, Macmillan, 1968.

Uhlig, H. H. *Corrosion and Corrosion Control*, Wiley, 1971.

# 13 Towards total quality assurance

## 13.1 Statistics and QA

Study and analysis of the past history of various types of plant and equipment, their performance during ageing, reliability, areas of trouble and possible trouble, failures in service, accident reports and statistics of all kinds can lead to the gathering of data which *inter alia* could help in improving the quality and safety of future material and in predicting the behaviour of existing material. Mistakes made in the past if properly recorded and analysed should not occur again.

## 13.2 Reliability

Breakdowns can sometimes be predicted by reference to past records, and perhaps anticipated and avoided by the adoption of suitable statistical and inspection techniques, possibly involving the use of components of known reliability.

*Reliability* can be defined as 'the probability that a system, or particular item, will perform its intended function without failure for a specified time under specified conditions of use.'

If there is a 'wear-out' life for an equipment, then replacement or overhaul before this (after say a predetermined number of operating hours) could prevent a breakdown, and this could form the basis of a planned maintenance policy. This failure pattern is known as the 'normal distribution'. However, it is becoming increasingly apparent that some systems and components, including those employing complex mechanical and hydraulic systems and electronic and electromechanical components, do not always exhibit a 'wear-out' period, and failures may occur at random, irrespective of the age of the components. The evidence is strong that such a failure pattern, the 'exponential distribution', is characterized by a *constant* mean time between failures (MTBF), which can be determined statistically. The inverse of MTBF is the failure rate.

But teething troubles may occur during introduction into service, and modifications to improve design or eliminate errors may be required before an equipment's failure rate falls to this steady value. Again, towards the end of its life there may also be instances where wear-out commences and the MTBF falls (and failure rate rises). This wear-out may be detectable by inspection, or it may occur on some equipment without warning.

Once a well-designed and reliable equipment has been 'run in' it should operate satisfactorily until the onset of wear-out, and need the minimum of attention—in fact, misdirected attention may cause failure by initiating another period of teething troubles (see Fig.13.1).

When the MTBF of an equipment exceeds the operating time or the working life, the probability of its failing during that period is small. The determination of MTBF's is a complex process, perhaps not fully applicable to large items of mechanical plant of individual design. Much effort, however, has recently been put into this matter and associated reliability studies and testing, particularly in the USA, and promising results have been attained, especially for equipment and components produced in quantity. Certain components, designed and tested for reliability, may be available commercially (particularly electronic components). The use of reliable components (e.g. components of assessed quality in the BS 9000 series: markedly reduces maintenance costs and increases plant availability and safety, but improvements in reliability cost money. Inspection for reliability is thus becoming of paramount importance and can be applied to systems as well as to components.

### 13.2.1 Specifying reliability

To obtain a qualitative or, more difficult, a quantitative assessment of the reliability of a plant or of its individual components it is first necessary to know something of its intended function and the conditions under which it is expected to work. These include:

(a) Environmental conditions—heat, cold, humidity, shock, vibration, chemical attack, etc.

(b) Stress conditions—loading—static or dynamic, likelihood of excessive loading or misuse.

(c) Life—in service and also in storage, and whether continuous or intermittent.

(d) Maintenance—will time and facilities be available for maintenance during service?

Such details should be specified initially in a contract which requires the setting up of any form of reliability programming. Guidance is now given in BS 5760 *Reliability of systems, equipments and components.*

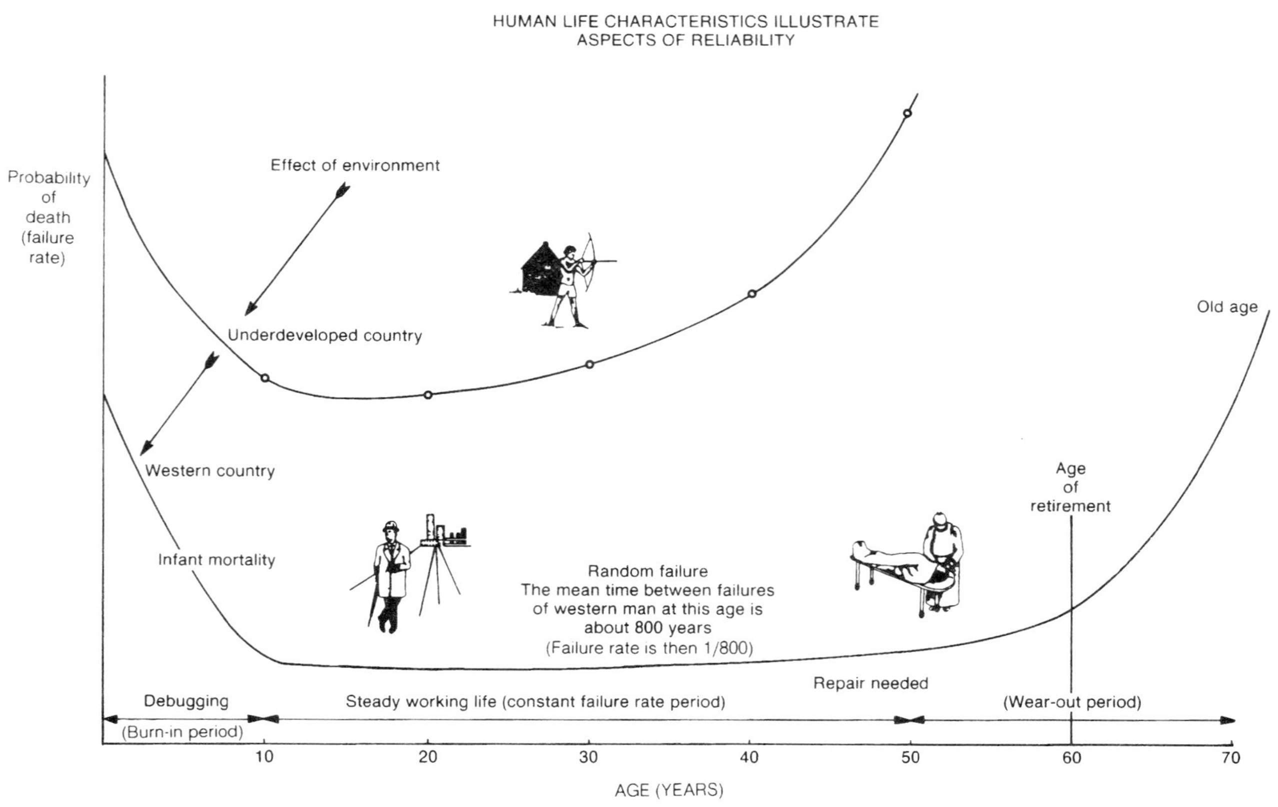

HUMAN LIFE CHARACTERISTICS ILLUSTRATE
ASPECTS OF RELIABILITY

Fig. 13.1    'Bath-tub' curve illustrating reliability by reference to man.

Part 1 Guide to reliability programme management.
Part 2 Guide to the assessment of reliability.
Part 3 Guide to reliability practices: examples.
Part 4 Guide to specification clauses relating to achievement and development of reliability in new and existing items.
Part 5 Failure mode.
Part 6 Effect and criticality analysis.
Part 7 Reliability of repairable systems.

The assessment of reliability in quantitative form involves *inter alia* a forecasting activity based on the collection and analysis of a mass of statistics including any available data on components, their failure modes and rates, design considerations, likely human errors, repair times, etc. A knowledge of the mechanism of failure is desirable. The sources of such data can be from operations in service of the same or similar components, from research, development or production testing, or even an estimate of the probability of failure (when for instance the components are of a new, untried design). The principle of *redundancy* is often used to increase a system's reliability, the system being provided with more items of one kind than are strictly necessary for its satisfactory functioning. One simple example of this is a four-engined aircraft, which can manage on three and get by on two—or maybe on one for a time. It is obviously more reliable than a single or twin-engined aircraft. Similarly a plant which has to run continuously is often provided with a standby emergency power supply which comes into operation automatically on failure of the normal power supply: but even here the automatic switching arrangements could fail!

From all the available data it is often possible to calculate or predict reliability (and hence failure rate and MTBF etc). Even with items or projects of new design an estimate can be made.

The confidence to be given to such figures depends greatly on the correct interpretation of the data.

To attain and maintain reliability may require periodic servicing involving performance checks and other tests to locate parts, etc. which require adjustment, repair or replacement before wear-out. Besides the British Standards quoted, many books and articles give information on the somewhat complex subject of reliability and its prediction. Reference to such as those listed below and to the 'bath-tub' curve (Fig. 13.1) should help.

However, a component or equipment is not likely to be reliable unless there has been good quality control during its manufacture. A poor specification, or a bad design or application may also cause unreliability, which no amount of quality control will correct. Similarly, complex mathematics will not produce reliability. As one rather eminent scientist and mathematician put it – 'making it right first time is worth a great deal of mathematics'.

However, an analysis of the data collected (modes and rates of failure

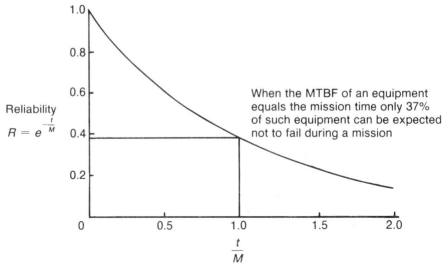

Reliability
$R = e^{-\frac{t}{M}}$

When the MTBF of an equipment equals the mission time only 37% of such equipment can be expected not to fail during a mission

Reliability is measured as the probability of a device to operate without failure for a specified period of time. When failures are random reliability is given by:

$$R = e^{-\frac{t}{M}}$$

Where $t$ is the operating or mission time
$\quad\quad M$ is the mean time between failures (MTBF)
$\quad\quad e$ is 2.718

The inverse of MTBF is the failure rate

**Fig. 13.2  Quantitative concept of reliability**

etc.) can lead to improvements in design, which give rise to improvements in reliability, maintainability and availability and, as relevant, to quality, health and safety, and loss prevention.

### 13.2.2 Methods of equipment reliability testing

Eng. Equip. Material Users Assoc. (EEMUA) Guide to reliability specifications. Issued by BSI as Draft for Development 57 (DD 57) (but not a British Standard), it contains provisional recommendations for *Equipment Reliability Testing* and is applicable to *all* types of equipment. The essential purposes of such tests are as follows:

(a) *Reliability determination test* to find the numerical value of a reliability characteristic (such as failure rate, MTBF, mean time to first failure (MTFF) of the equipment(s) being tested. (Note: as mentioned above the analysis of existing data (particularly from equipment in actual use) may also be used to determine reliability, and this may help to check the experimentally determined test value.)

(b) *Reliability growth test*, in which the equipment is run under specified conditions to expose and identify faults and weaknesses and *make arrangements for their elimination.*

(c) *Reliability compliance test* to show whether or not the value of the reliability characteristic obtained on test complies with the specified requirements. Note first, that close agreement between laboratory reliability test results, calculated reliability characteristics and those obtained from equipments in actual use is not to be expected, and second, that before commencing the formal test programme the equipment should be pre-conditioned, e.g. 'burn-in' should be completed in order to achieve the constant failure rate upon which statistical test plans are based.

### 13.3 Failure of engineering plant

In an engineering, and especially in a chemical, plant the failure of one unit, or even a small component, may result in complete shut-down or at least a serious loss of production, particularly if the plant is in continuous operation. The money value of this lost production may be far in excess of the cost of repair. Futhermore, a plant failure may lead to dangerous conditions to operators or others in the area, such as an explosion or the es-cape of noxious substances, with the possibility of expensive legal proceed-ings and/ or compensation. It may also result in damage to other, perhaps more costly, equipment.

#### 13.3.1 Primary causes of failure

Many analyses of failures have been made. Some simple but typical examples will be given. Table 13.1 shows in order of magnitude the causes of failures of a mechanical nature (taken from a paper by G.A. Cottell, 'Inspection and Testing of Metals', Institution of Metallurgists, 1954). It is worthy of study and comment.

The inspector at a manufacturer's works as such can do little to prevent a user operating plant under *abnormal conditions* for which it has not been designed although this may be noticed during any 'in-use' inspection. He will, however, endeavour to eliminate *defective workmanship* during manu-facture and repair; but good workmanship can never save *bad design*. He will also contribute to the reduction of failures by ensuring proper control of processes such as *welding*, and by careful attention to the problems of *corrosion* and *corrosion fatigue*.

Proper mechanical testing helps to eliminate material faults, but it is unlikely that the selected test pieces will show all the defects which may develop, as many will be due to cracks, inclusions, blow-holes, cavities, segregations and surface imperfections not present in the test samples. It is here that adequate inspection and non-destructive testing at the appropriate stage can help.

**TABLE 13.1**

*Causes of failure of engineering plant*

| Primary cause | Incidence (%) |
|---|---|
| Abnormal service conditions | 33 |
| Corrosion-fatigue | 20 |
| Defective workmanship | 14 |
| Corrosion | 7 |
| Unsatisfactory design | 5 |
| Misuse of welding | 4 |
| Faulty material | 5 |
| Unsuitable material | 2 |
| Miscellaneous | 10 |
| Total | 100 |

Referring to Table 13.1, it will be seen that if abnormal service conditions could be eliminated then corrosion-related problems would then cause some 27/67 or 40% of the failures, and defective workmanship and material problems some 30% of the failures.

Other, later analyses, from other sources, seem to give somewhat similar figures. In general, corrosion in metallic chemical process plants including piping may be said to cause over 50% of recorded failures; fatigue some 15% and defective workmanship and material some 7%.

**TABLE 13.2**

*Causes of failure in a refinery*

| Non-scheduled shutdowns (%) | | Significant non-shutdown equipment failures, etc. (%) | |
|---|---|---|---|
| Pipeline leaks and fires | 28 | Compressors | 30 |
| Pipeline leaks | 28 | Furnaces | 18 |
| Process | 12 | Exchangers | 17 |
| Utilities | 20 | Towers | 5 |
| Miscellaneous | 12 | Process | 18 |
| | | Process integration | 7 |
| | | Miscellaneous | 5 |
| Total | 100 | Total | 100 |

Table 13.2 analyses the causes of failure in a refinery. These failures were mainly due to faulty welding, leaks in high pressure pipes, foreign objects left in equipment, faulty fabrication and assembly, faulty supervision and human error. The relative contribution of items of equipment to the failures is of interest. Many somewhat similar analyses may be made of any plant and may well point to areas that need attention in respect of quality and reliability.

Table 13.3, deduced from HSE statistics, is of interest as it pinpoints the particular areas which contribute most to specific dangerous occurrences

## TABLE 13.3

*Annual return of failures and faults causing reportable dangerous occurrences at work (excluding mines, quarries, railways and offshore installations), listed in order of magnitude*

|  | No. of occurrences | Percentage of total |
|---|---|---|
| Failure, collapse or overturning of lifting machinery | 704 | 26·1 |
| Uncontrolled release or escape of potentially harmful substance | 671 | 24·9 |
| Explosion or fire due to ignition of process materials, waste, etc. | 340 | 12·6 |
| Explosion, collapse or bursting of any closed vessel | 277 | 10·25 |
| Electrical fault causing fire or explosion | 153 | 5·68 |
| Personal exposure to or contact with a harmful substance, or lack of oxygen | 147 | 5·45 |
| Uncontrolled release or escape of highly flammable fluids | 106 | 3·93 |
| Bursting, explosion or collapse of a pipeline etc. or ignition of its contents | 97 | 3·59 |
| Ignition or explosion of explosives | 86 | 3·18 |
| Collapse or part collapse of scaffold | 38 | 1·41 |
| Collapse or part collapse of any building or structure under construction | 29 | 1·07 |
| Overturning or serious damage to a tank while conveying prescribed dangerous substance | 28 | 1·04 |
| Ill health resulting from exposure to isolated pathogens or infected material | 13 | 0·50 |
| Failure or collapse of a lifted freight container or part thereof | 10 | 0·40 |
| Total | 2699 | 100 |

which must be reported to the HSE under statutory regulations. The figures were taken from one recent year, but other years around the same period tell the same general story. The number of dangerous occurrences for the previous year were 20% higher, and tend to drop in subsequent years, but the distribution of the types of failure is similar. Table 13.3 does *not* cover domestic gas incidents, for which see Table 13.5.

### 13.3.2   Power plant failures

A CEGB 2000 MW steam power station reported some 500 to 700 defects per week.

An analysis of these showed:

| | Percentage approx. |
|---|---|
| Serious defects requiring immediate attention with perhaps immediate shut down or within 24 hours | <1% |
| Defects requiring repair during a suitable outage | 9% |
| Defects affecting auxiliaries and causing high risk or loss of output | 11% |
| Defects affecting auxiliaries which can be held pending an outage | 20% |
| Other minor defects requiring attention which can wait perhaps until annual maintenance period | 60% |

The defects reported included those grouped below. (In each group the defects are listed in order of importance.)

*Turbine defects.* Turbine blade erosion and fatigue, detachment of blade shrouding or lacing wires; problems with alignment of blades, shafts and casings; bearing and gland problems.

*Boiler defects.* Tube failures due to overheating, restricted expansion and poor support; wastage due to corrosion and erosion problems; foreign bodies in steam and water spaces, tubes, etc. causing blockage or restrictions; defective welds (particularly with ERW tubes).

*Condenser defects.* Mainly leakage of condenser cooling water to steam side (and thus into boiler system).

*Alternator defects.* Vibration, mainly magnetic and electromagnetic, of the stator core and of conductors both within the stator slots and elsewhere may cause displacement and contact with moving parts; slip ring trouble; large alternators using water or hydrogen cooled conductors may experience leaking and cracking of these conductors.

Diesel generators are used widely in industry particularly for providing electricity in remote localities. In large power stations, such as steam-driven CEGB stations, they are used to provide auxiliary supplies in the event of the normal electricity grid supply failing or becoming disconnected for some reason. In such an emergency at least one such generator must be constantly available and must start up automatically with absolute reliability so that the full load of the electrically driven station auxiliaries (such as pumps) can be taken over very quickly.

Table 13.4 shows the approximate percentage of outage time due to faults in various components making the generator set not available for service (collected over a ten-year period, not counting the time spent out of service during its annual overhaul).

Perhaps surprisingly the alternator with its slip rings caused the most trouble, followed by the turbo-charger. Column, bedplate, cylinder block and crankshaft trouble were perhaps mainly due to vibration which could be (and was) reduced by accurate dynamic balancing.

Checking for cracked pistons by ultrasonic techniques was carried out annually (pistons being renewed as necessary). Similar techniques were used for bearing examination.

Valves and injectors were examined and serviced every 250/600 hours.

Knowing the pattern and likelihood of defects in any item of plant there is obviously great scope (and financial gain) for the use of inspection and NDT techniques in determining the growth and development of faults.

### TABLE 13.4

*Outage time due to faults in components of a diesel generator set*

| Component | Outage time (%) |
| --- | --- |
| Alternator | 36 |
| Turbo-charger | 18 |
| Cylinder blocks and liners | 10 |
| Pistons and cylinder heads | 9 |
| Columns and bedplate (vibration) | 6 |
| Crankshaft | 6 |
| Slip rings | 4 |
| Gears | 3 |
| Camshaft and cams | 3 |
| Cooling troubles | 2 |
| Air manifold | ·2 |
| Fuel pumps, ejectors, etc | 1 |
| Valves | 1 |

Some such techniques are dealt with in Chapter 10 and elsewhere in this book. In some cases the most sophisticated (and often costly) methods are well worthwhile.


### 13.4  Some modes of failure

Many failures, whether due to cracking, corrosion, poor design or fabrication, environmental conditions or other causes (alone or in combination), fortunately occur gradually. For instance, cracking may develop by three stages—(i) initiation, (ii) growth and (iii) propagation—each of which may be found by the use of suitable inspection techniques even though the initiating defects may sometimes be microscopic. The first stage should be searched for during manufacture, whilst all three stages may develop during operational use and are thus the province of 'in-use' inspection. The propagation stage is reached when the growth becomes unstable and comparatively rapid. With *ductile materials* the whole process may take years and an alert inspection organization should be able to give early warning so that precautionary measures can be taken.

With *brittle materials* however the process may occur with great rapidity, especially if unfavourable environmental conditions are suddenly imposed, and catastrophic failure may result. Such failures are normally associated with *notch-brittle behaviour*, particularly of certain mild and low-alloy steels in service at low temperatures (although some cases of failure have occurred at atmospheric and elevated temperatures).

Many steels, ordinarily considered ductile, may behave in a brittle manner under certain conditions, and sudden failures in pressure vessels, structures, piping, etc., often associated with welding (e.g. in the 'Liberty' ships), have occurred at stresses far below their normal yield point. Consequently continual vigilance should be exercised by the inspector regarding these potentially dangerous conditions. In general they involve, often in combination:

(i)  High stress concentrations—often due to poor design such as sudden changes in geometry, sharp corners, etc., or to notches, nicks, surface scratches, or defects (internal or external) such as discontinuities, cracks, etc.

(ii)  Low operating temperatures.

(iii) High rates of straining—resulting from, for instance, the fitting of connections or rigid anchor points to pipework which may limit free thermal expansion and contraction, or perhaps unrelieved residual tensile stresses present in the material.

(iv) Faulty welding and fabrication, e.g. lack of penetration or cracks in the root of the weld.

Care should be given to the selection of a suitable material for the service envisaged and its impact testing where necessary (e.g. to ensure a Charpy impact value of at least 15 ft lb (20·4 joules) at the design temperature), including possibly the determination of its ductile/brittle transition temperature (the temperature above which it behaves in a predominantly ductile manner and below which in a predominantly brittle manner: see 2.6 and Fig. 2.3).

Summarizing, *brittle fracture* requires the simultaneous occurrence of (i) high stress (ii) a notch or flaw, etc. and (iii) the presence of an environment in which the material is susceptible to fracture (such as a temperature below its ductile/brittle transition temperature).

Austenitic stainless steels, and copper, brass and aluminium, are not normally susceptible to notch-brittleness and may be used at low temperatures without impact testing.

The importance of heat treatment, where specified, should be realized. Fully annealed steels may have a comparatively high transition temperature, and thus would offer the poorest resistance to embrittlement. Normalizing improves matters, and optimum conditions can be obtained by quenching and tempering, and by stress relieving after welding.

Points of high stress concentration which may lead to the initiation of brittle or other fracture can sometimes be seen by the appearance of markings on the surface of the material. These markings may be in the form of a 'herring-bone' pattern pointing in the direction from which a crack has started. They are sometimes called Lueder's lines and may show up on the mill scale or paint on a surface, due to the metal underneath (or in the interior) undergoing deformation. Alternatively they may show up by polishing the surface of the material over a particular location. By applying a special brittle paint to the rough surface of, for instance, a pressure vessel before subjecting it to pressure the regions of high stress when under pressure will show up by the flaking or marking of the paint.

### 13.4.1 Failure due to high-temperature service

Cracking of carbon and carbon-molybdenum steel plate, piping and welds may occur after subjection to temperatures above some 800°F (426°C) owing to embrittlement caused by severe *graphitization*; the steel in the heat-affected zone becomes essentially pure iron and carbon. The graphite formation may be due to the addition of significant amounts of aluminium for deoxidation during steel manufacture (more than say 1 lb per ton of steel). The use of silicon or titanium for deoxidation does not appear to cause this trouble.

The degree of graphitization present can be assessed by a metallographic microscopic examination of a section of the specimen of weld metal. The results obtained from a guided bend test will also show the loss of ductility due to this embrittlement.

A mild degree of graphitization detected in a welded area may be corrected by suitable heat treatment, and this may also help to suppress its formation. A more severe degree may necessitate cutting out of the weld and heat-affected zones and rewelding, or even complete replacement.

Cracking troubles may arise in high-temperature service owing to *dissimilar metal* weldments. The dissimilarity may only be slight, e.g. the use of welding electrodes of different composition from that of the base metal, or the use of a corrosion-resisting welded overlay. With dissimilar metal pipe joints, cracking usually starts on the inside of the pipe, where detection is difficult. To help in the prevention of this cracking, weld-filler metals similar to the base metals should, if possible, be used, and any notch conditions avoided. Where dissimilar metals must be joined, the selection of a filler metal which does not cause trouble may be possible (e.g. Inconel). Alternatively, specially designed mechanical joints or prefabricated transition sections may be employed. Embrittlement due to *sigma phase formation* in certain stainless steels may also occur (see 2.13.2.). *Hydrogen embrittlement* can also take place under appropriate conditions (see 6.15) For zinc embrittlement see 5.9. In all cases hardness tests to check for localized areas of differing hardness may help to detect possible sources of trouble.

### 13.4.2 Fatigue failure

This is probably the commonest mode in welded construction. Most fatigue failures experienced in practice arise from bad detail design (such as abrupt changes in geometry) leading to stress concentrations, or to incomplete penetration through the plate thickness of butt welds. These faults are as dangerous in respect of fatigue as they are in respect of brittle fracture; they are relatively of far greater moment, and generally more obvious, than such defects as porosity, etc., revealed by non-destructive testing. Changes in section, welds transverse to the direction of stress, and intermittent welds, are particularly prone to fatigue failure.

The exceptional importance of surface condition on fatigue behaviour should be appreciated by the inspector—a rough surface can lower the fatigue strength of steel by as much as 20%.

### 13.4.3 Fracture appearance

*Brittle* fracture generally occurs suddenly and requires relatively little energy: the fracture appears bright, granular and crystalline and shows little or no evidence of plastic deformation or necking, and may be called a cleavage fracture. *Ductile* fracture occurs gradually and requires a high impact energy for its propagation: the fracture appears dull and fibrous and shows considerable plastic deformation or contraction of area.

In a similar manner a *fatigue* fracture is characterized by its comparatively smooth appearance as compared with the coarse appearance of a static fracture. Fatigue cracks are propagated at right-angles to the applied load; necking is negligible, but may be considerable with a static fracture.

Expert metallurgical opinion should be sought if making a detailed diagnosis.

### 13.4.4 Failure of cast iron pipe

Cast iron pipe for water, sewage or gas, laid in the ground many years ago frequently gives rise to trouble today, because of failure due perhaps to the combined effects of corrosion, frost, coupled with fatigue and vibration resulting from modern traffic conditions. Often the exact route of the pipe is uncertain and trouble is only made known by leakage. Then, at best, a comparatively simple but expensive digging and replacement job (perhaps using plastic pipe) puts things in order again. But catastrophic failure can and does occur, as for instance failure causing leakage from a gas main with subsequent ignition and explosion with fatal results.

It is difficult to guard against all such catastrophes, as they may occur at any time, perhaps over a hundred years after installation. Some of the methods for checking pipeline leakage given in 4.28 may be applicable. With large diameter pipe or sewers human visual inspection may be possible, or perhaps cameras with illumination may be sent through on a moving 'pig'. It may be possible to run a somewhat smaller plastic pipe through the old and worn original pipe. This will cut down the amount of excavation (and its cost) considerably, as this will only be necessary at strategic points to enable the new plastic pipe to be inserted in suitable lengths and joined with cemented couplings. Inspection will be involved throughout: in determining the location of the faulty pipeline; in checking the type of pipe used (e.g. polyethylene 230/50°C 24 sec ALDYL A (Dupont) BGC/PS/P62); in supervising the method of jointing; and in testing the completed job.

With small diameter water and perhaps sewage pipes it may be the practice to wait until considerable leakage is evident and then carry out leisurely replacement. But, with gas, speed in finding a leak and taking corrective action is vital. Replacement with smaller plastic pipe run through the older original pipe will not suffice if it cannot carry the necessary flow, and a larger diameter pipe is required. To cater for such cases, a machine known as a 'percussive mole' has been developed by the Avon Rubber Group which can be forced down the old pipe drilling it and the surrounding soil away, before feeding in new plastic pipe to replace it. This method, somewhat akin to the boring of a tube railway, can save much time and heavy labour in excavating trenches when used to replace for instance, large diameter sewers.

*13.4.5 Failures and dangerous occurrences in gas distribution and installation*

Table 13.5 summarizes the number of fatalities, injuries and incidents and prosecutions taken under gas safety legislation (particularly the *HSW Act* and the Gas Safety Regulations 1972 and Gas Safety (Installation and Use) Regulations 1984) during 1985. Many of these were due primarily to leakage, often caused by failure of cast iron gas mains.

In 1984 the HSE (HMFI) took over responsibility for gas user safety from the Department of Energy. From April 1986 relevant gas incidents are reported to HSE in accordance with the Reporting of Injuries, Diseases and Dangerous Occurrences Regulations 1985 (SI No. 2029).

**TABLE 13.5**

*Injuries and incidents due to use of British gas 1985*

| | |
|---|---|
| Fatalities due to carbon monoxide poisoning | 78 |
| Fatalities due to fire/explosion | 42 |
| Injuries due to carbon monoxide poisoning | 106 |
| Injuries due to fire/explosion | 184 |
| Incidents causing property damage only | 51 |
| Incidents reported | 300 |
| Major leaks, defective flues and other hazards | 830 |
| Prosecutions under gas safety legislation | 15 |

*Note*: The coal gas used before Britain's conversion to natural gas (completed by 1977), as it contained a proportion of carbon monoxide, was very lethal. In 1970 no less than 811 people died from carbon monoxide poisoning, (presumably mainly from inhaling gas from the mains, either accidentally or purposely).

Today's natural gas (largely methane) is not itself poisonous although fatalities *could* occur by asphyxiation in an atmosphere consisting mainly of natural gas. The carbon monoxide casualties now occurring are due to the formation of this gas by incomplete combustion through lack of oxygen/ventilation, and/or blocked chimneys, etc. causing the carbon monoxide to spill back into the room (i.e. the installation is faulty). Several lethal gas main explosions occurred in 1985 due mainly to fracture of ageing pipes. Obviously there is still plenty of work for the inspector in seeking leaks and operational safety and in preventing faulty gas installations.

### 13.5  Collection and analysis of defect and accident data

Carried out over a period, defect analysis can help in pinpointing areas which require investigation and improvement. As an example, Table 13.6 shows a distribution analysis of all defective components reported after inspections carried out on certain sophisticated machines (adapted from M.J. Lighthill, 'Reliability and a Research and Development Establishment's measures to promote it', *Journal of the Institution of Engineering Inspection*, August 1965).

**TABLE 13.6**

*Distribution of defects*

| System, area, etc., in which found | Component defects reported (%) |
|---|---|
| Mechanical systems and controls | 29 |
| Electronic equipment | 28 |
| Instrumentation (including electrical) and control | 25 |
| Structure | 14 |
| Power supply arrangements, etc. | 4 |
| Total | 100 |

All such defects are not, of course, of equal importance in causing machine failures. Most may be found during inspections, before they cause any failure or real trouble. Others may cause minor failures, inconveniences, etc.; some more serious failures, shut-downs or accidents; and a very few may cause catastrophic failure. This is brought out in Table 13.7 relating to the same systems, and based on reported machine failures of three categories of severity. It will be seen that the power system, with by far the lowest percentage of component defects, contributes out of all proportion to major failures.

This type of machine, with much instrumentation and electronics, is peculiarly susceptible to power failures. The analyses of defects in other machines or plants would each show its own pattern. The more complex a plant, the greater will be the number of minor defects continually arising, and the greater the need for systematic inspection, testing and diagnosis of faults, and for more reliable components. If a 'fail-safe' design philosophy has been used, however, it could well be that some such minor shut-downs may have prevented a major accident. Moreover, on some plants, such as the type considered, it may be well worth while to provide alternative power supply arrangements, and duplicated control systems.

**TABLE 13.7**

*Distribution and consequences of failure*

| System, area, etc., found to have caused the failure | Type of failure reported (%) | | |
|---|---|---|---|
| | Minor | Serious | Catastrophic |
| Mechanical systems and controls | 21 | 32 | 20 |
| Electronic equipment | 7 | 9 | 7 |
| Instrumentation (including electrical) and control | 54 | 8 | 12 |
| Structure | 6 | 20 | 4 |
| Power supply arrangements, etc. | 12 | 31 | 57 |
| Total | 100 | 100 | 100 |

### 13.5.1 Some accident statistics

An analysis of serious fires and explosions particularly in the process industries seems to show that perhaps the most frequent initial cause of the accident is a leaking or fractured pipe, flange or coupling. Should this leak be of flammable or dangerous material and an ignition source be in the vicinity disaster can occur. Fire statistics show that the most frequent sources of ignition are electricity (including static) and hot surfaces. Proper inspection (including NDT) both during manufacture and in service should be able to prevent most of such fires and explosions. (see particularly 6.9–6.12 for electrical hazards, also Fire Protection Association Research Reports).

Analysis of statistics also shows that pump etc. failures contribute considerably (perhaps some 30%) to process plant and equipment shut-downs and accidents. Such failures may be due to bearing and gland trouble or the result of a failure of the electrical supply, which may also affect certain vital heating circuits. Failure of thermostats or other electrical control equipment may also cause trouble. Leaks with or without fires may account for over 50% of refinery non-scheduled shut-downs. Human failures can also contribute to accidents. Statistics also show that seal failures outnumber bearing failures by about 5 to 1. In many cases seal failure can be readily observed by leakage, and a minor leakage can be tolerated; but in other cases, where for instance dangerous fluids may be released, leakage cannot be allowed. Hence special designs of seal and careful leak testing during service may be necessary, and a maximum leak rate may be specified (see Chapter 8 (Table 8.7) and Chapter 11).

Statistically there is also a tendency for more accidents to occur at the start of a shift, and particularly for an incident to develop after normal shut-down time (perhaps due to something being left on or not noticed). Maintenance and inspection personnel should be alert to such possibilities. See also *Major Loss Prevention in the Process Industries*, Inst. Chem. Engineers, 1971 and *Incidents resulting from Process Design and Operating Deficiencies*, by Taylor & Redpath.

### 13.5.2 Accident rates by occupation

To put matters into perspective statistics have been used to show that it is almost as safe to go to work in British industry generally as to stay at home.* The fatal accident frequency rate (FAFR)—the number of deaths from injury expected in a group of 1000 people during their working lives— sometimes taken as 40-hr/week $\times$ 50-week/year $\times$ 50 years $\times$ 1000 people $= 10^8$ exposed hours or 100,000 man-shifts (which is the HSE incidence rate) for various selected occupations is shown in Table 13.8 together with later but generally comparable HSE incidence rates for certain of these occupations.

An updating of these figures would show a relatively similar position except that the record for the UK chemical industry was spoilt in 1974, the year of the Flixborough accident, the FAFR rising to 5. Abroad, figures for the USA and Sweden seem roughly twice those for the UK, and for Canada and West Germany four times as great. Holland and Japan have figures comparable to the UK. However, the disaster at Bhopal in India, the Seveso

**TABLE 13.8**

*Accident rates by occupation*

| Occupation | FAFR* | HSE incidence rate (per 1000 employees)[†] |
|---|---|---|
| Staying at home | 3 | |
| Chemical industry | 3·5 | 1·6 |
| British industry generally | 4 | 2·3 |
| Coal mining | 40 | 21·6 |
| Travelling by car | 57 | |
| Construction industry | 67 | 10 |
| Travelling by air | 240 | |
| Travelling by motor cycle | 660 | |
| Professional boxing | 7000 | |

*Extracted from Sowby, F.T., *Symposium on the Transporting of Radioactive Material* p.89 Institute of Transport, 1964.
[†]Extracted from HSE Statistics for 1982.

disaster in Italy, several major chemical accidents in the USA, and the Chernobyl nuclear power station disaster in the Ukraine, with its effects spreading to countries hundreds of miles away, and the prediction of many deaths to come in the long term, give no grounds for complacency.

However, staying at home is far from safe in spite of its low FAFR. Other statistics show that some 7000 people a year die in the UK from accidents in the home, over a tenth from fire. This is comparable with the number killed on the roads (some 6000 in 1984). Over 100,000 received hospital in-patient treatment and several hundreds of thousands received treatment as out-patients or by their own doctor as a result of accidents in the home. The number injured on the roads in the UK in 1984 is given as 327,276. (In the USA the number killed on the roads is some 45,000 annually with perhaps ten times that number seriously injured. The incidence rate (at some 250 deaths per million per year) is some twice that of the UK. Yet neither country would seriously consider banning the automobile.)

It will be seen that far more people are killed or seriously injured on the roads or at home than in industry. The low value of FAFR in the home is due in part to the great number of people at risk.

Various authorities have different methods of collecting and expressing accident data. Most HSE statistics now give incidence rates for fatal and other injuries in terms of numbers per 100,000 employees (sometimes expressed as 'at risk', and previously restricted to 'operatives'.

Numbers for various industries are based on the latest available Census of Employment (probably 1981) returns, and the applicable Standard Industrial Classification (SIC). Table 13.8 gives some relevant fatal incidence rates alongside the FAFRs, but comparison of one set of statistics with another is fraught with difficulties and should be carried out (if at all) with great care.

Most HSE statistics from 1981–1986 arise from injuries and occurrences reported to them or their agencies under the Notification of Accidents and Dangerous Occurrences (NADO) Regulations (SI 1980 no. 804). Statistics obtained before these regulations may not be comparable in many cases. But accidents involving over a three day absence from work had to be first notified to the Department of Health and Social Security (DHSS) under NADO Regulations, and feedback of this information to HSE had become broken, reduced or unreliable, due also to sick pay legislation. Consequently the Reporting of Injuries, Diseases and Dangerous Occurrences Regulations (RIDDOR) 1985 (SI 1985 no. 2023) replaced NADO Regulations to restore the situation, and came into force in April 1986. These new regulations also deal with the notification of diseases, incidents arising from the supply of flammable gases, and include the self-employed and trainees within their scope.

UK government statistics indicate that of persons smoking 10 cigarettes per day, 1 in 400 ($2 \cdot 5 \times 10^{-3}$) may expect to die annually (it is presumed that those who die have been addicts for some years). Generally speaking hazards involving a risk of death greater than 1 in 1000 ($10^{-3}$) per year are considered completely unacceptable, whilst much government money would be expected to be spent on seeking methods of reducing risks of 1 in 10,000 per year ($10^{-4}$). Risks less than 1 in 100,000 per year ($10^{-5}$) are often accepted with little comment by the general public; deaths annually from poisoning are of this order. Deaths annually at work in British industry are around 1 in 30,000 ($3\cdot3 \times 10^{-5}$), and deaths per year from being struck by lightning are 1 in 2,000,000.

US statistics for the coal industry show one fatal accident per million man–hours from which the FAFR would be 100, assuming a 50-year working life, but with a shorter working life at the coal face the FAFR might drop to some 50. When comparing such statistics it is not always known whether the figures refer to workers at the 'sharp end' of the coal face, underground workers or whether they include surface workers and clerks. The frequency rate (deaths per 100 million man–hours) in US coal mines for 1977 is given as 30. The incidence rate (deaths per 100,000 employees for coal mines in the UK for the same year is given as 23.

Perhaps it is unnecessary to say that caution is required when studying statistics as it is often difficult to compare like with like. Remember Churchill's words—"There's lies, there's damn lies—and there are statistics!"

Some accident statistics abstracted from those issued by HM Inspector of Factories and other HSE enforcement authorities for the manufacturing and service industries covering the year 1983 are given in Table 13.9.

Table 13.9 does not include the large number of deaths and major injuries from road accidents sustained in the course of work; these are reportable under the *Road Traffic Act* and not under NADO Regulations. However a casualty caused by a person engaged for instance in road construction or repair was reportable under NADO Regulations and should appear in the table. (NADO Regulations (SI 1980 No. 804) were replaced in 1986 by RIDDOR Regulations (SI 1985 No. 2023)—see p. 638.

From Table 13.9 it will be seen that using the Standard Industrial Classification (SIC) mining and quarrying has the highest fatal and major incidence rate, followed by the construction industry which however has the highest number of fatalities.

Totalling 'all manufacturing industries' (SIC III–XIX) gives a number of fatalities closely approaching that of construction alone.

The comparatively large number of fatal and major accidents suffered by the self-employed and others (including the public) should be noticed, particularly in the construction industry and in agriculture, forestry and fishing. This seems to indicate that the larger, well organized firm with an adequate quality and safety organization has a better safety record; this will more than pay for the cost of its administration.

## TABLE 13.9

*Injuries in industry to employees and non-employees reported to HM Inspector of Factories or other HSE appointed enforcement authorities for the year 1983*

| Order no. | Standard industrial classification | Employees | | | Self-employed | | Non-employed | |
|---|---|---|---|---|---|---|---|---|
| | | Fatal injuries | Major injuries | Fatal and major incidence rate (per 100,000) | Fatal injuries | Major injuries | Fatal injuries | Major injuries |
| III–XIX | All manufacturing industries | 111 | 4,238 | 79·3 | 10 | 18 | 8 | 60 |
| V | (Chemical*) | (10) | (373) | (105·7) | – | – | – | (1) |
| VI | (Metal manufacture*) | (13) | (483) | (183·5) | (1) | – | – | (16) |
| XX | Construction | 118 | 2,176 | 220·7 | 20 | 57 | 11 | 66 |
| I | Agriculture, forestry, fishing | 29 | 200 | 65·8 | 26 | 25 | 9 | 31 |
| II | Mines and quarries | 46 | 1,005 | 330·7 | – | – | – | – |
| XXII | Transport and communications | 40 | 559 | 44·7 | 2 | 2 | 5 | 14 |
| XXI | Gas, elec. and water‡ | 6 | 163 | 52·4 | 1 | 1 | 6 | 7 |
| XXIII | Distributive trades | 12 | 195 | 7·5 | 2 | 1 | 1 | 1 |
| XXV | Prof. and scientific services | 7 | 1,019 | 27·3 | – | 3 | 12 | 4,418 |
| XXVI | Miscellaneous services | 11 | 494 | 19·9 | 3 | 3 | 29 | 235 |
| XXVII | Public admin. and defence | 15 | 1,197 | 87·7 | – | 4 | 7 | 1,252 |
| XXIV | Insurance, banking and business | | 19 | 1·4 | | | | – |
| | Unclassified† | 48 | 1,182 | – | – | – | – | 247 |
| | Total all industries and services | 443 | 12,447 | 62·4 | 64 | 114 | 88 | 6,331 |

\*Also included in the figures for all manufacturing industries.

†Mainly casualties reported by local authorities; includes self-employed and the general public.

‡Obviously does not include gas user casualties (mainly the public—see Table 13.5).

Some casualty figures seeming to require more explanation are those classified as professional scientific and miscellaneous services, public administration and defence and unclassified (but see footnote [†] on p. 640). Together they account for:

81 deaths amongst employees and 51 amongst non-employees;

3892 major injuries amongst employees and 6152 amongst non-employed; plus 10 self-employed.

This makes a grand total of 132 deaths and 10,054 major injuries. This is more than the total for all manufacturing industries, while major injuries total more than twice those incurred in manufacturing!

An analysis of more detailed statistics for *all* injuries reportable to enforcement authorities (derived from *HSE Statistics Health and Safety 1981–82*, Tables 1.1A and 3.2 (HMSO, 1985) is given in Table 13.10 and makes interesting reading.

Surprisingly public administration and defence (SIC no. XXVII of which no further details are given in the statistics) heads the list with the greatest number of reported injuries, slightly more than the construction industry or mining and quarrying, and greater than the combined totals of the heavy industries of mechanical engineering, metal manufacture and vehicles!

Furthermore total injuries in the professional and scientific services (SIC no. XXV) are reported (in Table 3.2 of *HSE Statistics*) to include 9975 sustained by educational service employees (including 2 deaths) and no less than 20,298 sustained by medical and dental sevice employees (including 3 deaths).

Seemingly, judging by the number of injuries, working in education is slightly more dangerous than working in the chemical industry; and working in the professional medical and dental service is more dangerous than being employed in the mechanical engineering manufacturing industry. But, of course, one has to look at the incidence rate (given in Table 13.10) and this depends upon the number of employees in each SIC classification (not necessarily detailed in the statistics); on this basis the most dangerous industry is mining and quarrying, following by metal manufacture and the construction industry. The incidence rates in Table 13.9 however give the same three industries but with construction taking second place.

The incidence rate for professional and scientific services given in Table 13.10 is 860 per 100,000 employees and the number of all reported injuries is 31,485. This implies a total of some $(31485 \times 100,000)/860 = 3,650,000$ employees.

Assuming there are some 600,000 employed in education and as there are 9975 reported injuries of all kinds this gives an incidence rate of $9975/6 = 1662 \cdot 5$ per 100,000 employees (or some 1 in 60 per annum). Note that the minimum serverity of a reportable injury is not mentioned.

Perhaps it should be noted that whilst there seems to be a steady decline in the number of fatal and serious reported accidents each year amongst

**TABLE 13.10**

*Injuries reportable to enforcement authorities*

| SIC order | SIC | All reported injuries | Fatal plus major injuries | Incidence rate, all reported injuries (per 100,000 employees) |
|---|---|---|---|---|
| XXVII | Public administration and defence | 47,795 | 1,181 | 3,160 |
| XX | Construction | 45,868 | 1,796 | 4,190 |
| II | Mining and quarrying | 44,344 | 1,087 | 13,240 |
| XXIII | Distributive trades | 35,342 | 252 | 1,300 |
| XXV | Professional and scientific services | 31,485 | 1,328 | 860 |
| XXVI | Miscellaneous services | 29,697 | 550 | 1,200 |
| III | Food, drink and tobacco | 25,514 | 503 | 4,080 |
| XXII | Transport and communication | 20,549 | 610 | 1,450 |
| VII | Mechanical engineering | 19,178 | 471 | 2,490 |
| VI | Metal manufacture | 13,685 | 558 | 4,280 |
| XI | Vehicles | 13,509 | 339 | 2,250 |
| V | Chemical and allied industries | 9,278 | 331 | 2,300 |
| Part of XXV | { Educational services | 9,975 | 850 | * |
|  | { Medical and dental services | 20,298 | 436 | – |
| III–XIX | All manufacturing industries | 151,966 | 4,218 | 2,550 |
|  | Total: all industries | 434,792 | 12,764 | 2,050 |

*Assuming some 600,000 teachers and staff the incidence rate may be estimated at 1700.

642

employees, there seems to be an increasing number of reported accidents to the self-employed and others. Perhaps employees are subject to better control and supervision!

### 13.5.3 Improvement and prohibition notices and convictions

Improvement and prohibition notices were issued by or on behalf of HM Factory Inspectorate in accordance with the *HSW Act* 1974 (see Sects 21 and 22) as shown in Table 13.11.

### TABLE 13.11
*Improvement and prohibition notices*

|  | 1982 | 1983 | 1984 | 1985(prov) |
|---|---|---|---|---|
| Improvement notices | 3800 | 3405 | 3329 | 2993 |
| Prohibition notices | 1472 | 1673 | 1805 | 1662 |
| Total all notices | 5272 | 5078 | 5127 | 4655 |

Notices were also issued by other HSE inspectorates and agencies and by authorized local authorities. These amounted to some 16,000 per annum.

For failure to comply with such notices, or for other offences or requirements, prosecutions may be taken out under the *HSW Act* or earlier legislation.

Table 13.12 lists the number of convictions obtained by HMFI for failure to comply with specific statutory regulations during two recent years. More than half the convictions were for offences against the various Construction Regulations (listed in Table 14.3).

### 13.5.4 The chemical industry

It will be seen from Tables 13.9 and 13.10 that the accident incidence rate for the chemical industry (employing some 400,000 workers) is not very different from that for 'all manufacturing industries', being lower for 'all reported injuries' but higher for 'fatal and major injuries'.

The HSE carried out a special analysis of accidents and dangerous occurrences in this industry for the year 1983, perhaps because of the industry's own reputed good record and the potential danger apparent to the public of some of its operations.

The results, summarized in Table 13.13, are amplified below:
(i) Some of the failures, incidents, etc. might have been prevented by more adequate in-service inspection procedures.

**TABLE 13.12**

*Convictions obtained by HMFI for offences against specific
Statutory Regulations*

| Code of Regulations | Convictions | | Total penalties (£) | |
|---|---|---|---|---|
| | 1983 | 1984 | 1983 | 1984 |
| Construction (general provisions) Regs 1961 | 66 | 62 | | |
| Construction (health and welfare) Regs 1966 | 27 | 10 | 94,055 | 99,075 |
| Construction (lifting operations) Regs 1961 | 61 | 69 | | |
| Construction (working places) Regs 1966 | 263 | 189 | | |
| Woodworking machinery Regs 1974 | 64 | 59 | 13,850 | 9,615 |
| Asbestos Regs 1969 and 1983 | 55 | 57 | 14,750 | 20,260 |
| Electricity (Factories Act) Special Regs 1908 and 1944 | 50 | 57 | 14,650 | 9,920 |
| Power Presses Regs 1965 and 1972 | 32 | 40 | 5,000 | 13,025 |
| Ionizing Radiation Regs 1969 | 13 | 24 | 4,900 | 13,800 |
| Notification Accident and Dangerous Occurrences Regs 1980 | 35 | 21 | 3,770 | 2,975 |
| Highly flammable liquids Regs 1972 | 9 | 12 | 2,225 | 4,900 |
| Control of Lead Regs 1980 | 8 | 9 | 2,500 | 1,350 |
| Total (including those under regulations not listed) | 731 | 644 | £166,635 | £187,920 |

(ii) 17 of the 643 incidents involved failures of permit-to-work procedures.

(iii) There were 30 pipework failures and 37 incidents involving flexible hoses or insecure temporary joints.

(iv) Over 34% of investigated incidents involved loss of containment, whether through failed vessels or pipework or in the course of maintenance work or manually decanting chemicals, etc. Of the 222 releases of chemicals 68 (30%) occurred during maintenance, repair or cleaning; 127 (57%) affected people; 92 (41%) occurred during process operation without involving work people; 64 (29%) occurred during process operation with direct involvement of work people. (Note: totals exceed 100% for obvious reasons.)

(v) 17 incidents involved tanker vehicles or tank containers.

(vi) 62 incidents (9·6%) involved non-employees, i.e. contractors, visitors, etc. but with the exception of road accidents involving road vehicles carrying chemicals no off-site fatalities were reported, although the potential for off-site casualties from explosion and release of chemicals may in some cases be great (as was the case with Flixborough in 1974 and more so at Bhopal, India in 1984).

## TABLE 13.13

*Analysis of accidents and dangerous occurrences in the chemicals industry in 1983*

| Type of incident | No. | % |
|---|---|---|
| Accidental release of chemicals (including 97 toxic, 51 corrosive, 45 flammable, 23 hot & 6 other materials) | 222 | 34·5 |
| Machinery faults and incidents | 77 | 12·0 |
| Process related fires and explosions | 66 | 10·3 |
| Falls from a height | 56 | 8·7 |
| Falls at same level and striking against objects | 39 | 6·1 |
| Pressure system and other equipment failures (main risk not from chemicals released) | 24 | 3·7 |
| Hit by falling objects | 23 | 3·6 |
| Failure or overturning of lifting equipment | 22 | 3·4 |
| Struck or trapped by vehicle | 15 | 2·3 |
| Affected by chemicals during work (e.g. decanting, charging, etc., without significant escape or spill) | 13 | 2·0 |
| Runaway exothermic reactions (with no major release of chemicals) | 9 | 1·4 |
| Manual handling and strains | 8 | 1·2 |
| Non-process related fires and explosions | 7 | 1·1 |
| Confined space incidents—people overcome | 5 | 0·8 |
| Electric short circuits | 5 | 0·8 |
| Not classified elsewhere | 52 | 8·1 |
| Total | 643 | 100% |

Table based on returns by inspectors of all directly reportable and all investigated accidents and dangerous occurrences (courtesy of HM Chief Inspector of Factories/HSE).

## 13.6 Failures attributed to poor inspection

Investigations tend to show that the causes of failures and hence of unreliability often fall into one or more of the following categories:

(i) Faults arising out of manufacturing processes, due mainly to inadequate supervision.

(ii) The misuse of plant and components of good quality.

(iii) The use of plant and components of poor quality.

(iv) The use of plant and components of poor design.

The first and third categories directly concern the inspector during manufacture, but all four may be high-lighted by 'in-use' inspection.

This pattern is largely confirmed by the following reports of catastrophic failures which are of great significance particularly to inspection.

### 13.6.1 The Tay Bridge disaster

An early major failure of the first, third and possibly fourth categories was the Tay Bridge disaster. An experienced civil engineer, Thomas Bouch, using such information as was then available, had designed and constructed the two-mile long railway bridge across the River Tay at Dundee. He was knighted by Queen Victoria after she herself had travelled over the bridge. But, after 18 months of use, on a stormy night in December 1879 the bridge collapsed taking with it an entire train and all its passengers, none of whom survived.

Investigation showed that many of the cast iron members of the bridge were faulty. Voids, cracks, etc. in them had been filled in with a mixture of rosin, beeswax, iron filings and swarth, with a little lamp black, and then painted over. Inspection and supervision must have been almost entirely lacking.

During use, bolts and fittings were seen to fall from the bridge and cracks in large cast iron columns were observed, but not reported to higher authority. The unfortunate designer was blamed, lost his reputation, money and perhaps his reason and died four months later as a result. The official Board of Trade Court of Inquiry largely blamed Sir Thomas Bouch for faults in design, construction, and maintenance. It seems that after the receipt of not very clear advice from the Astronomer Royal regarding expected wind pressures the bridge *may* have been designed to withstand 10 lb/ft$^2$ over its whole surface, although momentary wind pressures of over 40 lb/ft$^2$ upon very limited surfaces might be expected. Obviously on the night of the great storm very high wind pressures of unknown magnitude occurred, which acting on the bridge *and* the train (the rear coaches of which were lighter than the rest and could have been tilted over) in conjunction with the faults in the castings, known cracks in the structure (*which had been seen to be developing*), loose and unsecured ties and fallen bolts, caused the collapse, one after the other, of all 13 centre spans of the bridge. Possibly the last straw, which may have initiated the collapse, could have been a hammer blow struck by a tilting or overturned rear carriage on the already strained girders of the bridge. Although the coupling connecting these last two carriages was broken and they fell to the river bed some distance behind the rest of the train this matter was never fully brought out by the Court of Inquiry (who could not fully explain the exact course of events).

### 13.6.2 Ronan Point

Somewhat similarly a century later in 1968 a high rise block of flats at Ronan Point, East London, collapsed after a small gas leak and an explosion, killing five people and causing widespread consternation and fear for the safety of other high rise flats. Eighteen years later it was fully confirmed during dismantling operations that load bearing wall joints were packed with soft materials, including wadding, cigarette ends, tin cans and newspapers. Support bolts were not installed correctly leaving wall panels to rest on the soft padding. An engineer stated that the structural strength and stability of this type of building was very workmanship-dependent, and workmanship was poor generally. Obviously supervision and inspection, if any, was entirely inadequate.

As a result of the early misgivings following Ronan Point many similar buildings have been and will be demolished and millions of pounds have been wasted. One can comment that the immediate postwar temporary housing programme was engineered, supervised and inspected by the government—but not the high rise flats. Even some early postwar building components and equipment for general use were subject to a form of government design approval and checked to British Standards before the granting of licences for the scarce material required for their manufacture. (The British Electrical Approvals Board (BEAB) was a 'spin-off' from this arrangement and now tests samples and issues its own approval certificates and documentation.) Many of the early temporary houses may be seen today in out-of-the-way places, long after their planned lifetime. Of course, high rise flats are somewhat different, but proper supervision and inspection would have made a great difference and would have saved not only lives, but millions of pounds.

*13.6.3 The Flixborough disaster—Report of the Court of Inquiry (HMSO 1975)*

On Saturday 1 June 1974 an explosion occurred at a chemical works at Flixborough, Humberside, killing 28 people, injuring some 53 others and causing widespread damage. The casualties would have been far greater if the accident had occurred on an ordinary working day and if the site had been less remote. The causes of the accident were complex, but were due amongst other things to failures on the part of supervisory, design, inspection, maintenance and operating staff. The classic conditions for an explosion were present—a leak (developing from a crack), the presence of a hazardous atmosphere, a source of ignition, plus human failings.

The chain of events started on 27 March when a reactor vessel constructed of metal-clad plate (mild steel with stainless steel bonded to it on the inside (see 5.7)) was found to be leaking cyclohexane. It was shut down and the following morning inspection revealed that the crack had extended by some 6 ft. It was decided to by-pass the reactor (one of six) to enable production to continue. It so happened that the works engineer had left and had not been replaced; no qualified mechanical engineer capable of dealing with the situation was available for supervision. In consequence a make-shift modification was made using three lengths of 20 in pipe welded together to form a dog-leg connection between two 28 in flanges at different levels which were connected by expansion bellows to serviceable reactors. No design calculations were made and no approved procedure for the modification was carried out as would be required by BS 5750. In particular the minimum requirements of BS 3351 *Piping systems for petroleum refineries and petrochemical plants* had not been met, specifically clause 4.6.2. 'For axial bellows, the piping shall be guided to maintain axiality of the bellows and anchored at adjacent changes in direction to prevent the bellows being subjected to axial load due to fluid pressure.'* No pressure test was carried out on the modification before fitting it into the installation. The installation itself was not given the full specified test pressure before being put back into service.

On 29 May, following an untraced leakage of nitrogen (used in the process) and a leaking isolating valve, the plant was shut down to investigate and the leaking valve repaired. On the morning of 1 June the plant was started up again, and the pressure and temperature rose, at first apparently normally. But it seems there was some difficulty in control and the pressure rose somewhat above normal, perhaps due to not venting off nitrogen (because stocks of this were in short supply due to the unexplained leakage).

During the afternoon of 1 June the unanchored 20 in diameter dog-leg pipe assembly, perhaps under more than normal pressure, began to squirm badly, jack-knifed and finally ruptured and flashed, releasing large quantities of hot cyclohexane vapour ($C_6 H_{12}$) into the atmosphere. This rupture may have been assisted (or even caused) by a complex series of events involving *inter alia* a fire in the galvanized wire-covered thermal insulation causing zinc embrittlement of an 8 in stainless steel pipe which split and directed a flame of cyclohexane at the pipework. This hypothesis, and others, were considered in detail by the Court of Inquiry, but the 20 in diameter dog-leg was regarded as the primary cause of the accident.

The rapidly expanding cloud of cyclohexane vapour (normally a colourless, pungent toxic liquid which boils around 80°C and is flammable and explosive in the presence of oxygen) spread around the site and soon found a source of ignition. What this source was is uncertain, but the resulting massive explosion seemed to emanate from the hydrogen plant. There seems to have been two explosions, first from the dog-leg and then a larger one from the vapour cloud near the hydrogen plant. Like many massive explosions the resulting heavy damage destroyed much evidence which would have been of use to a Court of Inquiry in firmly establishing the cause and sequence of events. Consequently much of the detail will never be known for sure.

---

*As a result of the accident BSI prepared a Code of Practice: *The selection and application of bellows expansion joints for use in pressure systems* which gives much information and guidance, together with diagrams of safe and unsafe piping systems, etc. This was published as BS 6129, 1981. A slight amendment to BS 3351 was made at the same time.

As mentioned the initial cause of the trouble had arisen some months before with the initiation of cracking in the metal-clad plate reactor vessel (see 5.7). This was probably due to the premeditated constant pouring of water over it because of a leaking stirrer gland; this cooling effect condensed the escaping cyclohexane vapour to liquid form and enabled operations to continue without toxic fumes. But it may have set up nitrate stress corrosion cracking (see 12.7.6) because the local water contained nitrates. It may have caused hydrogen embrittlement or some other form of corrosion. The net result was that cracking was initiated and on 28 March was found to have spread extremely rapidly, causing the reactor to be taken out of service.

The unapproved and badly executed modification then led to disaster.

*13.6.4 Some remarks on the Chernobyl disaster*

The use of water for cooling purposes is commonplace, but as at Flixborough it may have undesirable effects. For instance the Russian nuclear reactor at Chernobyl used a graphite (carbon) moderator interspersed and cooled by many tubes (also containing the fuel elements) through which water was passed so producing steam to drive turbo-alternators. For some reason in May 1986 the nuclear fuel rods became grossly overheated (perhaps the cooling water had ceased to flow). The graphite (carbon) and the uranium fuel rods became red (or white) hot and then maybe the water supply was re-instated.

But the water tubes by this time may have melted or partly so. Consequently the resumed water supply (as steam) would have played on the white hot carbon (and uranium) core (aided possibly by water from the firemen's hoses). The reaction would have been similar to that used to produce water gas—large quantities of hydrogen and carbon monoxide would be evolved, both highly combustible and explosive; the reaction of steam on the very hot zirconium outer cladding of the fuel elements would also produce hydrogen. The reactor core would then burn fiercely in the presence of air. Hydrogen would have risen quickly and filled the area under the containment vessel. A source of ignition being readily available, the resulting explosion ruptured the roof of the containment vessel, releasing a great cloud of radioactive material into the atmosphere. The nuclear fire continued to burn for some days whilst frantic efforts were made to cool it down and stop further emission.

A full 'official' report is awaited, and if and when available will be (like the Flixborough report) very complex. Like Flixborough (but perhaps more so) its effect on industrial health, safety and inspection will be profound.*

---

*The Soviet report and much information has been issued and commented upon world-wide. Amongst its findings it states that 'unauthorized experiments' were carried out. The chief engineer and other top level people implicated were given heavy prison sentences.

### 13.6.5   Report of the Royal Commission on the Failure of King's Bridge, Melbourne, Australia (Cmd 6352/1963)

This report, relating to the collapse of a bridge costing over four million pounds, embodies material of great value to designers and inspectors of engineering structures, plant, pressure vessels, etc. Its salient facts and conclusions will be summarized briefly here.

(i) The *design* was considered basically sound.

(ii) The *structure collapsed catastrophically* under load after 15 months' service, investigations revealing widespread cracking throughout its length. Toe cracks had occurred immediately after welding, and extended by brittle fracture through the lower flanges and in some cases into the web plates of girders. Later some of this brittle fracture was further propagated up the web plates, complete severance of a bottom flange occurring at one point, and further normal fatigue cracks developed and extended, eventually resulting in complete rupture.

(iii) *Reasons for failure:*

(a) *Lack of an overall supervisory authority.* No single authority had been appointed to supervise the project as a whole, a matter which is essential if co-ordination is to be effected between the purchaser, designer, steel producer and the contractor and sub-contractors. In consequence, many important acceptance tests were omitted, and neglect in inspection occurred owing to the various parties concerned thinking that these matters were not their responsibility.

(b) *Material not up to specification.* A low-alloy steel was specified to BS 968:1941, * having the composition: carbon 0·23% max., manganese 1·8% max., chromium 1·0% max., manganese and chromium 2·0% max.

In fact, a large portion of the steel actually provided differed substantially from the specification. Carbon content ranging up to 0·28% was found; this resulted in a decreased resistance to brittleness, particularly when associated with a high manganese content, which in several cases was around the maximum specified.

The Izod notch brittleness figure had been fixed at 20 ft lb at 32°F, although the structure suffered ambient temperatures at times as low as 22°F. The Izod value for much of the steel supplied was substantially below that specified. Even so, the report recommends that a more realistic figure would have been 40 ft lb at 32°F.

(c) *Lack of control of welding operations.* The low-alloy steel used necessitated special welding techniques and specially trained operators. These matters were neglected and, in particular, little effort appears to have been made to ensure adequate preheat temperatures. Welding electrodes were not kept dry.

---

*Now superseded by BS 4360

(d) *Poor inspection.* Insufficient attention was given to inspection standards and to the action to be taken on any faults revealed by inspection and acceptance tests. Steel was accepted even though this was found by test not to comply with the specification demanded. A large degree of cracking was found after the failure which must have occurred at the time of, or very shortly after, fabrication. Some 50% of a particularly vital component (cover plates) had developed cracks, which could have been seen before the failure.

(e) *Stresses imposed by welding and sharp changes of section and brittle fatigue.* The final welding of the ends of the cover plates was the culminating factor in creating a complex system of stresses which, in conjunction with the static and variable loads imposed by the operating conditions, was favourable to the development of brittle fracture. Amongst the factors involved were stresses imposed by sharp changes of section at the cover plate ends and the effects of welding, especially transverse welding of cover plates, and of welding girder webs to lower flanges.

(f) The *immediate result* was the development of toe cracks which constituted ideal stress raisers, and all the conditions were then present for the development of embrittlement cracks. The ability of a structure to withstand the propagation of this latter form of crack is largely a function of the material, which in this case, as noted, was unsuitable owing to its poor notch embrittlement resistance as shown by the Izod test.

*Conclusions.* Failure occurred owing to cracking, extended by brittle fracture and fatigue, which could have been avoided, or at least seen and corrected, by adequate supervision. The trouble should have been evident during any pre-commissioning or 'in-use' inspections, had these been carried out.

## 13.6.6 The R101 disaster

The high technology project now considered is a classic case of how, in spite of good inspection, disaster occurred because today's requirements of total quality assurance were not then approached owing to political interference.

The project was the British Empire Airships programme, started in 1924. The government scheme was to span the Empire by giant passenger- and mail-carrying airships (aeroplanes were not then capable of operating a commercially viable all-weather trans-oceanic service). After the 1919 double Atlantic crossing of the British-built R34 (a design based on German Zeppelin principles) and trials with her sister ship R33, it was planned to build initially two huge airships of 5,000,000 cu. ft capacity, over 700 ft long and with a cruising speed of some 70 m.p.h. They would carry some 50 or 100 passengers in comfort, with dining saloon, smoking room, music and state rooms with real beds—all in first-class transatlantic liner style.

Orders were placed, one (the R101) with the Royal Airship Works at Cardington, Bedfordshire and the other (the R100), with a subsidiary company of Vickers Ltd at Howden, Yorkshire. The government-built ship with Lt Col. V.C. Richmond in charge of design would embody the latest in high technology and would use five or six diesel engines for propulsion, thus lessening the fire risk inherent with petrol-driven airships; both airships would of course rely on highly flammable hydrogen, then the only feasible gas for lifting purposes. The designer of the R100 was Barnes Wallis, later known as a very gifted but somewhat eccentric genius. He had to use an existing type of reconditioned Rolls Royce petrol engine. Both designers excelled themselves with their differing but advanced structural designs, their use of materials (such as stainless steel) and particularly the design of R101's 'netting' by which the thrust of some 16 gas bags was transferred to the airship structure.

Inspection, acceptance into service and recommendation for the issue of a Certificate of Airworthiness for civil flying was the responsibility of the Aeronautical Inspection Directorate (AID) of the Air Ministry, and in particular that of Mr McWade, Inspector-in-charge AID at the Royal Airship Works, Cardington. He was responsible through the H.Q. Assistant Director/Aircraft (Major Bishop) to the Director of Aeronautical Inspection (Lt Col. H.W.S. Outram) the man largely responsible for the development of the AID approved system of inspection described in Chapter 9. Col. Outram was answerable to the Air Member for Supply and Research (a serving officer's post), held by Air Vice-Marshal Higgins.

Now McWade was a very experienced airship man. He had worked on airships in the early days as an assistant works manager at Farnborough, flying to London in Cody's first airship and in other later ships. He was conversant with the process of making gas bags from animal intestines using gold beaters skin; with the use of hydrogen and with the vagaries of doped fabric used for the outer covering of aircraft. Neither Col. Outram nor Major Bishop had had such experience; they were both aeroplane men.

The manufacture and inspection of materials, components, structural wire rope, etc. went ahead under normal AID procedure. (Some concessions were given.) The first major trouble came with the diesel engines—they failed to meet their specified horse-power output and were considerably overweight. Furthermore, no satisfactory method of reversing could be found, so it became necessary to mount one engine with its propeller giving backward thrust for use only during manoeuvring—it was an idle and useless dead weight during normal flight. As no other suitable engines were available a concession for their use had to be given.

Consequently a trial flight showed that the underpowered airship was slower than specified and the useful lift available was much less than required. In an attempt to improve these matters articles were removed from the airship; its passenger accommodation was reduced and orders were given that the restraining 'netting' around the gas bags should be loosened so that they could be expanded to take more hydrogen, so increasing the lift.

A further trial flight showed some slight improvement, but Inspector McWade noticed chafing of the now less restrained gas bags during movement in flight, with consequent loss of gas. Tests he made in the airship shed showed a continuing undue loss of gas. (Changes in atmospheric temperature and pressure complicate such leakage calculations— (see 6.6). However, drastic measures were required to bring the lift of the ship up to the required standard. So it was decided to cut her in two and to insert a new 50 ft section with extra gas bags increasing her gas capacity to $5\frac{1}{2}$ million cu. ft.

Meanwhile her half-sister the R100 on completion was sent across the Atlantic on a trial trip. Inspector McWade went with her. He found that chafing and leakage of her gas bags also occurred, especially in rough weather. At one time atmospheric conditions (a storm near Quebec) caused her to rise and then fall nose down at 25° some 4000 ft. Long lengths of her outer fabric were forcibly torn away and had to be repaired in the air (McWade had already found that under certain conditions he could push his finger through the outer covering of both ships). After a stay in Montreal and a trip to Niagara the ship returned home (with one engine out of action).

The world greeted it as a highly successful flight. Meanwhile Lord Thomson, the Air Minister (and a wartime General RFC/RAF) was getting impatient. He desired to fly to India, using the new airship mooring masts at Cairo and Karachi, and return in time for the Imperial Conference where he hoped to get approval for more airships. Owing to tropical conditions the use of the petrol-driven hydrogen-filled R100 was ruled out. Thomson's timetable required the R101 to depart from England by 4 October. Completion of the extension to R101 was hurried forward. Meanwhile Inspector McWade had followed up his earlier reports on troubles with a scathing indictment of the ship. The gas bags were leaking and would leak increasingly in flight and in rough weather due to their largely unrestrained chafing against the structure, rigging, etc. The gas valves would also release gas if tilted beyond a certain angle. The outer fabric was rotten, particularly in places where patches had been inserted; in fact rubber solution left on un-covered fabric seemed to set up rapid deterioration. All those things could cause trouble in rough weather. The necessary trials, especially those after modification, had not yet been carried out. In short, he could not recommend the issue of the necessary Certificate of Airworthiness for the flight.

Col. Outram (DAI) called a meeting with the designer (Col. Richmond) and the other interested parties at Cardington (perhaps we can call this a design review meeting on the lines of BS 5882). The officials at Cardington (including the Director of Airship Development—W/Cdr Colmore) and the service officers of the ship all knew of Lord Thomson's immutable date and were perhaps 'frightened' of crossing him; in any case, they said, it was always an inspector's job to look for trouble and make a fuss! They would take a 'sporting chance'.

As a result of the meeting McWade was instructed in writing by DAI to see that projections, etc. were bound up as far as possible to prevent chafing of the gas bags, and that the fabric cover was patched up where necessary. Trials could take place en route to India and McWade himself should supervise them! McWade carried out the first part of his orders but refused to obey the order to sail in the ship he had condemned! He did not consider that padding and patching was an effective way of preventing leaks.

On 1 October R101 made a short trial flight of some 16 hours in calm weather but a full speed test could not be carried out because of a minor failure of an engine oil cooler. McWade did not fly, but another inspector gave the captain a generally guarded but satisfactory report under the prevailing conditions. Travelling on this trial was the newly appointed AMSR, Air Vice-Marshal Hugh Dowding, who had replaced Higgins. Dowding did not know of McWade's troubles. Returning to Cardington the ship loaded up for her voyage to India and her distinguished passengers came aboard. AID sent Major Bishop and another man to replace McWade. On the evening of 4 October R101 left for India, facing gusty, wet and increasingly deteriorating weather. Over the Channel she seemed so unbelievably low that when calcium flares were dropped from the control cabin to enable navigational drift measurements to be made (they would ignite on contact with water), they showed clearly the waves not far below. Ballast was dropped to increase her altitude to nearer 1000 ft but she continually lost height across France (remember the ship herself was 778 ft long, and that undoubtedly the leaking gas bags were having an effect).

Head winds of some 50 m.p.h. (gusting to 70 m.p.h.) and rain now reduced her speed over the ground to about 25 m.p.h. Approaching rising ground near Beauvais at a low altitude it seems that something happened to cause the bow to drop suddenly in a slow dive towards the ground, 'assuredly caused by a massive deflation of a forward gas bag, perhaps after failure of the outer cover on top of the ship.' A man was sent forward to release half a ton of water ballast in the nose but he did not get there. The engines were ordered to slow, and perhaps to stop. Comparatively gently the nose and forward control car slid into the wet grass of the hillside. Someone shouted 'We're down lads', and a few of the crew just walked on to the land. However, in a flash, the escaping hydrogen ignited. 48 died, some after surviving burns for some time. Only three lived to tell the tale.

The disaster was a classic case of the almost simultaneous occurrence of failures, human, structural, etc. in the presence of leaks, a hazardous gas, a hostile climatic environment, and a source of ignition.

Many questions remained unanswered by the official Court of Inquiry.

What was the source of ignition? There were no petrol engines and the diesels had been slowed, perhaps stopped, and in any case their hot exhaust pipes were low down, far beneath the gas bags—and the leaking hydrogen would normally immediately rise skywards and escape through vents. Was there a structural failure? Did the bending metalwork initiate a spark? Was it static electricity? But the ground was thoroughly wet, and surely a spark at ground level would be quickly doused. Was it due to the escaping hydrogen heating up by the reverse Joule–Thompson effect and spontaneously igniting? (see 7.2 and 7.7). Another suggestion has been made. Was a calcium flare, suspended from the control cabin, released by the crash and/or ignited by contact with the sudden wet grass?

The ship theoretically should not have sailed. Its Certificate of Air-worthiness had not been cleared by the responsible AID inspector McWade. It is true that Colonels Outram and Richmond had held a meeting to discuss McWade's report and McWade had been given his orders which, in effect, overruled his objections. It is said that the newly appointed AMRD Air Vice Marshal Sir Hugh Dowding (the ultimate chief) had cleared the issue of the certificate after discussion with his technical experts (but had not seen McWade's reports) and had sent it to Air Marshal Sir Sefton Brancker, the Director of Civil Aviation, aboard the ship just before departure.

In retrospect, if the requirements of a specification for a total quality assurance programme (similar to BS 5882 (see 13.10) could have then been applied, Inspector McWade's reports might have received more consider-ation and been brought to notice at higher level. Perhaps the decision to fly would not have been subject to such political pressure. The full trials programme, with its full speed and adverse environmental conditions tests, would have been insisted upon, and the faults might then have become more apparent and perhaps disaster could have been averted. The inspector did not fail, but his reports were overruled at high level and by political pres-sure. He refused to sail in the ship he had condemned.

Similar considerations apply today in any area of high technology whether it be a jet airliner, a space shuttle, an explosives factory, a nuclear installation or a large hazardous chemical plant. All should be subject to approved design and quality assurance procedures including full-scale acceptance tests conducted by competent, trained professionals. The authorized inspectors, in possession of all relevant information, should be fully independent, and seen to be so by the general public. Perhaps both Dowding and Outram (and their organizations) learnt something from the R101 disaster. Both men rendered yeoman service in technical command and administrative preparations for and during World War II.*

---

*I find that in his book *To Ride the Storm* (Kimber, 1982) Sir Peter Masefield gives as the thirteenth and final reason for the R101 disaster the ignition of calcium flares when the ship hit the wet ground at some 10 m.p.h. and broke them open.

### 13.6.7 Report of the US Presidential Commission on the Space Shuttle Challenger Accident of 28 January 1986

The report on this accident, which interrupted the development of the massive US space programme, causing widespread loss of confidence in the system, is of great interest to all concerned with quality assurance and safety, especially in connection with any high technology project involving risks. It shows the continuing detailed QA diligence necessary during design, assembly and operation.

The cause of the accident was found to be the failure of a pressure seal (made by two rubber-like 'O' rings of 0·280 in diameter ($+0·005$, $-0·003$) fabricated from a fluorocarbon elastomer) which was intended to prevent hot gases from leaking through the aft 'field' joint of the right hand solid fuel rocket motor. This failure was due to a faulty design unacceptably sensitive to a number of factors including the effects of temperature, physical dimensions, characteristics of materials, and possible distortion and incorrect assembly on the launching site of components which had designedly been used before. All of these factors were known, as is shown by ample documentary evidence in the report.

---

(Footnote continued.)

These were and had been used for dropping into the sea and calculating drift, so as to assist navigation. The tearing of the poor outer fabric cover had let in storm-force winds and this in conjunction with the leaking gas bags caused grounding and provided the hydrogen gas to cause the major fire.

A further reason for the disaster now seems evident, which might be termed an unfortunate lack of *good housekeeping* in the control cabin. According to a surviving eye-witness a box of calcium flares, originally containing one dozen, had clearly been left open on the control room floor and not safely put away or returned to the protection of the rack provided. He states, '. . . judging by the box he had on the floor I should say that he had used seven, because I think the box held a dozen and there were only five left in it'. Each flare consisted of 5 lb of calcium phosphide contained in a perforated cardboard cylinder to allow the penetration of water. But would the wet grass have been sufficient to penetrate the cardboard so quickly? It might, but there is a better explanation.

This same survivor tells us that at the moment of impact he had been resting on a settee in the smoking room from which he could see down the ladder into the control cabin. Within a few seconds there was a bright flash of flame in the control cabin: '. . . it was very white, and not at all like a hydrogen flame . . . No flame at all (came into) the smoking room, but thick choking smoke'. [This seems clear evidence that it was a calcium flare.] Trying to get up off the settee the survivor found that the deck above had collapsed to within 4 ft. of the floor, no doubt breaking various services, as the lights had gone out. Now in the control cabin, adjacent to the spot where the box of flares had been seen on the floor, were the supply line pipes and valves of the ship's main water supply system. These pipes of thin aluminium $2\frac{1}{2}$ diameter were almost certainly ruptured under the crushing weight of the collapsing deck above and thus quickly flooded and ignited the open box of flares on the floor (Chamberlain, G., *Airships – Cardington* Terence Dalton, Lavenham, Suffolk (1984)).

The rocket motor formed part of a booster assembly (of which two were attached to the shuttle) which gave the additional thrust needed at take off. Each booster assembly (150 ft long) consisted of 11 cylindrical sections (segments) which were joined together by a form of circular tongued-and-grooved (tang and clevis) joint (see Fig 13.3). The rubber 'O' rings fitted into grooves machined in the circumference of the steel segment (some 12 ft in diameter) which sealed the joint. The two segments joined at the aft 'field' joint (the joint which failed) were assembled on site but were often known to have significant out-of-round dimensions. The segments were held in place by over a hundred steel pins connecting tang and clevis around the circumference.

The intended launching procedure was that the booster rocket motors would fire, using solid fuel, for the first two minutes of flight and would then be automatically released and brought to the ground by parachute for refurbishment and re-use. The shuttle would then continue in flight powered by liquid hydrogen and liquid oxygen supplied from an external tank which would be automatically detached and jettisoned after some $8\frac{1}{2}$ minutes. Further manoeuvring would be carried out by small rocket motors.

But, due to various factors, the compression on the 'O' rings was not such as to maintain the seal and consequently fuel passed through, smoke being seen very early in the flight above the field joint as the rubber burnt away. After nearly a minute an increasingly large flame appeared, which eventually played on the external tank—burning through this and igniting and exploding the liquid hydrogen and oxygen. No firm action had been taken to remedy the known defects perhaps because previous take-offs had been successful (and after all the seal only had to be maintained for some two minutes).But examination of recovered boosters from recent flights had shown clear evidence that hot gases had blown past the 'O' rings, burning the rubber—fortunately without causing a catastrophe. No person or organization had sufficient authority to insist on immediate re-design. The 'O' rings themselves were made from material whose performance was affected by temperature (both high and low). A recommendation had been made (and overridden) advising against launch at temperatures below 53°F because of the lack of resilience of the 'O' rings at such temperatures. Faulty 'O' rings (perhaps having voids, blemishes, inclusions or out of tolerance dimensions) could have been used; and furthermore it is easy to mishandle, contaminate, misplace or trap metal slivers and other foreign bodies when assembling a long and unwieldy rubber into a groove in the open in icy weather, particularly when the segment with its tang and clevis joint had been used before and could be somewhat distorted.

Much pressure from high levels had been applied to quickly launch and complete the mission; the flight had already been postponed some four times for weather and other reasons. But high-level people would not necessarily know of the technical troubles and could override the technical

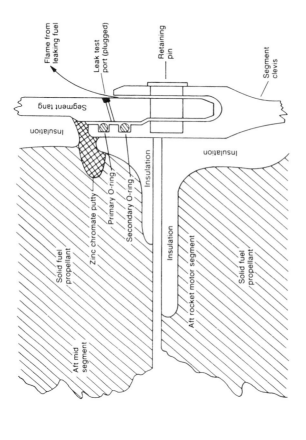

**Fig. 13.3   Cross-section of space shuttle field joint connecting two 12 ft diam. segments of solid fuel rocket motor (SRM) showing tang, clevis and 'O' rings and the path of the destructive flame which passed through due to a combination of distortion and resulting inadequate sealing, and the effects of low temperature on the 'O' rings.**

*Note:* The putty was intended to transmit the combustion gas pressure to actuate the 'O' ring seal, and also to act as a thermal barrier to prevent direct contact and consequent burning of the rubber 'O' rings.

To ensure that the two 'O' rings were properly seated a leak test was applied through the leak test port at 50 lb/in². This was later increased to 200 lb/in², and when initially applied (in the instant before the primary 'O' ring became properly seated) possibly caused blow holes in the putty so allowing burning of the 'O' rings in flight.

658

people (as was the case with the airship R101) to avoid further embarrassing delays.

In the author's experience somewhat similar technical troubles with 'O' rings and leak-tight seals were encountered in the UK during the early atomic energy programme (see 1.4). Re-design, the use of new materials, methods and manufacturing techniques, often under near clinical conditions, plus visits to 'O' ring manufacturers and rigorous inspection instructions for surface condition, voids, inclusions, blemishes, etc. and dimensions (both of 'O' ring and groove) to secure optimum compression— followed by leak testing, were necessary. High vacuum techniques (see 11.7.2) aided the development of leak-tight seals, including those used for hazardous situations. Decisions involving delays were necessary and were *not* overruled by those responsible for production.

The US Presidential Commission comments that it was surprised that after many hours of testimony NASA's safety staff was never mentioned, and no witness related the approval or disapproval of the reliability engineers, and none expressed the satisfaction or dissatisfaction of the quality assurance staff.

Amongst its findings the following points should receive particular attention by everybody concerned with hazardous plant and machinery:

(i) Reductions in the safety, reliability and quality assurance force seriously limited capability in those vital functions.

(ii) Organizational structures placed safety, reliability and quality assurance offices under the supervision of the very organizations and activities whose efforts they are to check.

(iii) Problem reporting requirements were not concise and failed to get critical information to the proper levels of management.

(*Author's comment*: It is obvious from the mass of reports and information quoted by the Commission that many hours must have been spent in writing them. One cannot help thinking that a few authoritative shouts at the sharp end might have been of more use and could possibly have averted disaster.)

Accordingly, amongst the Commission's recommendations was the establishment of an *independent* Office of Safety, Reliability and Quality Assurance to deal with all such matters. In addition an independent national design committee should be made available to oversee the design effort.

The necessity for quality assurance in design and the full operation of a quality system complying with the requirements of a standard such as BS 5750 Part 1 or its equivalent will be apparent (see 9.4.7).

### 13.7  Failure in pressure vessels and risk estimation

Table 13.14 shows the result of an investigation covering inspection over a period of 5 years.*

Most of the cracks occurred at branches and fillet welds and 54% of these involved fatigue mechanisms (i.e. mechanical, thermal or corrosion), whilst 7·6% of the cracks had existed from the manufacturing stage.

Thus inadequate inspection and quality control, faulty material selection, etc., *could possibly* have accounted for 7·6% of the cracks plus 2·3% material or fabrication defects—making a total of 9·9% of the recorded service failures.

Of the grand total of service failures 5% were catastrophic operational failures, 29% were discovered owing to leakage, 57% were found by visual examination, 7·5% during non-destructive testing and 1·5% during hydraulic testing.

### TABLE 13.14

*Distribution of service failures in pressure vessels*

| Cause of failure | % |
| --- | --- |
| Cracks | 89·3 |
| Corrosion | 1·5 |
| Mal-operation | 6·1 |
| Material or fabrication defects, etc. | 2·3 |
| Creep failure | 0·8 |

### 13.7.1  Estimation of failure rate of pressure vessels

Of the sample of 12,700 vessels having an operational service of 100,300 vessel years investigated by Philips and Warwick: 7 suffered catastrophic failure (4 cases of mal-operation, 2 of fatigue and one only because of defects (material or fabrication) pre-existing during construction, and which might perhaps have been found during inspection at works). 125 vessels suffered potentially dangerous failures in service. From this the catastrophic failure rates were given as:

*For further information see Philips (UKAEA) and Warwick (AOTC), *A Survey of Defects in Pressure Vessels Built to High Standards of Construction and its Relevance to Nuclear Primary Circuit Envelopes*, UKAEA Health and Safety Branch, 1968, obtainable from HM Stationery Office.

During construction: $2 \cdot 3 \times 10^{-4}$ failures/year (approx $2 \cdot 3 : 10,000$)
During service: $0 \cdot 7 \times 10^{-4}$ failures/year ($7 : 100,000$)
Potentially dangerous failures in service: $1 \cdot 25 \times 10^{-3}$ per year ($125 : 100,000$)

An analysis of the data as it might be applicable to nuclear reactor primary circuit envelopes concluded that many of the failures given in the survey would not then apply. Consequently the total number of service failures applicable was reduced from 132 to 62; and the number of catastrophic failures from 7 to 2. The service failure rates then became:

Potentially dangerous failures: $6 \times 10^{-4}$ failures/year
Catastrophic failures: $2 \times 10^{-5}$ failures/year.

Note: a further survey covering a later 5-year period gave somewhat similar results of yearly failure rates in service, i.e.

Potentially dangerous: $1 \cdot 1 \times 10^{-3}$; catastrophic $1 \cdot 5 \times 10^{-4}$

Other continental and American surveys (for ASME Code vessels) give somewhat similar but variable results which may be very roughly averaged as:

Disruptive failures: somewhat less than $1 \times 10^{-5}$ (ranging up to $4 \times 10^{-5}$ for less severe failures).

### 13.7.2 Estimating risks

By making use of event data, failure studies, accident statistics, data banks, etc. such as those already described, complex hazard studies for a variety of components and complete plants, involving foreseeable and even improbable happenings, may be made and from them estimates of specific risks can be assessed.

The HSE commissioned a most comprehensive hazard assessment study of the already complex refineries and chemical plants centred on Canvey Island in the Thames Estuary with a view to determining the overall risks to health and safety particularly in the light of requests for planning permission for additional works (see *Canvey: An Investigation of Potential Hazards from Operations in the Canvey Island/Thurrock Area (the Canvey Study)*, HSE–HMSO, 1978).

An investigating team of inspectors appointed by the HSE and drawing on expertise from the Systems Reliability Directorate of UKAEA (Culcheth, Warrington) carried out the work. Its report is a model of 'the state of the art' of hazard assessment and shows what at present can be done (and perhaps what cannot be done) in estimating risks without the use of a crystal ball.

It makes recommendations and outlines certain measures necessary for the reduction of these risks which should be adopted before approval of any new construction could be given.

It will of course be realized that this study, or any other such study, gives only *estimates* of risk, and that these may not all be borne out by events. Furthermore the estimates are based on past data, and any further changes in specifications, quality assurance, procedures, materials etc. may affect them (for better or even worse). And then there is the unknown 'fate factor'.

No doubt with this in mind the report expresses some reservations: 'Practical people dealing with industrial hazards tend to "feel in their bones" that something is wrong with risk estimates . . .'.

As has been said elsewhere 'Making it right first time is worth a ton of mathematics', and the practical inspector should attempt to see that this is done; he is not necessarily a prophet and cannot *always* predict (or calculate failure). A man, like an engineering component, has a finite life which may be shortened by events, or may crack under undue strain. So the motto is 'Keep watch . . . and assess and predict by all possible means any approaching trouble'.

In the Canvey Study the risks of failure for pressure vessels were based on those given above and in 13.2. The catastrophic failure rate used was $10^{-5}$ per year. The risk of vessels developing a fault requiring repair or withdrawal from service used was $3 \times 10^{-4}$ per year. It was of course essential that a proper system of inspection be in operation.

Failures of pressure pipes, pumps and suction lines around the refineries, and of lengthy incoming/outgoing pipelines had to be considered, and they could cause fires and explosions.

The frequency of pipe fracture was assessed generally as $5 \times 10^{-3}$ per year. The frequency of catastrophic rupture of LPG pumps was assessed as $10^{-4}$ per year. With, typically, 20 LPG pumps in a refinery, the risk of one rupturing and developing a fire and directing a fire plume at a nearby LPG storage vessel was assessed at:

$$5\% \text{ of } 20 \times 10^{-4} \text{ per year}$$

The frequency of serious failure of a pipeline was assessed at:

$$3 \times 10^{-4} \text{ per km per year}$$

The risk of a major refinery fire was assessed at 0·1 per year, and of an explosion following a fire as 0·5 of this.

The risk of an unconfined vapour cloud explosion was assessed at $10^{-3}$ per year. Many other risks and possible calamities were investigated and approximate frequency rates quantified, including aircraft crashes, missile hits, rail and road tanker and shipping accidents, toxic release, estimated casualties, evacuation plans, etc. For further details the full report must be consulted.

Following this report the *Control of Industrial Major Accident Hazards Regulations* 1984 (SI no. 1902) was issued. This requires identification and assessment of hazards, action to prevent or limit them, preparation of emergency plans and demonstration of safe operation for specified plants and materials. It applies particularly to refineries and many chemical plants.

## 13.8 Approach to total QA

In any area of human endeavour we can hope to approach perfection but not to reach it. So with QA. Like engineering efficiencies a full 100% total QA is (or seems to be) against natural laws.

Procedures for achieving a measure of QA were discussed in Chapter 9, whilst some actual methods have been dealt with in other chapters. Chapter 9 mainly covers inspection (and QA) during manufacture, although BS 5750 Part 1 describes a scheme approaching closer to total QA, embracing not only QA during manufacture, etc. but also during design, development, installation and field trials.

Chapter 12 deals with the important additional QA necessary during commissioning and operation. But all this is not enough—to approach total QA it is necessary to consider almost every aspect and possible circumstance affecting quality from 'before' the cradle to 'after' the grave. Consideration of these matters will also help towards the achievement of safety and of loss prevention.

All three of these aims, QA, safety and loss prevention, rely very largely on inspection and the study and analysis of a variety of statistics and reports. But there are subtle differences:

(i) An automatic lathe might run for hours producing intricate but undersized components from expensive material which, after *inspection*, would be rejected and scrapped because proper *quality control* arrangements were not in force.

(ii) A product might perform its function perfectly and safely with a long and useful life; but during manufacture some material may have been processed in an *unsafe manner*.

(iii) An article may have been specially designed, and made from necessarily costly materials, to enable it to operate in a hostile environment—but money would have been spent unnecessarily (lost) if it was then only required for use in a normal environment.

(iv) A chemical or other high technology plant might have been designed and built incorporating all the latest technology, and might have been put into *operation* apparently successfully. But if the plant used dangerous materials which in a hazardous environment might come into contact perhaps through a leak and/or some failure (human or material) or even poor maintenance and/or modification procedure, then disaster could and has followed.

(v) In 1893, in peacetime, Britain lost its latest and largest battleship and some 400 men, with near loss of a second battleship, due to *human error*. The Mediterranean Fleet was on manoeuvres steaming at full speed in two parallel lines, eleven ships in all. The Admiral wanted to practise a rapid reversal of the Fleet by turning the two lines inwards towards each other. He did not realize the large turning circle required by his new flagship *Victoria* and some of his ships. He gave the fleet the order to turn inwards. The very disciplined navy obeyed—nobody dared to warn the Admiral of any danger! Even the Rear Admiral, second in command, leading the parallel column dutifully turned his battleship *Camperdown* inward towards the *Victoria*. As they neared each other, and the danger became increasingly apparent, nobody took any corrective action. Disaster followed.

Perhaps the Royal Navy learnt something from this. The new German Navy certainly did. In the succeeding years they carefully practised somewhat similar maneouvres—and used them to good effect at Jutland in 1916 to extract their fleet under fire from almost certain destruction!

The greatest loss resulting from a human failure, or a failed component or project could—apart from human life—well be the financial loss arising thereby, perhaps increased by expensive litigation (see Chapter 14). Nothing in life can be performed without risk, and the use of any device, component or service involves such a risk, even if the commodity concerned is of the highest quality. QA can involve calculating risks, etc. by studying failure, accident and reliability figures etc. for almost every conceivable article, component or happening (a computer data bank is desirable) and making use of them to improve and/or predict the quality and safety, reliability and/or life of a component or project, suggesting methods of design, inspection, testing, operational use, maintenance, etc. to this end.

The field of investigation is wide and many would say somewhat confusing—so why bother—why not make things right first time? But how exactly does one do this? Hazard and stress analysis, operability and reliability studies, analysis of data on failures and defects, etc. provide a wealth of information which can be of use (see for instance 13.4–13.7). One angle of approach is to study accidents and failures, evaluate if possible their causes and institute (not just recommend) methods for preventing them. Do we learn from past mistakes? Some people would say NO; but the QA man must see that the answer is YES.

Some details are given in this book/chapter regarding certain accidents and occurrences. Case studies of many more can be found in the references and elsewhere. It is an interesting exercise to try to determine the causes and what lessons we can learn and what action we would take.

Reading about the collapse of Tay Bridge and, a century later, of Ronan Point, seems to indicate that we have learnt little. We can learn much from the case of the airship R101. It stopped UK airship development; the hydrogen-filled German *Hindenburg* met disaster, but so did the even larger US helium-filled *Akron* and *Macon*. But today, jumbo jet disasters with much greater casualties do not stop civil flying. The Chernobyl disaster, with its potential for similar disasters and for long-term casualties, may stop or at least slow down nuclear power developments; it has made more impact on world opinion than for instance the Bhopal disaster (see 12.10) with its far greater immediate casualty list. In this book the details and causes of the Chernobyl disaster have been left as written (see 13.6.4) within a few days of their occurrence; but the Soviets now attribute its main cause to the carrying out of unauthorized experiments and tests (i.e. to human error). They probably soft pedal on the possibility of poor design.

Guarding against the results of human error can be extremely difficult. However, something can be done by elaborate systems of interlocking, fail-safe mechanisms, or even a simple indicator system. But even so, as with railway signalling, interlocks may prevent a wrong setting, but may not prevent a dozing driver ignoring a signal. A further mechanism, or a dead man's handle, may shut off the power; but this—in the millionth chance—may cause the train to stop in a most dangerous position!

A second man to watch for errors (and tell the Admiral he is wrong!) may help (i.e. a duplicate, or redundant, system). So also can an all-seeing safety officer. It was once said that the most important duty of a safety officer at a large research establishment was to prevent mad scientists from killing themselves (and others)! But little can be done to stop some sudden, unexpected wrong actions of a human (except perhaps regular medical examinations and suitable training and discipline). However, with plant, regular in-service examinations can help to check the onset of deterioration, and the use of components of assessed quality (where available—see 9.4.3), and other techniques, should help to prevent unexpected failures.

However, accidents will happen, even in the best of regulated circles, and little can be done to prevent natural disasters (or acts of God as they were called), but precautions can be taken to mitigate their effects. By law the owners/operators of hazardous plants in the UK must make plans to deal with any conceivable emergency (see Chapter 14).

Statistical studies can work out the accident frequency rate (perhaps once in a million years), but do not necessarily tell us when (see 13.5). Reliability studies etc. (see 13.2) and/or in-service inspection (see Chapter 12) may indicate when. Obviously then, if total QA is desired, in-service inspection and testing must go on throughout the life of a plant; highly sophisticated test equipment may be essential if the need for total QA is great. Much help with statistical studies etc. can be obtained from S and RD, UKAEA Culcheth Warrington (see 13.2.1). It may be possible to develop, say, microprocessor-based hazard and security monitoring and control systems using fault detection and protection elements if the need is great, and money and the necessary techniques are available.

In this difficult often 'beyond the state of the art' area the organization of a meaningful total QA and safety programme may tax man's ingenuity. The Director General of the British Safety Council has stated: '... 90% of accidents are caused by people rather than things ... , but safety officers, engineers, etc. tend to spend 90% of their time correcting things rather than people'.

It was reported that in the USA a man was found asleep in a nuclear power station. The Regulatory Authority shut down the whole system! No faults or casualties had occurred, but the shaken utility company probably lost revenue and probably lost jobs.

At Zeebrugge in 1987 a British cross channel car ferry flooded and overturned with the loss of some 200 lives. The man who normally should have closed the bow doors was asleep in his cabin. The captain did not know the bow doors had been left open! However, apart from the sacking of a guilty and/or negligent employee, it is generally the business of the legislation, a court martial, etc. to adjudicate and award punishment, perhaps tempered or otherwise with mercy.

In World War I sentries found asleep at their post were often shot!

### 13.9 Continuing fitness for service—remanent life

One important aspect of any total quality assurance programme is the assessment and demonstration of the continuing fitness for further service of any item of a plant or of the complete plant. Coupled with this, but more complex, is the assessment of remanent life (e.g. the percentage of the designed life still remaining). Some items of plant found to be deteriorating may not reach their designed life; others could exceed it by a large margin. The regular periodic in-service inspection of plant, carried out either as a statutory obligation and/or as laid down by the inspection authority or by considerations of good practice, includes visual inspection and usually some form of non-destructive testing.

The purpose of such in-service inspections is to identify when and where any deterioration is occurring. Defects and/or changes to be looked for include distortion (including dimensional changes), corrosion and scale formation, metallurgical changes, performance changes, etc. Areas of overheating and stress concentration, or where repairs have been carried out, or where faults and cracks, etc. have been previously found or suspected should receive particular attention.

A simple dimensional change may in some cases be used to estimate remanent life. First the change of dimensions (strain) is measured accurately between clearly established and later recognizable datum points (taking care that the method of marking does not itself cause trouble, and that the temperature is recorded). This strain is then compared with the strain necessary to cause failure (fracture) for the relevant material at the appropriate temperature. A number of strain measurements may be taken over a period to establish strain rates.

An increasing rate of strain may give warning of approaching failure. On the other hand no strain or no increase of strain rate may indicate that the plant is not yet approaching the end of its useful life. From the data obtained a measure of the rate at which remanent life is being expended can be estimated. For many materials a simple relationship exists between strain rate and time to failure.

Coupled with the visual tests are non-destructive tests to determine particularly the presence (or absence) of cracks and similar faults. Specific areas of concern are welds and points of stress concentration along with those areas which operating experience may have shown to be suspect. If cracks are found it is necessary to ascertain their size and direction and their cause. It may be necessary to call in expert advice, and in any case the inspection authority will normally have to be consulted as to whether and if so for how long the plant can continue in operation before specific remedial measures are taken. If repairs involving rewelding are authorized it is necessary to ensure that the parent metal is damage-free and has sufficient remanent life to make the repair economically worthwhile. Official authorization procedure will of course have to ensure that the design intention is maintained. The actual NDT techniques used may include all those dealt with or hinted at in Chapter 10, including those beyond the 'state of the art'.

Records of the operational history of a plant are essential to the assessment or analysis of fractional life usage. Certain plant and components are designed for a finite life and may be subject to review then if continued service is required. More usually such an assessment would be made at not later than two-thirds of the design life. If the review shows no appreciable deterioration and none is suspected from other studies the plant or component may continue in service perhaps for an extended period. If deterioration or trouble is evident then a more complex analysis may be necessary. For instance an analysis of past records may show that known periods of operation under somewhat higher than normal temperatures and stresses have recurred. For a given material data are available which relate these factors with time to rupture.

Thus, simplifying matters: if $t$ is the time spent under certain specific conditions, and $t_r$ is the corresponding time to rupture: then fraction of life utilized under these conditions is $t/t_r$. This calculation can be repeated for all other periods of the plant's operating history. Then total fractional life utilized =

$$\sum_1^n \frac{t}{t_r}$$

Calculations of the above type can become very complex, and perhaps unnecessary or imprecise in some cases. But where safety or financial considerations are involved they may be essential, in which case much effort must be directed towards their accuracy. (This may perhaps be illustrated by considering a simple component such as an electric lamp made to a standard specification for a life of 1000 hours. When operating under abnormal conditions calculations as above may show that it should be replaced (perhaps for safety or financial reasons) before its normally expected life has been utilized.)

Statistical studies (reliability) help in the assessment of remanent life and the prediction of failure rates (see 13.9).

### 13.10  A total QA programme

As an early example of the organization of a total QA programme covering a complete large project, which could equally be suitable for a large chemical plant, refinery or an off-shore installation, consider BS 5882 *Total quality assurance programme for nuclear power plants/nuclear installations*. This specifies principles for the establishment and implementation of QA programmes during all phases of design, procurement, fabrication, construction, commissioning, operation, maintenance and decommissioning of structures, systems and components of installations such as nuclear power plants, fuel fabrication, processing and reprocessing plants and fuel storage facilities.

It states: 'Many practical methods are in existence to implement the principles set out in this standard ... BS 5750 "Quality Systems" ... may be applied (see Chapter 9) as and where appropriate, for the procurement of plant items and services'. BS 5882 attempts to establish compatibility of QA principles between known existing documents such as USA *Code of Federal Regulations* 10 CFR 50, ANSI N45·2, and the International Atomic Energy Code of Practice 50–CQ–A. It is based on ISO DIS 6215 *Nuclear Power Plants; Quality assurance*. 'It is the responsibility of the owner of the installation to ensure that a QA programme ... is established and executed in a manner consistent with the provisions of this standard. . . . He can delegate this work (e.g. to some independent approved inspection authority) ... but retains responsibility for its overall effectiveness. This in no way diminishes the responsibility of any participant (e.g. a designer or inspector) for the quality of his services.'

Details are given of the organization, management and documentation required: staffing and training; design control, verification and change including any on-site changes; control of purchasing, supplier evaluation, identification of materials etc.; process control, inspection, testing and surveillance, including in-service inspection and operational testing;

calibration of measuring equipment; inspection stamps and markings; review of non-conforming items—reject or repair; keeping of inspection/ QA records throughout the life of the plant or of particular items; audits to check and verify the effectiveness of the QA programme and organization etc.

Apart from the style and legal language employed in the specification it is easy to see that the requirements of BS 5750 Part 1 are incorporated, and that the old AID requirements of approved firms and suppliers, the relative independence of the inspector, his supervision over processes, the maintenance of identity of materials (and inspectors) are also contained therein.

*13.10.1 Necessity for QA in design* (see also BS 5750 Part 1 (9.4.7)

An item of plant, a component or even a complete project may have been produced and completed exactly in accordance with drawings; the processes of manufacture, welding, etc. may have been carried out perfectly and checked by the latest NDT techniques (all in accordance with the appropriate chapters in this book!) *but* if the intention in the designer's mind has not been fulfilled, i.e. if the design is inadequate, then all will be of no avail. The item or project may not function as intended (if at all); it may be unsafe and even cause loss of life or property; it may cause trouble and fail before reaching its intended life.

Consequently a total QA programme must include thorough checking and surveillance of design. In such a programme today the QA man should be called in with the designer at an early stage, and should learn his intentions. Perhaps even the designer's intentions may be ill-founded, or more likely, there are more ways than one of meeting them. All such questions must be sorted out in the project definition stage, and then preliminary sketch plans and/or designs drafted with the assistance, where required, of research and development and specialist support services.

Design specification and procurement of perhaps standard items may then go ahead, together with planning of the complete project or assembly in conjunction with any required time scale. Inspection arrangements can be made. Design of the complete scheme can then be argued out (if necessary) and changes and amendments made until the final design and drawings are made and approved (and perhaps 'frozen'). Manufacture and construction, testing and commissioning then follow according to plan, all subject to passing the necessary inspection and testing procedures.

If all has gone well the plant or project will go into operation and perform its function, subject, like a human being, to periodic checks and diagnosis of any troubles with treatment and repair as necessary, until the expected period of life has been reached. But if not there may be major trouble, complete breakdown or even disaster with loss of life, property and money. There may be expensive litigation and costs to meet perhaps due to infringement of safety regulations and consumer protection legislation (see Chapter 14). The question may then be asked—was it due to a design or an inspection failure?

### 13.10.2 QA in design control and planning

Quality assurance in manufacturing areas is comparatively well understood (and has been covered elsewhere in this book, in particular in Chapter 9— BS 5750). Quality assurance in design is newer and less well understood. It smacks of a QA man (with perhaps comparatively little specialized knowledge) standing by a genius like I.K. Brunel and continually questioning his every action and decision.

> QA man: 'Why do you want three forms of propulsion on your ship *Great Eastern*—wind, steam driven paddles *and* screw?'
> Brunel: 'That's redundancy—one system may fail.'
> QA man: 'Then why not let the screw propeller act on the air to produce wind?'

If the designer's intentions (which normally will correspond with the customer's requirements) are completely satisfied by compliance with some standard specification for a component then QA surveillance of design is straightforward. Verification of design compliance with a complex code (such as the ASME Boiler and Pressure Vessel Code) is relatively straightforward although some problems, alternatives, etc. may have to be settled.

It is when a customer calls clearly and concisely, but without supporting detail, for a project, say, 'to put a man upon the moon' that QA surveillance of design becomes difficult. One approach is to include in the surveillance some formalized procedure the principles of which may be given in some such standard as BS 5750 *Quality Systems* Part 1 (and the guide to it—Part 4) which has been dealt with in Chapter 9. But obviously much more will be required.

As the involvement of QA at the design stage is relatively new and unique, difficulties may be expected. A high degree of mutual understanding is needed and it may depend upon circumstances as to whether QA's role should be passive or active. Basically QA has to assess the design. That there is room for argument, delays and ambiguity regarding the responsibility of designers and assessors (QA) was brought about in the official Layfield Report on the Public Inquiry into the proposed PWR for Sizewell B (see for instance Chapter 49 of the report).

A former Superintending Inspector of the Nuclear Installations Inspectorate had stated: '. . . decisions on matters of design and operation had to be reached by debate among designers, operators and safety assessors . . . characteristic of this type of statutory safety surveillance is a measure of shared responsibility . . . the inspector participates in and contributes to the decision making process'. But later NII thought that this was incompatible with CEGB's statutory responsibility and stated: 'we have to be most careful that we are not influencing the designers, rather explaining ... what our requirements might be ...'. Subsequently NII stated: 'Of course we influence the safety design, for example, by some of our requirements ...'

Summarizing, perhaps it can be said that an inspector involved in QA does *not* design plant and equipment. He may have to carry out an assessment and if not satisfied he will state his requirements which may well influence or even totally change the design.

It will be evident that such an inspector must at least be like Caesar's wife—above suspicion. But in addition he should be diplomatic, of sound common sense, uninfluenced by pressures and politics, and of superior knowledge and experience such that his decisions are correct and acceptable to all and sundry!

BS 5750 Part 1 (see 9.4.7 and Table 9.2) besides covering QA during manufacture also covers QA in design particularly in Clause 4.8—Design control, Clause 4.9—Documentation and change control and also in Clause 4.7—Corrective action, Clause 4.6—Records and Clause 4.5—Work instructions. Part 4 gives some guidance in principle on these matters but is not exhaustive. Part 1 infers that QA may also be involved in installation and trials, but neither part gives details of these or of operational inspection. BS 5882 also gives some guidance in principle on QA in design, particularly in Clause 3—Design control, and will be referred to later.

BS 5750 Part 1 also covers the quality system organization (Sections 4.1 and 4.2) which includes design; it must generate evidence to demonstrate compliance with design quality. This may include records of compliance with relevant codes of practice, design standards, material certificates, statutory regulations and test reports not only on materials but ranging up to highly technical reports on research, performance of samples, prototypes, etc.

Minutes of meetings will give background to decisions made, etc. The surveillance of drawings and their approval, independent checking of calculations, etc., all with a view to seeing that the design intent is continually maintained, are all required. Much of this work is the normal duty of the design office and its chief. QA has to be seen to be checking, seeing that all this is verified. Similarly with documentation and change controls QA must ensure that concessions, deviations and corrective action are agreed by the designer and do not infringe the design intent.

Stress analysis, defect and accident statistics, the consequences of malfunction or failure, reliability matters and the latest research will be studied and/or analysed. If problems arise and a review of design is necessary or called for, QA can help in seeing that appropriate specialists are invited to attend and that a proper decision is made.

BS 5750 Part 1 recognizes that design may be specified principally in terms of the performance required and that in some cases it has not yet been formulated. It may be necessary to establish a design and development programme, providing new or making use of existing codes and standards of design (in whole or part); completely new or little known techniques may have to be developed, making the best use of any available scientific or specialist advice; statutory requirements including those for health and safety must be studied and designs framed to comply with them. In-service inspection and maintenance requirements must be borne in mind. Eventually all of this will be translated into drawings, specifications and procedures for contract action, criteria for acceptance and instructions for operation, etc. which may well be for a project requiring total QA similar to that covered by BS 5882.

The QA organization must ensure verification of the adequacy of design for the purpose intended, seeing to the carrying out and documentation of design analyses and reviews, and checking calculations (sometimes by the use of alternative methods); they must arrange that relevant quality requirements are specified in design and contract documents, naming the authorized inspection body responsible.

A suitable test programme may have to be devised and documented, so that the required performance can be demonstrated under perhaps specified adverse environmental conditions. If results do not come up to the specified standard, modifications may have to be devised and approved, carried out under supervision, and retested as necessary to ensure an agreed satisfactory performance. Such design changes as may be necessary, including on-site changes, must be reviewed and carried out by established procedures and subject to full design control measures, approval and documentation.

The object of QA design control and planning is not to do the designer's work for him (prima donna designers would rightly resent any hint of this!) but to ensure that everything possibly required has been done and documented in a disciplined manner, and nothing has been forgotten.

Process controls (see BS 5882 Clause 9) will be implemented for processes used in construction, fabrication, testing, commissioning, operation and decommissioning (e.g. for welding, heat treatment, electroplating, corrosion protection and testing, non-destructive testing including detection of surface cracks, chemical analysis, mechanical testing, vacuum testing and any tests of a special nature).

Another aspect of QA in design is the carrying out of hazard and operability (Hazop) studies on the complete project or process and its component parts to ascertain in advance what can conceivably go wrong (i.e. where there might be a deviation from the design intention) and to consider the causes of such deviations, their possible consequences and what can be done to prevent the deviation and perhaps to lessen the consequences if such a deviation occurs.

Such studies will involve the critical questioning (preferably by a multidisciplinary independent team ) of everything in the design and in the operation of the project (pity the poor designer!) and analysis of the answers (yes, no or maybe) with a view to seeing that the designer's intentions are attained and maintained, with safety.

Much ingenuity, thought and understanding of processes, materials and test and inspection methods are needed in making such studies. Major hazards should be readily identifiable and suitable precautions taken. It is often recognition of minor and possibly developing faults and their causes which is more difficult, as these often (perhaps quickly) develop into major hazards.

A simple illustration might be the hazard involved if a maintenance worker accidentally drove a pick into a particular pipe conveying fluid, or a particular electric cable. If the study showed the creation of a major hazard, one solution would be a protective shield over the pipe or cable. Failure of cooling water on a car engine might be inconvenient, but on a nuclear reactor it could be disastrous.

Plans must be made to deal with the worst possible consequences which could arise from the major hazards identified, such as evacuation, casualties and countermeasures. Further information can be found in:

Guide to Hazard and Operability Studies, 1977.
Chemical Industry Safety and Health Council, *Hazard and Operability Studies*, 1974.
ICI, Guide to the Control of Industrial Major Accident Hazards Regulations, 1984.

*13.10.3 Inspection, surveillance and testing for total QA (BS 5882 Clauses 10 and 11)*

The inspection and testing programme for the components, equipment and for the complete plant will be executed by or for the organization responsible, who may later carry out and report on any trials programme required, before and/or after commissioning. In general such activities will be under the surveillance of individuals other than those doing the actual work. Certain individuals or organizations may require to witness specific tests. Prototype qualification tests, proof tests prior to installation, pre-operational and start-up tests may be required, to ascertain that the specified design requirements and acceptance limits have been met. After acceptance and being put into operational use the plant will be subject to in-service inspection and tests on a regular basis throughout its life to ascertain that the designer's intentions (and statutory requirements etc.) are still being met (see Chapter 12). Any discrepancies, etc. found by in-service inspection will have to be dealt with, perhaps by a planned maintenance programme, or immediately if necessary. Control and surveillance of this work must be carried out as part of the total QA programme.

### 13.10.4 QA records (and audits)

Documentary evidence of the conformance of material, etc. must be available on site, together with reports, analyses, reviews on all matters relating to QA throughout the life of the plant (Clauses 7.3 and 17).

To verify compliance with all aspects of the QA programme and its effectiveness a system of internal and external audits (spot checks) must be carried out (sometimes at random) covering all work areas and activities by an independent auditing organization having no responsibility for the activities which they audit. The documented results of such audits must be reviewed by management, who must take any necessary corrective action to an agreed time scale (Clause 18).

### 13.10.5 Training and qualification of staff

BS 5882 under clauses 1.2.2 and 2.3 requires that staff should be qualified by education and training so that suitable proficiency is achieved and maintained in performing specific tasks affecting quality. With some projects this may necessitate the setting up in good time of suitable training courses or schools dealing with perhaps new skills or techniques (see Clause 9.2.2). It will be realized of course that BS 5882 is only a procedural specification and gives no technical details. These will have to come from the user/owner plus the design authority, and will eventually take the form of their own specifications and drawings, supplemented by standard specifications (BSI etc.) for specific materials and components. Perhaps the only major technical specification for nuclear plant is the ASME Boiler and Pressure Vessel Code (particularly Sections III and XI) which is much used in North America and worldwide for largely American style designed plant. Section III is used for design, construction and inspection during construction purposes. Section XI deals with in-service inspection (see Chapter 12), which will feed in details to a planned maintenance programme. However checking of radiation levels, radioactive wastes, etc. is left in the hands of the appropriate regulatory authorities.

When the planned economic life of the plant has been reached (or before if failures or other factors have influenced matters) arrangements will be made for its de-commissioning. It is likely that for a period it will be used on standby duties, not working at its full output. But the day will come when it is shut down finally and prepared for scrapping. With normal plant the scrap value may be high, but with nuclear plant there will be areas which cannot be worked on, perhaps for years, and even then with the most elaborate and expensive precautions. A de-commissioning programme will have to be planned in the light of the legislation prevailing at the time, and it may well be a very expensive and profitless business.

Similar problems may arise with other hazardous plant in this last phase of total quality control. The dangers and costs of dismantling may be prohibitive, and in some cases the plant cannot just be left to rot!

Battersea Power Station, London, once one of the largest and best in the country, was phased out finally in 1984–5, but safety problems arose in dealing with the removal of asbestos cladding of pipework, etc. when dismantling Battersea A, the first half of the station. A large wall or cofferdam had to be built to segregate it from the rest. The site, with its elegant cathedral-like structure, has now been sold as a form of amusement park! See also *Decommissioning of Radioactive Facilities*, papers presented at a Seminar held by I. Mech. E., Mech. Eng. Pub., 1984 (also in 1988).

In what follows some attempt will be made to examine what was done in the past on some large high technology projects to secure some overall measure of inspection and quality assurance, and what can now be accomplished by the implementation of a total quality assurance programme as outlined in some such specification as BS 5882.

### 13.11 The UK atomic programme (total QA in retrospect)

The UK atomic programme, started in secret by the Attlee government in 1946 as a military requirement, was carried out under security conditions by the Ministry of Supply's newly formed Division of Atomic Energy Production (DatEn) under the part-time control of Marshal of the Royal Air Force Lord Portal, the former wartime Chief of the Air Staff. Answerable to him were three remarkable men, Hinton, Cockcroft and Penny (who later all became Lords). The Industrial Group (based at Risley, near Warrington under Hinton) designed and engineered the factories, first for the production of fissile material, aided by the scientists etc. of the Research Group (based at Harwell under Cockcroft). This fissile material then went to the Weapons Group (based at Aldermaston under Penny) for the production of atomic and later hydrogen bombs. It must be remembered that with the passing of the American *McMahon Act* in 1946 no atomic information was available from the USA, so that the UK had to rely on her own resources (plus the Smyth Report (an American report, *Atomic Energy for Military Purposes*, published jointly by the USA and the UK (HMSO) in 1945 price 2/6) which Hinton instructed all his staff to buy!). Building, design and construction work (civil, mechanical and electrical) of the actual factories etc. was carried out by a special (security) section of the Ministry of Works. Inspection of plant and equipment at works was carried out independently, generally under the supervision of the Ministry of Supply (MOS) Inspectorate of Electrical and Mechanical Equipment (IEME) many of the senior officers in the newly formed section having had extensive AID experience. They were able to liaise effectively with design departments (especially after Hinton had insisted on the relevant IEME HQ officers being based at Risley with them) they could ensure that specifications and documents included applicable inspection requirements. They could call on the service of field inspectors from the area offices of the Ministry of Supply, instructing them as to inspection requirements at contractors' works and liaising at works with them to ensure that technical details and difficulties (often of a nature then new to most people) were assimilated and overcome. Many problems had to be solved.

The whole series of projects formed an early example of what would now require a total quality assurance programme. However today, working to BS 5750 and 5882, more detailed and searching QA requirements concerning not only inspection but such matters as design, reliability, safety, design reviews, etc. (and more paperwork!) would be insisted upon—and possibly more time would have been required for completion.

Construction of the several atomic energy factories required started at Windscale (Cumberland) in September 1947 where a graphite shop was set up (supervised by IEME) for the production of blocks, to be used as the moderator for the huge piles being built. A welding school was also established. A uranium processing plant for the production of canned uranium slugs for the piles was built at Springfields (near Preston). The IEME organization there later set up a training school for inspectors, dealing amongst other things with vacuum techniques and the leak testing of welds and equipment. Later still a gaseous diffusion plant for the production of the uranium isotope U-235 was built at Capenhurst (Cheshire) and came into operation in 1953. Two large conventional electric power stations were built by the CEGB to supply its needs. The Aldermaston site (an RAF airfield taken over in 1950) came into operation and produced the weaponry required for the first tests at Monte Bello Island (Australia) in September 1952. Concurrently with this military programme, the world's first large commercial atomic energy power station was constructed at Calder Hall (Windscale) and opened by the Queen in 1956. A similar power station was constructed at Chapel Cross (Dumfries).

IEME HQ inspection officers based at Risley visited the many contractors engaged on the various projects, liaising with the various atomic energy establishments, etc. Any contractor having an inspection organization (perhaps approved by AID) was able to use this organization at the discretion of the IEME officer, but with large and complex items of plant an acceptance inspection at works in the presence of the IEME officer often proved necessary. In many cases, after acceptance of 'first off' items the acceptance of follow-up items was delegated to the IEME field inspector from the local office. Field inspectors often became resident at many contractors to carry out such activities as weld inspection and vacuum testing. Very often vacuum test equipment, made by industry to Risley's requirements and operated by trained IEME inspectors, would pump away day and night to check that components could reach the high standards of leak tightness demanded. Many contractors would at first not believe that their components could possibly be leaking, and all had much to learn. From time to time IEME Risley HQ officers would call in specialist staff from IEME main HQ Chislehurst, or other establishments for particular advice, such as on metallurgical and radiographic problems but final decisions remained with them. Another IEME branch dealt with specialized electronic components for the Weapons Group.

In 1952/3 (according to Margaret Gowing, the official historian) IEME HQ staff at Risley numbered 82, but this did not include the many local office field inspectors throughout the country who worked full or part-time on the project. The MOS Chemical Inspectorate (according to the same source) also employed on atomic work some 545 non-industrial plus 132 industrial staff (a good proportion of their total staff). They were engaged upon the most rigorous analysis of materials and products at every stage of the processes in all the factories, employing instruments of all kinds, including elaborate high vacuum mass spectrometers, etc. (much of which equipment was inspected at works by IEME).

Some of the inspection work for Calder Hall and Chapel Cross, being of a semi-conventional nature, was sub-let to the engineering inspectors of a boiler insurance group. Inspection in service is now carried out continuously generally to the requirements of the Nuclear Installations Inspectorate, which was set up in 1959.

### 13.11.1 The Windscale piles

In order to produce the quantity of plutonium urgently required by government priority, designs were quickly prepared for two air-cooled piles with chimneys some 46 ft in diameter rising to a height of over 400 ft. The weight of concrete and contents was some 57,000 tons each. Eight large 2300 h.p. electric motor-driven fans were to force air through the graphite-moderated reactor and up each chimney, the heat being wasted on the mountain air. The best then available scientific information was used in the design, with much attention paid to safety (as far as it was then known), and construction went ahead rapidly. But at a design review (a practice now covered by BS 5882 Clause 3.3.1 and 3.4) the somewhat apocryphal story is told that Sir Christopher Hinton (as he then was) in the light of his intuition (and perhaps the latest information some of which was conflicting) sat down at the drawing board of a draughtsman and sketched a huge filter on the top of the chimney and told the draughtsman to fill in the details and get the thing installed ( a characteristic action on the part of Sir Chris!). To the consternation of the Ministry of Works this modification was actually insisted upon—some 200 tons of steel and much equipment, bricks and concrete had to be lifted and erected on the top of each chimney (the chimneys were already rising high over the Cumberland countryside and the filters could now *only* be put on top). When completed and put into operation in October 1950 the piles seemed to work well and successfully produced the required plutonium on time. But it was found that extra blower power costing some £3000 per week was required and that, because of the restriction of the filter, less plutonium was produced than expected. Consequently these distinctive chimneys with their curious tops (still much in evidence today) became known (at least amongst the staff) as Hinton's Folly!

A form of design review was even held to consider removing the filters as being unnecessary, but the filters were kept and the piles worked steadily for nearly 7 years. A few of the 70,000 uranium cartridges burst from time to time but these incidents were dealt with reasonably safely by established techniques.

Then in October 1957 an incident arose in Pile No.1 following a release of stored Wigner energy (a known phenomenon) causing a fire involving cartridges being processed, and radioactive particles went up the chimney. If the filter installed due to 'Hinton's folly' had not been present then very serious contamination would have been spread around a wide area. But even as it was, the level of radioactive contamination found on grass in the area was well above that permissible, and in consequence all cow's milk had to be thrown away for some weeks. So, due to 'Hinton's folly', what might have been a major national disaster was only a serious incident. Soon after both piles were closed down for good, the necessary plutonium now coming from the Calder Hall nuclear power station completed in 1956. Earlier Hinton himself had predicted the ultimate closure of the piles, expecting their life to be some five years. He said they would stand for a century as 'monuments to our initial ignorance'.

Throughout construction of the piles IEME, although present, took a comparatively minor part certainly in design problems, confining themselves mainly to normal inspection. However some problems which could have come under QA surveillance today can be mentioned. The graphite used as a moderator had to be exceptionally pure—industrial graphite was no use. During an urgent redesign of the graphite structure the quality of the graphite deteriorated alarmingly for no apparent reason. For some time it had been made from petroleum coke produced in Canada from exceptionally pure crude oil from one specific group of wells. The matter was urgent, so Hinton with a Harwell man visited the oil refinery in Canada and quickly diagnosed the trouble as poor industrial housekeeping—the oil had become contaminated by contact with slight traces of other materials which had previously passed through the same pipelines and containing vessels. Somewhat similarly on other nuclear projects slight contamination of many other materials has been found, by inspection, to be the cause of many troubles (see Chapter 2 for contamination of PTFE).

Trouble and mistakes in the laying of the concrete structure of the first Windscale pile and the possible wasting of £2 million could have been avoided, according to Hinton, by the employment of more adequate supervision (largely by MOW rather than IEME).

A problem arose over the choice of whether to use a water-cooled graphite-moderated pile for plutonium production (as had the Americans in remote Hanford (with a four-lane highway 30 miles long to permit rapid evacuation in the event of an emergency!) or an air-cooled graphite-moderated pile, as tried experimentally on a small scale by Harwell. Portal was in favour of using a water-cooled pile, as it was known to work satisfactorily on production. Hinton however was against it and would not relax his remote siting restrictions if forced to have water cooling. A panel was set up to review the matter (in which a QA man today, under BS 5750 and 5882 procedure, would have an interest). They decided in favour of the air-cooled pile (which was later developed into the gas-cooled and AGR reactors of the UK power programme). Incidentally a combination of circumstances were foreseen (including failure of the water supply) which, however unlikely, could lead to a violent temperature rise, vaporizing of the fuel elements and wide scattering of radioactivity causing a major disaster similar to that which occurred in 1986 at Chernobyl.*

Yes, Hinton certainly made the right decision!

*Note:* if one considers BS 5882 *Specification for a total quality assurance programme for nuclear power plants/installations* as applying to the project for the Windscale piles (1947–57) it will be seen that Section 3—Design Control—covers in general what actually happened under Hinton's administration. In particular Sections 3.3—Design verification, design reviews, use of alternative calculating methods, and 3.4—Design changes, including on-site changes, cover the last minute decision to install the filter, the struggle with calculations involving conflicting information on graphite expansion and other effects, and the later design review that might have implied that Hinton had been over-cautious. But, as has been shown, the action taken changed what might have been a serious catastrophe into 'an incident'. Although at the time no direct casualties were reported it has been estimated (by NRPB) some 25–30 years later that some 33 people may have died prematurely as a result (meaning perhaps that of the people in the plant and its vicinity at the time some 33 more than the nationally expected average number may have died from cancer, leukemia, etc. during the intervening period). The Atomic Authority has paid compensation to some employees without admitting liability.

This emphasizes the necessity of keeping accurate records of individual workers' (and others) exposure to radiation. If, for instance, these showed

---

*The Chernobyl disaster was additionally complicated by the formation of hydrogen which, on ignition, blew off the containing roof (see 13.6.4).

that a dose well above the then permitted amount for the period involved had been received then liability might be difficult to dispute.[†]

## 13.11.2 The Capenhurst gaseous diffusion plant

Perhaps a few extracts (with notes in brackets) quoted from Margaret Gowing's official history (*Britain and Atomic Energy, Independence and Deterrence*, vol. 2, *Policy Execution*, Macmillan, 1974) concerning the gaseous diffusion plant for the separation of the uranium isotope U-235 from natural uranium which was built at Capenhurst, will illustrate something of the nature of the technicalities facing inspection/QA staff engaged in total quality assurance for a nuclear installation (or for that matter any major project involving high technology of or beyond the 'state of the art' complexity). Gowing states: 'A gaseous diffusion plant is still, many years later, considered to be one of the most complex and taxing scientific engineering tasks' The material in the form of a very obnoxious gas uranium hexafluoride (hex) had to be pumped through a succession of hundreds of units each comprising a compressor and its motor, a control valve and a membrane system. The lighter U-235 isotope would tend to diffuse more quickly through the porous membrane. The units, starting large, got successively smaller as the degree of separation increased (there is only 0·7% of U-235 in normal uranium). 'The engineers . . . were faced with problems about the basic processes, the materials used and the development of crucial new components . . . There was one common factor. This was the importance of keeping the plant vacuum tight and leak proof to standards never known before in an industrial plant of this size.' (It was said that the site contained the largest building under one roof in Western Europe and consumed as much electricity as a city the size of Birmingham.) 'The plant had to work under vacuum to avoid the need to operate at inconveniently high temperatures, in order that hex would not condense. Working under vacuum there was a danger of air leakages; any moisture thus introduced would react with hex to form solid uranium compounds which would block the membranes. The necessary vacuum pumps and testing equipment were made available from industry' but manufacturing industry at large knew little or nothing of the complexities of high vacuum technology and at first refused to believe that the testing equipment really found leaks in the components they produced. They had to learn the hard way (as did many of

---

[†]The release of papers in early 1988 under the 30 year rule shows that a technical report by Sir William Penny (Director of Aldermaston) on the Windscale incident was suppressed at the time. Amongst many things he criticized shortcomings in the organization, such as the preparation of operational procedures, many of which today are covered by BS 5750 and BS 5883. The attention of lawyers is drawn to the Product Liability section of the Consumer Protection Act 1987 which allows an organization charged with negligence to plead 'state of the art' or 'development risks defence' in any civil proceedings brought against them (see 14.6.2).

the authority's own staff—a training programme was necessary). 'Risley, however, had to develop the use of argon arc welding on a scale never before used and to an unprecedently high standard . . . The plant was to have many miles of piping . . . there were two alternatives—nickel plated steel or aluminium (after various trials aluminium was finally chosen but welders had to be specially trained to produce clean leak tight welds and the standards of cleanliness, inspection and testing were very high) . . . Problems came with the compressors and their motors . . . and the glands where the motor shaft entered the compressor casing . . . nitrogen could be used as a buffer gas, some small motors and their compressors were both run in hex ... a large refrigeration plant was required . . . most thorough testing of the main components and measurement of performance were essential.'

### 13.12  Nuclear installations and total QA

One essential requirement of a total QA system for nuclear installations is that there should be very good technical and *personal* co-ordination between the many organizations involved, and a well recognized chain of command from the highest to the low, so that conflicting orders or decisions are not given.

In the past there have been complaints, particularly from BNFL and CEGB, about the central government inspectorates. They have been accused of conflicting interests and decisions, or of seeming incapable of making a decision; or duplication of visits by different inspectorates to check almost identical matters, or even of adopting different standards.

It was alleged that a failure of communication between inspectorates (or between different departments of CEGB, BNFL or contractors) may arise.

Investigation and government scrutiny put forward two alternatives to improve matters:

(i) the brigading of all nuclear inspection functions within HSE (this would have advantages and disadvantages);

(ii) joint top management action to achieve a better system of co-ordination across existing departmental lines of command.

Alternative (ii) was accepted and it was arranged that a joint DoE (RCI), Welsh Office, MAFF, HSE (NII) memorandum be issued, and a Joint Review Committee set up to improve matters.

It should be realized that BNFL and CEGB (together with UKAEA), having been in the business at the sharp end for a long time, may look askance at perhaps relative newcomers with little 'hands-on' experience telling them what to do. Therefore it is essential that the inspectorates, etc. should be staffed and particularly controlled by people of the highest quality and experience whose decisions will be acceptable to industry.

Besides the desirability that a total QA system should be in operation for all nuclear projects it is also highly desirable (if not essential) that QA (including that in design and development) should be backed up by authoritative and independent sources of information.

One such source is the Advisory Committee on the Safety of Nuclear Installations (ACSNI). ACSNI seeks to advise Ministers and the Health and Safety Commission on broad issues of safety policy and on the resources needed to implement such policy. It is composed of some 20 members (scientists, professors, and professional engineers of standing such as FRS) who are regarded as independent, plus representatives of the Trades Union Congress and the Confederation of British Industry, together with assessors and observers as may be necessary.

It should be able to give unprejudiced but technically competent advice, and keep a watching brief on all nuclear and related matters. As far as is humanly possible it regards itself as independent; it stresses the vital importance of the independence and competence of the NII, and has recommended a 50% increase in their numbers (see ACSNI's report for 1984–1986, HMSO, 1987). Note that the independence of QA/inspection organizations and their decision-making authority is receiving increasing attention today (e.g. see space shuttle accident report, 13.6.7).

### 13.12.1 Nuclear Installations Inspectorate procedure

No nuclear installation in the UK may be constructed without a site licence, issued by the NII of HSE under the Nuclear Installations Act 1965, nor operated without certificates of authorization issued by the Department of the Environment (DOE) and/or the Ministry of Agriculture, Fisheries and Food (MAFF) under Section 6 of the *Radioactive Substances Act* 1960. The certificates incorporate terms regulating discharges which are intended to ensure that the public do not receive radiation doses (now expressed in sieverts (Sv)) above the given dose limits (see Table 6.10 and 6.11 (1/10 of that of a worker)). The terms of the certificates and their enforcement lies with the Authorizing Departments (monitoring being done by DOE's Radiochemical Inspectorate) guided by advisory bodies like the National Radiological Protection Board (NRPB) and the Nuclear Installations Inspectorate (NII).

NII will be involved from the start in the control of plant design and also during construction and operation. Whilst inspection during manufacture and installation is primarily the responsibility of NII, inspection by approved firms' organizations, insurance companies inspection etc. will also be involved.

However, NII's powers do not theoretically extend to UKAEA sites*, where UKAEA use their own organization, although NII will be consulted and advise on safety and other matters. The storage of waste at nuclear sites

---

*Nor to Crown Premises, but the protection standards applied (by MOD) are at least as high as those applied to civil organizations.

falls within the responsibility of NII, but its discharge and disposal comes under the jurisdiction of the authorizing departments. There seem to be a few grey areas regarding responsibility, but with co-operation and mutual advice and assistance there should be few problems. In general NII is responsible for safety inside a plant and the authorizing department (DOE and MAFF) outside.

The recommendations on dose limitation of the International Commission on Radiological Protection (ICRP) have been incorporated in UK legislation as laid down in Ionizing Radiation Regulations 1985 (see Table 6.10, Part 1, Dose Limits for the whole body) which gives a dose limit of 50 mSv (5 rem) per year for a worker aged 18 or over, and of 5 mSv (0·5 rem) per year for any other person. In addition the UK now accepts the advice of the NRPB that use of this 5 mSv limit per year combined with techniques striving to reach levels as low as reasonably achievable (ALARA) or the best practicable means (BPM) will result generally in an average dose rate equivalent of around or less than the 1 mSv per year received by the local fishing and/or fish eating community.

Perhaps, surprisingly, MAFF Monitoring Reports on Radioactivity in Coastal Waters around UK Nuclear sites during 1984 were all below this limit (Sizewell A for instance being less than 0·01 mSv whilst the largest (Sellafield) was 0·84 mSv). Seeing that the natural background level of radiation in Dartmoor Forest has been recorded as 0·964 mSv (gamma) there would seem to be little to worry about regarding the *normal* operation of nuclear installations. But, as always, some experts will be found to disagree, particularly regarding some of the more harmful radionuclides discharged from Sellafield, such as ruthenium–106, strontium–90, and plutonium (the respective authorized discharges for which were 533 TBq, 204 TBq, and 331 TBq in 1983). However steps are being taken to install new plant at Sellafield which will substantially reduce these discharges, and in any case the dose limits given in Schedule 1 Part 1 of Ionizing Radiation Regulations 1985 (see Table 6.4) now include the intake of radionuclides.

There is a somewhat complex relationship between the discharge limits for various radionuclides worked out by MAFF/DOE and the 1985 ICRP limits which supposedly now include them. It has been pointed out (by NRPB) that readings below these limits do not indicate a safe situation; rather that readings above them indicate an unacceptable situation. To illustrate the widely varying and often highly charged views on the subject some 44 appendices in the Parliamentary Report on Radioactive Waste 1986 give memoranda from many different organizations. Extracts from two memoranda will have to suffice.

In Appendix 31 the Head of Medical Physics of the Northern Regional Health Authority and its Radiation Protection Adviser (responsible for serving the population of a huge area including Windscale/Sellafield, a nuclear submarine facility, several atomic power stations, reactors and chemical plants), in a lengthy memorandum mentions, when discussing a government proposal for reducing the discharge of liquid radioactive waste from Sellafield, that:

> If the *present* level of radioactive waste discharge from Sellafield were continued for a lifetime this would give a risk of death in the worst case (that of a voracious eater of seafood in the Sellafield area) comparable with:
>
> smoking an extra $\frac{1}{2}$ cigarette per month, or
>
> spending a 5 week holiday per year in a high natural radiation background area of the UK (such as Cornwall or Aberdeen)
>
> For an ordinary member of the general public the risk would be comparable with:
>
> smoking an extra 2 cigarettes per lifetime, or
>
> spending 1 hour per year in say Cornwall or Aberdeen.

In Appendix 32 a short memorandum from an Irish organization in Dublin gives its opinions and states its objections to Windscale/Sellafield:

> (i) There is no proven safe level of exposure to nuclear radiation and yet the radioactive waste from Windscale/Sellafield is discharged directly into the Irish Sea and environment where it enters the food chain and endangers human, animal and plant life.
>
> (ii) The potential danger to life and the environment in the case of an accident at the plant.
>
> (iii) The danger of the plant coming under attack—whether from a nuclear war or from terrorists.

In due course, in such matters, parliament through its committees and with the advice of government experts and others will have to decide from the evidence submitted which of the many often conflicting views are acceptable. Not all of the evidence/reports make light of the situation to such an extent as that expressed in Appendix 31. In some cases well qualified doctors and scientists representing other organizations take a somewhat contrary view. Some give lengthy explanations regarding their views. As was once said in another connection: 'To a believer no explanation is necessary; to an unbeliever no explanation will convince'.

Eventually legislation on the subject may be forthcoming and it will then be up to the inspectors, advised as necessary by the scientists, to interpret and enforce this legislation.

Today nuclear installations are subjected to continuous surveillance under the control of the NII. The requirements of BS 5882 (particularly Section 10—Inspection and Surveillance) are fully met, together with much else (see Whitehead, *IEE Journal*, Oct. 85—Long Term Safety Review of Nuclear Power Stations). Perhaps the rapid design and putting into service and the continued successful trouble-free long-running (30 years) of the original Calder Hall Magnox type power stations is a fitting tribute to

Hinton's organization; whilst the continued satisfactory condition and performance proved by constant NDT surveillance and the latest techniques (for instance at one station 5·5 km of fabrication welds have been inspected and found to be still free of significant defects) must be a tribute to the original design, workmanship and inspection. Obviously constant vigilance is necessary at all nuclear and any other hazardous installations. Minor faults, cracks, leaks etc. will develop, and it is the aim of the inspectorates to detect (or even predict) them before they can cause serious trouble.

### 13.13 The Sellafield thermal oxide reprocessing plant

An example of total QA as it might be applied to a hazardous chemical plant of a most complex nature which has caused much public and political agitation on the grounds of safety will now be considered.

This is the thermal oxide reprocessing plant (Thorp) now under construction at Windscale (Sellafield), Cumbria for BNFL and currently regarded as one of the largest projects underway in Western Europe. A total quality assurance programme complying at least with BS 5750 and BS 5882 is essential.

The design intent is to take spent fuel from nuclear reactors, recover the valuable uranium and plutonium and other materials, and separate and store the fission product wastes in a permanent and safe manner. Specifically it will deal with fuel from AGR and perhaps other reactors. Magnox fuel is dealt with by an existing plant.

Spent fuel arrives normally in two-ton loads shielded in a railway container weighing about 100 tons. Several thousand tons of fuel will be stored on site under water which acts as a radiation shield and cooling medium. The length of stay under water before reprocessing may be specified (possibly at least 3 years) together with the maximum expected rate of processing. The heat due to radiation from the spent fuel heats the cooling water; this heat (to the extent of some tens of megawatts) must be removed (the question arises: should it be wasted?) and the contaminated water (it may be radioactive) has to be disposed of as effluent.

Design, manufacture and installation of the plant and its components must be carried out fully in accordance with the procedures laid down in BS 5750 Part 1 and as detailed earlier in this book (see 9.4.7), QA staff undertaking their full supervisory duties.

The materials of the process vessels, etc., the methods of design, construction, welding, testing and inspection must be selected on lines similar to those for pressure vessels (e.g. BS 5500) and other items of plant. Safety, fault analysis and Hazop studies etc. should be carried out, including design allowances for earthquake (seismic) shock. Full use of computers will undoubtedly be made. They are and will increasingly be used for design calculations, and for solving complex problems and analysing data of such a nature that would be impracticable by other means. Surveillance of these latter problems may create difficulties for QA staff, who may not be that 'au fait' with computers, because a rough check for the right order of answer by ordinary arithmetic would be impossible. If the computer, or its programming is doubted, and the calculation is of importance, then it must be reviewed by an independent body preferably using a different method and computer program.

Leakage from the plant must be controlled, including leakage of contaminated water through the concrete of the fuel storage ponds. Strict control and inspection of the laying of this concrete is essential. The actual processing begins with the removal of the fuel rods from their heavy container, removal of their outer cladding and their processing with nitric acid through the various process vessels, etc. all with much remote handling gear. The bulk of the material recovered is uranium which can be enriched and used again. The plutonium finally extracted by the plant is toxic and fissile and must be closely controlled and contained. The fission products are intensely radioactive and emit heat which must be removed. Stringent criteria on the accumulation and interaction of fissile material (plutonium and uranium) must be met, which defines in some areas the geometry of the plant and/or the maximum mass which can be handled (so as to prevent criticality and the danger of nuclear reaction—see BS 3598). The release of radioactive effluents, solid, liquid and gaseous has to be closely controlled within limits specified by the appropriate ministries (including the Department of the Environment (DoE), and the Ministry of Agriculture and Food (MAFF) and other authorities).

The remaining radioactive liquid waste (perhaps some 3% of the original spent fuel) is concentrated and processed for storage and perhaps eventual disposal. Some may be stored in solid form by a process of vitrification (25% waste to 75% glass). Like industrial slag-heaps (such as Aberfan), problems will remain.

Safety standards, inspections, etc. are controlled by the NII. Throughout the plant the workers must be shielded and protected from radioactivity and prevented from breathing radioactive contamination, dust etc. A suitable ventilation system must be provided. Instrumentation to measure radioactivity levels and to warn of danger is required. Personal monitoring and recording of radiation dosage received by workers is essential to ensure that the internationally agreed levels are not exceeded. Remote handling equipment with television control must be provided.

In-service inspection with the latest NDT equipment to check for any possibly developing defects, and facilities for the carrying out of maintenance are required. Perhaps hundreds of kilometres of piping and many vessels will have to be checked; the number of radiographs and other NDT records required may well run into hundreds of thousands.

Measurement of contamination on surfaces, walls, etc. must be carried out periodically, together with any necessary decontamination (see BS 4247).

A monitoring service to detect the extent of any leakage of radiation and radioactive waste into the environment outside the site must be operated. Primary responsibility for this rests with the plant operator, but MAFF and the Radio-Chemical Inspectorate (RCI) of the DoE will carry out independent monitoring as a 'spot check' to verify that the limits they have set in their certificate of authorization are being met. The NII will also carry out their own on-site inspections. In addition the stored material in the cooling ponds and elsewhere is subject to inspection by the International Atomic Energy Agency to assure them that there has been no unauthorized diversion of fissile material (which could be stolen for military purposes!)

The storing of the fission products and radioactive waste, particularly their storing and/or disposal elsewhere, is a highly political problem (see 6.17.9(ix)).

All the inspections described above must be carried out periodically throughout the life of the plant and must be continued even after the plant has been closed down, until (and perhaps after) the site has been demolished. Some comparisons with the original UK Atomic Programme (see 3.11) may be of interest. (see Table 13.15).

## TABLE 13.15
### The UK nuclear programme

|  | Thorp (estimates) | Windscale (1946 to 1953 prices)[†] | Risley HQ |
|---|---|---|---|
| Cost (say) | £1,350 million | £34 million | Share of £8m (say 1/3) |
| Staff (incl. professional and design etc.) | 3000 (a high proportion being contractors' staff) | 1036 non-industrial and 1730 industrial* |  |
| Timescale | 8 years | 8 years |  |
| Completion | over 3 years behind schedule | On time |  |

*Includes share of Chemical Inspectorate and 82 IEME officers allocated to Risley projects.

[†]*Notes:* The total cost of the whole nuclear programme over these years was several hundred million pounds sterling. The staff total (nationwide) of the NII in 1984 numbered 106. The Windscale and Risley figures have been adapted from M. Gowing's *Official History*. The Thorp figures and account are adapted from published sources (including IEE Journals).

Today besides assessing and monitoring new plant such as Thorp and stressing QA requirements, RCI (now part of HM Inspectorate of Pollution) have also to review and monitor discharges and disposal of radioactive waste from non-nuclear premises such as hospitals and industrial sites. Far too many such sites, although normally having trivial approved discharges, etc., suffer accidental releases due to poor housekeeping, or may lose material due to poor security or stock/record keeping.*

## 13.14 Total quality assurance and the Sizewell B Report

Some of the contents and conclusions of the Inspector's Report on the CEGB's application for consent for the construction of a pressurized water reactor (PWR) at Sizewell may be applied, as may be relevant, to any hazardous industrial plant. (Sizewell A, a Magnox reactor station, had been constructed in 1960 and came into operation in 1966).

The CEGB applied for consent for the PWR in January 1981. Previously in 1971 consent had been given to construct a British advanced gas cooled reactor (AGR) on the site, but the CEGB later abandoned this.

The government appointed the Inspector in July 1981. The Public Inquiry started in January 1983 and finished in March 1985. The Inspector's Report was published in January 1987 and consisted of 8 volumes (109 chapters). The associated paperwork, evidence, etc. was enormous. Oral evidence comprised some 16 million words. The Nuclear Installations Inspectorate of necessity had to attend and provide evidence, reports, etc. Many man–hours of inspectors' time were spent on the inquiry, hopefully without detriment to their exacting duties elsewhere.

The Public Inquiry resulted in the Inspector (Sir Frank Layfield QC) giving his consent for the construction (subject to various conditions and recommendations). The government gave permission and the CEGB put the wheels in motion to initiate construction in March 1987.

In reaching his decision the Inspector and his assessors were primarily concerned with the engineering analysis of safety, based on established engineering practice and standards and the reliability and competence of NII and the CEGB's designers and safety assessors. Accident probability analysis and risk estimation were taken into account (see Chaps 2c and 47c of the report) but too much weight was not placed on the results, which, states the Inspector, are subject to substantial uncertainty.

---

*The resulting collective hazard from non-nuclear premises may be comparable or greater than that from a properly regulated installation. For instance, Oldbury nuclear power station in 1985 released 1TBq ($10^{12}$ Bq) of tritium and some 1·7 GBq (1.7 × $10^9$ Bq) of other liquid effluent. A West London non-nuclear manufacturer *accidentally* released 35 TBq (35 × $10^{12}$ Bq) of tritium; he was prosecuted by the inspectorate for infringing regulations, but the nuclear power stations kept well within the limits laid down.

The Inspector's report states:

Quality assurance is the means by which the CEGB seeks to ensure that the general design intention is met at all stages from detailed design (through manufacture, inspection, commissioning and operation) to decommissioning, and that significant shortcomings are detected and corrected. It is important to ensure that a satisfactory position (regarding QA) is reached and sustained over a long period. The QA programme would need to be carried out in many places by several organizations and by a large number of individuals. A great number of items would be involved, and each would require meticulous care ... I place great importance on the NII's role in monitoring the development and implementation of the QA programme and on the use of independent expertise and regular reviews of the programme.

A complete assessment of human factors (human error) in the design and operation of plant ... will be needed ... and NII must ensure that it is carried out thoroughly and its implications ... considered and acted upon where necessary.

Managerial arrangements for training ... of staff and operators [are necessary] ... I recommend that ... fuel loading shall not start until at least one year after a simulator has been installed and is ready for use for training operators.

Furthermore, with hazardous nuclear plant, total QA organizations at *all* stages are not only a commercial necessity, but a national and international necessity (remember, French PWRs are in operation all along the Channel Coast and are nearer to British centres of population than many British reactors—and certainly nearer than Chernobyl!). High technology and costly test equipment and procedures must be developed and used in the interests of both quality and safety in an endeavour to guard against all faults, likely and unlikely.

The Layfield report sidetracks somewhat the question of the disposal of radioactive waste, but a realistic answer *must* be agreed as this waste *exists* and continues to increase.

The Layfield report does not adjudicate as to whether the British AGR is safer than a PWR, it merely states in effect that in the Inspector's opinion, using the techniques indicated and relying on the competence of the CEGB and NII, the PWR proposed for Sizewell could be built and operated without undue risk (British Magnox and AGR reactors have operated safely for up to 25–30 years without undue trouble).

The Layfield report (when written) estimated that the PWR would be cheaper than an AGR or a coal-fired power station (presumably incorporating equipment to reduce 'acid rain' to EEC limits), all of the same output. The possibility of building further stations of the well proved AGR design is not considered. (Many US-designed PWR and BWR have been built and many exported. They are now somewhat under a cloud due to Three Mile Island troubles, etc. Only two British reactors (both Magnox) have so far been exported.)

Obviously in order to design, construct and operate a hazardous industrial plant, QA organizations that can competently oversee *all* relevant activities (generally to at least the requirements of for instance BS 5750 Part 1 and also to BS 5882 in the case of nuclear installations) are an absolute commercial necessity. Such organizations must be able to maintain their efficiency over the years and successfully satisfy any audits, reviews, inspections, etc. carried out by any supervisory authorities; their staff must be adequately trained and experienced, and controlled by leaders with enthusiasm, patience and integrity.

Unless a firm involved in the hazardous industrial plant field can comply with the above requirements it might as well close down, before it is too late and bankruptcy or disaster overtakes it (because it would not attract orders from discerning buyers, and/or its plant could fail, perhaps bringing financial disaster).

**References and further reading**

Billinton, R. and Allan, R.N., *Reliability evaluation of power systems*, Pitman, 1984.

Carter, A.D.S., *Mechanical reliability*, Macmillan, 1986.

*Condition Monitoring in Hostile Environments*, Seminar Proceedings (ERA Report No. 85-0118), ERA Technology Ltd, Leatherhead, 1985.

Cane, B.J., 'Remanent Life Assessment by Strain Measurement of Plant', *International Journal Pressure Vessels & Piping*, vol. 20, 1982.

*Chernobyl – a Technical Appraisal*, British Nuclear Energy Soc., 1987.

*Condition Monitoring of machinery and plant*, Seminar, Mech. Eng. Pub., 1985.

Dummer, G.W.A. and Griffin, N.B., *Electronics reliability—Calculation and design*, Pergamon, 1966.

Ireson, W.G., *Reliability Handbook*, McGraw-Hill, 1988.

Jardine, A.K.S., *Maintenance, replacement and reliability*, Pitman, 1973.

Lees, F.P., *Loss Prevention in the Process Industries*, Butterworth, 1980.

Mann, L. (ed.), *Maintenance Management*, Lexington, Mass., 1984.

Nixon, Frank, *Managing to achieve quality and reliability*, McGraw-Hill, 1971.

*QA in Design*, Symposium Mech. Eng. Pub., 1982.

Singh, C. and Billinton, R., *Systems reliability, modelling and evaluation*, Hutchinson, 1979.

Truscott, W.T., *Analytical Methods in Reliability Engineering*, Industrial & Commercial Techniques, London, 1970.

(from PD 6510 1980):

I. Mech. E., *Refurbishment and Life Extension of Steam Plant*, Mech. Eng. Pub. 1987.

I. Mech. E., *Conference on Engineering Aspect of Creep*, Oct. 1980.

Bolton, B.S. and Verrier, K., *Determining the Residual Life of Boiler Components working under creep conditions.*

Williams, K.R. and Plastow, B., *The Creep Life Assessment of Boiler Components.*

Phillips, I.I., Hutchins, C.A. and Williamson, J., *The Practical Use of and Extrapolation Technique to Aid Life Assessment of a 2 1/4 Cr 1 Mo Superheater.*

Moles, M.D.C., Leemans, D.V. and Westwood, H.J., *Residual Life Estimation of Boiler Tubing in Thermal Power Plants.*

BS 4200 *Guide on the reliability of electronic equipment and parts used therein.*

The UKAEA through its Safety and Systems Reliability Directorate runs the National Centre for Systems Reliability (located at Wigshaw Lane, Culcheth, Risley, Warrington) which can provide a wealth of information; it operates a consultancy service and a failure data bank and is now managed jointly with the HSE to carry out research and development work for the purpose of Section 1 of the *HSW Act* 1974.

# 14 The legal framework

## 14.1 Liabilities of the engineer/inspector

It is expected by the courts that engineers and others involved in industrial concerns should have sufficient practical working knowledge of the law affecting their particular profession as will enable them to carry out their duties effectively.

Engineers, surveyors, inspectors, etc. should know that they may risk criminal prosecution if they breach any of the statutory duties assigned to them particularly under the *Health & Safety at Work (HSW) Act*, 1974 and its related Acts and statutory regulations. A case against them could be taken under criminal law, the state itself prosecuting the offender; fines or imprisonment could result. The injured party could also sue for damages under civil law. As well as these liabilities the engineer may, if he is also an employer, have liabilities in respect of the health and safety of his employees and of the general public. *The Employer's Liability (Defective Equipment) Act*, 1969, states:

> Employers are also strictly liable for all personal injuries to their employees which may arise from defective equipment even though such equipment was supplied or serviced by a third party ... even if the employer is unaware of the defect and could not have been expected to find it.

Under the *HSW Act* Section 3 he could be liable for death, injuries or damage to the general public caused by any activities carried out at his undertaking. Furthermore, as a producer, he would be liable for prosecution by purchasers under the *Consumer Protection and Safety Acts* (see 14.8) which now include the product liability Directive of the EEC.

But first the legislation (statutory and otherwise) regarding health and safety at work will be considered—particularly its effect on inspection.

### 14.1.1 Statutory requirements—health, safety and inspection

At Common Law an employer is bound to take reasonable care of the safety and health of his work people, and to this end he must provide safe plant and machinery, a competent staff, a safe system of work and a safe place of work.

He must comply strictly with the requirements of the *HSW Act* 1974, its associated *Factories Act* 1961 and the *Offices, Shops and Railway Premises Act* 1963, and such other Acts as may be applicable. The most important of these, relevant to industry, are included in Table 14.1.

In addition, there are numerous Statutory Instruments, Orders and Regulations made under the appropriate Acts; examples include regulations covering chemical works, building construction and electricity—made under the *Factories Act*, and the Prescribed Dangerous Machinery Order 1964—made under the *Offices, Shops and Railway Premises Act* 1963.

## TABLE 14.1

*Some Acts of Parliament relevant to industry involving health, safety and inspection*
(All as amended by any later legislation)

---

The Atomic Energy Authority Act 1954
*The Factories Act 1961
*The Explosives Act 1875, and the Explosive Substances Act 1923
*The Boiler Explosions Act 1882 and 1890
*The Alkali, etc., Works Regulation Act 1906
The Clean Air Act 1956
*The Nuclear Installations Act 1959 and 1965
*The Petroleum (Consolidation) Act 1928
*The Radioactive Substances Act 1960
The Lead Paint (Protection against Poisoning) Act 1926
*The Mines and Quarries Act 1954
*The Public Health Acts 1936, 1937 and 1961 (includes legislation dealing with Trade Effluent)
*The Public Health (Smoke Abatement) Act 1926
The Rivers, Prevention of Pollution, Act 1951
The Thermal Insulation (Industrial Buildings) Act 1957
*The Offices, Shops and Railway Premises Act 1963
The Weights and Measures Act 1963
The Young Persons Employment Act 1938
*The Petroleum (Transfer of Licences) Act 1936
*The Hydrogen Cyanide (Fumigation) Act 1937
*The Pipelines Act 1962
*The Employment Medical Advisory Service Act 1972
The Fire Precautions Act 1971 and 1974
The Disposal of Poisonous Wastes Act 1972
The Control of Pollution Act 1974

---

*Indicates taken over or relevant to the *HSW Act* 1974, operating under the control of the Health and Safety Executive.

Many of these requirements may involve inspection in its various forms, either directly or indirectly.

For instance the *Factories Act* 1961 and other statutory requirements state that a 'competent person' shall test and examine various appliances and items of plant (see 12.4) often at specified intervals.

Some of the legislation and regulations relating to building and construction are listed in Table 14.3 and to electricity supply in Table 14.4; for some relating to gases and dangerous environments see 6.15 and 6.18. For legislation regarding pressure vessels see 3.2 and 14.8, and regarding 'in-use' inspection see 12.4 and 12.5.

### 14.1.2 The Robens Report

In May 1970, following criticism and disquiet over the somewhat tangled legislation dealing with health and safety at work, a government committee of inquiry under the chairmanship of Lord Robens (a former trade union leader and Chairman of the National Coal Board) was appointed to 'review the provision made for the safety and health of persons in . . . employment . . . , consider any changes needed . . . and any further steps required to safeguard members of the public from hazards . . . and to make recommendations'.

The Robens Committee reported in July 1972. Amongst their criticisms were:

(i) There is too much law (the main statutes are backed by some 500 detailed statutory instruments).

(ii) Much of this law was intrinsically unsatisfactory, 'written in a language and style largely unintelligible'

(iii) Administration of existing laws between many government departments was complex and created confusion.

Following the committee's recommendations the *HSW Act* 1974 was passed by Parliament.

### 14.2 The HSW Act 1974

This Act, which has already been briefly summarized in 1.2 is a lengthy legal document. It does, however, attempt to whittle down some of the complexities complained of in the Robens Report. Administration and control is put into the hands of a single independent body, the Health and Safety Commission (and its Health and Safety Executive). Some 31 existing Acts of Parliament are taken over and in effect replaced by one (the *HSW Act*), but much of the substance of the old Acts remains in force, at least until modified or replaced. The law is still backed by some 500 detailed statutory instruments (probably more now); whether there is still too much law and whether it is now satisfactory and intelligible are questions which industry itself must answer in due course.

The summary of the Act (see 1.2) states its objects (given in Sect. 1 of the Act), the general duties of employers and their employees (Sects 2–9) and the methods of enforcement used by inspectors, etc. (Sects 18–26). Further details with notes and some comments (in square brackets) will now be given.

Although the *HSW Act* 1974 in effect takes over much of the legislation of the *Factories Act* 1961 and other relevant Acts (see Table 14.1) its requirements often go much deeper. For instance under Section 2(3) every employer has to prepare and keep revised a written *safety policy statement* with respect to the health and safety at work of his employees showing the organization and arrangements for so doing, with detailed documents, rules and safety procedures, etc., applicable to his business. This statement must be brought to the notice of all his employees.

Under Section 2(4) the Act provides for the appointment by recognized trade unions of *safety representatives* from amongst the employees. This is implemented by SI 1977 no.500 Safety Representatives and Safety Committees. Regulations and a Code of Practice and *Guidance Notes* have been issued by the Health and Safety Executive.

Section 2(5) provided for the election by employees of safety representatives from amongst the employees to represent them in consultations with the employers. This was obviously to cater for non-union representatives, but Sect 2(5) has now been revoked.

It would now seem that in the case of a non-union shop (or otherwise) there should be no objection to the appointment of safety 'persons' from amongst the employees. But they would not have the 'statutory rights' (including pay and time off for safety duties) enjoyed by a trade union-appointed safety representative as outlined below.

The functions of safety representatives include:

(i) taking all reasonably practicable steps to keep themselves informed of the legal requirements, hazards and safety measures applicable to the workplace, and the health and safety policy of their employer;

(ii) encouraging co-operation between their employer and his employees in these health and Safety matters and checking the effectiveness of the measures taken (Sect. 2(6));

(iii) bringing to the employer's notice any unsafe or unhealthy conditions or practices or unsatisfactory arrangements for welfare (this can be done by day-to-day observations and/or by carrying out inspections; a typical inspection report form is shown in Figure 14.1).

The safety representative should receive some training (by his employer's staff, by his trade union or by an outside college) and must receive pay and time off from his normal duties for his safety work. It is possible he might be an experienced worker and a shop steward. His employer is required to give

**Health and safety at work**
**Safety representatives: Report form**

| Notification to the employers (or his representative) of conditions and working practices considered unsafe or unhealthy and of arrangements for welfare at work considered to be unsatisfactory | | | This column to be completed by the employer |
|---|---|---|---|
| Date and time of inspection and matter observed *10.1.88. 8 a.m. Unusual odour with some heat in compressor room* Building C.9. Access to plant rendered dangerous by oil spillage and obstructions | Particulars of matter(s) notified to employer or his representative *Matters notified to Principal foreman W. Green* | Name of safety representative, notifying matter to employer *J. Smith* | Remedial action taken or explanation if not taken. This information to be relayed to the safety representative(s) |
| (This report does not imply that the conditions are safe and healthy or that the arrangements for welfare at work are satisfactory in all other respects) | | | Signature of employer or his representative: |
| Signature(s) of safety representative(s): ............................................................................ | | | |
| Date ............................................................ | | | Date .................... |
| Record of receipt of form by the employer or his representative: Signature ............................................................ Date ............................................................ | | | |

**Fig. 14.1   Safety representatives' report form**

him technical information about hazards, processes and future policy and plans, and he must have access to any relevant records.

If two or more safety representatives request it the employer must establish a *safety committee* to promote co-operation between employers and employees and to provide a forum for studying and investigating accidents, diseases, reports, etc. on health and safety matters (Sect. 2.7), and a link with the appropriate inspectorates of the enforcing authority.

In the past it has not been uncommon for large organizations, factories, etc., to have such a committee which could deal with health and safety matters. Senior management, departmental heads, safety specialists, line management, the company doctor etc. would be appointed to such a committee and often workers' representatives (as with Whitley councils, etc.). Other specialists might be co-opted as necessary. But now it is a legal requirement that trade union safety representatives be appointed. This is all to the good if effective co-operation is to be achieved between workers and management (see 14.10—safety officers).

Every employer must conduct his undertaking in such a way as to ensure, as far as is reasonably practicable, that not only his employees but *all other persons* who may be affected thereby are *not exposed to risks to their health or safety* (Section 3). The best practicable means must be employed for preventing the *emission into the atmosphere of any noxious or offensive substance* or for rendering any such emissions harmless (Section 5). The employer would be expected to limit such emissions to within the maximum permissible concentrations recognized by some code or standard.

For the inspector and all engaged upon total quality assurance Section 6 of the Act is perhaps the most relevant. This requires that any person who designs, manufactures, imports or supplies any article or substance, must ensure, *so far as is reasonably practicable*, that by testing and examination *it is safe and without risks to health when properly used*, and that adequate information to this end is made available and that any necessary research to eliminate or minimize any such risks is carried out. Under Section 7 it is the duty of every employee to take reasonable care for *the health and safety of himself at work*, and of other persons who may be affected by his acts or omissions. No person shall *interfere with or misuse* anything provided in pursuance of relevant statutory requirements in the interests of safety etc. (Section 8). The Commission has power to direct *investigations and enquiries* into any accident, occurrence or other matter (Section 14).

No real technical details are given in the sections of the Act but the Commission is empowered to make health and safety regulations (by Section 15), to approve and/or issue (after consulting any appropriate bodies) codes of practice and publications giving practical guidance and information on technical matters (Section 16). A list of *Standards significant to Health and Safety at Work* is published by the HSE. In any *civil or criminal proceedings* failure by a party to observe any provision of a relevant approved code of practice (or its equivalent) *may* render him liable to prosecution (see Section 17). Or, putting it briefly, compliance with a relevant approved code of practice, etc. would be an extremely good form of defence.

Various codes of practice together with guidance notes (including those dealing with safety representatives, lead and asbestos) have been and are being approved by the Health and Safety Commission, who have also approved various British Standards as codes of practice.

Very wide-ranging powers are given to inspectors appointed by any relevant enforcing authority (Section 20). If an inspector is of the opinion that a relevant statutory provision (regulation) is or has been contravened he may serve an *improvement notice* on the party concerned requiring him to remedy the situation within a stated time (Section 21).

An inspector may issue a *prohibition notice* if there is a risk of serious personal injury arising from, or likely to arise from, a contravention of any relevant statutory provision. Such a notice may take effect immediately or at the end of a specified period (Section 22). Any notice served may (but need not) include directions as to remedying the situation (such as complying with an approved code of practice (Section 23).

An inspector may seize, and if necessary render harmless, any article or substance he has reason to believe is a cause of imminent danger (Section 25).

An inspector may prosecute the firm and/or the individuals responsible for an offence under any relevant statutory provisions (Section 39). On conviction the maximum fine for most offences is currently £2000, but higher fines and/or imprisonment for up to two years are possible (Section 33). Directors, managers, etc. should note that if an offence results from the consent, connivance or neglect of 'some other person' (who might well be themselves) then that person can be prosecuted (Section 37). In all cases costs, of course, may have to be met.

## TABLE 14.2

*Some regulations (statutory instruments) issued under the HSW Act 1974*

---

Fire Certificates (Special Premises) Regulations 1976 (SI 1976 no. 2003).
Safety Representatives and Safety Committees Regulations 1977 (SI 1977 no. 500)
Health and Safety (Enforcing Authority) Regulations 1977 (SI 1977 no. 746)
Notification of Accidents and Dangerous Occurrences Regulations 1980
    (SI 1980 no. 804)
    (replaced by Reporting of Injuries, Diseases and Dangerous Occurrences Regulations (SI 1985 no. 2023))
Control of Lead at Work Regulations 1980 (SI 1980 no. 1248)
Safety Signs Regulations 1980 (SI 1980 no. 1471)—requires safety signs to comply with BS 5378 Part 1
Notification of Installations Handling Hazardous Substances Regulations 1982
    (SI 1982 no. 1357)
Health and Safety (Emissions into the Atmosphere) Regulations 1983 (SI 1983 no. 943)
Asbestos (Licensing) Regulations 1983 (SI 1983 no. 1649)
Freight Containers (Safety Convention) Regulations 1984 (SI 1984 no. 1980)
Control of Industrial Major Accident Hazards Regulations 1984 (SI 1984 no. 1902)
Gas Safety (Installations and Use) Regulations 1984 (SI 1984 no. 1358)

---

Details of some of the existing Acts of Parliament taken over by the *HSW Act*, and some others which also have relevant statutory provisions appertaining to health, safety and inspection are given in Table 14.1. (Those marked therein with an asterisk are relevant to the *HSW Act.*) Some statutory regulations issued under the *HSW Act* are listed in Table 14.2.

Many earlier Acts, regulations, etc. are continually being revoked, repealed, replaced and amended as new legislation is issued. There is a continuing process of removing references to Imperial measurements, and of amending regulations issued under earlier Acts (such as the *Factories Act*)

### TABLE 14.3
*Some legislation and regulations relating to construction and building operations*

---

Issued originally under the Factories Act 1961 (and earlier Factories Acts):

The Construction (General Provisions) Regulations, 1961 (SI 1961 no. 1580)

The Construction (General Provisions) Reports Order 1962 (SI 1962 no. 224)

The Construction (Lifting Operations) Regulations 1961 (SI 1961 no. 1581) (Certificates of test, on prescribed forms, are required for hoists, cranes, winches, pulley blocks, wire ropes, chains and similar gear)

The Construction (Working Places) Regulations 1966 (SI 1966 no. 94)

The Construction (Health and Welfare) Regulations 1966 (SI 1966 no. 95)

Chains, Ropes and Lifting Tackle (Register) Order 1938 (SR and O 1938 no. 599)

Lifting Machines (Particulars of Examinations) Order 1963 (SI 1963 no. 1382)

The above regulations apply to building operations and/or works of engineering construction, and elaborate the requirements of the Factories Act regarding, amongst other things, the provision, construction, inspection and testing of scaffolds, cages, lifting appliances, etc., and the safety of operations.

The Construction (General Provisions) Regulations/Reports Order 1962 contains the only legislation requiring the appointment by the employer of a safety officer/advisor—any building or civil engineering contractor employing more than 20 workmen is obliged to appoint a safety supervisor. Although the duties/functions of a safety representative appointed by a *trade union* at his employer's works are laid down in some detail in the legislation attached to the *HSW Act* 1974 (see Sect. 2(4)), the duties of the professional safety officer/advisor employed by a firm are not directly mentioned (but see 14.6.3).

The Building Regulations first made under the *Public Health Act* 1961, then under Part III of the *HSW Act*, are now consolidated in the *Building Act* 1984 Section 1. They take the place of or are similar to the model bye-laws adopted by local authorities who enforce them by their own inspectors. They include such matters as structural fire precautions, sound insulation, refuse disposal and ventilation.

Mandatory requirements and 'deemed-to-satisfy' provisions, in some cases referring to schedules detailing materials and methods of construction (often by quoting British Standards and Codes of Practice), are given.

---

## TABLE 14.4

*Legislation and regulations relating to electricity supply, etc.*

---

*The Electricity Supply Regulations* 1937, issued under the *Electricity (Supply) Acts* 1882 to 1936 (revised 1947 by the Electricity Commissioners), deal amongst other things with insulation resistance tests, maintenance of insulation, earthing, inspections, examinations and tests.

*The Factories Act* 1961, and earlier acts, include the following regulations:

Electricity (Factories Act) Special Regulations, 1908 and 1944 (SR and O 1908 no. 1312 and 1944 no. 739)

(*N.B.* Regulation 27 dealing with 'Fire and explosion hazards', is covered generally by 6.11). Reg. 29 deals with 'Treatment for electric shock' (see 6.9.1). (See also Form SHW 928 *Memorandum by the Senior Electrical Inspector of Factories on the Electricity Regulations.*)

*The Regulations for the Electrical Equipment of Buildings*, issued and revised periodically by the Institution of Electrical Engineers, and known familiarly as the 'I.E.E. wiring rules', represent good up-to-date electrical installation practice. They are often quoted in specifications and codes, and are related to and supplement relevant statutory regulations. A section deals with testing and inspection.

---

to bring them into line with the newer *HSW Act* 1974. Details of all regulations and of the current legal position, may be had by reference to the official publications, and such works as the latest issue of Redgrave's *Health and Safety in Factories*. Some regulations may be of vital importance to industrial safety and inspection.

## 14.3 The Factories Act

*The Factories Act* 1961 (Consolidating the *Factories Acts* of 1937, 1948 and 1959) lays down various requirements regarding such matters as safety, health, welfare, etc., which may be enforced by HM Inspectors of Factories. In addition to the Act itself, there are also a great many statutory instruments, regulations, rules and orders prescribing special precautions for particular kinds of work or plant and dealing with a great variety of other points of detail. These are all obtainable from HM Stationery Office. Those currently applicable are listed and reprinted periodically in such publications as Redgrave's *Health and Safety in Factories* (formerly Redgrave's *Factories Acts*). For convenience some which may involve the inspector are listed in Table 14.5.

Some relevant detail from the *Factories Act* is given below (with acknowledgements to HMSO) together with (in square brackets) some comments. The appropriate section of the Act, and any reference relevant to the Chemical Works Regulations (CWR), has been noted.

## TABLE 14.5
*Sundry statutory regulations and orders issued under the Factories Acts*

---

The Asbestos Regulations 1969 (SI 1969 no. 690) (see 6.16)

The Blasting (Castings and other articles) Regulations 1949 (SI 1949 no. 2225)

The Breathing Apparatus, etc. (Report on Examination) Order 1961 (SI 1961 no. 1345)

The Chemical Works Regulations 1922 (SR and O 1922 no. 731 and SI 1961 no. 2435)

The Chromium Plating Regulations 1931 (SR and O 1931 no. 455)

The Electric Accumulator Regulations 1925 (SR and O 1925 no. 28)

Examination of Steam Boilers Regulations 1964 (SI 1964 no. 781)

Examination of Steam Boilers Reports (No. 1) Order 1964 (SI 1964 no. 1070) (These regulations give requirements for boiler inspection when cold and when under normal steam pressure)

Factory Electricity Regulations (see Table 14.4)

Grinding of Metals (Miscellaneous Industries) Special Regulations 1925 and 1950 (SR and O 1925 no. 904 and SI 1950 no. 688)

The Indiarubber Regulations 1922 and 1955 (SR and O 1922 no. 329 and SI 1955 no. 1626)

The Ionizing Radiations Regulations (see 6.17)

The Kiers Regulations 1938 (SR and O 1938 no. 106)

The Lead Smelting and Manufacturing Regulations 1911 (SR and O 1911 no. 752)

The Paint and Colour Manufacture Regulations 1907 (SR and O 1907 no. 17)

The Vitreous Enamelling of Metal or Glass Regulations 1908 (SR and O 1908 no. 1258)

The Work in Compressed Air Special Regulations 1958 (SI 1958 no. 61)

Magnesium (Grinding of castings and other articles) Regulations 1971 SI 1971 no. 1040)

The Highly Flammable Liquids and Liquefied Petroleum Gases Regulations 1972 (SI 1972 no. 917, SI 1973 no. 897).

---

### 14.4 Some health provisions

*1. Cleanliness*

Every factory must be kept clean. In particular, accumulations of dirt and refuse must be removed daily from floors and benches, the floor of every workroom must be cleaned at least once a week and all inside walls, partitions and ceilings must (a) if they have a smooth impervious surface, be washed with hot water and soap or cleaned by other approved method every 14 months, or (b) if kept painted in a prescribed manner or varnished, be repainted or revarnished at prescribed intervals (of not more than 7 years) and washed with hot water, etc., every 14 months, or (c) in other cases be whitewashed or colourwashed every 14 months (certain factories and parts of factories are excepted from these provisions because of the nature of the work carried on). The prescribed particulars must be entered in the General Register (Sect. 1).

['Good housekeeping' is essential with inspection work, and also in many chemical processing plants. A well thought out scheme of internal decoration making the best use of light colours, etc., will result in increased tidiness and safety, and will boost morale.]

## 2. Overcrowding

A factory must not be overcrowded. There must be in each workroom at least 400 cubic feet of space for every person employed, not counting space more than 14 ft from the floor (Sect. 2).

## 3. Temperature

A reasonable temperature must be maintained in each workroom by non-injurious methods. In rooms in which a substantial proportion of the work is done sitting and does not involve serious physical effort, the temperature must not be less than 60°F after the first hour, and at least one thermometer must be provided in a suitable position (Sect. 3).

[The *Offices, Shops and Railway Premises Act* 1963 and other Regulations state 16°C (60.8°F).]

## 4. Ventilation

Adequate ventilation of workrooms must be secured by the circulation of fresh air. All practicable measures must be taken to protect workers against inhalation of dust, fumes and other impurities likely to be injurious or offensive, and local exhaust ventilation must be provided and maintained where practicable (Sects. 4 and 63).

[The use of new materials and processes invariably requires some initial surveillance to ensure that no serious health hazards are introduced.

The risk of inhalation of obnoxious dust particles, etc., is now well recognized in many industries, and the use of suitable extraction hoods and enclosures, an efficient exhaust draught or ventilating plant and effective protective clothing is either recommended or required (CWR 2 and 3).

In a very few cases maximum acceptable concentrations (MAC) of a particular hazard in the atmosphere may be laid down by regulations; in other cases suggested figures for guidance may be published by various authorities.

However a number of regulations are now in force to minimize such effects. These include The Pottery (Health and Welfare) Special Regulations 1950, No. 65, which under Regulation 17(8) requires a thorough examination and test of all ventilating plant and dust collecting apparatus by a 'competent person', at least once every 14 months.]

## 5. Lighting

There must be sufficient and suitable lighting in every part of the factory in which persons are working or passing (Sect. 5 (now revoked) and CWR 4(a) and also 4(b)—safety precautions)

[S.R. and O. 1941 no. 94 (now revoked) prescribes in general not less than 6 ft candles where persons regularly work, or 0·5 ft candles where they pass. However, inspection requires much higher levels of illumination: the Illuminating Engineering Society recommended 50–200 ft candles (lumens/ft$^2$) according to the fineness of the work. These recommendations have been revoked by BS 8206 Part 1: Code of practice for artificial lighting which recommends illuminance of from 50 lux (for walkways, cable tunnels, etc.) to 500 lux for offices, laboratories, etc. and up to 2000 lux for fine assembly and inspection.]*

## 6. Drainage of floors

Where wet processes are carried on, adequate means for draining the floor must be provided (Sect. 6).

## 7. Sanitary accommodation

Sufficient and suitable sanitary conveniences, separate for each sex, must be provided subject to conformity with standards prescribed by regulations. The conveniences must be maintained and kept clean, and effective provision must be made for lighting them (Sect. 7).

## 8. Meals in certain dangerous trades

A person must not partake of food or drink or remain during meal times in workrooms where any poisonous substance is so used as to give rise to dust or fumes; nor may a person remain during meal times in any room in which is carried on any process prescribed by regulations as one which gives rise to siliceous or asbestos dust. Suitable provision must be made to enable persons employed in all such rooms to take their meals elsewhere in the factory (Sect. 64).

## 9. Underground rooms

No work is to be carried on in any underground room (unless used only for

---

*SI units are used in the latest recommendations, values being given in lux. 1 lux (lumen/metre$^2$) = 10·76 lumens/ft$^2$.

storage or other specially excepted purpose) if the District Inspector certifies that it is unsuitable as regards height, light or ventilation, or on any hygienic ground, e.g. because the means of escape in case of fire are inadequate. Notice must be given to the District Inspector before an underground room is used as a workroom in a factory if it was not so used on 1 July 1938 (Sect. 69).

### 10. *Lifting excessive weights*

No one must be employed to lift, carry or move any load so heavy as to be likely to cause injury (Sect. 72).

### 11. *Lead processes*

A woman or young person must not be employed in certain lead processes or in cleaning workrooms where any of the processes are carried on (Sect. 74).

Where women or young persons are employed in any other process which involves the use of a lead compound producing dust or fume, or, if they are liable to be splashed with any lead compound, (a) the dust or fume produced must be drawn away by an efficient exhaust draught; (b) they must undergo medical examination as prescribed and may be suspended from further employment in lead processes; (c) no food, drink or tobacco may be brought into the workroom; (d) protective clothing must be provided by the occupier and worn; (e) suitable cloakroom, messroom and washing accommodation must be provided as prescribed; and (f) all tools and apparatus must be kept clean. (Sect. 75—requirements are now given in SI 1980 no. 1248—The Control of Lead at Work Regulations.)

### 12. *Notification of industrial poisoning or disease*

Cases of poisoning by lead, phosphorus, arsenic, mercury, carbon bisulphide, manganese or aniline; chronic poisoning by benzene; compressed air illness; anthrax; toxic jaundice due to tetrachlorethane or nitro- or amido-derivatives of benzene or other poisonous substances; toxic anaemia; epitheliomatous ulceration, and chrome ulceration, must be reported immediately to the District Inspector and to the appointed factory doctor and entered in the General Register (Sects 82 and 140, and Reporting of Injuries, Diseases and Dangerous Occurences Regulations, SI 1985 no. 2023).

## 14.5 Some safety and welfare provisions

### 13. *Fencing*

Every part of the transmission machinery and every dangerous part of other machinery, and all parts of electric generators, motors, rotary converters and flywheels directly connected to them, must be securely fenced unless in such a position or of such construction as to be as safe to every person employed or working on the premises as if securely fenced; and any part of a stock-bar which projects beyond the head-stock of a lathe must be securely fenced unless it is in such a position as to be as safe to every such person as if securely fenced. A male person over 18 may, however, approach unfenced machinery in motion in certain strictly limited contingencies (e.g. for lubrication and maintenance purposes, etc., in certain continuous processes as in the chemical industry) and subject to conditions specified in regulations (Sects 12 to 15). Moving parts of other prime movers and flywheels directly connected to them, and the head and tail race of a water wheel or water turbine, must be securely fenced irrespective of their position (Sect. 12).

Fixed vessels, pits, etc. containing scalding, corrosive or poisonous liquids must, unless the edge is three feet above the adjoining ground or platform, be securely fenced to at least that height or be securely covered; where this is impracticable, other precautions, so far as practicable, must be taken. Where any such vessel is not securely covered, no ladder, stair or gangway may be placed above, across or inside it which is not at least 18 in wide, securely fenced to a height of at least 3 ft and securely fixed. When any such vessels adjoin each other, and the space between them either is less than 18 in in width or is not securely fenced to at least 3 ft, barriers must be placed so as to prevent passage between them (Sect. 18 and CWR 1).

All fencing must be of substantial construction, maintained in an efficient state and kept in position while the parts required to be fenced or safeguarded are in motion or use (Sect. 16).

## 14. Further requirements in connection with transmission machinery

Devices or appliances for promptly cutting off the power from the transmission machinery must be provided in every room or place where work is carried on. Efficient mechanical appliances must be provided to move driving belts to and from fast and loose pulleys. Driving belts must not rest or ride on revolving shafts when the belt is not in use (Sect. 13).

## 15. New machines

New power-driven machines must not be sold, let on hire, or used unless certain parts are effectively guarded (Sect. 17).

BS 5304 (previously BS CP 3004) *safeguarding of machinery* gives guidance on principles applicable to all sectors of industry and should help in meeting current legislation.

## 16. Cleaning machinery

A woman or young person must not clean (a) a prime mover or transmission machinery while it is in motion or (b) any part of any machine if there is risk of injury from any moving part of that machine or of any adjacent machinery (Sect. 20).

## 17. *Training of young persons*

A young person must not work at any machine specified by the Minister to be dangerous unless (i) he has been fully instructed as to the dangers and precautions and (ii) he has received sufficient training in the work or is under adequate supervision by an experienced person (Sect. 21).

## 18. *Hoists or lifts*

Every hoist or lift must be of good mechanical construction, sound material and adequate strength and must be properly maintained. It must be thoroughly examined every six months by a competent person whose report must be entered in or attached to the General Register.

Every hoistway must be efficiently protected by a substantial enclosure and landing gates, with efficient interlocking or other devices. The safe working load must be marked conspicuously on each hoist. Additional safeguards (e.g. devices to prevent overrunning) must be provided on hoists used for carrying persons, whether with goods or otherwise. The requirements are somewhat less stringent in the case of hoists constructed before 30 July 1937, hoists not connected with mechanical power, and continuous hoists.

Every teagle opening or similar doorway used for hoisting or lowering goods must be fenced (except when the hoisting or lowering is going on at that opening) and be provided with a secure hand-hold on each side of the opening (Sects 22 to 25).

## 19. *Chains, ropes and lifting tackle*

No chain, rope or lifting tackle used for raising or lowering persons or goods may be used unless it is of good construction, sound material and adequate strength and free from patent defect. Tables of safe working loads (SWL) must be posted in the stores and elsewhere, but need not cover any lifting tackle, the safe working load of which is marked on the tackle itself. Tackle must not be used for any load exceeding its stated safe working load. Chains, ropes and lifting tackle in use must be thoroughly examined by a competent person every six months, and must not (excepting fibre ropes and fibre rope slings) be taken into use for the first time in the factory unless they have been tested and certified. Factory form F87 Certificate of Test and Examination of Wire Rope should be used as appropriate.

Periodic annealing (generally at least every 14 months) is required except in the case of ropes and rope slings and other tackle exempted by HM Chief Inspector.

**TABLE 14.6**

*Steel chain—strength and identification*

| Chain | Normal SWL (tonnes) | Proof load (tonnes) | Minimum breaking load (tonnes) | Grade identifying markings |
|---|---|---|---|---|
| Mild steel | $6d^2$ | $12d^2$ | $30d^2$ | 3 |
| Higher tensile steel Grade 40 | $8d^2$ | $16d^2$ | $40d^2$ | 4 for normalized chain 04 for quenched and tempered chain |
| Alloy steel chain Grade 60 | $12d^2$ | $24d^2$ | $60d^2$ | 06 |
| Alloy steel chain Grade 80 | $14d^2$ | $32d^2$ | $80d^2$ | 08 |

($d$ = diameter of cross-section of a link in inches)

A register of all chains, etc., and also the certificates of tests, must be kept (Sect. 26).

Each item of lifting tackle should be clearly marked with its number (in a circle) so that its safe working load can be readily ascertained (see Table 14.6). [Grade 80 is specially designed for use as the load chain of pulley blocks since it results in the use of a smaller block for a given safe working load.

The other grades are all suitable for general lifting purposes. In any case of doubt users should either consult the makers or the relevant British Standard (see Table 14.7).]

[Over the years the custom has developed of proof loading all items and then setting a maximum safe working load equal to half this proof load. This takes care of any additional loading imposed by acceleration, or by shock caused by the load slipping or catching.

However, heavy loads above 25 tonnes would normally be lifted with great care and shocks would be avoided. Consequently it has been agreed internationally (by the International Labour Office) that a new scale of proof loading would be introduced. Above 25 tonnes safe working load the ratio of proof to SWL falls steadily from 2 to 1·33 at 180 tonnes SWL and above.]

**TABLE 14.7**

*Some British Standards dealing with chains, cranes and lifting tackle*

| BS No. | Description |
|---|---|
| 302 | Wire ropes for cranes, excavators and general engineering purposes |
| 1290 | Wire rope slings and sling legs |
| 1663 | Higher tensile steel chain, Grade 40 |
| 1757 | Power-driven mobile cranes |
| 2573 | Permissible stresses in cranes and design rules |
| 2830 | Suspended safety chairs and cradles for use in the construction industry |
| 2902 | Higher tensile steel chain slings and rings, etc. |
| 2903 | Higher tensile steel hooks for chains, slings and blocks |
| 3032 | Higher tensile steel shackles |
| 3113 | Alloy steel chain, Grade 60, Short link for lifting purposes |
| 3114 | Alloy steel chain, Grade 80, Polished short link calibrated load for pulley blocks |
| 3243 | Hand-operated chain pulley blocks |
| 3458 | Alloy steel chain slings |
| 3551 | Alloy steel shackles |
| 4436 | Reach and straddle fork lift trucks—stability tests |
| 5655 | Lifts and service lifts |
| 5744 | Code of practice for safe use of cranes (overhead/underhung and goliath, high pedestal and portal jib dockside, etc.) |
| 6166 | Recommendations for rating of lifting gear for general purposes |
| 6210 | Code of practice for the safe use of wire rope slings for general lifting purposes |
| CP3010 | Safe use of cranes (mobile, tower and derrick). |
| 6405 | Non-calibrated short link steel chain (grade 30): Class 1 and 2 |
| 6521 | Guide for proper use and maintenance of calibrated round steel link fitting chains |

*20. Cranes and lifting machines, etc.*

All parts and working gear (including anchoring appliances) of cranes and other lifting machines must be of good construction, sound material and adequate strength, free from patent defect and must be properly maintained. A thorough examination of all such parts and gear by a competent person must be made every 14 months. A lifting machine must not be taken into use for the first time in the factory unless it has been tested and certified. A register of examinations and tests must be kept. The safe working load or loads must be shown on every lifting machine; in the case of cranes with a derricking jib an automatic indicator or a table of safe working loads must be attached to the crane. A lifting machine must not be loaded beyond its safe working load, except for the purpose of test. Rails and tracks of travelling cranes and transporters must be of proper size and construction. If any person is working near the wheeltrack of an overhead travelling crane, steps must be taken to ensure that the crane does not approach within 20 feet.

Effective measures should also be taken to give warning of the approach of such a crane to anyone working above floor level and liable to be struck by it or by its load (Sect. 27).

[Under the Docks Regulations 1934 (S.R. and O. 1934 no. 279) every crane and other hoisting machine with its accessory gear shall be tested with a proof load which shall be exceed the safe working load as follows:

| Safe working load | Proof load |
|---|---|
| Up to 20 tonnes | 25% in excess |
| 20 to 50 tonnes | 5 tonnes in excess |
| Over 50 tonnes | 10 % in excess] |

Under the Construction (Lifting Operation) Regulations 1961 after each erection of a crane, or alteration affecting its anchorage or ballasting, tests should be carried out to establish its security. A 25% overload at a position where there is a maximum pull on each achorage (or an equivalent reduced load at an increased radius) should be imposed and the test recorded in the appropriate register. Any defect, damage or abnormality should be reported immediately to a responsible person.

## 21. Construction of floors, etc.

Floors, steps stairs, passages and gangways must be soundly constructed, properly maintained and, so far as is reasonably practicable, kept free from obstruction and any substance likely to cause persons to slip. Handrails must be provided for stairs. All ladders must be soundly constructed and properly maintained. Openings in floors must, wherever practicable, be securely fenced (Sect. 28).

## 22. Safe means of access and place of work

So far as is reasonably practicable (i) there must be provided safe means of access to every place at which any person has at any time to work, (ii) every such place must be made and kept safe for anyone working there, (iii) fencing or other means must be provided to ensure the safety of any person who is to work at a place from which he would be liable to fall more than six feet six inches and which does not afford secure foothold and, where necessary, secure handhold (Sect. 29). [Ladders must be provided where necessary and suitably secured, access paths etc. must be gritted during icy weather.]

### 23. Precautions against gassing

Special precautions are laid down for work in confined spaces where men are liable to be overcome by dangerous fumes (Sect. 30).

[*Manholes and inspection openings.* Sect. 30 of the *Factories Act* states 'where work in any factory has to be done inside any chamber, tank, vat, pit, pipe, flue or similar confined space, in which dangerous fumes are liable to be present to such an extent as to involve the risk of persons being overcome thereby, the confined space shall, unless there is other adequate means of egress, be provided with a manhole, which may be rectangular, oval or circular in shape, and shall be not less than 18 in long and 16 in wide or (if circular) not less than 18 in diameter, or in the case of tank wagons and other mobile plant, not less than 16 in long and 14 in wide, or (if circular) not less than 16 in diameter.'

The Chief Inspector may, however, grant exemption where he is satisfied that compliance with these requirements is unnecessary or impracticable.

Consequently, vessels and confined spaces may be required by statute to have openings. In addition, all vessels subject to corrosion should have inspection and/or access openings to permit a complete visual examination of the interior (this is required by BS 5500 (and other specifications) which also requires that vessels over 36 in diameter shall have at least one manhole, and that vessels to which the aforementioned statutory regulation applies should have at least two, in order to facilitate rescue operations. Manholes and inspection openings shall comply with the requirements of BS 470).

On use of breathing and rescue apparatus see 12.8 (18) and CWR 6, 7 and 8. Facilities have to be kept available.]

### 24. Explosions of flammable dust or gas

Precautions against explosion are laid down for certain processes, and for welding or soldering or other operations involving the application of heat to containers which hold or have held any explosive or flammable substance (Sect. 31). (See also 6.9, 6.16, 6.17 and Chemical Works Regulations 4(b)–(d).)

[A sufficient supply of non-metallic (non-sparking) spades, scrapers and pails should be provided for cleaning out or removing residues from any vessel or place where an inflammable vapour or dust is likely to arise. (Sometimes the risk is not obvious, as for instance, where acid may cause the production of hydrogen.) (CWR 9.)]

### 25. Steam boilers, steam receivers, etc.

Every part of every steam boiler and steam receiver must be of good construction, sound material, adequate strength and free from patent defect. Detailed requirements are laid down as to the valves and other fittings. The outlet of every steam container must at all times be kept open and free from obstruction.

Steam boilers and steam receivers and their fittings must be properly maintained and (unless the Minister provides otherwise in an exemption order) must be thoroughly examined by a competent person: boilers every 14 months and after extensive repairs, receivers every 26 months [but see 12.5]. A report of each examination must be attached to the General Register. New boilers must be certified and second-hand boilers must be examined before being taken into use (Sects. 32 to 35, 37 and 38, and Sixth Schedule, Para. 3).

[Where the examination report indicates repairs are necessary the inspecting authority must send a copy to the factory inspector. For protective devices and pressure tests, etc., see 3.19 and 3.20; for Chemical Works Regulation No. 5—Safety valves on vessels containing gas under pressure—see 6.16.]

## 26. Air receivers

Every air receiver and its fittings must be of sound construction and properly maintained. Detailed requirements are laid down as to the fittings.

Air receivers must be thoroughly cleaned, and be examined or tested by a competent person, every 26 months, and a report entered in or attached to the General Register. In some cases a longer period is allowed (Sects. 36 and 37 (2)).

[Pressure tests, etc., are dealt with in 3.20. See also 3.22.]

## 27. Fire

Every factory falling within one of the classes defined in Section 45 of the Act must have a certificate from the fire authority that the means of escape in case of fire are such as may be reasonably required. The means of escape specified in the certificate must be properly maintained and kept free from obstruction. Effective fire alarms must be provided and maintained; they must be tested or examined every three months, and a report attached to the General Register.

The contents of workrooms must be so arranged that there is a free passageway to the means of escape.

In factories employing more than 20 workers in the same building above the first floor or more than 20 feet above ground level, or where explosive or highly flammable substances are used or stored in the building, effective steps must be taken to ensure that the workers are familiar with the means of escape and their use and the routine to be followed in case of fire.

Fire fighting equipment must be provided, maintained and kept readily available in every factory irrespective of the number of persons employed.

Hoistways and liftways inside buildings constructed after the end of June 1938 must be completely enclosed with fire-resisting materials and the means of access to them must be fitted with fire-resisting doors, except that the top of unvented hoistways and liftways must be enclosed by material easily broken by fire. While any person is in any factory for the purpose of employment or meals, doors must not be so locked or fastened that they cannot be easily and immediately opened from the inside. Any doors opening onto a staircase or corridor from any room in which more than 10 persons are employed must open outwards unless they are sliding doors. The same requirement applies also to all other doors affording a means of exit from factories constructed or converted after 30 June 1938. Fire exits must be distinctively and conspicuously marked by a notice printed in letters of adequate size (Sects. 40 to 52).

(Note: in consequence of the coming into operation of the *HSW Act* 1974 and of the *Fire Precautions Act* 1971–4 the above referred to Sections 40 to 52 have been repealed and superseded by the Fire Precautions (Factories, Offices, Shops and Railway Premises) Order 1976, SI 1976 no. 2009, and by SI nos 2003 and 2010 (referred to in 14.7.1—The *Fire Precautions Act* 1974)).

[Many types of fire fighting equipment are used in industrial and chemical plant. The periodic inspection of these items is an important task sometimes carried out by firemen as part of their duties; but, with specialized equipment often employing electric and electronic principles coming increasingly into use, advice and assistance from the inspection department can be helpful.

It should be realized that many methods of fire fighting employ substances which are themselves dangerous, toxic or asphixiating.

For instance, carbon dioxide is commonly released from high-pressure gas cylinders into enclosed spaces containing machinery, electrical equipment, etc., to stifle a fire. In many cases, such as in unmanned electrical sub-stations, the outbreak of a fire causes a fusible plug to melt and thus initiates the discharge of the $CO_2$ gas cylinders. Should there be a possibility of personnel being in the area a klaxon horn may be arranged to sound a warning for them to get clear prior to the discharge taking place. Normally, however, if $CO_2$ fire protection is used in a space where men may be working, the automatic discharge arrangements are switched over to manual operation.]

The following BS Codes of Practice may be consulted:

BS 5306 (formerly CP402) *Fire extinguishing installations and equipment on premises*—some 8 parts deal with hydrant, sprinkler, carbon dioxide and halon systems.

BS 5588 Part 4 *Smoke control in protected escape routes using pressurization.*

BS 5839 (formerly CP1019) *Fire detection and alarm systems in buildings*

BS 5908 *Code of Practice for fire precautions in chemical plant*

## 28. Protection of eyes

Suitable goggles or effective screens must be provided in processes specified by the Minister (Sect. 65).

[The Protection of Eyes Regulations 1974 (SI 1681) give a schedule of processes for which appropriate protection is required (the main types of eye protection being spectacles, goggles, screens and face shields). The processes include cleaning and blasting, grinding; operation, maintenance and dismantling of plant which contains or has contained dangerous substances; operations involving hot or molten metals and substances, and those producing glare or other forms of radiation. When using grinding wheels personal spectacles (with prescription or plain lenses as appropriate) should invariably be worn.

Besides protecting the eyes from glare or the entry of foreign matter, eye-wash bottles filled with distilled water or suitable liquid must be provided, clearly indicated, in places where there is danger from corrosive or harmful liquids, etc. (see CWR 10 (a) (ii). This equipment must be inspected regularly and its contents checked.]

## 29. Notification of accidents and dangerous occurrences

Accidents causing loss of life or disabling a worker for more than three days from earning full wages at the work at which he was employed must be reported forthwith to the District Inspector (on Form 43) and entered in the General Register. Certain dangerous occurrences must also be reported whether disablement is caused or not, e.g. the bursting of a revolving vessel, wheel or grindstone moved by mechanical power, the collapse or failure of a crane, hoist or other lifting appliance, or any part thereof (except the breaking of chain or rope slings), or the overturning of a crane; and explosions of fires in certain circumstances (now covered by Reporting of Injuries, Diseases and Dangerous Occurrences Regulations SI 1985 no. 2023).

## 30. Drinking water

An adequate supply of wholesome drinking water, with an upward jet convenient for drinking or suitable drinking vessels with facilities for rinsing them, must be provided (Sect. 57).

## 31. Washing facilities

Adequate and suitable washing facilities (to include a supply of clean running hot and cold or warm water, soap and clean towels or other suitable means of cleaning or drying) must be provided, maintained and kept in a clean and orderly condition (Sect. 58).

> [Where there is danger from corrosive or obnoxious substances means should be provided for bathing, or for drenching with water or a suitable neutralizing agent any person (including his clothing) who becomes so contaminated (see also CWR 29.]

## 32. Accommodation for clothing

Adequate and suitable accommodation for clothing not worn during working hours, with such arrangements as are reasonably practicable for drying such clothing, must be provided (Sect. 59).

## 33. Facilities for sitting

Where any employed persons (irrespective of sex) have in the course of their employment, reasonable opportunities for sitting without detriment to their work, there must be provided for their use suitable facilities for sitting sufficient to enable them to take advantage of those opportunities. There are detailed requirements as to seats and seating arrangements for work of which a substantial proportion can properly be done sitting (Sect.60).

## 34. First aid

In every factory there must be provided a first-aid box or cupboard of the prescribed standard, containing nothing except first-aid requisites. Where more than 150 persons are employed at one time an additional box or cupboard for every 150 additional persons or fraction of that number is required. Each box or cupboard must be placed in the charge of a responsible person who, in the case of a factory, where more than 50 persons are employed, must satisfy prescribed conditions as to training in first-aid treatment. The responsible person must always be readily available during working hours and a notice must be affixed in every workroom stating the name of the person in charge of the box or cupboard provided in respect of that room (Sect. 61). [See also Health and Safety (First Aid) Regulations 1981, SI no. 917.]

## 35. Notice of occupation or use of premises as a factory

At least one month before beginning to occupy or use premises as a factory or introducing mechanical power into a factory, the occupier must furnish the District Inspector with certain particulars. The occupier may, however, begin to use the premises before the month's notice has elapsed, provided the District Inspector gives written permission or, subject to certain conditions, where an existing factory is taken over from another person (Sect. 137).

### 36. General Register

The occupier must keep a General Register in the prescribed form (Sect. 140).

Codes of regulations and orders made for particular factories, industries, processes, plant, etc., must be observed. Printed copies or prescribed abstracts of any codes of special regulations in force in any factory must be kept posted in the factory (Sect. 139).

### 37. Inspection

HM Inspectors have power to inspect every part of a factory by day or by night. They may require the production of registers, certificates and other papers. They may examine any person found in the factory, either alone or in the presence of any other person as they think fit, and may require him to sign a declaration of the truth of the matters about which he is examined. They may also exercise such other powers as may be necessary for carrying the Act into effect, including certain powers of taking samples for analysis. Every person obstructing an inspector is liable to a penalty.

The officers of local authorities and fire authorities have similar powers so far as required for their duties under the Act (see *HSW Act* 1974, Sect. 20).

### 14.6 Chemical works regulations, codes of safe practice, etc.

The Chemical Works Regulations 1922 (S.R. and O. 1922 No. 731 as amended by SI 1961 no. 2435), issued under the *Factories Acts*, are divided into two parts, Part I applying to all chemical works, and Part II to specific processes or types of work. The regulations in Part I may be said to amplify and, in Part II particularly, to specify details regarding safety generally covered by the Factories Act. They deal with such matters as fencing, efficient exhaust draught, dust enclosures, lighting, explosive risks, safety valves, breathing apparatus, lifebelts, entry into dangerous places, rescue, non-sparking tools, protective clothing, and facilities for first aid, training, welfare, etc. Reference has already been made to these regulations in 14.3, 14.4 and 14.5 and in 6.16 and 12.8.

In addition to statutory requirements certain rules and regulations affecting operational inspection, etc. may be enforced by local management. These could include:

Model Safety Rules for Chemical Works (issued by the Association of British Chemical Manufacturers).

Model Code of Safe Practice in the Petroleum Industry (issued by the Institute of Petroleum).

BS 5908 (previously CP 3013) *Fire precautions in chemical plants.*

Most large organizations (particularly ICI) issue their own regulations, safety codes and orders, often very comprehensive.

All these are designed to encourage efficient and safe operating practices and to eliminate as far as possible any infringement of statutory obligations.

### 14.6.1   The Alkali Act—noxious emissions, etc.

The *Alkali, etc., Works Regulation Act* 1906 as extended by the Alkali, etc., Works Orders 1928 to 1966 in conjunction the *HSW Act* 1974 contains legislation dealing with the minimization of emissions of noxious or offensive gases, smoke, grit and dust from certain specified classes of works, which include alkali, cement and smelting works (non-scheduled works), and a wide variety of scheduled works ranging from those dealing with acid and chemical manufacture, petrochemicals, oil refining, and metal working, to gas and electricity production (from thermal fuel fired power stations). Such works have to be registered annually and are subject to visits and inspection by the government HSE inspectors, who may take samples for analysis and obtain details of processes, etc. Additional works may be added to the Schedule of the *Alkali Act* and to the list of noxious or offensive gases included in it.

The provisions of the *Public Health (Smoke Abatement) Act* 1926, and of the *Clean Air Act* 1956 relating to dark smoke, grit and dust, etc. emanating from works controlled under the *Alkali Act* were originally administered by the Alkali Inspectorate (now absorbed in the HSE), but local authorities, who control normal industrial and domestic installations, may also be involved. 'Dark smoke' is defined as that which, if compared in the appropriate manner, would appear to be as dark as or darker than Shade 2 on the Ringelmann Chart (relaxations covering lighting up periods, etc., are allowed by the Dark Smoke (Permitted Periods) Regulations 1958).

The printed Ringelmann charts comprise a number of shades corresponding to number 0 (white), through shades of grey (increasing by 20% for each whole number), to 5 (black). By suitably mounting the charts at a distance the observer compares the smoke at the point where it leaves the chimney and selects the number of the shade which appears most closely to match the darkness of the smoke. Under favourable conditions estimates can be made to the nearest quarter Ringelmann number (see BS 2742 *Use of the Ringelmann and miniature smoke charts*). The actual charts are obtainable in packets from BSI as BS 2742C, or as a simple miniature chart to be held by an observer, as BS 2742M. BS 2741 deals with simple smoke viewers to give a visual indication to the fireman.

BS 2740 describes *Simple smoke alarms and alarm metering devices* required for the control and limitation of smoke. These comprise a light source projecting a beam across the chimney with a photoelectric cell to indicate and if necessary record the smoke obscuration/density, and/or to give an alarm if a particular value is exceeded. Measurements of optical density of smoke can be converted to standard Ringelmann numbers.

BS 2811 describes *Smoke density indicators and recorders* of a more comprehensive type to measure and continuously record the optical density of or percentage obscuration caused by smoke. Any calibration in terms of the Ringelmann scale must be carried out on site after installation.

In conjunction with the *HSW Act*, particularly Section 5 and the Health and Safety (Emissions into the Atmosphere Regulations 1983 SI no. 943), the sampling and measurement of grit and dust emissions to check the performance of arresting equipment is carried out by inspectors generally using the iso-kinetic sampling technique (British Coal Utilization Research Association method) to BS 3405.

Battersea Power Station which finally closed in 1983 was also notable as the world's first power station to have a system of washing the flue gases to remove $SO_2$. Although nearly 90% was removed there was a snag: under adverse weather conditions the washed and cooled chimney smoke with its remaining 10% $SO_2$, etc. fell on the surrounding neighbourhood instead of being carried high into the air and dispersed—perhaps widely over Scandinavia!

The Chief Inspector Industrial Air Pollution or other HSE agreed Inspectorate must be satisfied, in general, that plant is furnished with the 'best practical means' for minimizing and rendering harmless all offensive discharges. All alkali processes must be such that a minimum of 95% of the hydrogen chloride gas generated is trapped. In a few cases statutory limits of acidity in the waste gases from certain processes are prescribed (e.g. $0.2$ grains/ft$^3$ ($0.46$ gram/m$^3$)); in other cases provisional standards ('presumptive limits') for the offensive substance may be agreed with the Inspector (see Mahler, E.A. 'Standards of emission under the Alkali Act', *International Clean Air Congress Proceedings*, Part 1, National Society for Clean Air, London 1966).) Consequently management and the inspector are vitally concerned to see that the plant is designed, operated and efficiently maintained to such standards. This involves not only the discovery and measurement of the escape of noxious substances, but the cause of their escape and the development of remedial measures. A series of inspections and tests to be carried out during each shift, etc. may be evolved.

The escape of noxious substances represents waste, so in general its prevention may be sound economics; the penalties for any infringement of the Acts and the cost of legal proceedings may also be heavy.

Substances deemed to be noxious or offensive for the purpose of Section 5(1) of the *Control of Pollution Act* 1974 are specified in Schedule 2 of the Health and Safety (Emissions into the Atmosphere) Regulations 1983 SI no. 943. These regulations also give (in Schedule 1) a list of premises in which specified works of a noxious or offensive kind are carried on (including those dealing with substances mentioned in Schedule 2).

Amongst the means for minimizing the concentration of noxious and offensive gases, smoke, etc., in the atmosphere may be mentioned scrubbers, filters, electrostatic precipitators, absorption into some disposable sludge, burning, and dilution by dispersion from high chimneys (see *Clean Air Act* 1956, *Memorandum on Chimney Heights*, HMSO 1963, which deals particularly with flue gases from sulphur-containing fuels). Good housekeeping of course plays an essential part. Although maximum acceptable concentrations (MAC) of toxicity may be recommended, quite often widespread public complaint may arise from malodorous compounds present in the air to the extent of even less than one part per million.

Concentration of gases or vapours, etc., in the atmosphere may be measured as the ratio of weight to volume (W/V), or volume to volume (V/V). In metric units weight to volume may be expressed in milligrams per cubic metre ($mg/m^3$), whilst in English units it may be expressed as grains per cubic foot ($gr/ft^3$). Volume to volume concentrations may be expressed in parts per million (p.p.m.).

$$\text{Concentration (p.p.m.)} = \frac{mg/m^3 \times 24{\cdot}45}{\text{molecular weight (mg)}}$$

$$[1 \ mg/m^3 = 4{\cdot}37 \times 10^{-4} \ grains/ft^3]$$

### 14.6.2 Air pollution ('acid rain')

In the UK, control of air pollution from industrial plant is divided between local authorities, exercising powers under the *Clean Air Acts*, and the Industrial Air Pollution Inspectorate (IAPI) which enforces relevant sections of the *Alkali Acts* and the *HSW Act* 1974 (Sections 1(1)(d) and 5. IAPI itself deals mainly with the heavy and chemical industries, but cooperates with local authorities on their work of dealing with the major proportion of industrial premises in the light and other manufacturing industries. The main requirement is to ensure the use of the 'best practicable means' to prevent nitrogen discharges, etc. into the atmosphere. Sulphur and nitrogen oxides and hydrocarbons (mainly from fuel burning) are amongst the most significant pollutants in the formation and deposition of 'acid rain' (it is pointed out that rain, snow (and soil) are already naturally somewhat acid).

Today 'acid rain' causes damage to buildings and materials, freshwater aquatic life, vegetation and forests in particular. This form of damage has occurred for centuries, but was accelerated by industrialization. It has been stated that at the close of the Victorian era some 269 belching mill chimneys could be seen from the heights of the centre of Oldham, Lancashire (and available photographs seem to prove this!). However the extent of acid concentrations ('smog') etc. has fallen in recent years in the UK, as will be apparent to those who remember, for instance, the thick 'pea-souper' fogs of pre-war industrial London culminating in the London 'smog' of December 1952 alleged to have caused the death of some 6000 people. This improvement has been due *inter alia* to the enforcement of clean air legislation, etc., the more efficient burning of industrial fuel (particularly coal), and the huge reduction in the use of coal for domestic fires (triggered by the declaration of 'smokeless zones' in towns).

Nevertheless damage allegedly due to acid rain has occurred particularly in Southern Norway and Sweden and elsewhere, resulting in a reduction in the freshwater fish population and loss and damage to forests. A recent selective survey of UK forests by the Forestry Commission did not confirm the presence of damage similar to that found in continental Europe. Test figures of the acidity level (pH value)* of UK lakes give variable results. One remote lake in Southern Scotland shows a gradual increase over the years, whilst a lake in remote Cumbria (used to supply water to Manchester) shows very little change over a period of 50 years.

Scandinavia blames the UK (and particularly her power stations) as one of the major contributors to the trouble. But Scandinavia (particularly Norway) is fortunate in that she has much water power available to supply her needs. And Sweden has been meeting some 42·2% of her industrial and domestic requirements by the use of acid rain-free nuclear power (but now intends to phase out all nuclear power). The position is highly political as well as technical, and more research and investigation is necessary.

Under EEC directives the UK must comply with air quality standards for smoke, $SO_2$ and $NO_2$, and the Community has proposed measures which would progressively reduce national emissions of sulphur and nitrogen oxides (and dust). At present the UK is the largest single emitter of $SO_2$ (27% of the total) and possibly the second largest emitter of nitrogen oxides in the EEC.

Many EEC and other states have undertaken to reduce their $SO_2$ emissions to 30% below their 1980 level by the mid-1990s. The UK, although not necessarily accepting responsibility and uncertain about the environmental benefits which might result in continental Europe and not initially giving a formal undertaking, has announced its intention to achieve a 30% reduction (in both sulphur and nitrogen oxides) by the late 1990s. UK $SO_2$ emissions in 1985 were 25% below their 1980 level, and 43% below

---

*The midpoint on the pH scale (7) is neutral. Numbers higher than 7 are alkaline and those lower than 7 are acidic. Clean, unpolluted rain has a pH usually of 5·6 (i.e. it is naturally acid because of its absorption of atmospheric carbon dioxide). A change from pH 6·0 to pH 5·0 indicates a tenfold increase in acidity.

their 1970 level. The relevant UK Inspectorate (IAPI of the HSE, splintered off from the Alkali Inspectorate and to transfer back to Department of the Environment) states that it does not offer alternative approaches to pollution control based on either prevention or dispersion; reliance on dispersion (and hence dilution into the atmosphere) alone is only permitted *when there are no practicable methods of preventing emissions.* Tall chimney stacks for dispersion date from a period when control technology was not 'practicable' within the meaning of the Act. Today, technologies are available to reduce substantially $SO_2$ emissions from large combustion sources (e.g. power stations) but with an increased cost to the consumer.

The CEGB, in evidence before a Parliamentary environment committee, stated that to secure a 60% reduction in their $SO_2$ emissions would raise the price of electricity by 5%.

Action which HM Government have now agreed to undertake to further reduce emissions could include:

(i) use of more advanced and efficient fuel- (particularly coal-) burning techniques, such as fluidized bed combustion, coal gasification, etc.;

(ii) combined heat and power generation;

(iii) energy conservation techniques;

(iv) complete elimination of 'acid rain';

(v) non-fossil fuel power generation (e.g. water, nuclear, wind power).

The only immediately available large-scale UK source of (v) would be nuclear power (which has its own problems) and can kill or bring disease to people, not just fishes & trees!) A longer-term UK source of (iv) might be tidal power (e.g. a Severn Barrage, which would bring problems including disturbing people and the ecosystem).

Some major reduction (perhaps 50% in the UK's emission of 'acid rain') could be achieved by making extensive use of combined heat and power (CHP) methods of generating electricity in future power stations (see 8.4). Heat energy (in the form of hot water and steam) of an amount approximating to that of the electrical energy generated would be available for domestic and industrial use in the vicinity of the power station without any further expenditure of fuel.

Air pollution from road vehicle emissions, particularly hydrocarbons and lead, is another highly sensitive problem subject to increasing legislation and attention from the inspectorates and local authorities. Reductions in the permissible amounts have been agreed by the EEC and will no doubt be implemented by HM Government. The arguments for and against lead in fuel and general information on the subject are contained in an information pack available from the Information and Library Service, Institution of Mechanical Engineers. Further information on acid rain and related matter can be obtained from the National Society for Clean Air, 136 North Street, Brighton, from whose policy statement some of the above material has been extracted.

*14.6.3 Industrial Pollution Inspectorate: Pollution and Safety*

Arising from a recommendation of the Royal Commission on Environmental Pollution and a government scrutiny it was agreed to form (from April 1987) a new Pollution Inspectorate (HM Inspectorate of Pollution (HMIP) to undertake the work of HM IAPI, the Hazardous Waste Inspectorate (HWI), set up in 1983 to oversee waste disposal authorities and mainly run or privately licensed by local government under the *Control of Pollution Act* 1974), HM Radiochemical Inspectorate (RCI) (on both nuclear and non-nuclear sites), and a new Water Pollution Inspectorate. All would be under the common management of the Department of the Environment (DoE) but would also serve the Welsh Office. DoE, the department responsible for policy on environmental protection, would thus also be charged with investigating compliance with legislation. Amendments to existing legislation to meet the requirements of EC Directive 84/360/EEC on combating air pollution from industrial plants became necessary from July 1987.

It was necesssary to arrange coordination between HMIP and the HSE Inspectorates, particularly for their field forces which are often located in the same building. Similar coordination is necessary with HM Industrial Pollution Inspectorate for Scotland (HMIPI) which comes under the control of the Scottish Development Department. This is particularly necessary to ensure a consistent and common standard of approach and effectiveness to all inspection matters (especially those involving the *Radioactive Substances Act* 1960) both north and south of the border.

**14.7 Further legislation concerning inspection**

(i) *The Fire Precautions Act* 1974 arose in part from the large number of fires involving loss of life, particularly in hotels and buildings used for residential and entertainment purposes. Like the fire requirements of the *Factories Act* 1961 in general it requires the provision of means of escape and of fire fighting and warning equipment. The fire authority has to inspect the premises and when satisfied grant a fire certificate.

From 1977 the scope of the Act was extended to cover factories, offices, shops and railway premises (previously covered under the 1961 (*Factories*) and 1963 (*Offices, Shops and Railway Premises*) Acts). These premises in general come under the responsibility of the (local) fire authority. However where factories include a process risk, or where (specified) large quantities of (specified) dangerous materials are processed or stored, all responsibility for these special premises (including the issue of fire certificates) will remain with the Health and Safety Executive. (See SI 1976 no. 2003 Fire Certificates (Special Premises) Regulations 1976, particularly Schedule I Part I which details the materials and processes involved.)

Where a fire certificate is not required under the Act and is not specified in SI 2003 the provisions of SI 2010 Fire Precautions (Non-Certificated Factory, Offices and Railway Premises) Regulations 1976 apply and cover means of escape and provision of fire fighting equipment). Building Regulations also require certain structural fire precautions for new factories and other buildings. The *Radioactive Substances Act* 1960 may include fire precautions in its conditions for storage of such materials. The *Petroleum (Consolidation) Act* 1928 (see also 14.8) makes provision for fire hazards, etc. See also Chemical Works Regulations 1922 (see 14.6).

Suitable provision must be made for giving warning in the event of fire. Fire detection and alarm systems may be installed and must be inspected, maintained and given operational tests regularly (and sometimes without prior notice). Fire detection equipment is usually operated by convected heat, radiation (infra-red, ultra-violet or visible) or smoke (see also 14.4.27).

BS 4547 *Classification of fires* designates four classes:

Class A.　Fires involving solid materials usually of a carbonaceous nature but excluding those which readily liquefy on burning. The usual extinguishing agent is drenching with water.

Class B.　Fires involving flammable liquids or liquefiable solids. Suitable extinguishing agents include foam, dry powder, carbon dioxide, halogenated hydrocarbons and water spray.

Class C.　Fires involving gases. The most effective method of extinguishing these is to cut off the gas supply.

Class D.　Fires involving burning metals, such as aluminium, magnesium, titanium, calcium, sodium and potassium. Most extinguishing agents are ineffective and often may be dangerous to use. The heat produced by the burning metal is intense and there may be toxic fumes. Perhaps the only sure method is to isolate the fire from the atmosphere, but this in many cases is clearly impossible. The hazards of toxic fumes, etc. produced by burning plastics are well known.

(ii) *The Explosives Act* 1875 and the Explosive Substances Act 1923 and relevant subordinate legislation (including parts of the *HSW Act* where applicable) deals with the manufacture, handling, storing, conveyance and supply of explosives. It is enforced by HM Explosives Inspectorate (under the control of the HSE) most of whose work is centred on factories, etc. but it also has responsibilities for the sale of fireworks.

Licences have to be issued by the Inspectorate to authorize any work with explosives; safety distances around relevant buildings are specified to protect neighbouring buildings and people; and liaison with local authorities is usually necessary to plan for any emergency.

In the past government establishments, including Royal Ordnance Factories, have been exempt from the licensing requirements, but with any privatization of ROFs this will not be so.

(iii) *The Nuclear Installations Act* 1965, etc. and the work of the NII of the HSE have already been mentioned (see 6.18 and 12.10) but, as with explosives, etc. government establishments are exempt from licensing requirements (and this includes the UKAEA but not BNFL or the CEGB). The perhaps unwritten rule is that establishments under the Crown are conducted to at least the highest standards *imposed* upon any private establishment. Much of the work of the NII has been concerned with the inspection and assessment of safety of CEGB nuclear power stations, both during construction and operation, but a part of its resources was engaged for some three years on the Public Inquiry into the proposed PWR for the Sizewell 'B' nuclear power station (see 13.14).

Both the Explosives Inspectorate and the NII show nil returns for fatal accidents in recent years. But their potential for major accidents and heavy casualties is of course great. Munitions explosions in World War I killed some 3000 in Halifax, Canada and some hundreds at Chilwell ROF, Notts.

(iv) *Legislation concerning pressure vessels, etc.* UK legislation for pressure vessels, boilers, gas cylinders, etc., is based on the *Health and Safety at Work Act* 1974, the *Factories Act* 1961, the *Boiler Explosions Act* 1882 and 1890, the *Mines and Quarries Act* 1954–1961 and the *Petroleum (Consolidation) Act* 1928.

The UK is one of the few major industrial countries which does not embody within its legislation the mandatory use of a national design standard for the construction and inspection of pressure vessels, etc., its legislation being largely confined to periodic examinations throughout service (see 12.5) by a 'competent person' (12.4).

Even so, a wide range of pressure systems and vessels do not come under the requirements of the *Factories Act* 1961 and whilst there may be no statutory requirements at present covering pre-commissioning inspection, this is covered generally by the requirements of the *HSW Act* and the HSE's 'recognition' of BS 1113, BS 2790, BS 5500 etc. and by the formation of the PVQAB (see 3.4.2, 3.23 and 9.4.8).

The *Boiler Explosions Acts* 1882 and 1890 provided for enquiries to be held into the cause of an explosion, and copies of reports were sent to the Factory Inspectorate for any necessary legal action and/or recommendations. Similar legislation is now carried out under the *HSW Act* 1974 by the HSE under, *inter alia*, the Reporting of Injuries, Diseases and Dangerous Occurrences Regulations 1985. Deaths, injuries and accidents at work have to be reported immediately and some 14 categories of notifiable dangerous occurrences (including boiler explosions, etc.) *wherever they occur* are scheduled for notification and reporting by the 'responsible person' to the HSE and other authorities who will undertake any necessary investigations and legal action (see also 3.2).

Figures for these 'reported' casualties now form the basis of the statistics issued by the Inspectorates of the HSE—see 13.3.

*The Mines and Quarries Act* 1954–61 consolidates earlier legislation and contains detailed safety (and therefore inspection) provisions expanded in the regulations made under it. It differs in some respects from the *Factories Act* in its regulation of the system and of the qualifications for management and its imposition of personal criminal liabilities upon management. It requires, under Section 84, that 'all apparatus . . . which contains or produces air, gas or steam at a pressure greater than atmospheric pressure shall be so constructed, installed, maintained and used as to obviate any risk from fire, bursting, explosion or collapse, or the production of noxious gases.' HM Mines and Quarries Inspectorate (under the HSE) enforces all the relevant regulations. Reported fatal accidents average some 50 per year (of which some 8 were surface accidents) in coal mines; 5 in other mines, and 15 in quarries.

The *Petroleum (Consolidation) Act* 1928, through the Gas Cylinders (Conveyance) Regulations 1931 (as amended 1947 and 1959) controls, in general, the conveyance by road of gas cylinders of the types specified. These Regulations lay down in considerable detail specifications for materials, design, construction and testing of cylinders. The bulk of these specifications are embodied in British Standards, which are restated in the schedules to the order. It should be noted that these British Standards largely embody Home Office requirements for design and inspection, and where appropriate, are mandatory. Such gas cylinders etc. may only be manufactured by approved manufacturers after official approval of prototype samples; inspection is carried out by independent inspection organizations approved by the Health and Safety Executive (see 6.7).

The Factories Inspectorate normally wishes to see Home Office Regulations followed on factory sites, whilst British Railways do, in effect, observe them.

The storage and conveyance of dissolved acetylene in cylinders containing a homogeneous porous mass is subject to the requirements of Order of Secretary of State no. 9 made under the *Explosives Act* 1875 (S.R. and O. 1919 no. 809).

Thus it will be seen that the Home Office Regulations for Gas Cylinders may cover both inspection during manufacture as well as 'in-use' inspection, and that, in some cases, the use of approved firms and inspection organizations and of approved specifications is mandatory.

At present legislation does not cover all aspects of a pressure system but tends to concentrate on boilers, pressure vessels, air receivers and gas cylinders. Obviously the components and pipework, etc. of a pressure system could be just as much at risk; certain hazardous fluids are also not adequately covered. Consequently the Health and Safety Commission are considering with industry proposals for new legislation for pressurized systems which are meant to be all-embracing, and would cover such matters as approved inspection organizations and the enforcing authority, assessment of hazards, periods between examination and testing, and record keeping.

Legislation regarding the conveyance by road of hazardous substances is also increasing; it is intended to cover all dangerous goods in due course.

Although the legislation of many foreign countries makes the use of certain national standards mandatory, UK opinion generally feels that such a practice should be avoided, particularly for pressure vessels, as it can inhibit technical innovation. Without it, however, an additional onus is put upon the 'competent' inspection organization in deciding whether a vessel, etc., is safe and fit for service.

Various bodies such as the ISO prepare standards and the EEC issues directives to its member states requiring them to promulgate legislation to secure a measure of conformity regarding regulations and legislation. For instance Council Directive 77/767/EEC of 27 July 1976 relates to the provision of common laws for pressure vessels and the methods of inspecting them. All such directives, etc. should in due course be applicable in the UK.

*Agriculture (Safety, Health and Welfare Provisions) Act* 1956 provided for the first time provision for the safety, health and welfare of those employed in agriculture and related areas. Regular inspection of agricultural machinery and methods of use is obviously a necessity. Fatal injuries (mainly arising from machinery) amount to some 30 per year. The use of agricultural pesticides and poisonous substances is controlled by regulations. Enforcement of all relevant regulations, etc. is carried out by HM Agricultural Inspectorate of the HSE.

*Offices, Shops and Railway Premises Act* 1963 is somewhat akin to the *Factories Act*, although less extensive in some directions (Add further note) Detailed safety standards for hoists and lifts have been made in regulations under this Act. (They require the thorough examination by a competent person of hoists and lifts at least once every six months, and safety precautions similar to those in the *Factories Act* (see 12.5) Much of the work of enforcement of regulations, prosecutions, etc. is carried out by local authority inspectors. Some 40 fatalities are reported per year.

*Employment Medical Advisory Service Act* 1972 sets up a medical service which, *inter alia*, supersedes the factory doctors and the medical inspectors of the Factory Inspectorate. The Medical Division of the HSE and the Medical Advisory Committee of the HSC carry out investigations on such occupational health matters as noise, dangerous organisms, etc. and the use of visual display units (VDUs).

## 14.8 Consumer protection and safety legislation

A purchaser (consumer) of an item of plant, or some other product or service, may not be satisfied. Perhaps it is not as ordered, it does not function or it is unsuitable for the required purpose, etc. Furthermore it may have caused trouble, loss, damage or injury.

UK law allows persons injured or who have suffered loss or damage by reason of a defective product, to seek redress through (i) breach of contract, (ii) the tort (civil wrong) of negligence, or (iii) breach of statutory duty.

Obviously manufacturers, suppliers, engineers, designers and inspectors may be involved either directly or indirectly. Under the *Sale of Goods Act, 1979* liability in (i.e. breach of) contract can arise if conditions relating to the quality and fitness for purpose of the goods are not met. If an article is defective and leads to the buyer suffering personal injury or damage to property the buyer can then sue for damages, *irrespective of whether the seller has been negligent.* Such a case for damages will normally be taken under civil law, the state providing the legal framework.

The *Unfair Contract Terms Act* 1977 provides:

(i) that no person may by any contract term limit or exclude his liability for death or personal injury caused by negligence on his part;

(ii) the conditions of merchantable quality and fitness for purpose cannot be excluded;

(iii) in respect of other forms of loss or damage, e.g. damage to property, he can only exclude liability to the extent that it is reasonable to do so.

(Note: the burden of proving it is reasonable is placed upon the person seeking to show it is reasonable.)

If a manufacturer markets a defective product which causes loss or damage or injures the user then the manufacturer is open to an action in the tort of negligence; the onus of proving negligence rests with the plaintiff (but see the Consumer Protection Act 1987, p. 728).

Negligence may be simply forgetting to carry out some operation, etc.; it may be professional negligence, e.g. not using the professional skills and knowledge expected of a professional engineer in designing and/or testing a product to ensure its fitness for the purpose specified. And, of course, any breach of safety or statutory regulations made under the *HSW Act* 1974 is a criminal offence and civil action for damages may also be taken by any affected consumer.

Under the *Consumer Protection Act* 1961 and 1971 it is a criminal offence for retailers, manufacturers, importers or wholesalers to offer for sale goods which did not comply with regulations laid before Parliament (i.e. statutory regulations). If the failure to comply was due to the act or default of his supplier, proceedings could be taken against the supplier as well as or instead of the retailer.

Amongst the first of the regulations made were those relating to the colour coding of flexible electric cable cores and the description and marking of certain electrical goods which were required to comply with particular British Standards if cited in the regulations. The Electrical Equipment (Safety) Regulations 1975 and 1976 were introduced under the

Act, and are written in very general terms and can cover a wide range of goods including equipment not yet on the market. Guidance can be obtained showing the standards considered to afford the degree of safety required, but this has no statutory force, and in general manufacturers are free to meet these requirements in any way they choose. If trouble arose only a Court could decide if a piece of equipment complied, and compliance with British Standards would obviously influence the Court. (As an example, equipment complying with BS 415 *Safety Requirements for mains operated electronic apparatus* is recognized as meeting the requirements of the Electrical Equipment (Safety) Regulations 1975 and 1976 (see 6.9.2). It was not practical or desirable to make regulations for every type of consumer product; therefore a general safety requirement became applicable.

The *Consumer Safety Act* 1978 took over from the *Consumer Protection Act* 1961 and 1971, but the Electrical Equipment (Safety) Regulations and other regulations remained in force. This act provided a framework for certain actions by the Secretary of State for Prices and Consumer Protection making regulations, etc. to ensure that goods are safe by design, construction and labelling, etc. These regulations may refer to published Standards, which 'may be deemed to satisfy' the prescribed requirements; they may require 'approval' by a specified body: 'A person shall not be guilty of an offence unless it is proved that goods do not conform to a particular standard'. Reference is made to testing and inspection, and to manufacturers' quality control arrangements.

The Act can give rise to civil and criminal liabilities; it enables quick action to be taken to ban dangerous supplies by the use of prohibition orders, notices to warn, etc. It provides an element of strict product liability on producers for personal injury and damage to property arising from a defective article. It enables safety regulations to be made for any class of goods. Breach of these regulations is not only a criminal offence, but is also actionable as a breach of statutory duty owed to any person who may be affected by the breach. A product which fails to comply with the regulations is ipso facto defective. Any officer of the body corporate (e.g. company) who through neglect, or with consent or connivance commits an offence will be also guilty of that offence as well as the body corporate. Thus directors, managers, professional engineers, designers, QA surveyors and inspectors, etc. will risk criminal prosecution and claims for damages if they ignore regulations.

Safety regulations can cover a wide field including design, construction, finish, marking, testing, inspection, packaging, operating instructions, servicing and marketing. Those under this Act are produced by the Department of Trade and Industry (DTI) in consultation with trade associations and other interested bodies. Details can be obtained from the Consumer Safety Unit of the DTI.

*Defensive measures (for manufactures, etc).* The successive Acts of legislation described here aimed to safeguard the consumer from products that do not reach a reasonable level of safety. Also there has been the increasing threat (to the manufacturer) of the imposition of stringent product liability, making him liable for damage and injury caused by defective products.

To protect a company or organization and its employees (including directors, managers, designers, inspectors and surveyors) from the full rigours of the law which could arise from defects and other infringements certain defensive measures can be taken. Besides having the services of a good lawyer these measures could include:

(i) An analysis of design to assess the possibility of unforeseen defects.

(ii) A review of type tests and possibly life tests (remembering that product liability ends after ten years).

(iii) A structural failure analysis of particular designs.

(iv) A check of bought-out components for compliance with specifications, etc.

(v) A check for any possible dangers to the user and preparation of suitable warning notices, instructions, etc.

(vi) The provision of an effective QA organization, (e.g. to BS 5750), with quality control of relevant components.

(vii) The permanent identification of individual products and their correlation with dated test records.

(viii) Insurance — obviously employers (and employees!) should have some insurance to cover their various liabilities.

*The Employers Liability (Compulsory Insurance) Act* 1979 and related acts, require employers to have approved insurance cover for accidents which cause injury to their employees. Cover for claims from the public for personal injury and/or damage, and for insurance against product liability risks, are also desirable.

'No-fault' product liability legislation had been proposed by the EEC and has been developed in the USA. In the USA some unfortunate aspects of this system have appeared, and punitive damages have been inflicted by the juries (in the UK damages would be assessed by the judges).

It is no doubt expecting too much for a person or company to provide services without faults. (A doctor for instance would never commit errors. If he did, or his patients died, he could be sued under such legislation.) In industry, however, much can be done towards a perfect world by strict compliance with safety regulations, design and inspection standards and strict adherence to quality plans, as outlined in much of this work.

*The Consumer Protection Act* 1987 makes provisions with respect to the liability of persons for damage caused by defective products and in effect took over the earlier acts and legislation with amendments, including the *Consumer Safety Act* 1978. It imposes EEC product liability law.

It is divided into two main parts:

(a) *Product liability* (implemented under Directive 85/374/EEC) provides for the right of a person injured or who has suffered damage by reason of a defective product to sue for damages.

This Act removes the need to prove a manufacturer negligent (a customer can already sue a supplier without proof of negligence under the Sale of Goods Act).

A plaintiff must begin his court action within three years of the incident and cannot sue after ten years from the date of supply.

Besides the protective measures a manufacturer or supplier can take during design and manufacture (mentioned previously) it would be a defence in any civil proceedings arising if he could prove that:

(i) the state of scientific and technical knowledge ('state of the art') at the time of supply was not such that another producer in the same field might be expected to have discovered the defect (a so called 'development risks defence')

(ii) the defect was caused by complying with the law, or any regulation or specification (it might be necessary to show that the defect was the inevitable result of compliance)

(iii) the defect was not in the product at the time of supply (it may have become defective because of faulty treatment)

(iv) the producer of a component would not be liable if he was able to show that the defect was due to the design of the finished product or to defective specifications given to him

(b) *Consumer Safety.* The Act consolidates and improves the regulating making powers under previous consumer safety law. A person shall be guilty of an offence if he fails to comply with the general safety requirement or specific regulations. He will not be regarded as failing to comply if he can prove that the consumer goods

(i) conform in a relevant respect with a European Community obligation

(ii) conform to any applicable safety regulations or standards approved by DTI (who publish a list of such standards).

## 14.9 Foreign legislation

In many foreign countries inspection and approval of design is compulsory by law in respect of boilers, pressure vessels, air receivers, gas cylinders and containers, etc. In some cases the design and materials have to be in accordance with national or approved specifications and the manufacturer's works facilities, welding procedures and welders have to be approved. Often inspection is carried out by a government or officially recognized independent inspection organization, or an inspector acting under its authority; inspection during manufacture and final testing is generally required. Countries which impose legislation similar to that outlined include West Germany, USA, Canada, France, Holland, Italy,

Norway, Sweden, Switzerland and the USSR. Some countries accept pressure vessels constructed to the standards of the exporting country (see 3.3), although inspection and final documentation may be required. Further details of the statutory requirements, regulations and codes applicable abroad, not only for pressure vessels but for electrical equipment for flammable atmospheres, gas equipment, etc., are given in the *Technical Digests* issued by the Technical Help to Exporters Section of BSI at PO Box 391 Milton Keynes MK14 6 LW.

## 14.10 Safety officers and their duties

The Construction (General Provisions) Regulations (SI 1961 no.1580) issued under the *Factories Act* 1961 seemingly contains the only direct legislation requiring an employer to appoint a safety officer/adviser. This applies only to a building or civil engineering contractor employing over 20 workmen (see note in Table 14.3).

Although the *HSW Act* does not directly require that an employer should employ the services of a safety officer (and only goes into detail including regulations and a Code of Practice concerning the wide ranging powers of trade union appointed safety representatives employed by the employer under Sect. 2(5) of the Act) many large firms and organizations have for years past found it increasingly desirable to appoint one, either full or part-time (i.e. having other duties, often in the same organization). However, the statement on safety policy which every employer is required to make by the *HSW Act* necessitates a description of the organization and arrangements for carrying it out, and this could be useless unless it contained details of individual/s experienced, knowledgeable and preferably qualified enough to advise senior management on safety matters (i.e. safety officers or advisers). Consequently there has been an increasing demand by employers for qualified professional safety officers. It is generally accepted that his duties are mainly advisory and that he reports to top management who theoretically carry the final legal responsibility for safety (i.e. they may not always accept his advice but would be foolish if they went against any such firmly expressed and re-iterated advice and would be criminally responsible at law if trouble subsequently arose). In order to keep in touch with what is happening he needs to inspect not only the plant, by making tours of inspection, but anything and everything—if necessary down to the last detail. He has to talk to people and give advice to all and sundry. Obviously he has only one pair of eyes and ears so he must make use of anyone who can help him (from top management to shop-floor labourers and of course trade union appointed safety representatives); he must be a good listener, and well known, respected and contactable.

So management and safety officers will then have extra eyes looking for 'trouble' and helping them in their work. As an example, a certain keen electrician as a worker's representative was a great help to a safety officer, but another worker's representative was always conscious of the difference between 'them' and 'us' and needed at least careful, handling. Both were trade union men. 'Unbiased' health and safety education is vital but like unbiased history is often difficult to obtain. A shop steward on a safety committee (this was before the implementation of SI 500 in October 1978) seemed to be waging a permanent personal vendetta against a certain principal foreman also on the committee and much time was consumed with their 'crossfire'. There was often some merit on both sides, but the safety officer in the privacy of his office had to spend a lot of time trying to educate both!

Under the latest legislation (and the Code of Practice) management should realize that a safety representative has the right to report unsafe conditions, etc. to the employer (normally in writing, but orally if need be). Whether he does this direct or through the safety officer is not stated. (But see safety representatives inspection report, Figure 14.1).

In comparatively small organizations the safety officer may have other related duties. For instance he may be a plant manager very knowledgeable about the hazards of the plant. This has advantages and disadvantages. He could for example take immediate action (as plant manager) to stop a process reported as erratic, which (as safety officer) he could only *advise* management was apparently becoming dangerous. On the other hand his position and experience as plant manager might incline him to continue the process for a time as an acceptable risk.

In many larger organizations a full-time professional safety officer could have part-time safety officers reporting to him from each of many departments. These departmental part-time officers would have other responsible duties in their respective departments and should contribute a wealth of detailed knowledge and experience. Also properly trained trade union safety representatives should contribute down-to-earth common sense from the shopfloor.

With the tremendous amount of inspection and safety work required or implied by the *HSW Act* it would seem that there should be a large increase in the number of HSE inspectors employed to see to its enforcement. But this would involve great public expenditure and an increase in the number of perhaps hard to find suitably experienced civil servants. The position could be similar to that faced by AID in earlier days (see 9.1.1) and there would seem to be a case for the appointment by firms of 'approved' safety officers, to carry out some of the duties imposed on the firm by legislation. Like an approved chief inspector they would work under the general supervision and with the advice of the HSE inspector from the local regional office, and would themselves have the control and assistance of a number of full and part-time representatives of many skills from various departments and organizations.

## 14.11 Responsibilities of inspectors, designers, etc.

Inspectors, design engineers, etc. have always had great moral responsibilities. Under current legislation it will be realized that they have many responsibilities for which they may be held legally liable. Nevertheless in many organizations they may come under intense pressure at times from their superiors and other influential people in an attempt to alter or influence their decisions (these people may have the power of hire and fire, or perhaps also of recommending advancement). Maybe an inspector finds that some apparently minor specification clause, regulation or statutory requirement has not been strictly complied with, or something he regarded as defective has brought forth a flood of invective and objections from such people. The inspector, etc. has been called a fool, a pedantic ass with no practical knowledge, or even a coward. However he should remember that if an accident or fatality occurs, everybody, including his superiors, etc. will be looking for a scapegoat. The inspector and designer and their work will be subject to close scrutiny. Any defects or non-compliance with specifications or regulations which come to light will be seized upon, perhaps by an official enquiry, as a possible cause of the accident. Any verbal pressurizing of the inspector or designer which may have influenced him to accept something incorrect will no doubt be denied or conveniently forgotten and the inspector, etc. may be left 'carrying the can'.

Many accidents destroy much of the evidence which caused them and it is often difficult to determine the true cause or causes (but it is surprising how many result from the juxtaposition of a leak, explosive or hazardous material and a source of ignition). Any inspector, designer, etc. faced with such pressurization as described above should, after careful thought and if then his considered judgement is still not accepted, insist that the situation is recorded in writing perhaps in the minutes of a meeting giving the name of the proposer and details of the fault or intended breach of regulations etc. (the proposer is unlikely to agree openly to do this). However should the inspector's decision and/or requirements still be over-ruled he should report the matter in writing to the highest level possible.* It might be thought that with the great attention now given to the approval of quality systems (e.g. as in BS 5750) and the apparent independence of the inspector such situations would not arise; but human nature being what it is, they do—even in the highest circles—and must be guarded against.

An inspector should not expect any credit for doing his job—often the reverse. In some organizations he may be marked by the 'higher ups' as a troublesome and awkward person, difficult to get on with. They will note this particularly if his objections have sometimes been over-ruled and no

---

*Perhaps after drawing the attention of the proposer to Sect. 37 of the *HSW Act* 1974 (see 14.2).

trouble of note has arisen; but should trouble or disaster occur and if the inspector is covered in writing then blame will lie elsewhere.

Attention is drawn to the classic case of the inspection of the airship R101 (see 13.6.6). The inspector made many reports of the endemic leakage of hydrogen from gas bags, particularly in flight. The matter was discussed by his superiors and his director with the designers and operational staff. Under intense political pressure they told the inspector to, in effect, 'bodge' up the leakage and fly with the ship to India and report. He carried out the first order but refused to clear the certificate of airworthiness required for further flying and refused to fly in her. Another inspector was appointed for the voyage and flight clearance was approved by the newly appointed 'man at the top'—Air Marshal Sir Hugh Dowding (later of Battle of Britain fame). It is doubtful whether he saw all the inspector's reports and heard the full story. The airship crashed, with the loss of 48 lives including the politician mainly responsible and two AID inspectors. However the inspector who rejected the ship as unsafe and refused to fly in her apparently got no more promotion!

A somewhat similar but more recent case is that of the American space shuttle accident (see 13.6.7). Leakage had been known or suspected for some time, and possible reasons for such leakage and possible methods of prevention had been put into writing. The 'state of the art' to begin with was such that a 'development risks defence' might have been put forward to avoid liability. But as further *apparently* successful operational flights were made, higher management took 'a calculated risk' in approving them.

The disaster *may* have been due to compliance with a new test specification (which, whilst proving a leak tight joint, blew the protective putty away (see Fig. 13.3) and exposed the seal to heat during operational flight). But (under UK law) to avoid legal liability the defence would have to show that the defect was the *inevitable* result of compliance with the new specification. However, a manufacturer of components could disclaim liability if the defect was due to the design of the finished product or to defective specifications supplied to him.

In accidents such as those described and any others particularly those involving hazardous plants, official inquiries may result in penalties to those considered guilty parties; much depends upon the legislation applicable. For instance, contravention of the General Safety Requirement of the UK Consumer Protection Act 1987 can result in a fine not exceeding £2000, up to six months' imprisonment, or both; in the USA the widow of the pilot of the space shuttle Challenger sued the makers for $1.5 billion!

Rather than end on a somewhat sour note it should perhaps be pointed out that those concerned with inspection and safety have a very worthwhile and often psychologically rewarding job to perform. They are often in a position to spot and prevent trouble before it has a chance to cause perhaps disaster, death, injury and loss of money. With the right personality, training and experience (which should include knowledge of design and manufacture) they can carry out their duties in such a way as to take a great load off the minds of top management.


**References and further reading**

Lewis, J.R., *Quality assurance and the law*, Brit. Inst. Management, 1985.
Redgraves *Health and Safety in Factories* (Butterworth/Shaw)
Mitchell, Ewan, *The employer's guide to the law on health, safety and welfare at work*, Business Books, 1985.
Whincup, M., *Product Liability Law*, Gower, 1985.
*Guide to product liability and safety provisions of the Consumer Protection Act*, Consumer Affairs Division, DTI, 1987.

The Building Regulations 1985. Package comprising the manual; materials and workmanship; means of escape in case of fire; approved documents, etc., HMSO: Dept. of the Environment.
The Building (Approved inspectors, etc) Regulations 1985 (SI 1985 no.1066), HMSO.
Air Pollution Control in Great Britain, review and proposals: a consultation paper, HMSO.

# Appendix   Legal metrology

That field of knowledge concerned with *measurement* in all areas of science and technology is termed *metrology*.

In a more restrictive sense it is often regarded in industry as the science of *accurate* measurement, particularly of length.

That part of metrology which treats of *units of measurement, methods of measurement* and of *measuring instruments*, particularly in relation to mandatory technical and legal requirements which have the object of ensuring a public guarantee from the point of view of the security and of the appropriate *accuracy of measurements*, is termed legal metrology (see BS PD 6461: Part 2).

Obviously the inspector will be vitally interested in all such matters. Legal metrology is enforced by Inspectors of Weights and Measures acting under government and/or local authority.

## A.1   Units of measurement

Since 1965 the Système International d'Unités (SI) has been gradually introduced and used in the UK (as in countries of the EEC and most other countries except the USA) and was accepted by the UK in 1969 as the principal and legal system of measurement for all purposes. It has in effect replaced the old Imperial (ft/lb/sec) system and many units from the metric centimetre/gramme/sec (CGS) system previously much used in scientific circles.

EEC directives including those concerning units of measurement (based on the General Conference on Weights and Measures (CGPM) decisions) are issued from time to time (and confirmed by UK Statutory Instruments) detailing such matters as SI units for permanent use, other units (including most Imperial and certain technical metric units which cannot be used for legal purposes), and certain other units which may be used with SI, perhaps temporarily. Consequently most familiar Imperial and many other units are not now strictly legally acceptable in EEC countries (although still much in evidence in the UK). However, the USA still makes much use of Imperial units, although SI units are being increasingly employed there.

In the past the standards of measurement employed in both the metric and Imperial systems were somewhat arbitrary; for instance, both the international metre and the Imperial standard yard were based on the distance between two lines on a certain bar at a certain temperature and kept respectively in Paris and London. However, the 11th General Conference of Weights and Measures (CGPM), meeting in Paris in October 1960, decided upon the adoption of six units to serve as a basis for the establishment of a practical system of measurement for international purposes. This system, a development of the earlier rationalized Giorgi or MKSA (metres/kilogramme/seconds/ampère) system but including the kelvin and candela, was adopted by the International Organization for Standardization (ISO) and is known as the Système International (SI) d'Unités (International System of Units). Although the kilogram is still arbitrary, being the mass of a certain international prototype kept at Sèvres, Paris, its other fundamental (base) units are precisely defined. For instance the metre was defined by reference to 1650763.73 wavelengths emitted in vacuum by a discharge lamp using krypton 86 under specified conditions,* whilst the second is defined as the interval occupied by a certain number of cycles of radiation corresponding to the transition of the caesium-133 atom.

The use of SI units should secure a measure of uniformity with European and other countries. But change-over and re-education is taking time, and as the USA still in general uses the Imperial system, particularly for engineering work, English units will no doubt remain in evidence for many years.

However, it is the policy of the American Society for Testing and Materials (ASTM) and many other official US bodies to work towards the simplification of units of measurement. To this purpose, it is generally stated that SI units should be more widely used, but they do not advocate any immediate mandatory change in established dimensions, etc., rather that both present units and their converted SI equivalents be published and included in new and revised standards, etc. This policy is being generally followed by many US technical and scientific bodies. For instance, ASME, having included both present (Imperial) and SI units in their publications, now publish a separate SI edition of their Boiler and Pressure Vessel Code. Canada, with its official dual English/French system, in general uses SI. Its 'mileposts' etc. are now in kilometres and these change to miles on crossing into USA. In the UK, however, although SI is 'official' for legal purposes mileposts and other Imperial units are still much in evidence!

The SI system now includes 7 base units (the seventh base unit being the mole (symbol mol)—the amount of substance of a system which contains as many elementary entities as there are in 0.012 kilogram of carbon 12) plus many derived units (some of which have received names).

The whole forms what is known as a 'coherent' system of units, meaning

---

*See A.4, redefined 1983

the product or quotient of two (or more) of its base units give *directly* the SI unit for the derived quantity (which is a distinct advantage over the older systems).

In practice it may be convenient to employ (as prefixes) decimal multiples and sub-multiples of the base SI unit, but only recommended and named powers of 10 should normally be employed (e.g. $10^6$ = mega (M)). However, in order to avoid errors in calculation it is advisable to express quantities *only in terms of their base SI units*, prefixes being replaced by powers of ten (i.e. these multiple and submultiple units are *not* the coherent base SI units).

Another dangerous source of error when dealing with continental documentation is confusion between the British decimal point and the comma used on the continent for the same purpose; also in the UK the comma is commonly used for separating groups of three figures, whereas a space is used for this purpose on the continent. For example consider: 32·021 and 32,021 or 32 021—these may be the same or may differ by one thousand times! Note: 299 792 458; 1/31 556 925,974 7; 0,012; 4,185 5; 2204,6. Note also: 1401 Pa can be written as 1,401k Pa in continental style, but 1·401k Pa in UK style (i.e. the continental 1,401k Pa would be one thousand times greater read as English notation).

Certain ISO and IEC standards have been accepted as suitable for publication without deviation as British Standards (they have dual, but different, standard numbers). BSI draws attention to the fact that 'the comma has been used throughout as a decimal marker. In British standards it is current practice to use a full point (full stop on the baseline) as the decimal marker'—so be warned!

Certain units outside the SI may be used with SI units. Thus days and hours are used as well as the basic second; volume may be expressed in litres (its symbol can now be L or l to avoid any confusion with 1 (one). 1 litre = 1 $dm^3$; tonne (symbol t and pronounced 'tunny') represents 1000 kg (and at 2204·6 lb is close to the English ton of 2240 lb and the American short ton of 2000 lb). Certain other units may be used temporarily with SI (e.g. the nautical mile, knot and bar).

Details of SI units, and conversion tables for various systems and units are given in many publications, particularly those of the BSI, etc. (see Tables A.1 and A.2) and elsewhere in various chapters of this book where relevant. Particular attention is drawn to conversion Table A.3 taken by permission from BS 5316 Part 1 which is based on an ISO specification. This uses the continental type of 'comma' decimalization and figure spacing as explained above. It should be studied *very* carefully by those not conversant with the system. An inspector *must be familiar with all systems and units in current use*.

It is perhaps surprising to see the number of different units for pressure and stress, and related derived units such as leak rate (see Tables 8.6 and

## TABLE A.1

*Units and conversion tables*

| | |
|---|---|
| BS 3763 | International System (SI) Units |
| PD 5686 | The use of SI units |
| BS  350 | Conversion factors and tables |
| BS 2856 | Precise conversion of inch and metric sizes on engineering drawings |
| BS 5233 | Glossary of terms used in metrology (taken mainly from vocabulary published by the International Organization of Legal Metrology (OIML) which deals with the service of legal metrology (available from BSI as PD 6461) |
| BS 5555 | SI units and recommendations for the use of their multiples and of certain other units |
| BS 5775 Parts 0–13 | Specification for quantities, units and symbols |
| BS 5781 | Measurement and calibration systems |
| Bureau International des Poids et Mésures | Le Système International d'Unités (SI). (Sèvres France, 5th ed., 1985, English/French) |
| Royal Society of London | Quantities, Units and Symbols |

11.1), which have been used often with official blessing (maybe temporarily) in recent years.

Units used for expressing radioactivity, radiation dosage, etc. have also been changing to SI and have caused some confusion (see 6.17.2).

## A.2  The process of measurement

The control of manufacturing processes and the assessment of product quality depend largely upon the inspector's ability to measure or supervise the processes of measurement to required and known standards.

The process of measurement is carried out by comparing the quantity to be measured with a *standard* whose value is known (to a specific degree of accuracy) in terms of the *unit* of that particular quantity.

In general, components are first manufactured and checked using *workshop standard* gauges, instruments etc. Then the inspector checks for possible acceptance using *inspection standard* gauges etc, (of a higher degree of accuracy). The integrity of the inspector's task is founded upon his skill, the use of proper equipment and the establishment and maintenance of an effective system of control and *calibration*).

Calibration involves the periodic checking of the inspection standards, instruments or gauges against a calibration standard of an even higher

## TABLE A.2

*Values of some Imperial units in terms of SI units*

| Length | | Density | |
|---|---|---|---|
| 1 yd | **0·9144** m | 1 lb/in$^3$ | 2·767 99 $\times$ 10$^4$ kg/m$^3$ |
| 1 ft | **304·8** mm | 1 lb/ft$^3$ | 16·0185 kg/m$^3$ |
| 1 in | **25·4** mm | 1 lb/UKgal | 0·099 776 3 Mg/m$^3$ |
| 1 mile | **1·609 344** km | | (i.e. 0·099 776 3 kg/dm$^{3}$*) |
| | | | |
| **Area** | | **Force** | |
| 1 in$^2$ | **645·16** mm$^2$ | 1 pdl | 0·138 255 N |
| 1 ft$^2$ | 0·092 903 0 m$^2$ | 1 lbf | 4·448 22 N |
| 1 yd$^2$ | 0·836 127 m$^2$ | | |
| 1 mile$^2$ | 2·589 99 km$^2$ | **Pressure** | |
| 1 acre | 4046·86 m$^2$ | 1 lbf/in$^2$ | 6·894 76 kN/m$^2$ |
| | | 1 tonf/in$^2$ | 15·444 MN/m$^2$ |
| **Volume** | | | |
| 1 in$^3$ | 16 387·1 mm$^3$ | **Energy (work, heat)** | |
| 1 ft$^3$ | 0·028 316 8 m$^3$ | 1 ft pdl | 0·042 140 1 J |
| 1 UKgal | 4·546 09 dm$^{3}$* | 1 ft lbf | 1·355 82 J |
| | | 1 cal | **4·1868** J |
| **Velocity** | | 1 Btu | 1·055 06 kJ |
| 1 ft/s | **0·3048** m/s | | |
| 1 mile/h | **0·447 04** m/s | **Power** | |
| | | 1 hp | 745·700 W |
| **Mass** | | 1 ft lbf/s | 1·35582 W |
| 1 lb | **0·453 592 37** kg | | |
| 1 ton | 1016·0 kg | **Temperature** | |
| | | 1 Rankine unit | **5/9** of kelvin unit |
| | | (= 1 Fahrenheit unit) | (= **5/9** of Celsius unit) |

numbers printed in bold type are exact.

---

*By a resolution of the twelfth CGPM in 1964 the word 'litre' (symbol l, (but L may now be used) was recognized as a special name for the cubic decimetre but is not used to express high-precision measurements.

In 1901 the litre was defined as the volume of 1 kilogramme of pure water at normal atmospheric pressure and maximum density, equal therefore to 1·000 028 dm$^3$. This 1901 definition still applies for the purposes of the 1963 *Weights and Measures Act*. On the basis of the 1901 definition, 1 UKgal = 4·545 96 litres, but this small difference may be disregarded for most purposes.

Fahrenheit temperature in °F = $\frac{9}{5}$(Celsius in °C) + 32. The kelvin unit (symbol K) should be used to express temperature difference (or interval) and is equal to the unit 'degree Celsius' (°C). The degree symbol (°) is *not* used with kelvin. Use lower case for kelvin, as it is a base unit.

Thermodynamic temperature (kelvins) = Celsius temperature (°C) + 273·15
1 N/mm$^2$ = 1MN/m$^2$ = 1MPa    Adapted from PD 5686 by permission of BSI

## TABLE A.3
### Conversion to SI units

This table gives factors for conversion to SI units of some of the quantities expressed in multiples or sub-multiples of SI units and in units other than SI units. The conversion factor is the number by which the value expressed in various units should be multiplied to find the corresponding value in SI units.
Continental type decimalization is used in this table.

| Quantity | Symbol of SI unit | Various units Name | Various units Symbol | Conversion factors |
|---|---|---|---|---|
| Volume rate of flow | m³/s | litre per second | l/s | $10^{-3}$ |
| | | cubic metre per hour | m³/h | 1/3 600 |
| | | litre per hour | l/h | 1/3 600 000 |
| | | litre per minute | l/min | 1/60 000 |
| | | imperial gallon per minute | gal (UK)/min | 0,000 075 77 |
| | | cubic foot per second | ft³/s | 0,028 316 8 |
| | | gallon (US) per minute | gal (US)/min | 0,000 063 09 |
| | | barrel (US) per hour (petroleum) | barrel (US)/h | 0,000 044 16 |
| Mass rate of flow | kg/s | ton per second | t/s | $10^3$ |
| | | ton per hour | t/h | 1/3,6 |
| | | kilogram per hour | kg/h | 1/3 600 |
| | | pound per second | lb/s | 0,453 592 37 |
| Pressure | N/m² (also known as pascal : Pa) | kilopond per square centimetre | kp/cm² | } 98 066,5 |
| | | kilogram-force per square centimetre | kgf/cm² | |
| | | bar | bar | } $10^5$ |
| | | hectopieze | hpz | |
| | | torr | torr | } 133,322 |
| | | conventional millimetre of mercury | mmHg | |

| Quantity | SI unit | Unit name | Symbol | Factor |
|---|---|---|---|---|
| | | conventional millimetre of water | mmH$_2$O | 9,806 65 |
| | | poundal per square foot | pdl/ft$^2$ | 1,488 16 |
| | | standard atmosphere | atm | 101 325 |
| | | pound-force per square inch | lbf/in$^2$ (psi) | 6 894,76 |
| Density | kg/m$^3$ | kilogram per cubic decimetre | kg/dm$^3$ | 10$^3$ |
| | | gram per cubic centimetre | g/cm$^3$ | |
| | | pound per cubic foot | lb/ft$^3$ | 16,018 5 |
| Power | W | kilowatt | kW | 10$^3$ |
| | | kilopond metre per second | kp·m/s | 9,806 65 |
| | | I.T. kilocalorie per hour | kcal$_{IT}$/h | 1,163 |
| | | cheval vapeur* | ch | 735,5 |
| | | horsepower* | hp | 745,7 |
| | | British thermal unit per hour | Btu/h | 0,293 071 |
| | | kilogram-force metre per second | kgf·m/s | 9,806 65 |
| Viscosity (dynamic viscosity) | N·s/m$^2$ = kg/m·s | decapoise | daP | 1 |
| | | poise | P | 10$^{-1}$ |
| | | dyne second per square centimetre | dyn·s/cm$^2$ | |
| | | gram per second centimetre | g/s·cm | |
| | | kilopond second per square metre | kp·s/m$^2$ | 9,806 65 |
| | | centipoise | cP | 10$^{-3}$ |
| | | poundal second per square foot | pdl·s/ft$^2$ | 1,488 16 |
| Kinematic viscosity | m$^2$/s | stokes | St = cm$^2$/s | 10$^{-4}$ |
| | | centistokes | cSt | 10$^{-6}$ |
| | | square foot per second | ft$^2$/s | 0,092 903 0 |

*No international symbol exists for this unit; the symbol shown is the most common.

741

degree of accuracy; this may involve the preparation of a document, certificate and/or calibration curve permitting the estimation of any errors. Finally, the calibration standard, gauge etc. should have documentation showing that it has been checked for accuracy against a *reference standard* which itself has been compared with the *national* standard.

For most manufacturers measurement capability will be confined to the provision of workshop and usually inspection gauges, etc. Calibration and checking of these may, if necessary, be undertaken by an outside test house. Calibration and reference standards and gauges will be checked and calibrated periodically by test houses of the highest repute, such as those at the National Physical Laboratory (NPL) Teddington. By such methods all measurements are traceable by an unbroken chain of comparisons up to the national measurement standard.

### A.3  Approval of calibration systems

The Aeronautical Inspection Directorate (AID) pioneered the investigation and approval of contractors' and other test houses and laboratories for the measurement of specific quantities (such as length, electrical units etc.) and of equipment (such as jigs, tools and gauges). These 'approved test houses' were listed in Part II of the AID List of Approved Firms and were subject to supervision and verification of performance by normal AID procedures, check testing and monitoring being done generally by the AID Test House at Harefield, Middlesex.

In 1966 the British Calibration Service (BCS) was set up, whereby firms and laboratories were examined and, if suitable, approved for various types and grades of measurement. Such 'approved laboratories' (which included the AID Test House) could then undertake specified calibration work on a commercial basis. The audit of test samples is carried out generally by BCS staff (generally controlled by NPL) and checked periodically by reference to national standards (including those held by NPL).*

BS 5781 *Measurement and calibration system* Part I Specification for system requirements was issued in 1979, and Part 2 Guide to the use of BS 5781 was issued in 1981. These are based on UK Defence standards DEF STAN 05-26 *Calibration system requirements for industry* and DEF STAN 05-27 *Guide for the evaluation of a Contractor's Calibration System*, respectively.

The interval between checking, servicing or re-calibrating any item of test equipment depends on many circumstances and must be regularly re-

---

* NPL also operates the National Measurement Accreditation Service who accredit industrial laboratories throughout the UK. These laboratories cover most test and measurement activities and issue test reports and calibration certificates which can aid industrial quality assurance.

viewed. An increase in use of an item may warrant more frequent calibration checks, etc.; the interval may be laid down in a specification or some regulation or agreement. Records must be maintained showing the results and dates of all such checks, and the date when the next check is due. The essential information should be attached to the item by labelling or similar means.

Compliance with those requirements enables a contractor and his calibration laboratory to qualify for approval to BS 5750 *Quality systems*, as explained in 9.4.1 and for listing in the Department of Trade and Industry's *Register of Quality Assessed Companies.*

### A.4 Linear measurements

Linear measurements may be compared visually by using a calibrated divided scale. More accurately they can be checked by using some form of optical *line-standard comparator*. Another type of length standard commonly used is the *end standard*, usually a slip or block of hardened steel with flat and parallel faces. Johansson slip gauges are generally used in sizes up to 4 in (100 mm) between faces, but for longer end standards cylindrical steel bars are preferred in the UK. By 'wringing' together a suitable combination of end standards any required dimension can be built up. Precise dimensional inspection is basically dependent on such standards.

Measuring machines of different types and sensitivity are available for comparing end standards by contact measurement, and for calibrating ring gauges, etc.

Obviously the length of a standard is dependent on its temperature. Consequently it has been agreed internationally that industrial standards of length are adjusted to be correct at 20°C (68°F). For exact comparison, the article being checked, the standard and the comparator should all be at this temperature.

Actual checking of physical length standards with the fundamental unit of length, as defined by international agreement may be carried out by inspection laboratories and such bodies as the National Physical Laboratory (NPL) using light waves from a specified krypton 86 discharge lamp and a process of optical interferometry. Regular patterns of alternate bright and dark bands or fringes (lines or circles) are produced. By adjusting the optical system, knowing the wavelength emitted, accurate measurement of length is possible.

In 1983 the CGPM, recognizing the need for more precise realization of the length of the metre and the progress made in the stabilization of lasers, redefined the metre as the length of the path travelled by light in vacuum during 1/299, 792, 458 of a second (the reciprocal of the speed of light in metre/sec). Consequently accurate methods of length measurement using radiations of stabilized lasers as well as spectral radiations of krypton lamps, etc. have now been recommended (see *Le Système International d'Unités'* BIPM 5th ed., 1985 and documents quoted therein).

### A.5 Measurement of force

The tensile and compression testing machines used in industry can be checked by using proving rings inserted in place of the material specimen. A typical 50 tonf (500 kN)* steel proving ring of NPL design has an indicator and a large drum micrometer mounted within the ring for measuring its elastic deflection under tensile and compressive loads. It can be used as a secondary load standard, and is capable of reproducing the primary standard of load to an accuracy of 2 parts in 5000 under laboratory conditions (corresponding to a 0·5 grade device—see below). It may itself be calibrated at the NPL or other approved laboratory by means of a primary standard deadweight machine, the masses of the cast iron weights of which are adjusted, for buoyancy and gravity, so that they provide loads in terms of the internationally recognized units of force to an accuracy within 1 part in 25,000, or better.

Other secondary load standards, such as the electrical resistance strain gauge type, now much used in industry, may also be checked against a dead weight standard.

BS 1610 *Materials testing machines and force verification equipment* has been prepared taking cognizance of the requirements of ISO and of the International Organization for Legal Metrology (OIML). Part 1 specifies requirements for the grading of the forces applied by materials testing machines and the methods of verification. Part 2 specifies requirements for the grading of the equipment used for the verification of the forces applied by materials testing machines. Such equipment (i.e. 'proving devices') may be proving rings, electrical resistance strain gauge load cells or other devices (mechanical, electrical, electronic, optical, etc.) which determine force by measurement of the elastic deformation of a loaded member.

A numerical system of grading is specified for the maximum permissible errors of forces, for the error of zero force, and for their repeatability. The method of calibration for proving devices is specified.

Three grades (0·5, 1·0 and 2·0 for both testing machine and proving device) are recognized (see Table A.4).

For each grade of verification equipment (proving device) the maximum numerical value of repeatability (expressed as percentage of deflection) is defined as 5 times better than that of the corresponding grade of testing machine.

---

*With SI units the unit of force is the newton (N). For all practical purposes 50 tonf = 500 kN. More precisely 1 tonf = 9·964 kN = 9964N

**TABLE A.4**

*Grades for materials testing machines*

| Grade | Max. permissible repeatability of forces (as percentage of nominal force) | Max. permissible mean error (as percentage of nominal force) | Max. permissible error of zero force (percentage of max force) |
|-------|-------------------------------|-------------------------|-------------------------|
| 0·5 | 0·5 | ±0·5 | ±0·1 |
| 1·0 | 1·0 | ±1·0 | ±0·2 |
| 2·0 | 2·0 | ±2·0 | ±0·4 |

### A.6 Frequency of verification

A testing machine should be re-verified annually or after dismantling or major repair or adjustment.

A proving device should be re-calibrated every two years, or after any damage or adjustment. Its calibration should be corrected if necessary for the deflection sustained at 20°C.

The calibration forces must be traceable either directly or indirectly through laboratories approved by British Calibration Service to the national standards held by the National Physical Laboratory.

### A.7 Strain gauges

The development of the electrical resistance strain gauge facilitated the direct measurement of dynamic strain, thereby providing data for designs making more effective use of material.

The simple principle on which the resistance strain gauge depends is that the resistance of a conductor varies directly with its length, but inversely with its cross-sectional area. Consequently if a suitable wire conductor is bonded intimately to the surface of the specimen under test, the cement acting as an electrical insulator, then any subsequent tensile strain in the specimen will cause an increase in length of the conductor and a decrease in its cross-sectional area, thereby increasing its resistance. This change in resistance can be measured by a suitable Wheatstone bridge. Various arrangements of resistance strain gauges forming the bridge are possible.

Up to some 6 in (150 mm) of fine wire, wound parallel to one direction, may normally be required for each gauge; resistances of some 100 ohms or more are used. Gauges are generally packaged marked with the material lot number, resistance, and gauge factor (the ratio of unit resistance change divided by strain—$\triangle R/R \div \triangle L/L$). For any one job or measurement, gauges bearing the same lot number should be used if possible.

The method of cleaning the test specimen and attaching the gauge should be carefully standardized, and no air bubbles, inclusions or defects should be trapped between them. The insulation resistance between gauge and earth should be checked.

Instead of using wire-type strain gauges, metal foil gauges, perhaps manufactured by using printed circuit techniques, have been developed. They may have thicknesses of the order of 0·0005 in (12 $\mu$m), are made in a grid pattern, and are mounted on backing material (e.g. a film of epoxy resin). Their high surface-to-volume ratio enables them to be operated at higher current densities, giving more sensitivity than wire gauges.

Semi-conducting materials, such as silicon, are also used for the manufacture of strain gauges. They give a greater output than ordinary resistance gauges due to the *piezoresistance effect* (the change in electrical resistance with application of stress), being some 60 times more sensitive than most ordinary metal gauges. However, they have a non-linear strain-resistance characteristic.

Strain gauges of various types can also be used in transducers for measuring pressure, torque, etc.

**A.8  Coating techniques**

The use of *brittle coatings* for the location of regions of stress concentration and the directions of principal stresses is a technique which has been developed recently (although in 1850 Clark noticed the flaking away of paint from metal on the Britannia and Conway tubular bridges in regions of high strain). Resin-based coatings may be applied to structures, pressure vessels, etc., and, under strain, cracks in the coating will first appear at right-angles to the direction of the maximum principal tensile stress. If desired, quantitative information concerning the levels at which cracks just appear can be determined by reference to a calibration bar. Conditions of humidity and temperature may affect the results; ceramics coatings may be used at higher temperatures with perhaps some loss of sensitivity. However, brittle coating techniques are more often than not used qualitatively to show the general stress pattern.

*Photoelastic coating* techniques are now much used in industry, particularly in the USA and France where they were developed under the trade name Photostress. Components are coated with a specially developed bi-refringent plastic so that when subjected to a load the stress distribution and resulting strains on the surface are followed by the coating, and fringe patterns are made visible in colour when viewed under polarized light.

These colour patterns can be interpreted directly in terms of principal surface strain by means of a colour versus strain conversion chart. This method is analogous to using an infinite number of strain gauges of almost zero length distributed uniformly; it can be used at slightly elevated temperatures. However the interpretation of results, especially on complex components, may prove difficult and corrections are necessary if the coating is too thick.

By the use of appropriate instruments, accuracies up to ±10 micro strain (±10 $\mu$in/in), and ±2° strain direction may be obtainable.

## A.9 Grid methods (Moiré fringe)

Indication and measurement of strain can be carried out experimentally by noting the distortion of a grid.

A fine parallel grid of lines (or circles) of some 200–2000 lines/inch is formed on the surface of the specimen, and when loaded the grid deforms. The superimposition of this deformed grid on an underformed master grid produces an optical phenomenon—an interference fringe pattern—called the Moiré effect, which can be observed and photographed. The fringes are lines of constant displacement, and from them the strains can be derived.

## A.10 Measurement of electrical quantities

Electrical measuring instruments such as ammeters, voltmeters and watt-meters can be checked for accuracy by testing against a reference standard instrument of known accuracy. Having stabilized the instrument to be checked by running it for some half-hour under the specified reference conditions including ambient temperature (usually 20°C), adjusted its zero index and energized and adjusted the test circuit/s to produce an indication on the instrument under test at an exact numbered scale mark at the lower end of the scale, the reading of the reference standard instrument (corrected if necessary) is recorded. This process if repeated for further increasing exact figured scale marks up to the upper limit of the instrument's effective range, and then for decreasing values down to zero (noting any residual indication at zero quantity).

The accuracy class of an instrument is designated by its *class index* as follows:

| Class index | 0·05 | 0·1 | 0·2 | 0·5 | 1 | 1·5 | 2·5 | 5 |
|---|---|---|---|---|---|---|---|---|
| Limits of intrinsic error | ±0·05% | ±0·1% | ±0·2% | ±0·5% | ±1% | ±1·5% | ±2·5% | ±5% |

These percentage limits of error are related *not* to the maximum scale value (as was the practice until recently) but to a *fiducial value* which is defined for each type of instrument. Under the class index system permitted changes of error due to outside influences such as temperature, position, magnetic fields, etc. are implicit in the classification and are not dealt with separately. In general for many instruments the *fiducial* value *may* correspond to the upper limit of its effective range.

It is a requirement of BS 89 and BS 90 (which may be referred to for further information) that the limits of effective range must be recognizable without ambiguity, but the methods whereby this may be achieved have been left to the discretion of the manufacturer. For instance triangular marks thus can be printed on the scale indicating the upper and lower limits of the effective range, or the fine scale sub-divisions may be omitted outside the effective range.

Class index 0·05 is the most accurate specified for direct acting indicating instruments, and class index 0·2 is the most accurate specified for direct acting recording instruments.

In general, for indicating instruments, reference instruments are those from class index 0·05 up to but not necessarily including class index 0·5, whilst those used for industrial purposes are those perhaps including class index 0·5 but more generally from class index 1 to 5.

Tests may be divided into three categories:

(i) Routine tests, made on all instruments (including limits of intrinsic error).

(ii) Batch tests, made on samples of each production batch (may include limits of variation due to position).

(iii) Type tests, made on a sample or samples of each design (may include limits of variation due to various influence conditions, and damping, overload, also vibration tests, etc. if separately specified).

*A.10.1 Standard cells*

These may be used as a *reference standard* of electromotive force (e.m.f.). They are of two types, using an electrolyte of either (i) a saturated or (ii) an unsaturated aqueous solution of cadmium sulphate; in both cases the negative electrode is of cadmium amalgam and the positive electrode of mercury covered with a paste of $Hg_2 SO_4$.

The e.m.f. of a standard cell at 20°C will be within the range:

1·018 54V to 1·018 73V for saturated cells, and
1·018 8V to 1·019 6V for unsaturated cells.

The actual certification value being stated by the certification laboratory (certification temperatures other than 20°C may be agreed).

The accuracy class of a cell (its stability with respect to time) is defined by the maximum permissible deviation of its e.m.f. during a period of one year and is designated by its class index number (usually expressed as a percentage).

Thus unsaturated cells are made with class indices of 0·002, 0·005 and 0·10%, meaning that for a class index of 0·002 the permissible derivation of certified e.m.f. will be ±0·002%. Saturated cells can be made to a higher accuracy class, the most accurate standard cell specified by BS 5142 (IEC 428) having a class index of 0·0002%.

The e.m.f. of a saturated standard cell within its reference temperature range can be calculated by a formula taking account of the actual and certification temperatures and characteristics of the cell given by the manufacturer.

The standard cells described in BS 5142 are not intended to supply a current, nor to be used as national or international standards of e.m.f.

## A.11 Measurement of pressure

The latest revision of BS 1780 (1985) *Bourdon tube pressure and vacuum gauges* for ranges up to 1000 bar extends the emphasis on safety and requires compliance with a safety pattern for gauges for use with gases or steam above 25 bar. This safety pattern includes (i) a solid baffle wall, forming an integral part of the case; interposed between the bourdon tube and the dial; (ii) a blow-out device; and (iii) a window of non-splintering glass or plastics. For use with gases (including steam) at 25 bar or less a blow-out device has now to be fitted.

Gauges for use with oxygen in addition to being of the safety pattern must naturally be of materials resistant to the chemical action of oxygen; also all components must be thoroughly cleaned and degreased before assembly. Only oil-free fluids must be used in testing; the gauge must be marked OXYGEN with the warning USE NO OIL, or some equivalent symbol.

Gauges for use with steam should be connected to the tapping point of the system by means of a syphon formed of tubing bent through 180° and filled with water, as it is essential that steam is prevented from entering the bourdon tube. If a gauge cannot be grasped by hand without discomfort it is working at too high a temperature.

Of interest, in preparing this revised specification, particular consideration was given to the choice of units for expressing pressure and the marking of the gauge dials. It was decided to give first preference to the use of the bar, this being considered a more practical pressure unit than the SI unit, the pascal. If desired the pascal (Pa), kPa, MPa or Imperial units may be used and suitable scale ranges in bar, pascals (and their multiples), and in Imperial units are tabulated. The specification also states (in an appendix) that the standard atmosphere, technical atmosphere (at) i.e. $kgf/cm^2$, conventional inch of mercury, millimetre of mercury, foot of water (ft $H_2O$) and other units may be met in practice and it defines some of these. It makes no mention of EEC and CGPM's various rulings declaring that most of these units should cease to be used for legal purposes and the temporary use of the bar (see A.1, 8.2, 11.2).

### A.11.1 *Accuracy of pressure gauge measurement*

BS 1780 requires that when tested under specified reference conditions with either increasing or decreasing pressure:

(i) Test gauges should have an error in pressure indication not exceeding 0·25% of the maximum scale value.

(ii) Industrial gauges should have an error in pressure indication not exceeding 1% of the maximum scale value (from above 10% and below 90% of the maximum scale value) whilst for the rest of the scale the error must not exceed 1·5% of the maximum scale value.

For the smallest size of industrial gauge (nominal size 50 mm) the error must not exceed 1·5% of the maximum scale value.

Industrial gauges must withstand an overload on pressure test of 25% above the maximum scale value up to 160 bar, decreasing to 10% above on maximum scale values over 600 bar. After this test the gauge must again be tested for accuracy and must comply with the requirements stated above.

All tests have to be conducted at a temperature of 20 ±3°C and calibration certificates must be supplied.

For test gauges the testing apparatus should comprise a mercury manometer or a dead-weight tester, a dead-weight tester being used for maximum scale values above 2 bar. (Any necessary small corrections due to buoyancy of the air, local variations in gravity, etc. should be made.)

For industrial gauges a suitably calibrated test gauge may be used in lieu of other test apparatus.

As with other forms of legal metrology the calibration of the test apparatus must be traceable back to national standards.

Table A.5 lists some standards, etc. dealing with metrology, including those for the measurement of length (and dimensions), mass, weight and force, electrical quantities, temperature, fluid flow etc.

### A.12  Precision of test methods

The inspector may be faced with the fact that tests performed on apparently identical materials, etc., made under apparently identical and specified conditions, do not always produce identical results. Problems may therefore arise as to whether the material does or does not conform to specification (pedantically of course it does not) or whether the discrepancies may be

*Some standards dealing with legal metrology*

| BS Specification No. | Description |
|---|---|
| **Measurement of length (and dimensions)** | |
| 852 | Toolmakers' straight edges |
| 869 | Toolmakers' flats and high precision surface plates |
| 870 | External micrometers |
| 887 | Precision vernier calipers |
| 888 | Slip (or block) gauges and their accessories (4 grades—workshop, inspection, calibration and reference) |
| 906 | Engineers' parallels |
| 907 | Dial gauges for linear measurement (with plunger movement parallel to dial plane; scale divisions—0·001 in, 0·0001 in or 0·01 mm) |
| 2795 | Dial test indicators (lever type) for linear measurement |
| 919 | Screw gauge limits and tolerances (deals in 4 parts with *go* and *not go* plug, ring and caliper gauges for general and reference use for checking screw threads of Unified, Whitworth, BA and ISO metric form) |
| 5590 | Screw thread metric series measuring cylinders (for checking external screw threads—appendix covers use with Unified, Whitworth and BA thread forms—grades of accuracy etc.). Supersedes BS 3777. |
| 939 | Engineers' squares (three grades of accuracy—AA, A and B) |
| 957 | Feeler gauges |
| 958 | Spirit levels for use in precision engineering |
| 959 | Internal micrometers (including stick micrometers) |
| 969 | Limits and tolerances on plain limit gauges (tables for tolerances on plug, bar, rod, pin, ring and gap gauges, with examples showing principles of inspection using them). |
| 1044 | Gauge blanks: Part 1 Plug, ring and caliper gauges (notes on design features, dimensions etc of commonly used types of gauges) |
| 1054 | Engineers' comparators for external measurement (primarily comprising a rigid stand supporting a measuring head over a work table, the movements of the measuring tip being amplified by mechanical, electrical, electronic, optical, fluid or pneumatic means) |
| 1098 | Jig bushes |
| 1790 (obsolescent) | Length bars and accessories (cylindrical bar type; accuracy standards—reference, calibration, Grade 1 and 2 (inspection and workshop)). Includes inch sizes. |
| 5317 | Metric length bars and accessories (cylindrical bar type; accuracy standards—reference, calibration, Grade 1 and 2 (inspection and workshop) |

TABLE A.5 *concluded*

| BS Specification No. | Description |
| --- | --- |

**Measurement of force, etc.**

| 1610 | Methods for the load verification of testing machines |
| 4408 Part 2 | Strain gauges for concrete investigations |
| DD6 | Methods for calibration of bonded electric resistance strain gauges |

**Measurement of electrical quantities**

| 89 | Direct acting indicating electrical measuring instruments (identical with IEC51) |
| 90 | Direct acting indicating electrical recording instruments (based on IEC 258) |
| 5142 | Standard cells |
| 5164 | Indirect acting electrical indicating and recording instruments |
| 5685 | Electricity meters — class 0·5, 1 and 2 watt-hour meters |

**Measurement of temperature**

| 1041 | Code for temperature measurement (some 7 parts deal with expansion thermometers, industrial thermometry, thermo couples, radiation pyrometers, temperature/time indicators (change of shape devices, seger cones, etc.) |

**Measurement of fluid flow**

| 1042 | Methods of measurement of fluid flow in closed conduits<br>Part 1 Orifice plates, nozzles, venturi tubes (including a guide to their use)<br>Part 2 Pitot-static tubes, etc. |

**Measurement of pressure**

| 1780 | Bourdon tube pressure and vacuum gauges (test and industrial gauges with maximum scale readings up to 1000 bar; accuracy, test methods and apparatus) |

**Measurement of radio interference**

| 727 | Radio-interference measuring apparatus (based on CISPR 16 published by IEC and EEC Directives and intended for use as a specific reference to the legal implementation of regulations on permissible limits of radio interference, and as called for by current UK Statutory Instruments and relevant British Standards (e.g. BS 800 and BS 5394) |
| 4809 | Radio interference limits and measurements for R.F. heating equipment (applicable to many types of industrial equipment, including induction heaters and plastics welders) and follows closely the International (CISPR) Recommendations |

attributed to unavoidable random errors inherent in many test procedures. Such errors may be contributed to by vagaries of the operator, the equipment or the environment and by the calibration of the equipment. Attention is drawn to BS 5497 *Precision of test methods* which in Part 1 gives a *Guide for the determination of repeatability and reproducibility for a standard test method by inter-laboratory tests.* In general repeatability (r) refers to tests performed by one laboratory and giving similar results; whilst reproducibility (R) refers to the ability (or otherwise) of another laboratory to do likewise. The standard establishes basic principles for precision experiments for the estimation of r and R, and for their application. A computer program that may be used for the statistical analysis of precision data is outlined.

### References and further reading

Anthony, D.M., *Engineering Metrology*, Pergamon Press, 1986.

Dixon, W.J. and Massey, F.J., *Introduction to Statistical Analysis*, McGraw-Hill 1969.

Faraso, F.T., *Handbook of dimensional measurement*, Industrial Press, 1968.

Hume, K.J., *A History of Engineering Metrology*, Mech. Eng. Pub./I. Mech. E. 1950.

BS 5532 Statistical terminology.

*Directory of NAMAS accredited laboratories and their services*, National Measurement Accreditation Service, National Physical Laboratory, 1988.

# Index